College Mathematics with Applications to the Business and Social Sciences

College Mathematics with Applications to the Business and Social Sciences

Bodh R. Gulati

SOUTHERN CONNECTICUT STATE COLLEGE

HARPER & ROW, PUBLISHERS
New York, Hagerstown, San Francisco, London

Sponsoring Editor: Charlie Dresser
Project Editor: Eleanor Castellano
Designer: Rita Naughton
Production Supervisor: Will C. Jomarrón
Compositor: Syntax International Pte. Ltd.
Printer and Binder: The Murray Printing Company
Art Studio: Vantage Art Inc.

College Mathematics with Applications to the Business
and Social Sciences

Library of Congress Cataloging in Publication Data
Gulati, Bodh R
    College mathematics with applications to the business
and social sciences.

    Includes index.
    1. Mathematics—1961–   2.   Business mathematics,
3.   Social sciences—Methodology.   I.   Title.
QA37.2.G85   510   77-22205
ISBN 0-06-042538-5

To
Santosh, Anita,
and Sunil

Contents

Preface

There has been an increasing tendency to turn to quantitative techniques and models as a potential means for solving many of the problems that arise in business, management, and social sciences. Most of the students who populate courses devoted to these techniques and models have had limited exposure to mathematics in high school. Either the students were afraid of mathematics and elected as few courses as possible or they did not consider mathematics of any practical significance and, therefore, have forgotten most of what they learned. Consequently, many students find themselves inadequately trained for mathematics courses oriented to management and the social sciences at the college level. It is for such students that this text is intended. I have tried to adopt a "down-to-earth" approach and to present the fundamentals in a way that will facilitate an intuitive understanding of the basic concepts. Applications are drawn from economics, education, business, management, and social sciences.

From the abundance of worked examples, the student should be able to gain a firm grasp of the principles presented in the text. The book contains approximately 1600 problems of varying degrees of difficulty, with answers to odd-numbered exercises at the end of the text. Answers to even-numbered exercises are available in a separate booklet.

There is sufficient material for a sequence of three one-semester courses. However, the text is structured to be used in a variety of ways. It is my experience that material selected from the first seven chapters provides a good first quantitative course in management or the social sciences; Chapters 1 and 9 through 12 form a meaningful course in applied finite mathematics or probability, which is often a prerequisite for a course in elementary statistics. A course in linear mathematics and applied matrix algebra would cover Chapters 4 through 8 and could possibly include Chapter 13 on the theory of games and Markov chains (for those students who have had some exposure to basic concepts of probability and expected value). A short course in calculus would cover the first three chapters as the basis for the material presented in Chapters 14 through 19. The text is flexible so that an instructor can choose topics that best fit the needs of his or her students.

I thank my friends and colleagues at Southern Connecticut State College whose suggestions, criticisms, and comments helped me in this long and arduous undertaking. Special gratitude is expressed to Dr. J. Philip Smith, Dr. Michael Meck, and Dr. Robert Washburn for their careful review of the first draft of the book; to Dr. Dorothy V. Schrader and Dr. Kerry E. Grant for their words of encouragement; to Professors Karen Latil and Gary Bobb for class testing the manuscript; to Professors Leo Kuczynski and Richard DeCesare for providing solutions to the problems in some chapters; and to several students who made suggestions that have been incorporated in the final version. I also gratefully acknowledge the assistance of Professors Garret Etgen of the University of Houston, Lawrence A. Trivieri of Mohawk Valley Community College, and Ronald J. Harshbarger of Pennsylvania State University, whose penetrating comments improved the entire manuscript. Finally, I wish to express my deep appreciation to Mrs. Maryann Franco, who skillfully and cheerfully typed more than one version of this manuscript.

I must not forget my indebtedness to George Telecki, Charlie Dresser, Eleanor Castellano, and Rita Naughton of Harper & Row for their interest, encouragement, and cooperation; finally, thanks are also due to John Wiley & Sons, Inc., for permitting me to use certain tables from some of their publications.

New Haven, Connecticut   Bodh R. Gulati
June 1977

College Mathematics with Applications to the Business and Social Sciences

CHAPTER 1
Sets

1.1 CONCEPT OF A SET

The term set plays an extremely fundamental role in the development of mathematics. This concept possesses an intuitive counterpart in everyday experience and will be used to develop some of the major concepts.

A set is an aggregate or collection of objects of some kind. These objects are called the elements or members of the set. There are many examples of sets with which the reader is familiar. For example, the reader is an element of the set of students in the class. A student not in this class is not a member of this set.

A set must be well defined in the sense that we can determine whether or not an element belongs to a given collection. Some examples of well-defined sets are

   (i) the set of sales executives in Sears and Roebuck
  (ii) the set of vice-presidents in the First National Bank of Chicago
 (iii) the set of Congressional Representatives from the State of Connecticut
 (iv) the set of female employees in the Hartford Insurance Group
  (v) the set of teachers in Wayne High School
 (vi) the set of automobiles registered in the State of New York

Each of the above sets is so clearly defined that we can easily determine whether or not an element belongs to a given collection. Note, however, that the set of older folks in the State of Vermont is not well-defined.

Sets are designated customarily by capital letters $A, B, C, \ldots$, whereas members of a set are denoted by small letters $a, b, c, \ldots$. If a set A consists of the numbers 1, 2, 3, 4, 5, 6, we write

   $A = \{1, 2, 3, 4, 5, 6\}$

If a set has a large number of elements, we may abbreviate in listing its members. For example, we may denote the set of letters of the alphabet by

   $\{a, b, c, \ldots, y, z\}$

and interpret the dots to mean that the unlisted letters d through x, both inclusive, are also members of the set.

Essentially, a set may be specified in two different ways. One way is to list all the elements of a set as we have illustrated; another is to enclose in braces a defining property by which it can be determined whether or not a given member belongs to that set. Consider, for example, the set of five vice-presidents in the local insurance company,

{Adam, Brown, Charles, David, Edward}

A member must be one of the vice-presidents in the insurance company in order to belong to that set. We may denote this set by the following notation:

{$x|x$ is a vice-president in the insurance company}

and read this symbol: "The set of all x such that x is a vice-president in the insurance company." The vertical line in the notation is read "such that." The letter x of the alphabet in the notation is called a variable.

Example 1.1
List the elements of the set

$A = \{x|x$ is a day of the week\}

SOLUTION

$A = \{$Monday, Tuesday, Wednesday, Thursday, Friday, Saturday, Sunday\} ∎

Example 1.2
List the elements of the set

$B = \{x|x$ is a counting number less than 5\}

SOLUTION

$B = \{1, 2, 3, 4\}$ ∎

It is important not to confuse the concept of an element with the concept of a set. If A is a set whose only element is 3, we write $A = \{3\}$ so as not to confuse the counting number 3 with the set $\{3\}$ consisting of one element.

To express the fact that Kathy is a member of the set A, we write

Kathy $\in A$

where the symbol $\in$ is interpreted to mean "is an element of," "is a member of," or "belongs to." Thus, if $A = \{$Roger, Jeannie, Mary, Kathy\}, then

Roger $\in A$

Kathy $\in A$

Jeannie $\in A$

Mary $\in A$

but

Marilyn $\notin A$

The notation Marilyn $\notin A$ means that "Marilyn does not belong to the set A."

Definition 1.1.1: A set with no elements is called the null or the empty set; it is denoted by $\{\ \}$ or $\varnothing$.

The set of all secretaries who can type 800 words per minute, the set of sales executives over 300 years old, the set of all men who weigh more than 1500 pounds, and the set of all counting numbers greater than 10 and less than 11 are all examples of an empty set.

Universal Set

The set of all logical possibilities $\mathscr{U}$ in a given situation constitutes the basis for a discussion and must be agreed upon before the discussion proceeds in an unambiguous manner. For example, if we wish to discuss some of the students in Chico State College, the universal set would be the set of all students in that college. In case we wish to talk about some of the incorporated business firms in Illinois, the universal set would be the set of all incorporated business firms in that state, and firms incorporated in California or any other state of the Union are then excluded from the discussion in progress.

The universal set may be the set of the days of the week or the set of counting numbers less than 5. It could also be a very large set, such as the heights of all males in the United States; or it could be a relatively small set, such as the number of females in a household. Nevertheless, the concept of a universal set means the set of all possibilities under discussion.

Relations Between Sets—Subsets

Consider the sets

$\{$Sunil, Anita$\}$ and $\{$Sunil, Anita, Judy, Dick$\}$

How do these sets compare? Perhaps an obvious statement is that every element of the first set is also an element of the second set. Such a relation between sets is a common one. For example, each element of the set of consonants in the alphabet is also an element of the set of all letters of the alphabet.

Definition 1.1.2: A set A is a subset of B if and only if every element of the set A is also an element of the set B.

The notation $A \subseteq B$ or $B \supseteq A$ means that "A is a subset of B." Thus, we say that $A \subseteq B$ if $x \in A$ implies that $x \in B$, but if there exists some element $x \in A$ that does not belong to the set B, then A is not a subset of the set B.

Example 1.3

In the universe of counting numbers,

$$\{1, 2, 3\} \subseteq \{1, 2, 3, 4, 5\}$$
$$\{2, 4, 6, 8\} \subseteq \{2, 4, 6, 8, 10\}$$
$$\{6, 8, 9\} \subseteq \{6, 8, 9\}$$

but

$$\{1, 2, 3\} \nsubseteq \{1, 2, 4\} \qquad \blacksquare$$

The set A is a subset of itself, $A \subseteq A$, because every element in A is an element in A and the definition of a subset is satisfied. We also consider the null set as a subset of every set A, because there is no element of $\varnothing$ that does not belong to A; therefore, $\varnothing \subseteq A$. These relationships, $\varnothing \subseteq A$ and $A \subseteq A$, will be employed in the development of the important concept of a power set, which we discuss later in this section.

A set may contain a finite number of elements or it may contain infinitely many. The set of counting numbers

$$N = \{1, 2, 3, 4, \ldots\}$$

is an infinite set. To say that a set is finite means that either it is an empty set or its members can be counted. The set of students registered in a given course, the set of mathematics teachers in Hamden High School, and the set of books in a given library are all examples of finite sets.

Definition 1.1.3: Let A and B be two sets. The set A is a proper subset of B, written $A \subset B$, if $A \subseteq B$ and the set B contains at least one element that does not belong to the set A.

The null set is a proper subset of every nonempty set, whereas a set A is not a proper subset of itself. All subsets of $\mathscr{U}$, except $\mathscr{U}$ itself, are proper subsets of the universal set $\mathscr{U}$. Here are some examples.

Example 1.4

In the universe of counting numbers,

$$\{1, 2, 3\} \subset \{1, 2, 3, 5\}$$
$$\{2, 4, 6, 8\} \subset \{2, 4, 6, 8, 10\}$$

but

$$\{1, 2\} \not\subset \{1, 2\} \qquad \blacksquare$$

How many subsets does a given set have? If the set is empty, it has only one subset, itself. If the set has one element, then it has two subsets, itself and the empty set $\varnothing$. Before we generalize, we will consider a few more examples.

Example 1.5

(a) $A = \{1, 2\}$. The subsets of A are

$$\{ \ \}, \{1\}, \{1, 2\}$$
$$\{2\}$$

(b) $B = \{1, 2, 3\}$. The subsets of B are

$$\{ \ \}, \{1\}, \{1, 2\}, \{1, 2, 3\}$$
$$\{2\}, \{1, 3\}$$
$$\{3\}, \{2, 3\}$$

Notice that we systematically wrote the subset containing no element, then all subsets that have one element, two elements, and so on, finally including the original set itself. The following table points out a relationship between the number of possible subsets to the number of elements in a given set.

Number of Elements in a Set	Number of Subsets
0	$1 = 2^0$
1	$2 = 2^1$
2	$4 = 2^2$
3	$8 = 2^3$

Because the set $\{1, 2, 3\}$ is not a proper subset of itself, it follows that there are $2^3 - 1 = 7$ proper subsets of the set consisting of three elements 1, 2, and 3. This leads us to conjecture that if n is a nonnegative integer, then a set with n elements has 2^n subsets of which $2^n - 1$ are proper subsets. Readers should convince themselves by considering several examples that this conjecture is correct.   ■

We find it worthwhile to point out that the two symbols $\in$ and $\subseteq$ are distinct notions—one denotes the set membership and the other set inclusion. The difference between these concepts becomes evident if one compares the statements

$$x \in A \quad \text{and} \quad \{x\} \subseteq A$$

$x \in A$ states that x is an element of a set A, and $\{x\} \subseteq A$ means that the set containing one element x is a subset of set A.

Definition 1.1.4: Two sets A and B are said to be equal if A is a subset of B and B is a subset of A. In symbols,

$$A = B$$

This means that two sets A and B are equal if and only if every element of A is an element of B and every element of B is also an element of A.

Example 1.6

    Let A = {Brown, Charles, Dick, Gary} and

        B = {Gary, Dick, Brown, Charles}.

These sets are equal because each set is a subset of the other. This example illustrates the fact that equal sets have exactly the same members and that the order in which the elements of the set are listed is immaterial. ∎

EXERCISE 1.1

1. Determine which of the following are well-defined sets.
    a. smart students in a marketing course
    b. beautiful girls on the campus
    c. senators from the state of California
    d. older folks in Maine
    e. hogs in Omaha, Nebraska
    f. wheat farmers in the United States
    g. teachers in a high school
    h. counting numbers greater than 50
    i. residents in the state of Vermont
    j. new automobiles in Chicago, Illinois

2. Given that A = {1, 2, 3, 4, 5, 6, 7, 8}, which of the following statements are true and which are false?
    a. $5 \in A$ **b.** $12 \in A$
    c. $0 \in A$ **d.** $\{5\} \subset A$
    e. $\{5\} \subseteq A$ **f.** $A \subset A$
    g. $A \subseteq A$ **h.** $-2 \in A$
    i. $\{1, 2\} \subset A$ **j.** $\emptyset \in A$
    k. $\emptyset \subset A$ **l.** $\emptyset \subseteq A$
    m. $\{1, 2, 3\} \in \{1, 2, 3, 4\}$ **n.** $\{1, 2, 3\} \subseteq \{1, 2, 3, 4\}$

3. Classify the following statements as true or false.
    a. {Jodey, Tracey} $\subseteq$ {Jodey, Jeannie, Tracey}
    b. {Jodey, Tracey} $\subseteq$ {Jodey, Tracey}
    c. {Jodey, Jeannie, Tracey} $\subseteq$ {Jodey, Tracey}
    d. {1, 2, 3, 4, 5} $\subseteq$ {5, 3, 1, 2, 4}
    e. {2, 4, 6, 8} $\subset$ {2, 4, 6, 8}
    f. {2, 4, 6, 8} $\subseteq$ {2, 4, 6, 8}

4. List or indicate within braces the elements or members of the following sets.
    a. the set of senators from your state
    b. the set of states of the United States that border Canada
    c. the set of United States astronauts who have landed on the moon
    d. the set of mathematics teachers in your high school
    e. the set of females in your household

5. Determine whether the following sets are finite or infinite.
    a. the set of odd counting numbers
    b. the set of chickens in Cleveland, Ohio

    c. the set of savings and loan associations in the United States

    d. the set of all automobile manufacturers in Michigan

    e. the set of points on a line

    f. the set of dust particles in the air

    g. the set of Canadians visiting the United States in 1976

    h. the set of all business executives in Colorado

6. Which of the following sets are equal?

    a. $\{1, 2, 3, 4\}$ **b.** $\{2, 1, 4, 3\}$

    c. $\{3, 4, 1, 2, 5\}$ **d.** $\{4, 1, 2, 3\}$

    e. $\{3, 1, 4, 5\}$ **f.** $\{2, 4, 3, 1, 6\}$

7. Given that

$$A = \{x \mid x \text{ is a counting number between 3 and 8, both inclusive}\}$$

$$B = \{x \mid x \text{ is a counting number less than 6}\}$$

Which of the following sets are equal to A or B?

    a. $\{4, 5, 6, 7, 8\}$ **b.** $\{1, 2, 3, 4, 5\}$

    c. $\{3, 4, 5, 6, 7\}$ **d.** $\{3, 4, 5, 6, 7, 8\}$

    e. $\{4, 3, 1, 5, 2\}$ **f.** $\{3, 8, 6, 5, 7, 4\}$

8. Given that $\mathscr{U} = \{a, b, c\}$, list all subsets of $\mathscr{U}$. Which ones of these are proper subsets? Which ones of these are nonempty subsets?

9. Given that $\mathscr{U} = \{\text{Bob, Charles, Dick, Edward}\}$, list all the subsets of $\mathscr{U}$. Which one of these are proper subsets?

10. Given that $\mathscr{U} = \{\text{Bob, Carlson, Dick, Gary, Henry}\}$, list all subsets of $\mathscr{U}$ that have

    a. two elements

    b. three elements

    c. four elements

1.2 OPERATIONS ON SETS

We have introduced so far the concept of a set and notations for describing sets. We have also discussed some of the important relations on sets. It now seems reasonable to ask how we can form new sets from the sets under discussion. To answer this question, we consider a family of sets that are subsets of some fixed universal set $\mathscr{U}$. We now introduce the operations of union, intersection, and complement of sets.

Definition 1.2.1: Let A and B be the subsets of the universal set $\mathscr{U}$. The union of A and B, denoted by $A \cup B$, is the set of all elements that belong to A or to B or to both. In symbols,

$$A \cup B = \{x \mid x \in A \text{ or } x \in B\}$$

Example 1.7

Let $A = \{\text{Sunil, Anita, Mary}\}$, and let $B = \{\text{Mary, Susan, Joe, Dick}\}$. Then

$$A \cup B = \{\text{Sunil, Anita, Mary, Susan, Joe, Dick}\}$$ ■

Example 1.8

Let $A = \{2, 3, 5, 7, 8\}$ and $B = \{1, 2, 3, 4, 6, 8\}$. Then

$$A \cup B = \{1, 2, 3, 4, 5, 6, 7, 8\}$$ ■

It may be helpful to represent sets and their operations using a pictorial method known as Venn diagrams. In a Venn diagram, a rectangle is used to represent the universal set $\mathcal{U}$ whereas subsets of $\mathcal{U}$ are represented by regions bounded by closed curves within the rectangle $\mathcal{U}$. Because $A \cup B$ consists of elements that are either in A or in B or in both, the shaded region of Figure 1.1 represents the union of two sets, A and B.

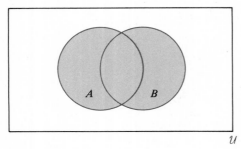

Figure 1.1

Sometimes two sets have elements in common. The shaded area of Figure 1.2 represents the elements common to both the sets.

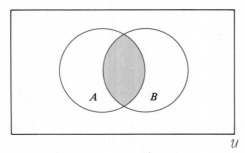

Figure 1.2

Definition 1.2.2: Let A and B be the subsets of $\mathcal{U}$. The intersection of A and B, denoted by $A \cap B$, is the set of all elements that belongs to both A and B. In symbols,

$$A \cap B = \{x | x \in A \text{ and } x \in B\}$$

Example 1.9

Let $\mathcal{U} = \{1, 2, 3, 4, 5, 6, 7, 8, 9, 10\}$ and $A = \{1, 2, 3, 6, 7, 8\}$ and $B = \{3, 7, 8, 9, 10\}$. Then

$$A \cap B = \{3, 7, 8\}$$ ■

Example 1.10

Let $\mathscr{U}$ be the set of all employees in an insurance company while A and B represent, respectively, the set of secretaries employed by that insurance company and the set of stockholders of that insurance company. Then $A \cap B$ is the set of all those secretaries who are stockholders of that insurance company. ∎

Frequently, two sets do not have any common element. For instance, if $\mathscr{U}$ is the set of all sales executives in a business firm and A and B represent, respectively, those attending a sales meeting in Chicago and those taking part in conferences at the head office in New York at the same time, then $A \cap B$ represents an empty set because no one can be at two places at the same time. Figure 1.3 represents that two sets have no common elements.

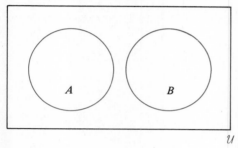

Figure 1.3

Definition 1.2.3: Let A and B be subsets of $\mathscr{U}$. The sets A and B are said to be disjoint if they have no elements in common; that is,

$$A \cap B = \varnothing$$

Example 1.11

Let $\mathscr{U} = \{4, 5, 6, 7, 8, 9, 10, 11, 12\}$ and $A = \{4, 6, 8, 10, 12\}$ and $B = \{5, 7, 9, 11\}$. Then A and B do not have any element in common. In other words, the intersection of A and B is the null set. ∎

A subset of the universal set $\mathscr{U}$ that is intimately related to the set A is the set called the complement of A. The region outside the circle but within the rectangle $\mathscr{U}$ in Figure 1.4 represents the complement of a set A.

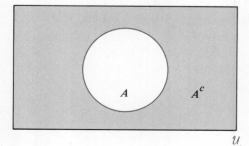

Figure 1.4

Definition 1.2.4: Let A be any subset of $\mathscr{U}$. Then the set of all elements in $\mathscr{U}$ that do not belong to A is called the complement of A and is denoted by A^c. In symbols,

$$A^c = \{x \mid x \in \mathscr{U}, x \notin A\}$$

Example 1.12

Let $\mathscr{U} = \{1, 2, 3, 4, 5, 6\}$ and let $A = \{1, 3, 5, 6\}$. Then $A^c = \{2, 4\}$. Note that

(i) $A \cup A^c = \mathscr{U}$
(ii) $A \cap A^c = \varnothing$
(iii) $\mathscr{U}^c = \varnothing$
(iv) $\varnothing^c = \mathscr{U}$

∎

Example 1.13

Let $\mathscr{U} = \{1, 2, 3, 4, 5, 6, 7, 8, 9, 10, 11, 12\}$ and let A, B, and C be subsets of $\mathscr{U}$ as given below:

$$A = \{1, 5, 6, 10, 11, 12\}, \quad B = \{2, 3, 7, 8, 9, 10\}, \quad C = \{2, 5, 8, 9, 12\}$$

Show that

$$A \cap (B \cup C) = (A \cap B) \cup (A \cap C)$$

SOLUTION

Clearly, $B \cup C = \{2, 3, 5, 7, 8, 9, 10, 12\}$. Thus

$$A \cap (B \cup C) = \{5, 10, 12\}$$

Now

$$A \cap B = \{10\}$$
$$A \cap C = \{5, 12\}$$

Then

$$(A \cap B) \cup (A \cap C) = \{5, 10, 12\}$$

Because $A \cap (B \cup C)$ and $(A \cap B) \cup (A \cap C)$ consist of the same elements, it follows that

$$A \cap (B \cup C) = (A \cap B) \cup (A \cap C)$$

∎

In the next example, we shall verify this assertion by Venn diagram.

We must, however, caution the reader that Venn diagrams are in no way intended to be a substitute for logical proofs. They only help in establishing the plausibility of a relation and provide the reader with an intuitive notion to test whether or not a particular relation holds among the sets.

Example 1.14

Using a Venn diagram, show that

$$A \cap (B \cup C) = (A \cap B) \cup (A \cap C)$$

SOLUTION

Let the sets A, B, and C be represented by interlocking circles enclosed in a rectangle that represents the universal set $\mathcal{U}$.

The shaded area in Figure 1.5(a) represents $B \cup C$, whereas Figure 1.5(b) shows how A intersects with $B \cup C$, and thus demonstrates how $A \cap (B \cup C)$ is obtained from the set A and the set $B \cup C$.

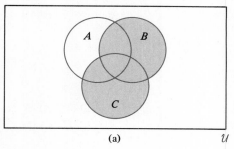 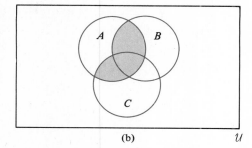

(a) $\mathcal{U}$ (b) $\mathcal{U}$

Figure 1.5

Now we begin shading the sets $A \cap B$ and $A \cap C$ in Figure 1.6(a) and Figure 1.6(b), respectively. To find $(A \cap B) \cup (A \cap C)$, we form the union of the shaded regions $A \cap B$ and $A \cap C$; this gives the shaded area in Figure 1.7.

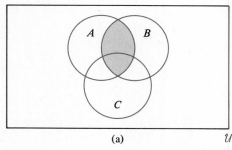 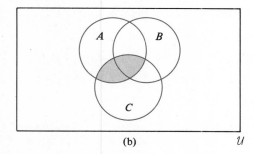

(a) $\mathcal{U}$ (b) $\mathcal{U}$

Figure 1.6

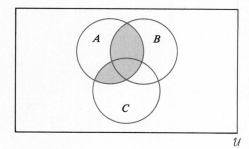

(b) $\mathcal{U}$

Figure 1.7

Because the shaded area in Figure 1.5(b) and Figure 1.7 is the same, it follows that

$$A \cap (B \cup C) = (A \cap B) \cup (A \cap C)$$

We shall now discuss two important results, called De Morgan's laws. If A and B are any two subsets of $\mathcal{U}$, then

$$(A \cup B)^c = A^c \cap B^c \quad \text{and} \quad (A \cap B)^c = A^c \cup B^c$$

The following examples illustrate these laws.

Example 1.15

Let $\mathcal{U} = \{1, 2, 3, 4, 5, 6, 7, 8, 9, 10, 11, 12\}$ and let A and B be defined as follows: $A = \{1, 2, 3, 4, 5, 6\}$ and $B = \{4, 5, 6, 7, 8, 9\}$. Then

$$A^c = \{7, 8, 9, 10, 11, 12\}$$
$$B^c = \{1, 2, 3, 10, 11, 12\}$$
$$A \cup B = \{1, 2, 3, 4, 5, 6, 7, 8, 9\}$$
$$A \cap B = \{4, 5, 6\}$$
$$(A \cup B)^c = \{10, 11, 12\}$$
$$(A \cap B)^c = \{1, 2, 3, 7, 8, 9, 10, 11, 12\}$$
$$A^c \cup B^c = \{1, 2, 3, 7, 8, 9, 10, 11, 12\}$$
$$A^c \cap B^c = \{10, 11, 12\}$$

Clearly, the set $(A \cup B)^c$ and $A^c \cap B^c$ are equal because they consist of precisely the same elements. Similarly, the sets $(A \cap B)^c$ and $A^c \cup B^c$ are equal. We shall now verify through Venn diagrams that in general

$$(A \cup B)^c = A^c \cap B^c$$

∎

Example 1.16

Using a Venn diagram, show that

$$(A \cup B)^c = A^c \cap B^c$$

SOLUTION

The set $(A \cup B)^c$ consists of all elements that do not belong to $A \cup B$. This is represented by the shaded region in Figure 1.8.

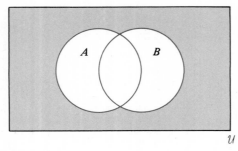

Figure 1.8

We have shaded the region A^c with horizontal lines in Figure 1.9(a) and the region B^c with vertical lines in Figure 1.9(b). Then the cross-hatched area in Figure 1.9(c) yields $A^c \cap B^c$.

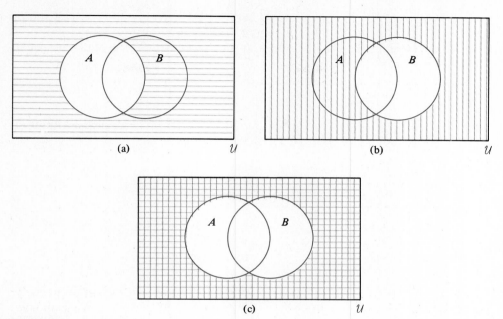

Figure 1.9

Because the shaded area in Figure 1.8 and the cross-hatched area in Figure 1.9(c) is the same, it follows that

$$(A \cup B)^c = A^c \cap B^c$$ ■

In a similar manner, it is easy to show that

$$(A \cap B)^c = A^c \cup B^c$$

We leave this as an exercise for the reader.

EXERCISE 1.2

1. Shade and label the portion of Figure 1.10 that will illustrate each of the sets listed below.

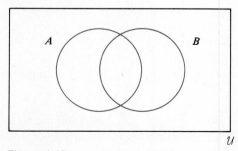

Figure 1.10

    a. $A \cap B$ **b.** $A^c \cap B$

    c. $A \cap B^c$ **d.** $A^c \cap B^c$

2. Shade and label the portion of Figure 1.11 that will illustrate each of the sets listed below.

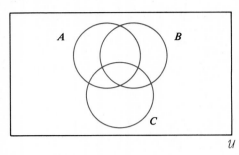

Figure 1.11

    a. $A \cap B \cap C$ **b.** $A \cap B \cap C^c$

    c. $A^c \cap B \cap C$ **d.** $A \cap B^c \cap C$

    e. $A^c \cap B^c \cap C$ **f.** $A^c \cap B \cap C^c$

    g. $A \cap B^c \cap C^c$ **h.** $A^c \cap B^c \cap C^c$

3. Let $\mathcal{U} = \{1, 2, 3, 4, 5, 6, 7, 8, 9, 10\}$ and suppose that we have the following subsets:

$$A = \{2, 3, 4, 5, 6\} \qquad B = \{4, 6, 7, 8, 10\}$$

Determine the elements in the following sets.

    a. A^c **b.** B^c

    c. $A \cup B$ **d.** $A \cap B$

    e. $A^c \cup B^c$ **f.** $A^c \cap B^c$

    g. $(A \cup B)^c$ **h.** $(A \cap B)^c$

4. Let $\mathcal{U} = \{1, 2, 3, 4, 5, 6, 7, 8, 9\}$ and suppose that we have the following subsets:

$$A = \{1, 3, 5, 7, 9\} \qquad B = \{2, 4, 5, 6, 8\} \qquad C = \{3, 6, 7, 9\}$$

Determine the elements in the following sets.

    a. A^c **b.** B^c

    c. C^c **d.** $A \cup B$

    e. $B \cup C$ **f.** $A \cup C$

    g. $A \cup B \cup C$ **h.** $B \cap C$

    i. $A \cup (B \cap C)$ **j.** $(A \cup B) \cap (A \cup C)$

    k. $A \cap (B \cup C)$ **l.** $(A \cap B) \cup (A \cap C)$

    m. $A^c \cup (B \cap C^c)$ **n.** $A^c \cup B^c \cup C^c$

    o. $(A \cup B \cup C)^c$ **p.** $(A \cup B)^c \cap (A \cup B)$

5. Let $\mathcal{U}$ be the set of employees in an insurance company. Suppose that we have the following subsets:

$$A = \{x | x \text{ is a secretary in an insurance company}\}$$
$$B = \{x | x \text{ is a stockholder of the insurance company}\}$$
$$C = \{x | x \text{ is a keypunch operator in the insurance company}\}$$

Describe each of the following sets in words:

a. $A \cup B$

b. $A \cap B$

c. $B \cap C$

d. $B \cup C$

e. $A \cup C$

f. $A \cap C$

g. $A \cap (B \cup C)$

h. $A \cap B \cap C$

6. Let $\mathscr{U} = \{$all students in the college$\}$

$A = \{$all students taking a course in accounting$\}$

$B = \{$all students taking botany$\}$

$C = \{$all students taking chemistry$\}$

Describe each of the following sets in words:

a. A^c

b. B^c

c. $A \cup B$

d. $A \cap B$

e. $A \cap B \cap C$

f. $A \cup (B \cap C)$

g. $B \cup (A \cap C)$

h. $A \cup B \cup C$

7. Using Venn diagrams, show that

a. $A \cap (A \cup B) = A$

b. $A \cup (A \cap B) = A$

c. $A \cap (A \cap B) = (A \cap B)$

d. $(A \cap B^c) \cup (A^c \cap B) \cap (A \cap B) = A \cup B$

8. Using Venn diagrams, show that

a. $A \cup (B \cup C) = (A \cup B) \cup C$

b. $A \cap (B \cap C) = (A \cap B) \cap C$

c. $(A \cap B)^c = A^c \cup B^c$

d. $A \cup (B \cap C) = (A \cup B) \cap (A \cup C)$

1.3 NUMBER OF ELEMENTS IN FINITE SETS

On the basis of a recent survey in San Diego, a market research organization claims that among 312 homemakers randomly selected in a suburb, 183 buy magazine A and 156 buy magazine B. How would you respond to the questions, "How many homemakers buy at least one of the magazines?", "How many homemakers do not buy any of the magazines?". If you are reluctant to answer these questions and conclude that you do not have enough information, you have an insight into these problems. What is missing in the data is information as to how many homemakers buy both the magazines. If we know that 94 homemakers buy both the magazines, then there are 245 homemakers who buy at least one magazine and there are only 67 of them who do not care for either of them. Surprised?

Let us examine the above questions in a formal manner. Let us associate $n(A)$ and $n(B)$ with the number of elements in the sets A and B, respectively. We wish to know the number of elements in sets related to the sets A and B by the operations of union, intersection, and complementation. Observe that

(1.1) $\quad n(\varnothing) = 0$

(1.2) $\quad n(A) > 0 \qquad (A \text{ is nonempty})$

(1.3) $\quad n(A \cup B) = n(A) + n(B) \qquad \text{if } A \text{ and } B \text{ are disjoint sets}$

These observations are rather trivial; the null set has no elements in it, a nonempty set A cannot have a negative number of elements and if two sets A and B have no common elements, then the union of these two sets will have all the elements of the set A as well as those of set B.

Example 1.17

Twenty-six Republicans and 17 Democrats have been invited to a special dinner at the White House. How many Republicans or Democrats attended this dinner?

SOLUTION

Let R and D represent the sets of Republicans and Democrats, respectively. Clearly, $R \cap D = \varnothing$ and $n(R \cap D) = 0$. Because $n(R) = 26$, $n(D) = 17$ and $n(R \cup D) = n(R) + n(D)$ we have

$$n(R \cup D) = 26 + 17 = 43$$ ∎

In case the sets A and B are not disjoint, then the number of elements in $A \cup B$ is not the sum of $n(A)$ and $n(B)$. Consider, for example,

$$A = \{1, 2, 3, 5, 7\} \quad \text{and} \quad B = \{3, 4, 5, 6, 7, 8\}$$

Then

$$A \cup B = \{1, 2, 3, 4, 5, 6, 7, 8\}$$

Because

$$n(A) = 5, \quad n(B) = 6, \quad \text{and} \quad n(A \cup B) = 8,$$

it follows that

$$n(A \cup B) \neq n(A) + n(B)$$

What sort of equality is true in such cases?

Proposition 1.3.1: Let A and B be subsets of the universal set $\mathcal{U}$, then

$$n(A^c \cap B) = n(B) - n(A \cap B)$$

PROOF

We partition the set B into disjoint sets such that

$$B = (A \cap B) \cup (A^c \cap B)$$

as illustrated in Figure 1.12. Then an application of (1.3) yields

$$n(B) = n(A \cap B) + n(A^c \cap B)$$

from which the assertion follows.

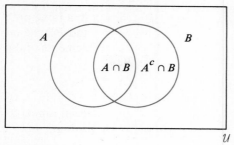

Figure 1.12

Proposition 1.3.2: Let A and B be subsets of the universal set $\mathcal{U}$, then

(1.4) $n(A \cup B) = n(A) + n(B) - n(A \cap B)$

PROOF

The union of two sets A and B may be represented as the union of two disjoint sets A and $A \cap B^c$. In symbols,

$$A \cup B = A \cup (A \cap B^c)$$

as shown in Figure 1.13. Then an application of (1.3) yields

$$n(A \cup B) = n(A) + n(A^c \cap B)$$
$$= n(A) + n(B) - n(A \cap B) \qquad \text{(Proposition 1.3.1)}$$

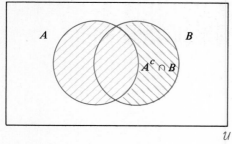

Figure 1.13

Because $n(A) = 5$, $n(B) = 6$, $n(A \cap B) = 3$, and $n(A \cup B) = 8$, in the preceeding example, the reader can verify that the (1.4) holds.

Returning to the example in the beginning of this section, notice that

$$n(\mathcal{U}) = 312, \quad n(A) = 183, \quad n(B) = 156, \quad n(A \cap B) = 94$$

Using (1.4), we obtain

$$n(A \cup B) = 183 + 156 - 94 = 245$$

To determine the number of homemakers who do not buy any of the magazines, we need to partition the universal set $\mathscr{U}$ into two disjoint sets such that

$$\mathscr{U} = (A \cup B)^c \cup (A \cup B)$$

Applying (1.3), we have

$$n(\mathscr{U}) = n(A \cup B)^c + n(A \cup B)$$

from which we obtain

(1.5) $\quad n(A \cup B)^c = n(\mathscr{U}) - n(A \cup B)$

Thus,

$$
\begin{aligned}
n(A^c \cap B^c) &= n(A \cup B)^c \qquad \text{(De Morgan's law)} \\
&= n(\mathscr{U}) - n(A \cup B) \\
&= 312 - 245 \\
&= 67
\end{aligned}
$$

One could also use Venn diagrams for problems of this type (See Figure 1.14). Starting with the information that $n(A \cap B) = 94$, place 94 in the region corresponding to $A \cap B$. Because $n(A) = 183$ and we have $n(A \cap B) = 94$, it follows that $n(A \cap B^c) = 183 - 94 = 89$. Again, $n(B) = 156$. We have $n(A^c \cap B) = 156 - 94 = 62$. Thus,

$$
\begin{aligned}
n(A \cup B) &= n(A \cap B^c) + n(A \cap B) + n(A^c \cap B) \\
&= 89 + 94 + 62 \\
&= 245
\end{aligned}
$$

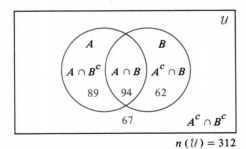

Figure 1.14

To obtain $n(A^c \cap B^c)$, we simply subtract 245 from a total of 312 and obtain 67 as the number of homemakers who do not buy any of these magazines.

The result obtained in (1.3) can be extended to any number of disjoint finite sets. Thus, if $A_1, A_2, A_3, \ldots, A_m$ are all disjoint finite sets, then

$$n(A_1 \cup A_2 \cup \cdots \cup A_m) = n(A_1) + n(A_2) + \cdots + n(A_m)$$

The results for sets that are not disjoint are difficult to visualize at this stage. However, we shall use (1.4) to develop a relation among three sets A, B, and C, which are not disjoint.

From the preceding discussion for two sets, we have

$$n[A \cup (B \cup C)] = n(A) + n(B \cup C) - n[A \cap (B \cup C)]$$
$$= n(A) + n(B) + n(C) - n(B \cap C)$$
$$- n[(A \cap B) \cup (A \cap C)] \quad \text{(distributive law)}$$

But

$$n[(A \cap B) \cup (A \cap C)] = n(A \cap B) + n(A \cap C) - n(A \cap B \cap C)$$

Thus, we obtain the following formula.

(1.6) $n(A \cup B \cup C) = n(A) + n(B) + n(C) - n(A \cap B) - n(A \cap C)$
$$- n(B \cap C) + n(A \cap B \cap C)$$

Example 1.18

In a survey of 55 students, the numbers studying different courses are given as follows:

marketing, 23; economics, 24; psychology, 19; marketing and economics, 12; marketing and psychology, 9; economics and psychology, 7; all three subjects, 4.

Determine the number of students who are

(a) enrolled in at least one course
(b) enrolled in exactly one course
(c) enrolled in exactly two courses

SOLUTION

We construct a Venn diagram. Let M, E, and P represent the set of students in marketing, economics, and psychology, respectively. The information that four students are enrolled in three courses is a starting point; that is

$$n(M \cap E \cap P) = 4$$

Because 12 students are enrolled in courses in marketing and economics, this leaves

$$12 - 4 = 8$$

who are enrolled only in marketing and economics. Similarly,

$$9 - 4 = 5$$

are enrolled only in marketing and psychology courses, whereas

$$7 - 4 = 3$$

are enrolled only in economics and psychology. These numbers are placed in the corresponding regions of Figure 1.15. Because the total number of students in the course in marketing is 23, the number of students enrolled only in the marketing course is

$$23 - 8 - 4 - 5 = 6$$

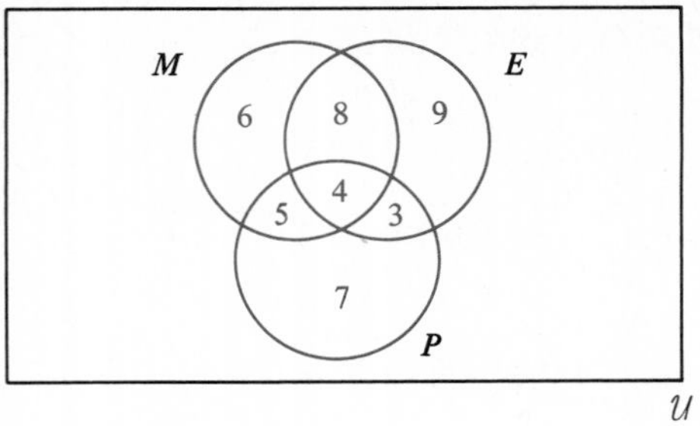

Figure 1.15

Similarly, the number of students enrolled only in the economics course is

$$24 - 8 - 4 - 3 = 9$$

Also, the number of students enrolled only in the psychology course is

$$19 - 5 - 4 - 3 = 7$$

Now we are in position to answer the questions raised in (a), (b), and (c).

(a) The number of students in at least one course is given by

$$6 + 8 + 4 + 5 + 9 + 3 + 7 = 42$$

Alternatively, we can obtain this information directly by using the formula (1.5) by which

$$n(M \cup E \cup P) = n(M) + n(E) + n(P) - n(M \cap E) - n(P \cap E) - n(M \cap P)$$
$$+ n(M \cap P \cap E)$$
$$= 23 + 24 + 19 - 12 - 9 - 7 + 4$$
$$= 42$$

(b) The number of students enrolled in exactly one course is given by

$$6 + 9 + 7 = 22$$

(c) The number of students enrolled in exactly two courses is given by

$$8 + 5 + 3 = 16$$

EXERCISE 1.3

1. Let $A = \{2, 3, 4, 5, 6\}$ and $B = \{4, 5, 6, 7, 8, 9\}$. Determine:
   a. $n(A \cap B)$
   b. $n(A \cup B)$
   c. Show that $n(A \cup B) = n(A) + n(B) - n(A \cap B)$.
2. Given that A and B are subsets of $\mathcal{U}$, where $n(\mathcal{U}) = 200$, $n(A) = 114$, $n(B) = 93$, $n(A \cap B) = 45$, determine the following.
   a. $n(A^c)$ b. $n(B^c)$
   c. $n(A^c \cap B)$ d. $n(A \cap B^c)$
   e. $n(A \cup B)$ f. $n(A^c \cap B^c)$

3. Given that A and B are subsets of the set $\mathscr{U}$, where

$$n(\mathscr{U}) = 50, \quad n(A) = 30, \quad n(B) = 21, \quad n(A \cap B) = 9$$

determine the following:

a. $n(A^c)$ **b.** $n(B^c)$

c. $n(A^c \cap B)$ **d.** $n(A \cap B^c)$

e. $n(A \cup B)$ **f.** $n(A^c \cup B^c)$

g. $n(A^c \cup B)$ **h.** $n(A \cup B^c)$

4. Let A and B be subsets of $\mathscr{U}$, where

$$n(\mathscr{U}) = 150, \quad n(A) = 93, \quad n(B) = 87, \quad n(A \cap B) = 42$$

Determine the following:

a. $n(A^c)$ **b.** $n(B^c)$

c. $n(A^c \cap B)$ **d.** $n(A \cap B^c)$

e. $n(A \cup B)$ **f.** $n(A^c \cup B^c)$

5. In a group of 170 college students, 89 are enrolled in a course in principles of accounting, 108 are registered in a course in psychology, and 46 are enrolled in both courses. Determine the following.

a. How many students are enrolled in at least one course?

b. How many students are not enrolled in any of these courses?

c. How many students are taking exactly one course?

6. A market research organization claims that among 285 homemakers randomly selected in a suburb of Cleveland, Ohio, 142 homemakers buy product A, 133 buy product B, and 69 buy both products. Determine the number of homemakers who buy

a. at least one of these products

b. none of these products

c. exactly one of these products

7. Let A, B, and C be three subsets of $\mathscr{U}$, where

$$n(\mathscr{U}) = 80, \quad n(A) = 32, \quad n(B) = 36, \quad n(C) = 38, \quad n(A \cap B) = 12$$
$$n(A \cap C) = 14, \quad n(B \cap C) = 20, \quad n(A \cap B \cap C) = 8$$

Determine the following:

a. $n(A \cup B \cup C)$ **b.** $n[A \cap (B \cup C)]$

c. $n(A^c \cap B^c \cap C^c)$ **d.** $n[A \cup (B \cap C)]$

8. An airline reported the following statistics about a group of 270 students on one of their chartered flights to Europe:

    90 students visited Paris
    90 students visited Rome
    90 students visited Lisbon
    30 students visited Paris and Rome
    30 students visited Rome and Lisbon
    30 students visited Paris and Lisbon
    10 students visited Paris, Rome, and Lisbon

Determine the number of students who visited
a. at least one city
b. at least two cities
c. exactly one city
d. exactly two cities
e. none of these three cities

9. A survey of 100 business executives revealed the following information on college majors for business students:

    45 take business courses
    30 take technical courses
    52 take liberal arts courses
    17 take business and technical courses
    15 take business and liberal arts courses
     8 take liberal arts and technical courses
     6 take all three

Determine the number of students who take
a. at least one of these courses
b. none of these courses
c. only liberal arts courses
d. only technical courses
e. business as well as technical but not liberal arts courses

10. A survey of 70 business executives in a firm gave the following results:

    30 read *The Wall Street Journal*
    25 read *Business Week*
    20 read *Changing Times*
    10 read *The Wall Street Journal* and *Business Week*
     7 read *The Wall Street Journal* and *Changing Times*
     8 read *Business Week* and *Changing Times*
     3 read all three

How many business executives read
a. at least one magazine?
b. at least two magazines?
c. exactly one magazine?
d. exactly two magazines?
e. none of these three magazines?

11. A new car dealer has 250 cars in stock. Some cars have additional optional equipment of power steering, air conditioning, and automatic transmission as listed below:

    90 cars with power steering
    95 cars with automatic transmission
    93 cars with air conditioning
    40 cars with air conditioning and automatic transmission
    28 cars with air conditioning and power steering
    35 cars with automatic transmission and power steering
    18 cars with all three accessories

How many cars have
a. at least one piece of optional equipment?
b. exactly one piece of optional equipment?
c. at most one piece of optional equipment?
d. none of this equipment?

12. A store specializing in "take-home" service keeps a supply of 100 prepared hamburgers available. The manager reports that he has on hand:

> 28 hamburgers with mustard
> 30 hamburgers with ketchup
> 42 hamburgers with pickles
> 8 hamburgers with mustard and ketchup
> 10 hamburgers with mustard and pickles
> 5 hamburgers with ketchup and pickles
> 3 hamburgers with all three

a. How many plain hamburgers are available?
b. How many hamburgers are available with pickles only?
c. How many hamburgers have exactly two of the three choices?
d. How many hamburgers have exactly one of the three choices?

1.4 CARTESIAN PRODUCTS

We recall that if $A = \{a, b, c, d\}$, then the set $\{a, b\}$ consisting of two elements, a and b, is a subset of A; further, $\{a, b\}$ is the same set as $\{b, a\}$ because the order in which the elements in the set are listed is immaterial. At times, the order in which the information is recorded plays an important role. Consider, for example, that an auditor wants to describe the financial status of an airline by listing a pair of numbers with the understanding that the first and second numbers of the pair represent, respectively, the total assets and its liabilities in millions of dollars. The pair $(6, 0)$ means that the airline is in an excellent financial position, whereas the pair $(0, 6)$ implies that the airline is on the verge of bankruptcy. Thus, the pairs $(6, 0)$ and $(0, 6)$ convey very different information because of the order.

Definition 1.4.1: Let A and B be two sets. Then an ordered pair (a, b) where $a \in A$ and $b \in B$ is a listing of two elements in a certain order. The element a is called the first component in the ordered pair and the element b is called the second component in the ordered pair.

Two ordered pairs (a, b) and (c, d) are equal if and only if

(1.7) $\quad a = c \quad$ and $\quad b = d$

Consider now two sets A and B and all the ordered pairs that can be formed by selecting the first element of the pair from the set A and the second element of the pair from the set B. The set of ordered pairs thus obtained is called the Cartesian product of the sets A and B and is written as $A \times B$.

Definition 1.4.2: If A and B are two sets, then the Cartesian product of A and B, denoted by $A \times B$, is the set of all ordered pairs (a, b), where $a \in A$ and $b \in A$. In symbols,

(1.8) $\quad A \times B = \{(a, b) | a \in A, b \in B\}$

Example 1.19
Let $A = \{1, 2, 3, 4\}$, $B = \{6, 7\}$. List the elements in each of the following Cartesian products.

   (a) $A \times B$ (b) $B \times A$

SOLUTION
   (a) $A \times B = \{(1, 6), (2, 6), (3, 6), (4, 6), (1, 7), (2, 7), (3, 7), (4, 7)\}$, and
   (b) $B \times A = \{(6, 1), (6, 2), (6, 3), (6, 4), (7, 1), (7, 2), (7, 3), (7, 4)\}$ ■

Notice that in the above example $A \times B \neq B \times A$. Further, observe that in the above example

$$n(A) = 4, \quad n(B) = 2, \quad n(A \times B) = 8$$

Thus,

(1.9) $\quad n(A \times B) = n(A) \times n(B)$

This formula can be extended to the Cartesian product of any number of finite sets. The formula for three sets A, B, and C, for example, is given by

(1.10) $\quad n(A \times B \times C) = n(A) \times n(B) \times n(C)$

Example 1.20
List the set of all possible outcomes that can be obtained when a coin is tossed (a) twice, (b) three consecutive times. How many outcomes are possible in each case?

SOLUTION
   (a) Let $A = \{H, T\}$. Then the ordered pairs of $A \times A$ have first components belonging to A and second components also belonging to A. Thus,

$$A \times A = \{(H, H), (H, T), (T, H), (T, T)\}$$

Note that

$$n(A \times A) = n(A) \times n(A) = 4$$

   (b) $A \times A \times A = (A \times A) \times A$
$$= \{(H, H), (H, T), (T, H), (T, T)\} \times \{H, T\}$$
$$= \{(H, H, H), (H, H, T), (H, T, H), (H, T, T), (T, H, H),$$
$$(T, H, T), (T, T, H), (T, T, T)\}$$

Observe that the first, second, and third components in each of the ordered triplets are elements of A. The number of different outcomes is

$$n(A \times A \times A) = 8$$

which is precisely the same as the one given by

$$n(A) \times n(A) \times n(A) = 2 \times 2 \times 2$$

∎

EXERCISE 1.4

1. Let $A = \{2, 3, 4\}$ and $B = \{5, 6\}$. List the elements in each of the following:
   a. $A \times B$ b. $B \times A$
   c. $A \times A$ d. $B \times B$

2. Let $A = \{2, 3, 4, 5\}$ and $B = \{6, 7, 8\}$. List the elements in each of the following:
   a. $A \times B$ b. $B \times A$
   c. $A \times A$ d. $B \times B$

3. Given that $A = \{1, 2, 3\}$, $B = \{3, 4, 5\}$, and $C = \{6, 7, 8\}$, list the elements in each of the following:
   a. $A \times B$ b. $A \times C$ c. $B \times C$
   d. $B \times A$ e. $C \times A$ f. $C \times B$

4. Let $A = \{0\}$ and $B = \{5, 6, 7\}$. List the elements in
   a. $A \times B$ b. $B \times A$
   c. Determine $n(A \times B)$ and $n(B \times A)$.

5. Let $A = \varnothing$ and $B = \{5, 6, 7\}$. What can you say about
   a. $A \times B$ b. $B \times A$
   c. Determine $n(A \times B)$ and $n(B \times A)$.

6. A car manufacturer advertises a model with a choice of four colors—green, yellow, blue, and red—for the top and three colors—green, yellow, and red—for the body. List all the nine possible two-tone color designs.

7. Compute $n(A \times B)$ without enumerating the elements of $A \times B$ in each of the following:
   a. $A = \{a, b, c, d\}$, $B = \{f, g, h, k, m\}$
   b. $A = \{$Roger, Dick, Bob, Henry, Steve$\}$
      $B = \{$Jodey, Tracey, Anita, Jeannie$\}$
   c. $A = \{$Xerox, Kodak, ITT, IBM, Westinghouse$\}$
      $B = \{$Adam, Brown, Charles, Dick, Mark, Bill$\}$
   d. $A = \{1, 2, 3, 4, 5\}$, $B = \{a, b, c\}$
   e. $A = \{1, 2, 3, 4, 5, 6\}$, $B = \{H, T\}$

8. Compute $n(A \times A \times A)$ without enumerating the elements of $A \times A \times A$ in each of the following:
   a. $A = \{1, 2, 3, 4\}$ b. $A = \{1, 2, 3, 4, 5, 6\}$
   c. $A = \{a, b, c\}$ d. $A = \{H, T\}$

9. For the set $A = \{1, 2, 3, 4, 5, 6\}$, find a subset of $A \times A$ such that
   a. the sum of the two elements in each ordered pair is 7
   b. the two elements in each ordered pair are equal

10. For the set $A = \{H, T\}$, find a subset of $A \times A$ for which
   a. no tail occurs
   b. one tail occurs
   c. two tails occur
11. For the set $A = \{H, T\}$, find a subset of $A \times A \times A$ for which
   a. no tail occurs
   b. two heads and one tail occur
   c. one head and two tails occur
12. For the set $A = \{0, 1, 2, 3, 4\}$ and $B = \{0, 1, 2, 3\}$, find a subset of $A \times B$ such that
   a. the sum of the two elements in each ordered pair is 5
   b. the two elements in each ordered pair are the same
   c. the sum of two elements in each ordered pair is even

CHAPTER 2
Functions

2.1 INTRODUCTION

With our greater appreciation for the language of sets, it is now possible to refine the notion of a function and make its meaning precise. Although some of the concepts may appear abstract, they are nevertheless motivated by several practical problems in diversified fields. We must, however, caution the reader that the word "function" has a technical meaning in mathematics and is not to be confused with our use of the word when we speak of the functions of the board of directors of a company, the function of a neurologist in a hospital, or the function of a switch in a television set.

In almost every field, scientists strive to establish relationships between quantities that can be measured or observed. Engineers develop formulas that tell them how many inches certain beams bend when subjected to a certain number of pounds of load; a psychologist asks for the relationship between the average time it takes an adult to react to a certain quantity of a given stimulus; physicians are interested in the relationship between blood pressure and heart attack, between smoking and cancer, and the like; a sociologist may determine a relation between a person's economic status and his or her integration into society or between the increase in crime and increase in the population in cities. In the physical sciences, the relation between pressure and volume of a gas at a constant temperature is expressed by Boyle's law. In education, researchers study the relation between the IQ of pupils and their achievement in the elementary grades, between their high school performance and their later accomplishments in college, or between some career-oriented college programs and any sharp increase in the general college enrollment. Economists strive to determine relationships between the demand and the price of a product, between consumption of a commodity and its supply in the market, between the money available for the construction industry and the current prime rate of interest, and so on.

In this chapter we concentrate on the essential features of such quantitative relationships and describe them by means of formulas and graphs.

2.2 FUNCTIONS AND EQUATIONS

Consider, for example, the set A of babies born in the United States in 1976 and let B be the set of real numbers between 0 and 100. For each baby in the set A, we have one and only one real number in the set B, that is, his or her weight in pounds at the time of birth. The rule that associates with each baby his or her weight (an element of B) describes a function.

Note that goods shipped to the warehouse is a function of the production capacity of the factory, the amount of money a family spends on entertainment is a function of its earnings, the distance that a car travels at a certain speed is a function of time, the grade a student can get in a course is a function of the number of hours he or she studies, the salary of a sales executive is a function of how long he has been with the company, and so on.

Consider next the equation $s = 16t^2$ describing the law of a falling body. If an object is released from rest in a vacuum near the surface of the earth, then 1 sec after its release it has traveled 16 ft below its starting point, 2 sec after its release it has traveled 64 ft, 3 sec after its release it has traveled 144 ft, and so on. Thus, if we know the time t in seconds after the release of an object, the formula $s = 16t^2$ gives us the distance s the object has traveled below its starting point. Notice that for each value of t, there is one and only one value of s corresponding to that value of t.

As another illustration, consider an equation $y = 3x + 2$. For each real number x, we obtain one and only one real number y corresponding to that value of x. For example, if $x = 1$, then $y = 5$; if $x = 2$, then $y = 8$; if $x = 10$, then $y = 32$, and so on. Thus, the equation $y = 3x + 2$ is a rule that assigns to each value of x one and only one value of y. Essentially, the rule is this: Take three times the value of x and then add 2 to it. This leads us to the practical origins of the abstract mathematical idea of a function, which we define informally as follows:

Definition 2.2.1: Let A and B be two nonempty sets. Then a function from A to B is a rule that assigns to each element $x \in A$ one and only one element $y \in B$. This element y is called the image of x (see Figure 2.1).

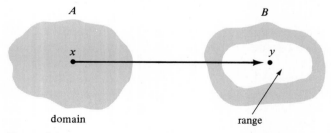

Figure 2.1

The set A is called the domain of the function, and the subset of B that contains all images of the elements of A is called the range R of the function. We may use any kind of objects to make up the domain and the range of the function. However, most of the functions we shall discuss will be ones for which A and B will be sets of real numbers. We call such functions real-valued functions of a real variable; that is, the domain and the range of the functions are sets of real numbers. The element x in the domain is called an independent variable and the corresponding element y in the range is called the dependent variable. Thus, in general, the notion of a function involves three things:

1. A set D_f called the domain of the function;
2. A set R_f called the range of the function; and
3. A rule of correspondence that assigns to each element of the domain one and only one element of the range.

We denote functions by small letters: $f, g, h, \ldots$. If f is a function, then the number that f assigns to an element x in the domain is denoted by $f(x)$. This symbol is read "f of x" or "f evaluated at x" or "the value of f at the point x." To point out the usefulness of this mathematical symbolism, suppose that we want to describe the demand for a commodity in a symbolic form. If p denotes the price of a commodity and q represents the quantity of that commodity demanded by consumers, then we can express this quantitative relationship by $q = f(p)$, which simply means that the quantity in demand depends, in some way, on the price of the commodity. Likewise, we may write the consumption function as $c = g(s)$, where c denotes the consumption of a commodity and s designates the supply of that commodity available at a point of time. The symbolic expression $c = g(s)$ is interpreted to mean that the consumption is a function of the supply.

To specify a function, we must give its domain and the rule that pairs each element x of its domain with one and only one value $f(x)$, thus determining the range. Generally, the rule of correspondence is expressed in the form of a mathematical equation, as is illustrated in the next few examples.

Example 2.1

Let f be a function defined by

$$f(x) = 4x + 5$$

with the set $\{2, 3, 4, 5, 6, 7\}$ as its domain. Then

$$f(2) = 4(2) + 5 = 13 \qquad f(5) = 4(5) + 5 = 25$$
$$f(3) = 4(3) + 5 = 17 \qquad f(6) = 4(6) + 5 = 29$$
$$f(4) = 4(4) + 5 = 21 \qquad f(7) = 4(7) + 5 = 33$$

The range R_f is the set $\{13, 17, 21, 25, 29, 33\}$. ■

Example 2.2

Let f be a function defined by

$$f(x) = x^2 + 3$$

with the set $\{-3, -2, -1, 0, 1, 2, 3\}$ as its domain. Then

$$f(-3) = (-3)^2 + 3 = 12 \qquad f(1) = 1^2 + 3 = 4$$
$$f(-2) = (-2)^2 + 3 = 7 \qquad f(2) = 2^2 + 3 = 7$$
$$f(-1) = (-1)^2 + 3 = 4 \qquad f(3) = 3^2 + 3 = 12$$
$$f(0) = (0)^2 + 3 = 3$$

The range R_f is the set $\{3, 4, 7, 12\}$. ■

Example 2.3

Let f be a function defined by

$$f(x) = 2x + 3$$

whose domain is the set of all real numbers. Then for some of the choices from the domain, we have

$$f(-3) = 2(-3) + 3 = -3 \qquad f(1) = 2(1) + 3 = 5$$
$$f(-2) = 2(-2) + 3 = -1 \qquad f(\sqrt{2}) = 2\sqrt{2} + 3$$
$$f(-1) = 2(-1) + 3 = 1 \qquad f(2) = 2(2) + 3 = 7$$
$$f(0) = 2(0) + 3 = 3 \qquad f(3) = 2(3) + 3 = 9$$
$$f(\tfrac{1}{2}) = 2(\tfrac{1}{2}) + 3 = 4 \qquad f(\pi) = 2\pi + 3$$

and so on. Intuitively, the range is also the set of all real numbers. ■

Example 2.4

Let f be a function defined by

$$f(x) = 3x^2 + 1$$

with its domain as the set of all real numbers. Then for some arbitrary choices from the domain, we have

$$f(-2) = 3(-2)^2 + 1 = 13 \qquad f(\sqrt{2}) = 3(\sqrt{2})^2 + 1 = 7$$
$$f(-1) = 3(-1)^2 + 1 = 4 \qquad f(2) = 3(2)^2 + 1 = 13$$
$$f(0) = 3(0)^2 + 1 = 1 \qquad f(3) = 3(3)^2 + 1 = 28$$
$$f(\tfrac{1}{2}) = 3(\tfrac{1}{2})^2 + 1 = \tfrac{7}{4} \qquad f(4) = 3(4)^2 + 1 = 49$$

Thus, intuitively, the range is the set of real numbers greater than or equal to 1. ■

We wish to remark that although the domain is an essential part of the function, it is frequently not mentioned, especially when the rule of correspondence between the sets is given by a mathematical equation. The general convention is that unless the domain is stated explicitly, it is understood to consist of all real numbers for which the defining equation makes any sense. The rule f that associates to each element x in the domain with one and only one value $f(x)$ determines the range.

Example 2.5

Let f be a function defined by

$$f(x) = \sqrt{4 - x^2}$$

Observe that this rule of correspondence does not yield a real number for $x > 2$ or $x < -2$. For example, if $x = 3$, then

$$\sqrt{4 - x^2} = \sqrt{4 - 9} = \sqrt{-5}$$

which is not a real number. Therefore, the domain D_f is the set of reals between -2 and 2, inclusive. The rule f assigns to each $x \in D_f$ one and only one number $\sqrt{4 - x^2}$ in the range. Intuitively, the range R_f consists of non-negative reals between 0 and 2, inclusive. ■

Example 2.6

Let f be a function defined by

$$f(x) = \frac{1}{x}$$

The domain D_f is the set of nonzero real numbers, because for $x = 0$ the function $f(x)$ is not defined. Observe that

$$f(0.1) = 10 \qquad f(0.001) = 1000$$
$$f(0.01) = 100 \qquad f(0.0001) = 10,000$$

and so on. Hence, if x is close to zero and positive, $f(x)$ is large and positive. Also,

$$f(1) = 1 \qquad f(100) = 0.01$$
$$f(10) = 0.1 \qquad f(1000) = 0.001$$

Thus, if x is positive and large, $f(x)$ is positive and near zero. Similar remarks apply to $x < 0$.

The range R_f consists of all nonzero real numbers. ∎

Let us now consider some practical illustrations of the functions. Suppose, for example, that the market demand function for a product is given by

$$f(p) = 400 - 10p$$

where $f(p)$ denotes the quantity demanded per year in thousands of units and p denotes the price per unit. Because p is an element of the domain of the function f and the corresponding element of the range is denoted by $f(p)$, we have for some choices of p,

$$f(0) = 400 \qquad f(10.3) = 297$$
$$f(1) = 390 \qquad f(12) = 280$$
$$f(1.5) = 385 \qquad f(15) = 250$$
$$f(2) = 380 \qquad f(20) = 200$$
$$\vdots \qquad\qquad \vdots$$
$$f(9.7) = 303 \qquad f(30) = 100$$
$$f(10) = 300 \qquad f(40) = 0$$

Because the price p per unit is charged only in dollars and cents, we conclude that the domain D_f is the set of all such numbers between 0 and 40, inclusive, that is, $\{0, 0.01, 0.02, 0.03, \ldots, 39.98, 39.99, 40\}$. The range R_f is the set $\{0, 0.1, 0.2, 0.3, \ldots, 399.8, 399.9, 400\}$, and for each value of p in the set D_f, there is one and only one value $f(p)$ in the set R_f.

Conversely, for each value $f(p)$ in the set R_f, there is one and only one element in the domain D_f. Thus, the relationship between the elements of two sets is not only a function but also a one-to-one correspondence. Other examples of one-to-one correspondences are the one between the employees in a company and their social security numbers, one between husbands and their wives, one between the 50 states of the United States and their governors, and so on.

To give an example of a function that is not a one-to-one correspondence, consider the set of 30 students who have taken a final examination in a philosophy course. After the tests have been graded, the instructor assigns to each test a letter grade A, B, C, D, or F. Note that because for each test there corresponds one and only one letter grade, the condition for the function is satisfied. The domain is the set of 30 tests and the range consists of only those letter grades that have actually been assigned. That this function is not one-to-one correspondence follows from the fact that more than one test may correspond to the same letter grade in the range.

As another illustration, consider a travel agency in New York that advertises an all-expense-paid 5-day cruise to Nova Scotia for certain special groups. The agency makes reservations for 50 couples on the boat. The charge is $600 per couple with an additional charge of $20 for each subsequent cancellation. If x is the number of cancellations received prior to the departure of the boat, then $(50 - x)$ couples plan to be on the boat and each pays $600 plus $20x$. Thus, the total receipts of the travel agency are given by

$$f(x) = \$(50 - x)(600 + 20x)$$

which on simplification yields

$$f(x) = \$20(1500 + 20x - x^2)$$

The domain of the function is the set

$$A = \{0, 1, 2, \ldots, 50\}$$

Let us now compute $f(x)$ for some values of x in the set A. For example,

$$f(0) = \$30,000 \qquad f(15) = \$31,500$$
$$f(5) = \$31,500 \qquad f(20) = \$30,000$$
$$f(10) = \$32,000 \qquad f(25) = \$27,500$$

and so on.

The reader can verify that for each value x in the set A, there is a unique value $f(x)$ in its range. Thus, the relationship between the two sets constitutes a function, but this function is not a one-to-one correspondence. (Why?) Notice that two values of x, $x = 0$ and $x = 20$ (for example), in the set A correspond to the same value $f(x) = \$30,000$. Similarly, $x = 5$ and $x = 15$ in the set A correspond to one value $f(x) = \$31,500$ in the range. Thus, we have some elements in the range of the function that correspond to more than one element in the domain, and this is precisely what we need in order to show that the function under consideration is not one to one.

So far, we have considered a function as a rule of correspondence that pairs with each element of its domain one and only one element of its range. This shows that a function is actually a set of ordered pairs. The following is a formal definition.

Definition 2.2.2: Let A and B be two nonempty sets. Then a function from A to B is a set of ordered pairs (x, y), where $x \in A$ and $y \in B$ such that every element of A appears as a first element of exactly one ordered pair.

Example 2.7

The set of ordered pairs

$$\{(1, 5), (2, 8), (3, 11), (4, 14), (5, 17)\}$$

is a function with the set $A = \{1, 2, 3, 4, 5\}$ as its domain and the set $B = \{5, 8, 11, 14, 17\}$ as its range. Figure 2.2 describes this function.

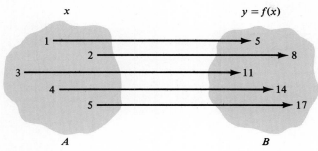

Figure 2.2

Another way to describe this function is

$$\{(x, f(x))/f(x) = 3x + 2, x \in A\}$$

where $A = \{1, 2, 3, 4, 5\}$. Note that $y = f(x)$, and this function is one to one. ∎

Example 2.8

The set of ordered pairs

$$\{(-5, 26), (-3, 10), (-1, 2), (1, 2), (3, 10), (5, 26)\}$$

is a function with the set $A = \{-5, -3, -1, 1, 3, 5\}$ as its domain and the set $B = \{2, 10, 26\}$ as its range. The rule of correspondence that pairs elements of the domain with the elements of the range is described in Figure 2.3.

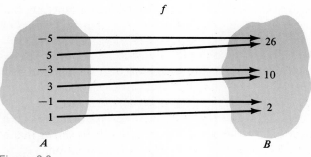

Figure 2.3

In a mathematical equation, we may express this function as

$$\{(x, f(x))/f(x) = x^2 + 1, x \in A\}$$

Example 2.9

The set of ordered pairs

$$\{(-1, 3), (2, 4), (3, 5), (2, 6), (4, 7)\}$$

is not a function because an element 2 in the domain is paired with both 4 and 6 in the range as illustrated in Figure 2.4.

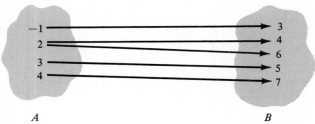

Figure 2.4

Notice that a function from set A to set B is given as a set of ordered pairs and this set of ordered pairs is a subset of the Cartesian product $A \times B$. In order for a subset of $A \times B$ to be a function from set A to set B, each element of A must appear as a first element in one and only one of the ordered pairs constituting that subset. Thus, the set of ordered pairs

$$\{(x, f(x))/f(x) = 2x^2 + 5\}$$

is a function from the set of real numbers to the set of real numbers greater than or equal to 5. ∎

It is instructive to think of a function as a machine that produces a unique output for a given input (see Figure 2.5). If f is a function, then we can interpret the domain of the function as the set of all those elements that can be entered into the machine. If we enter an element x in the machine, it produces $f(x)$ as its output. The range of the machine, thus, is the set of all outputs. As an example, consider the function

$$f(x) = 3x^2 + 2$$

with the set $A = \{-2, -1, 0, 1, 2\}$ as its domain. If a number $x \in A$ is entered, the machine squares this input, multiplies it by 3, and then adds 2 to the number thus obtained. Thus,

$$f(-2) = 3(-2)^2 + 2 = 14 \qquad f(-1) = 3(-1)^2 + 2 = 5$$
$$f(0) = 3(0)^2 + 2 = 2 \qquad f(1) = 3(1)^2 + 2 = 5$$
$$f(2) = 3(2)^2 + 2 = 14$$

and the range of the function is the set $\{2, 5, 14\}$.

Notice that in the notation $f(x)$, the independent variable x is "dummy" in the sense that $f(x)$ is the same as $f(a)$, $f(b)$, $f(c)$, and so on. Thus, if $f(x) = 3x^2 + 2$, then $f(a) = 3a^2 + 2$, $f(b) = 3b^2 + 2$, $f(c) = 3c^2 + 2$, and so on. Thus, no matter what

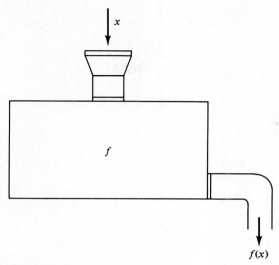

Figure 2.5

we put in the machine, that quantity is squared, then multiplied by 3, and finally 2 is added to the number obtained. We do assume that whatever is entered in the machine is a part of the domain of the function f.

Example 2.10

Suppose that f is the function defined by the equation

$$f(x) = x^2 + 3x + 4$$

Find (a) $f(0)$, (b) $f(1)$, (c) $f(2)$, (d) $f(3)$, and (e) $f(x + 2)$.

SOLUTION

    (a) $f(0) = 0^2 + 3 \cdot 0 + 4 = 4$
    (b) $f(1) = 1^2 + 3 \cdot 1 + 4 = 8$
    (c) $f(2) = 2^2 + 3 \cdot 2 + 4 = 14$
    (d) $f(3) = 3^2 + 3 \cdot 3 + 4 = 22$
    (e) $f(x + 2) = (x + 2)^2 + 3(x + 2) + 4 = x^2 + 7x + 14$

Example 2.11

Let $f(x) = x + 4$. Determine (a) $f(a)$, (b) $f(x + 2)$, (c) $f(x^2)$, and (d) $f(2x + 3)$.

SOLUTION

    (a) $f(a) = a + 4$
    (b) $f(x + 2) = (x + 2) + 4 = x + 6$
    (c) $f(x^2) = x^2 + 4$
    (d) $f(2x + 3) = (2x + 3) + 4 = 2x + 7$ ■

EXERCISE 2.1

1. Decide whether the situations described below constitute functions.
  a. the correspondence between the State Colleges in California and their presidents
  b. the correspondence between the professors at your college and the freshman courses they teach in one semester
  c. the correspondence between all homemakers in Hartford, Connecticut, and the grocery stores in which they shop
  d. the correspondence between the states and their Senators in the United States Senate
  e. the correspondence between authors and the books they publish
  f. the correspondence between the products sold in a department store and their prices
  g. the correspondence between the insurance companies and their senior vice-presidents
  h. the correspondence between salespeople and the sales territory they cover
  i. the correspondence between the churches and their pastors
  j. the correspondence between the residents of Boston and their telephone numbers
2. State which of the functions of Exercise 1 are one-to-one correspondences.
3. Determine whether or not the following rules of correspondence in Figure 2.6 are functions from A to B.

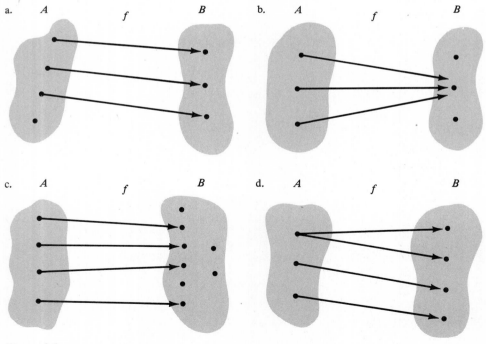

Figure 2.6

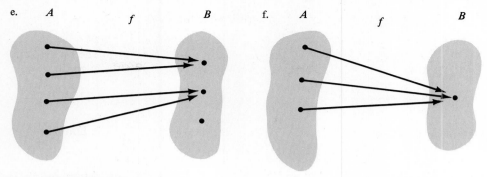

Figure 2.6 (*Continued*)

4. Determine whether or not the following sets of ordered pairs are functions.
   a. $\{(2, 3), (3, 4), (4, 5)\}$
   b. $\{(2, 3), (3, 4), (4, 5), (5, 4)\}$
   c. $\{(1, 1), (2, 2), (3, 3), (4, 4), (5, 5)\}$
   d. $\{(1, 1), (2, 1), (3, 1), (4, 1), (5, 1)\}$
   e. $\{(2, 4), (4, 6), (2, 6)\}$
   f. $\{(4, 2), (6, 4), (6, 2)\}$
   g. $\{(1, 1), (2, 4), (3, 9), (4, 16), (5, 25)\}$
   h. $\{(3, 5), (4, 5)\}$

5. Determine whether or not the following sets of ordered pairs $(x, f(x))$ define functions:

a.

x	1	2	3
$f(x)$	4	5	6

b.

x	1	2	3
$f(x)$	2	2	2

c.

x	1	2	3	3
$f(x)$	4	5	6	7

d.

x	0	2	3	4
$f(x)$	0	4	9	16

e.

x	1	2	3	4
$f(x)$	1	8	27	64

f.

x	1	2	1	2
$f(x)$	3	4	4	5

6. State which of the functions of Exercise 4 are one-to-one correspondences.

7. Find the domain and the range of each of the following functions.
   a. $f(x) = x$
   b. $f(x) = 4x + 5$
   c. $f(x) = x^2$
   d. $f(x) = x^2 - 4$
   e. $f(x) = \dfrac{6}{x}$
   f. $f(x) = \sqrt{9 - x^2}$

8. Find the domain and the range in each of the following functions.
   a. $f(x) = \dfrac{x}{2}$
   b. $f(x) = 3$
   c. $f(x) = \dfrac{1}{x - 1}$
   d. $f(x) = x + \dfrac{1}{x}$
   e. $f(x) = \sqrt{16 - x^2}$
   f. $f(x) = \sqrt{x^2 - 16}$

9. Given that $f(x) = x^2 - 2x + 3$, determine the following:

 a. $f(-2)$ **b.** $f(3)$ **c.** $f(8)$

 d. $f(0)$ **e.** $f(4)$ **f.** $f(12)$

10. Given that

$$f(x) = \frac{150 + 20x}{x}$$

determine the following:

 a. $f(1)$ **b.** $f(2)$ **c.** $f(3)$

 d. $f(4)$ **e.** $f(5)$ **f.** $f(6)$

11. Given that $g(x) = x^3 - 3x^2 + 3x + 8$, find the following:

 a. $g(0)$ **b.** $g(2)$ **c.** $g(3)$

 d. $g(-1)$ **e.** $g(-2)$ **f.** $g(5)$

12. Assuming that $g(x) = -2x + 40$ gives the number of students in a large class who require x hours of study weekly, determine the number of students who require the following amounts of study:

 a. $x = 0$ **b.** $x = 1$ **c.** $x = 2$

 d. $x = 4$ **e.** $x = 5$ **f.** $x = 10$

13. Suppose that the demand d for a certain product is given by

$$d(p) = 100 - 4p^2$$

where p is the price in dollars per unit. Determine the demand $d(p)$ for $p = 0$ to $p = 5$ inclusive.

14. The total cost of production for a firm producing a certain commodity is given by

$$c(x) = 100 + 10x$$

where x denotes the number of units produced and $c(x)$ is the total cost in dollars of producing x units. Determine the total cost schedule and the average cost schedule $A(x) = c(x)/x$ for $x = 1$ to $x = 10$ inclusive.

15. The total cost of production for a firm producing a certain commodity is given by

$$f(x) = 100 + 5x - 2x^2$$

where x denotes the output of the firm in hundreds of units per month and $f(x)$ is the total cost in thousands of dollars. Determine the total cost schedule and the average cost schedule for $x = 1$ to $x = 7$ inclusive.

2.3 COORDINATE SYSTEM

We choose an arbitrary point 0 in the xy plane called an origin and draw a pair of mutually perpendicular lines through 0, one horizontal and the other vertical. The horizontal line is called the x axis and the vertical line is called the y axis. The axes together are called the coordinate axes, and the plane in which the axes lie is called the coordinate plane. An arbitrary unit of length is selected, and starting from the origin a number scale is marked on the x axis, positive to the right and negative to the left, of the origin 0. Similarly, a scale is marked along the vertical axis with positive numbers marked upward and negative numbers marked downward. Although the units measured along the x axis have the same length as the units along the y axis in Figure 2.7, it is not necessary that they be equal.

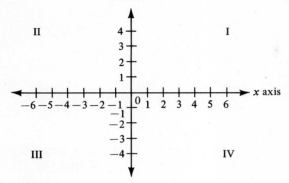

Figure 2.7

The coordinate axes divide the plane into four quadrants numbered as indicated in Figure 2.7. We are now ready to set up a one-to-one correspondence between a set of ordered pairs of numbers and the points of the plane. If P is a point in the plane (Figure 2.8), we draw two lines through P, one perpendicular to the x axis and the other perpendicular to the y axis. The intersection with the horizontal axis is at the point A, whereas the intersection with the vertical axis is at the point B. The point A is "a" units to the right of the origin if a is positive and on the left if a is negative. Similarly, the point B is "b" units above the x axis if b is positive and below the x axis if b is negative. Thus, the ordered pair associated with the point P in the plane is (a, b). The number a is called the x coordinate or abscissa of P and the number b is called the y coordinate or ordinate of P. Thus, P is a point with coordinates (a, b).

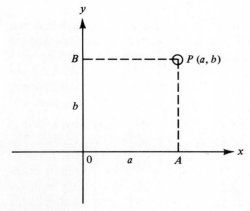

Figure 2.8

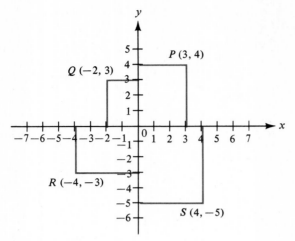

Figure 2.9

Figure 2.9 shows the coordinates of $P(3, 4)$, $Q(-2, 3)$, $R(-4, -3)$, and $S(4, -5)$. Because the coordinate axes divide the plane into four quadrants, it is easy to determine the quadrant from the signs of the coordinates of a point. A point with two positive coordinates lies in quadrant I; a point $P(c, d)$ with a negative c and a positive d lies in quadrant II; a point with both negative coordinates is located in quadrant III; and so on. Thus, if (c, d) is any ordered pair of real numbers, we start at the origin and go along the x axis to the right if c is positive and to the left if c is negative until we reach c units from the origin 0. Then we go d units along a line parallel to the y axis upward if d is positive and downward if d is negative. The point so located has coordinates (c, d). We have noted earlier that to each point in the plane there corresponds a unique ordered pair of real numbers, and, conversely, to each ordered pair of real numbers there exists exactly one point in the plane.

2.4 DISTANCE BETWEEN TWO POINTS

We shall now use the coordinate system to determine the distance between two department stores, between two warehouses, or between two cities. Consider, for example, that a furniture store in town A schedules a delivery on Monday of a bedroom set to a customer in town B. What will be the distance traveled in one round trip? To answer questions of this nature, we must first identify the coordinates of towns A and B. If the two towns, say $A(x_1, y_1)$ and $B(x_2, y_2)$, have the same abscissa, that is, $x_1 = x_2$, then the distance between them is $y_2 - y_1$ if $y_2 > y_1$ and $y_1 - y_2$ if $y_2 < y_1$. Thus, the distance between $A(20, 25)$ and $B(20, 32)$ is simply $32 - 25 = 7$ miles and the distance between $A(15, 12)$ and $B(15, -8)$ is $12 - (-8) = 20$ miles. Similarly, if the towns A and B have the same ordinate, that is, $y_1 = y_2$, then the distance between them is $x_2 - x_1$ if $x_2 > x_1$ and $x_1 - x_2$ if $x_2 < x_1$. Thus, the distance between $A(10, 12)$ and $B(23, 12)$ is $23 - 10 = 13$ miles and the distance between $A(10, 12)$ and $B(-6, 12)$ is $10 - (-6) = 16$ miles. Note that the distances measured are always positive.

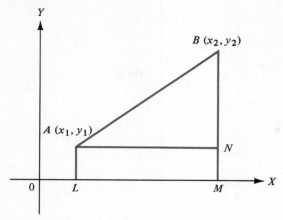

Figure 2.10

We now extend the concept of distance to the two points $A(x_1, y_1)$ and $B(x_2, y_2)$ that have neither the same abscissa nor the same ordinate. (See Figure 2.10.) Draw AL and BM perpendicular to the x axis and AN perpendicular to BM. The triangle ANB so formed is a right triangle with a right angle at N. Note that the sides AN and NB are of lengths $x_2 - x_1$ and $y_2 - y_1$, respectively. By the Pythagorean theorem,

$$(AB)^2 = (AN)^2 + (NB)^2 .$$

or

$$AB = \sqrt{(AN)^2 + (NB)^2}$$
$$= \sqrt{(x_2 - x_1)^2 + (y_2 - y_1)^2}$$

Hence, we have established the following proposition.

Proposition 2.4.1: The distance from $A(x_1, y_1)$ to $B(x_2, y_2)$, $x_1 \neq x_2$, $y_1 \neq y_2$, written as $d[A, B]$, is equal to

$$\sqrt{(x_2 - x_1)^2 + (y_2 - y_1)^2}$$

It can be shown that the Proposition 2.4.1 holds for $x_1 = x_2$ or $y_1 = y_2$. We shall leave this as an exercise for the student.

Example 2.12
Find the distance between $A(8, 10)$ and $B(20, 15)$.

SOLUTION
Letting $x_1 = 8$, $y_1 = 10$, $x_2 = 20$, and $y_2 = 15$ in Proposition 2.4.1, we have

$$d[A, B] = \sqrt{(20 - 8)^2 + (15 - 10)^2}$$
$$= \sqrt{(12)^2 + (5)^2}$$
$$= \sqrt{144 + 25}$$
$$= \sqrt{169}$$
$$= 13$$

Note the following properties of the distance function $d[A, B]$.

1. $d[A, B] = 0$ if B is the same point as A.
2. $d[A, B] > 0$ if $B \neq A$.
3. $d[A, B] = \sqrt{(x_2 - x_1)^2 + (y_2 - y_1)^2}$
   $= \sqrt{(x_1 - x_2)^2 + (y_1 - y_2)^2}$
   $= d[B, A]$.

EXERCISE 2.2

1. Graph the following points.
   a. $(2, 4)$ **b.** $(-3, 8)$ **c.** $(-4, -5)$ **d.** $(0, 1)$
   e. $(0, 3)$ **f.** $(12, 5)$ **g.** $(5, 12)$ **h.** $(-5, -12)$

2. Determine the coordinates of
   a. point A **b.** point B **c.** point C
   d. point D **e.** point P **f.** point Q
   in Figure 2.11.

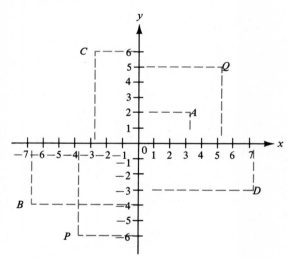

Figure 2.11

3. Determine the distance between each of the following pairs of points without using Proposition 2.4.1.
   a. $(2, 4)$ and $(8, 4)$ **b.** $(3, 5)$ and $(3, -4)$
   c. $(8, 6)$ and $(8, 12)$ **d.** $(8, 7)$ and $(8, -7)$
   e. $(12, 5)$ and $(-8, 5)$ **f.** $(4, -5)$ and $(-10, -5)$

4. Determine the distance between the following pairs of points.
   a. $(0, 0)$ and $(3, 4)$ **b.** $(6, 2)$ and $(10, 5)$
   c. $(3, 4)$ and $(9, 12)$ **d.** $(-2, 1)$ and $(10, 6)$
   e. $(-8, -9)$ and $(16, -2)$ **f.** $(4, -3)$ and $(20, 9)$

5. Some household furniture is to be shipped from town A to town B. It can be shipped directly by train at a cost of \$3.25 per mile or by moving van lines via

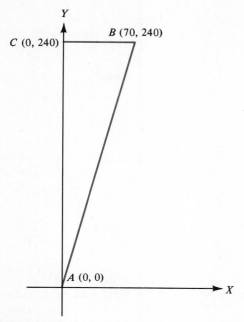

Figure 2.12

town C at a cost of \$3.00 per mile. Assuming that towns A, B, and C are located as shown in Figure 2.12, which way is cheaper?

6. A new automobile is to be shipped to town C from a plant located in town A. It can be shipped directly by a freight train at a cost of \$1.30 per mile or by truck via town B at a cost of \$1.25 per mile. Assuming that the coordinates of A, B, and C are (20, 11), (200, 11), and (200, 30), determine which mode of transportation is cheaper.

7. Show that the points (12, 8), (-2, 6), and (6, 0) are the vertices of a right triangle. (Hint: Use the Pythagorean theorem.)

8. Show that the points (0, -1), (2, 1), (0, 3), and (-2, 1) are the vertices of a square.

9. Show that the points (-5, 1), (5, 5), and (10, 7) lie on a straight line.

10. Show that the coordinates of the middle point C of the line joining $A(x_1, y_1)$ and $B(x_2, y_2)$ are given by

$$\left(\frac{x_1 + x_2}{2}, \frac{y_1 + y_2}{2} \right)$$

2.5 THE GRAPH OF A FUNCTION

A function may be represented graphically by using a rectangular coordinate system. Assuming that a function is given by a mathematical equation $y = f(x)$, it is possible to learn the simultaneous behavior of x and y by plotting a set of points (x, y), where x represents an arbitrary value selected from the domain of the function and y is the corresponding value determined by the rule of correspondence. Each of the ordered pairs $(x, f(x))$ corresponds to a distinct point in the plane. We shall follow the convention that if the domain consists of only a finite number of members, the points plotted in the plane represent the entire graph; but when the domain consists of rational numbers within a specified interval, we shall show the graph as a dotted curve drawn through the plotted points. The graph will be drawn as a solid curve if the domain of the function consists of all real numbers in an interval. Consider, for instance, a function

$$f(x) = x^2$$

with its domain as set of integers between -4 and 4, inclusive. Thus, we have a set of ordered pairs in the following table below, the first component of which is an element of the domain and the second component of which is the corresponding element in the range.

x	-4	-3	-2	-1	0	1	2	3	4
$f(x)$	16	9	4	1	0	1	4	9	16

Plotting the ordered pairs $(-4, 16), (-3, 9), \ldots, (4, 16)$, we have the graph in Figure 2.13. If the domain of $f(x) = x^2$ consists of all reals between -4 and 4 inclusive, then the graph consists of a smooth curve drawn through the plotted points. The graph is a curve of infinite extent if the domain consists of all reals. This is illustrated by the arrows in Figure 2.14.

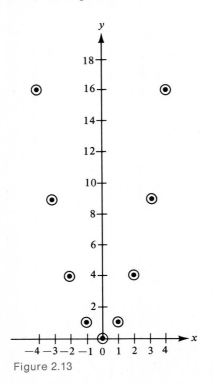

Figure 2.13

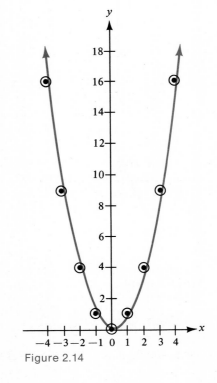

Figure 2.14

Example 2.13

Plot the graph of

$$f(x) = 2x + 3$$

where the domain is the set of all reals.

SOLUTION

Because we cannot list all possible pairs of real numbers satisfying the above equation, we shall use a partial list of points to determine the shape of the curve. The values of $f(x)$ for some values of x, say, $x = -1, 0, 1, 2$, and 3, are given in the following table.

x	$f(x) = 2x + 3$
-1	1
0	3
1	5
2	7
3	9

The graph, which consists of a smooth curve passing through the points $(-1, 1)$, $(0, 3), \ldots, (3, 9)$, is displayed in Figure 2.15.

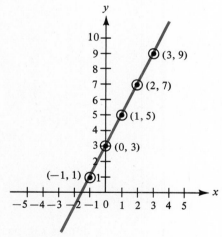

Figure 2.15

Example 2.14

Plot the graph of

$$f(x) = \begin{cases} 5 - x & x < 3 \\ 2x - 4 & x \geq 3 \end{cases}$$

where the domain of f is the set of real numbers.

SOLUTION

Note that the function has its domain separated into two disjoint sets upon each of which it is defined differently. The values of $f(x)$ for some values of x are given separately for each piece in the following tables.

$f(x) = 5 - x, x < 3$

x	$f(x)$
-2	7
-1	6
0	5
1	4
2	3

$f(x) = 2x - 4, x \geq 3$

x	$f(x)$
3	2
4	4
5	6
6	8

The graph consists of two straight lines—one passing through the points $(-2, 7)$, $(-1, 6), \ldots, (2, 3)$ and the other passing through the points $(3, 2), \ldots, (6, 8)$ as shown in Figure 2.16.

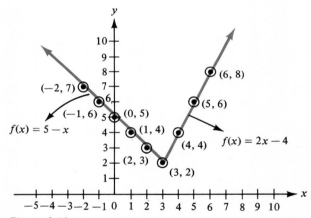

Figure 2.16

Example 2.15

The demand for a certain product is given by

$$f(x) = 100 - 20x$$

where $f(x)$ represents the demand of the product at a unit price of x dollars. Graph $f(x)$.

SOLUTION

Note that $f(x)$ must be non-negative. (Why?) Because the price per unit is charged in dollars and cents, the variable x may assume the values $0.01, 0.02, 0.03, \ldots, 4.98, 4.99, 5.00$. If $x > 5$, then $20x > 100$ and consequently $100 - 20x$ is a negative number. Thus, the domain of the function consists of only two-decimal-place numbers between 0 and 5, inclusive. The values of $f(x)$ for some values of x, say, $x = 0, 1, 2, 3, 4$, and 5, are given in the following table.

x	$f(x) = 100 - 20x$
0	100
1	80
2	60
3	40
4	20
5	0

The related set of ordered pairs (0, 100), (1, 80), (2, 60), (3, 40), (4, 20), and (5, 0) determine a set of points that are plotted in Figure 2.17. The dotted line, indeed, represents the corresponding graph of $f(x)$.

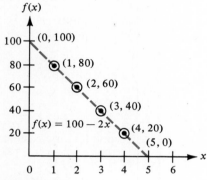

Figure 2.17

Example 2.16

The manager of a chain of bookstores has determined that the supply s of certain paperbacks is given approximately by

$$s(p) = 30 - \frac{60}{p - 1}$$

where $s(p)$ denotes the supply at the price p (in dollars) per carton of books.

a. Find the supply for $p = 3, 4, 5, 6, 7, 11, 16, 21$.

b. Graph $s(p)$ by plotting the corresponding points obtained in part a and joining them by a dotted curve.

c. Discuss the practical significance of the graph, if any.

SOLUTION

a. The calculated value of $s(p)$ for each of the given values of p is given below:

p	3	4	5	6	7	11	16	21
$s(p)$	0	10	15	18	20	24	26	27

b. Plotting the ordered pairs (3, 0), (4, 10), (5, 15), (6, 18), (7, 20), (11, 24), (16, 26), and (21, 27) and joining them by dotted lines, we have the graph in Figure 2.18.

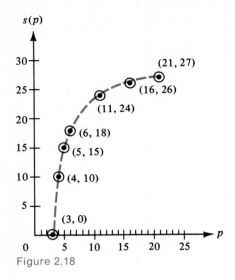

Figure 2.18

c. Notice that the supply "levels off." For $p = 31$, $s(p) = 28$ and for $p = 61$, $s(p) = 29$. Thus, it follows that as the price increases, the corresponding increase in the supply becomes very insignificant. ∎

Example 2.17

Because of raw material shortages and higher labor costs, it has become increasingly expensive to drill for oil found in relatively inaccessible locations. In fact, the profits (in millions of dollars) are determined approximately by the function

$$P(x) = 80x - 10x^2 \qquad 0 \leq x \leq 8$$

where x is the number of millions of barrels of oil produced and $P(x)$ is the corresponding profit. Determine the level of production that will yield maximum profit.

SOLUTION

Because we are unable to list all ordered pairs of real numbers in the specified interval that may satisfy $P(x)$, we shall use only a partial list of ordered pairs. The following table shows the value of $P(x)$ corresponding to some values of x.

x	0	1	2	3	4	5	6	7	8
$P(x)$ (in dollars)	0	70	120	150	160	150	120	70	0

Plotting the ordered pairs $(0, 0)$, $(1, 70)$, $(2, 120)$, ..., $(8, 0)$ and joining them by a smooth curve, we have the graph of $P(x) = 80x - 10x^2$ shown in Figure 2.19.

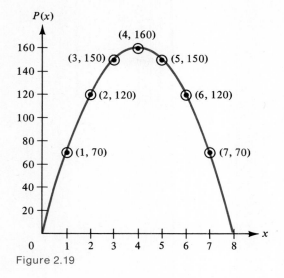

Figure 2.19

Perhaps you noticed that it appears as if the maximum profit of $160 million is obtained by producing 4 million barrels of "inaccessible" oil. Later on, we shall be able to apply some calculus concepts to verify that this is indeed true. ∎

Let us now return to the example in the preceding section of a travel agency that advertises an all-expense-paid 5-day cruise to Nova Scotia. The total receipts of the travel agency are given by

$$f(x) = 20(1500 + 20x - x^2) \qquad x = 0, 1, 2, \ldots, 50$$

where x is the number of cancellations received prior to the departure of the boat from New York.

The domain of f is the set of non-negative integers between 0 and 50, both inclusive. The values of $f(x)$ for several values of x in the specified interval are given in the following table.

Number of Cancellations x	Receipts $f(x)$
0	$30,000
5	31,500
10	32,000
15	31,500
20	30,000
25	27,500
30	24,000
35	19,500
40	14,000
45	7,500
50	0

Plotting the ordered pairs $(x, f(x))$, we have the graph of $f(x) = 20(1500 + 20x - x^2)$ in Figure 2.20.

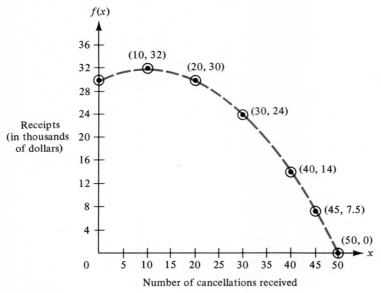

f(x)

Receipts
(in thousands
of dollars)

Number of cancellations received

Figure 2.20

Notice that the maximum value of $f(x)$ occurs at $x = 10$. Thus, the receipts of the travel agency are \$32,000 when 10 cancellations are received.

As a final illustration, consider a graph where $f(x)$ remains constant for some values of x.

Example 2.18

The management of a parking lot charges its customers according to the formula

$$f(x) = \$1.50 + \$0.50(x - 2) \qquad 2 \le x \le 8$$

where x is the number of hours the car is parked and $f(x)$ is the amount assessed for parking the car for x hours or part thereof subject to a minimum of \$1.50 and a maximum of \$4.50.

a. Determine the cost for parking up to 2, 3, 4, . . . , 24 hours.
b. Graph $f(x)$.
c. Find from the graph the cost for parking for $3\frac{1}{2}$ hours and for 4 hours and 45 minutes.

SOLUTION

a. Apparently, the management charges \$1.50 for the first 2 hours and \$0.50 for each additional hour or part thereof. The parking schedule is given in the table below.

Time in Hours x	Parking Cost $f(x)$
Up to 2 hours	$1.50
Up to 3 hours	2.00
Up to 4 hours	2.50
Up to 5 hours	3.00
Up to 6 hours	3.50
Up to 7 hours	4.00
Up to 24 hours	4.50

b. The graph of $f(x)$ is given in Figure 2.21.

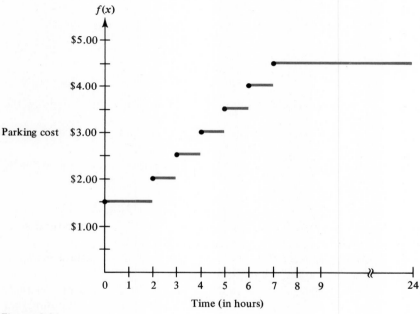

Figure 2.21

c. The parking for $3\frac{1}{2}$ hours costs $2.50, whereas the cost of parking for 4 hours and 45 minutes is $3.00. ■

EXERCISE 2.3

1. The demand for a certain product is given by

$$g(p) = 100 - \tfrac{5}{4}p$$

where $g(p)$ is the demand in units at a price p.

a. Calculate (i) $g(0)$, (ii) $g(20)$, (iii) $g(40)$, (iv) $g(60)$, and (v) $g(80)$.

b. Using the values of the function $g(x)$ for $x = 0, 20, 40, 60$, and 80, plot the graph of $g(p)$.

2. The market supply function for beer in Chicago is given by

$$s(p) = 300 + 40p$$

where $s(p)$ denotes the quantity of beer supplied in thousands of gallons per year at a price p in dollars per gallon.

a. Determine the supply schedule for beer for the price range $p = 1$ to $p = 8$ inclusive at $1 intervals.

b. Plot $s(p)$ for the same price range.

3. The market demand function for a product is given by

$$D(p) = 480 - 40p$$

where $D(p)$ denotes the demand of a product at the price p (in dollars) per unit.

a. Determine the demand schedule for $p = $1, $2, $3, $4, $6, and $12.

b. Plot $D(p)$ for the same price range.

4. Assume that the market demand function for unskilled labor in the United States is given by

$$f(x) = \frac{400}{x^2}$$

where $f(x)$ represents thousands of labor hours per month and x denotes the wage rate per hour in dollars.

a. Determine the demand schedule for $x = 1, 2, 4, 5, 10$, and 20.

b. Using the demand schedule in part a, plot $f(x)$.

5. The production function for a firm producing a certain commodity is given by

$$f(x) = 100 + 60x - 10x^2$$

where $f(x)$ denotes total cost in thousands of dollars and x represents the output in hundreds of units per week.

a. Determine the cost schedule $f(x)$ and the average cost schedule $g(x) = f(x)/x$ for $x = 1, 2, 3, 4, 5$, and 6.

b. Plot $f(x)$ and $g(x)$ for the same range of output.

6. A travel agency has arranged a trip to Niagara Falls by bus for a senior class. It has rented a bus with a seating capacity of 80 students with an understanding that at least 30 students sign up for the tour. The fare is $60 per student if the minimum requirement of 30 students is met, and the fare will decrease by $1 per student for each additional student who signs up.

a. Determine the total revenue, $R(x)$, as a function of x, the number of additional students who go.

b. Give the domain of the function.

c. Calculate $R(x)$ for $x = 0, 5, 10, 15, 20, 25, 30, 35$, and 40.

d. Using the revenue schedule in part b, plot $R(x)$.

e. What is the value of x for which $R(x)$ is maximum?

7. A travel agency advertises an all-expense-paid tour to Washington, D.C., for college students. The agency charters one car on a train with a seating capacity of 50 passengers. The fare is $100 per student plus an additional $5 for each empty seat.

a. Determine the total revenue, $R(x)$, as a function of x, the number of empty seats on the train.

b. Give the domain of the function.

c. Calculate $R(x)$ for $x = 0, 5, 10, 15, 20, 25, 30, 35,$ and 40.

d. Plot $R(x)$.

e. What is the value of x for which $R(x)$ is maximum?

f. How many students would have to go on the trip to give the travel agency a total revenue of $4320?

8. A charter flight charges a fare of $200 per person plus $5 for each unsold seat on the plane. The plane has a seating capacity of 100 passengers.

   a. Determine the total revenue, $R(x)$, as a function of x, the number of empty seats on the plane, and give the domain of the function.

   b. Plot $R(x)$.

   c. What is the value of x for which $R(x)$ is a maximum?

9. Taxis charge $0.50 for the first quarter-mile of transportation and $0.10 for each additional quarter-mile or part thereof. Determine the cost function, $C(x)$, where $C(x)$ is the cost in cents of taxi ride of x quarter miles. What will a taxi cost a passenger who needs to travel

   a. $\frac{1}{2}$ mile?

   b. 1 mile?

   c. $1\frac{1}{2}$ miles?

   d. 2 miles?

10. An attendant in a parking lot charges $2.00 for the first hour and $0.75 for each additional half-hour or part thereof. Determine the cost function $C(x)$, where $C(x)$ is the cost in dollars for parking x hours. What will it cost Mr. Smith if he parks his car for

    a. 2 hours?

    b. 3 hours?

    c. $3\frac{1}{2}$ hours?

    d. 4 hours?

Plot the graph of each of the following real valued functions.

11. $f(x) = 3x + 4$

12. $f(x) = x^2 - 4$

13. $f(x) = \dfrac{12}{x}$

14. $f(x) = \begin{cases} 7 - 2x & x < 2 \\ 4x - 5 & x \geq 2 \end{cases}$

15. $f(x) = \begin{cases} x & x \geq 0 \\ -x & x < 0 \end{cases}$

16. $f(x) = \begin{cases} x^2 & x < 0 \\ x & x \geq 0 \end{cases}$

2.6 SUM, DIFFERENCE, PRODUCT, AND QUOTIENT FUNCTIONS

Functions whose domain and range are sets of real numbers may be combined in several ways to obtain new functions. If f and g are functions with ordered pairs of the form $(x, f(x))$ and $(x, g(x))$, respectively, then the new functions $f + g$ and $f - g$

may be defined as follows:

$$(f + g)(x) = f(x) + g(x)$$
$$(f - g)(x) = f(x) - g(x)$$

Similarly, the product and quotient of two functions f and g are defined by

$$(fg)(x) = f(x) \cdot g(x)$$

and

$$\frac{f}{g}(x) = \frac{f(x)}{g(x)} \qquad \text{provided that } g(x) \neq 0$$

In each case, the domain is restricted to the intersection of the domains of the two functions f and g. In the case of f/g, the domain is further restricted to the set of those real numbers for which $g(x) \neq 0$.

Example 2.19

Let f be the function defined by $f(x) = x^2$ and let g be the function defined by $g(x) = 2x + 3$. Then

$$(f + g)(x) = f(x) + g(x)$$
$$= x^2 + 2x + 3$$
$$(f - g)(x) = f(x) - g(x)$$
$$= x^2 - 2x - 3$$
$$(fg)(x) = f(x) \cdot g(x)$$
$$= x^2(2x + 3)$$
$$\frac{f}{g}(x) = \frac{f(x)}{g(x)} = \frac{x^2}{2x + 3} \qquad \text{for } x \neq -\tfrac{3}{2}$$

■

Example 2.20

Sketch the graphs of $f(x) + g(x)$ in Example 2.19.

SOLUTION

Note that the domain of both f and g is the set of all reals. To obtain the elements of $f(x) + g(x)$, we simply perform the addition of $f(x)$ and $g(x)$ as shown in the following table. The graph of $f(x) + g(x)$ is given by the continuous curve in Figure 2.22.

x	$f(x)$	$g(x)$	$f(x) + g(x)$	$(x, f(x) + g(x))$
-4	16	-5	11	$(-4, 11)$
-3	9	-3	6	$(-3, 6)$
-2	4	-1	3	$(-2, 3)$
-1	1	1	2	$(-1, 2)$
0	0	3	3	$(0, 3)$
1	1	5	6	$(1, 6)$
2	4	7	11	$(2, 11)$

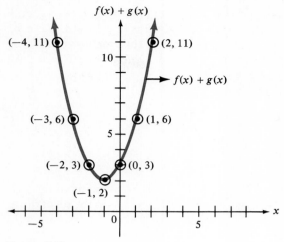

Figure 2.22

EXERCISE 2.4

For each of the functions f and g in Exercises 1 to 5, specify the functions $f + g$, $f - g$, fg, and f/g.

1. $f(x) = x^2; g(x) = 3x$
2. $f(x) = x^2 + 3; g(x) = 2x + 1$
3. $f(x) = x^2; g(x) = 1/x, x \neq 0$
4. $f(x) = x^2; g(x) = 1/x^2, x \neq 0$
5. $f(x) = x + 1/x, x \neq 0; g(x) = x - 1/x, x \neq 0$

For each of the functions f and g in Exercises 6 to 10, sketch the graphs of $f + g$, $f - g$, and fg.

6. $f(x) = x + 2; g(x) = x$
7. $f(x) = x^2; g(x) = x$
8. $f(x) = 2x; g(x) = \sqrt{x}$
9. $f(x) = 1 + 1/x, x \neq 0; g(x) = 1 - 1/x, x \neq 0$
10. $f(x) = x^2 + 3x + 2; g(x) = x + 4$

2.7 COMPOSITION OF FUNCTIONS

Another way of combining two functions to form a new function is the method of composition. When f and g are two functions, we may obtain another function h called the composition of g on f and denote it by $g \circ f$.

Definition 2.7.1: The composite of g on f, denoted by $g \circ f$, is defined by

$$(g \circ f)x = g[f(x)]$$

This implies that we first determine $f(x)$ under the rule of correspondence f and then apply the rule g to the element thus obtained. Because x is in the set A, $f(x) \in B$, which is the domain of the function g. Thus, the domain of the composite function $g \circ f$ consists of only those elements x for which $f(x)$ is in the domain of g. Figure 2.23 illustrates the characteristics of the composite function.

It may also be instructive to consider Figure 2.24.

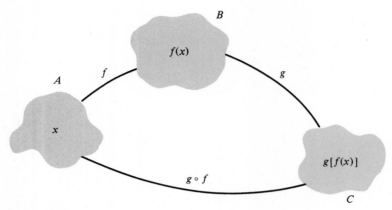

Figure 2.23

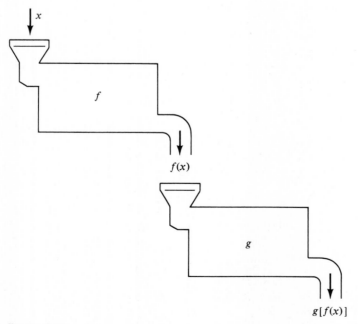

Figure 2.24

Thus, if an element x is entered into the machine f, the output from this machine becomes the input for the machine g, which yields $g[f(x)]$ as the final output corresponding to every x fed into the machine f.

Example 2.21

Let f be a function defined by

$$f(x) = x + 2$$

with the set $A = \{1, 2, 3, 4, 5\}$ as its domain. Determine $g[f(x)]$ for each $x \in A$ if $g(x) = 2x + 5$.

SOLUTION

First, we compute $f(x)$ for each $x \in A$. Because

$$f(1) = 3, \quad f(2) = 4, \quad f(3) = 5, \quad f(4) = 6, \quad \text{and} \quad f(5) = 7$$

the range of the function f is the set $B = \{3, 4, 5, 6, 7\}$ as illustrated in Figure 2.25.

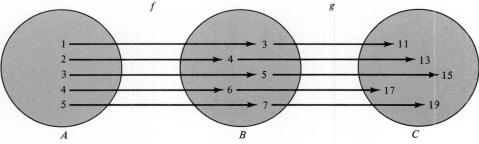

Figure 2.25

Now g is a function from set B to set C. We compute $g(x)$ for each element in B. Because $g(x) = 2x + 5$, we have

$$g(3) = 11, \quad g(4) = 13, g(5) = 15, \quad g(6) = 17, \quad \text{and} \quad g(7) = 19$$

Thus, the range of the function $g \circ f$ is the set $C = \{11, 13, 15, 17, 19\}$.

Alternatively, we can determine a formula for the composite function $g \circ f$ and then compute $g[f(x)]$ for each $x \in A$. Recall that because $g(x) = 2x + 5$, we have

$$(g \circ f)x = g[f(x)] = 2[f(x)] + 5$$
$$= 2(x + 2) + 5$$
$$= 2x + 9$$

Now

$$(g \circ f)(1) = 2 \cdot 1 + 9 = 11 \qquad (g \circ f)(2) = 2 \cdot 2 + 9 = 13$$
$$(g \circ f)(3) = 2 \cdot 3 + 9 = 15 \qquad (g \circ f)(4) = 2 \cdot 4 + 9 = 17$$
$$(g \circ f)(5) = 2 \cdot 5 + 9 = 19$$

Thus, the range of the composite function $h = g \circ f$ is precisely the same we established in Figure 2.25. ∎

As another illustration, consider the following example.

Example 2.22

Let $f(x) = x^2 + 1$ and $g(x) = 3x + 2$. Determine $g[f(x)]$ and $f[g(x)]$ for $x = 1, 2, 3,$ and 4.

SOLUTION

$$(g \circ f)x = g[f(x)] = 3[f(x)] + 2$$
$$= 3(x^2 + 1) + 2 = 3x^2 + 5$$

Thus,

$$(g \circ f)(1) = 3(1^2) + 5 = 8 \qquad (g \circ f)(2) = 3 \cdot (2^2) + 5 = 17$$
$$(g \circ f)(3) = 3(3^2) + 5 = 32 \qquad (g \circ f)(4) = 3(4^2) + 5 = 53$$

The range of $g \circ f$ is the set $\{8, 17, 32, 53\}$. Now,

$$(f \circ g)x = f[g(x)] = [g(x)]^2 + 1$$
$$= (3x + 2)^2 + 1$$
$$= 9x^2 + 12x + 5$$

Thus,

$$(f \circ g)(1) = 9(1^2) + 12(1) + 5 = 26$$
$$(f \circ g)(2) = 9(2^2) + 12(2) + 5 = 65$$
$$(f \circ g)(3) = 9(3^2) + 12(3) + 5 = 122$$
$$(f \circ g)(4) = 9(4^2) + 12(4) + 5 = 197$$

The range of $f \circ g$ is the set $\{26, 65, 122, 197\}$. Note that the range of $f \circ g$ is not the same as the range of $g \circ f$. ∎

Example 2.23

Let $f(x) = x^2 + 2$ and $g(x) = 1 - x$. Sketch the graphs of
a. $(g \circ f)(x)$
b. $(f \circ g)(x)$

SOLUTION

a. $(g \circ f)(x) = g[f(x)] = 1 - f(x)$
$$= 1 - (x^2 + 2) = -(x^2 + 1)$$
b. $(f \circ g)(x) = f[g(x)] = [g(x)]^2 + 2$
$$= (1 - x)^2 + 2 = x^2 - 2x + 3$$

We provide enough points in the following tables to sketch $g[f(x)] = -(x^2 + 1)$ and $f[g(x)] = x^2 - 2x + 3$, respectively.

$y = -(x^2 + 1)$

x	$-(x^2 + 1)$
-3	-10
-2	-5
-1	-2
0	-1
1	-2
2	-5
3	-10

$y = x^2 - 2x + 3$

x	$x^2 - 2x + 3$
-2	11
-1	6
0	3
1	2
2	3
3	6
4	11

The graphs of $(g \circ f)(x)$ and $(f \circ g)(x)$ are shown in Figure 2.26 and Figure 2.27, respectively.

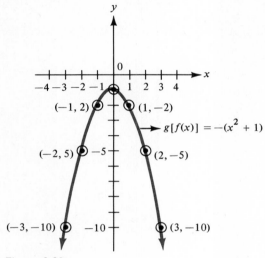

Figure 2.26

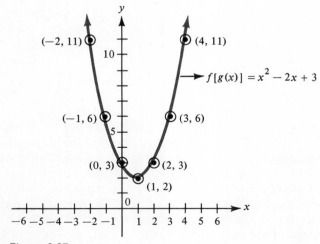

Figure 2.27

Examples 2.22 and 2.23 demonstrate the fact that, in general,

$$g \circ f \neq f \circ g$$

EXERCISE 2.5

1. Given that $f(x) = 3x + 2$ and $g(x) = 2x + 3$, determine the value of $g[f(x)]$ for $x = 1, 2, 3, 4, 5$, and 6.
2. Given that $f(x) = 4x + 5$, and $g(x) = 5x + 2$, determine the value of $f[g(x)]$ for $x = 1, 2, 3, 4, 5$, and 6.
3. Given that $f(x) = 3x + 4$, and $g(x) = 4x + 3$, determine the value of $g[f(x)]$ and $f[g(x)]$ for $x = 1, 2, 3, 4$, and 5.
4. Determine the values of $f[g(x)]$ and $g[f(x)]$ for $x = 1, 2, 3, 4$, and 5 in each of the following.
   a. $f(x) = x^2$, $g(x) = x + 1$
   b. $f(x) = (x + 2)^2$, $g(x) = 2x + 3$
   Determine $g[f(x)]$ and $f[g(x)]$ in Exercises 5 through 10.

5. $f(x) = 3x + 1$, $g(x) = \dfrac{x + 1}{3}$

6. $f(x) = x^2 + 1$, $g(x) = \sqrt{x + 1}$

7. $f(x) = 2x + 5$, $g(x) = x + \sqrt{x}$

8. $f(x) = x + \dfrac{1}{x}$, $g(x) = \sqrt{x - 1}$

9. $f(x) = \dfrac{2}{1 + x^2}$, $g(x) = 2x + 3$

10. $f(x) = x^2 + 2x + 2$, $g(x) = 1 - x^2$
    Sketch the graphs of $g[f(x)]$ and $f[g(x)]$ in each of the following problems.
11. $f(x) = 3x + 5$, $g(x) = 3x - 2$
12. $f(x) = x^2$, $g(x) = 1 - x$

2.8 INVERSE FUNCTIONS

The function f has been defined as a rule that assigns to each element in a set A one and only one element in a set B. Thus, if a is any arbitrary element in the set A (see Figure 2.28), then there is one unique element $b \in B$ such that $f(a) = b$. Geometrically, this means that a vertical line drawn through a meets the graph of the function in one point (a, b) where $b = f(a)$. To determine whether or not f is one to one, we need to ascertain whether or not each horizontal line meets the graph of the function at no more than one point. Note that this is equivalent to whether or not for each $b \in B$ there exists one and only one value $a \in A$ such that $f(a) = b$.

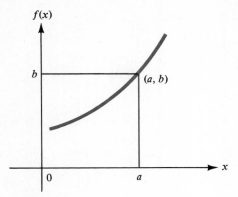

Figure 2.28

If the function f is one to one, we can define a new function g that is the inverse of the original function f. Thus, for each $a \in A$, if f carries $a \in A$ to $f(a) \in B$, then g is the function that brings $f(a) \in B$ back to $a \in A$, as shown in Figure 2.29. This implies that $g[f(a)] = a$ for each $a \in A$.

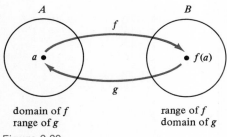

domain of f
range of g

range of f
domain of g

Figure 2.29

Definition 2.8.1: Let f be a one to one function with the domain as set A and the range as set B. Then a function g with domain as set B and range as set A is called the inverse of f if $g[f(x)] = x$ for all $x \in A$

The inverse function g of the function f is denoted by f^{-1}. Thus,

$$f^{-1}[f(x)] = x \qquad \text{for } x \in A$$

One can also show that

$$f[f^{-1}(x)] = x \qquad \text{for } x \in B$$

Example 2.24

The functions

$$f(x) = 3x - 2 \quad \text{and} \quad g(x) = \frac{x + 2}{3}$$

are inverses of each other, because

$$(g \circ f)x = g[f(x)] = \frac{f(x) + 2}{3} = \frac{(3x - 2) + 2}{3} = x$$

and

$$(f \circ g)x = f[g(x)] = 3g(x) - 2 = 3\left(\frac{x + 2}{3}\right) - 2 = x$$

Thus, the inverse function of f is f^{-1} such that

$$f^{-1}(x) = \frac{x + 2}{3}$$

■

Example 2.25

Let $f(x) = 2x + 3$. Does $f^{-1}(x)$ exist? If so, find $f^{-1}(x)$.

SOLUTION

To show that $f^{-1}(x)$ exists, it is necessary to demonstrate that f is one to one. Suppose that x_1 and x_2 are two distinct elements in the domain of f. Then, $2x_1 + 3$ and $2x_2 + 3$ will be two distinct elements of the range. Because only x_1 will go to $2x_1 + 3$ under the function f, we conclude that f is a one to one function.

If g is to be the inverse function of f, then

$$f[g(x)] = x$$

which implies that

$$2g(x) + 3 = x$$

Solving for $g(x)$, we have

$$g(x) = \frac{x - 3}{2}$$

Thus,

$$f^{-1}(x) = \frac{x - 3}{2}$$

■

We compare the graphs of $f(x) = 2x + 3$ and $f^{-1}(x) = (x - 3)/2$ in Figure 2.30. The ordered pairs

$$(-3, -3), (0, 3), (2, 7), (3, 9)$$

are elements of the function f, whereas its inverse f^{-1} contains the ordered pairs

$$(-3, -3), (3, 0), (7, 2), (9, 3)$$

Note that each ordered pair (x, y) of the original function f has been replaced by an ordered pair (y, x) in the inverse function and the graphs of $f(x)$ and $f^{-1}(x)$ are

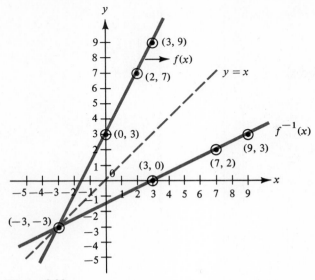

Figure 2.30

symmetrical about the line $y = x$. Thus, if f is a one to one function, then its inverse f^{-1} is obtained simply by interchanging the roles of x and y in the original expression, which is then solved for y. Consider, for example, a function

$$f = \{(x, y)|y = 3x - 4\}$$

Then

$$f^{-1} = \{(x, y)|x = 3y - 4\}$$
$$= \left\{(x, y)\middle|y = \frac{x + 4}{3}\right\}$$

EXERCISE 2.6

1. For each of the functions defined by the following equations, determine its inverse.

a. $f(x) = 5x - 4$

b. $f(x) = 4x + 3$

c. $f(x) = 2x + 1$

d. $f(x) = \dfrac{1}{x}, \quad x \neq 0$

e. $f(x) = \dfrac{x - 1}{x + 1}, \quad x \neq -1$

f. $f(x) = x^3$

2. For each of the given functions, determine its inverse.

a. $f(x) = 2x - 1$

b. $f(x) = x^2, \quad x \geq 0$

c. $f(x) = \dfrac{1}{x + 2}, \quad x \neq -2$

d. $f(x) = 4x \quad \text{for} \quad x \geq 0$

3. Graph $f(x)$ and $f^{-1}(x)$ for each of the following functions.

   a. $f(x) = x + 3$

   b. $f(x) = 3x + 2$

   c. $f(x) = 2x - 5$

4. Graph $f(x)$ and $f^{-1}(x)$ for each of the following functions.

   a. $f(x) = x^2, \quad x \geq 0$ **b.** $f(x) = x^3$

5. Given $f(x) = 4x - 5$, find the following:

   a. $f^{-1}(x)$ **b.** $f[f^{-1}(x)]$ **c.** $f^{-1}[f(x)]$

6. Given $f(x) = 3x + 2$, find the following:

   a. $f^{-1}(x)$ **b.** $f[f^{-1}(x)]$ **c.** $f^{-1}[f(x)]$

7. Given that $f(x) = mx + b$, find the following:

   a. $f^{-1}(x)$ **b.** $f[f^{-1}(x)]$ **c.** $f^{-1}[f(x)]$

8. Show that the function $f(x) = \sqrt{4 - x^2}, 0 < x \leq 2$, has an inverse function.

3
Linear Functions

3.1 INTRODUCTION

Linear functions play an important part in marketing, economics, and many other facets of the economy. These functions also form the basis for the study of linear programming and are used extensively in the cost analysis in which business firms keep careful control over the cost of the products they manufacture.

In this chapter, we introduce the concept of a slope of a line and then use it to develop the equation of a straight line. Later, we examine linear functions in relation to linear depreciation.

3.2 LINEAR FUNCTIONS

Any function of the form $(x, f(x))$, where $f(x) = mx + b$, is called a linear function. It can be shown that the graph of $f(x) = mx + b$ for fixed values of m and b is a straight line. Conversely, the equation of any nonvertical straight line can be represented in the form

$$y = mx + b$$

where m is the coefficient of x and b is the constant term.

The coefficient of x determines what we call the "slope" of a line. The concept of slope is important in business and economics because it measures the rate at which changes are taking place—the rate at which the price of gold is fluctuating in the international market, the rate at which unemployment is going up in the private sector of the economy, the rate at which enrollment is dropping in the liberal arts colleges, the rate at which crime is increasing in large cities, the rate at which the international economy is likely to recover from a recession, and so on. Consider, for example, the sales of three companies A, B, and C by comparing the rate at which their volume of sales have increased or decreased over a 3-year period. The following table shows the sales volume of these companies in 1971 and 1974.

| | Sales in | |
Company	1971	1974
A	$15,000	$24,000
B	10,000	13,000
C	5,000	2,000

We assume that the volume of sales of these companies is a linear function of time. Two points corresponding to each company are plotted on the graph and then connected by means of straight lines as displayed in Figure 3.1. The sales of company A

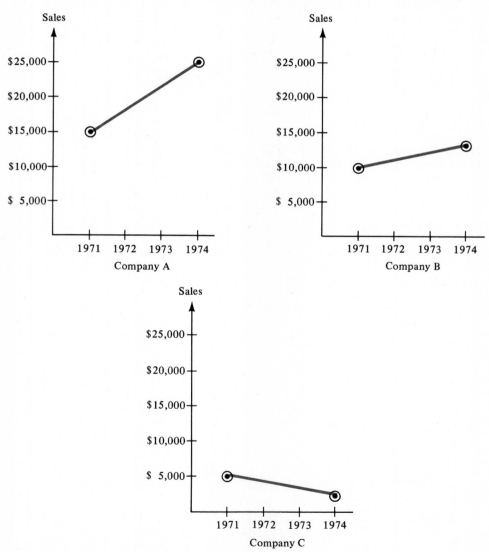

Figure 3.1

have increased from $15,000 in 1971 to $24,000 in 1974. Thus, the average annual increase in sales is $9000/3 = $3000. The sales of company B have increased by $3000 over this three-year period and the average annual increase in sales is $1000. This accounts for the fact that slope for company B is not as steep as it is for company A. Nevertheless, the upward trend of companies A and B reflects their growth. The line segment for company C, which slopes downward, shows a drop in sales during the period 1971–1974. Because sales have decreased from $5000 in 1971 to $2000 in 1974, the average drop in sales is $1000 per year. Thus, the slope of a line can be described as a measure of its steepness.

To determine the slope of a hill, for example, we simply divide its vertical height by the corresponding horizontal distance. Thus, if an automobile going uphill has to climb 1 mile while covering a horizontal distance of 50 miles, then the slope of the hill is 1/50 = 0.02. In short,

$$\text{slope} = \frac{\text{vertical rise}}{\text{horizontal run}}$$

Example 3.1
Two towns A and B are 5 miles apart along a horizontal base. The elevation of town A and town B is 560 ft and 3200 ft, respectively. Assuming that an automobile is going uphill from A to B on a road with a constant slope, determine the slope of the hill.

SOLUTION
The vertical rise = 3200 ft − 560 ft = 2640 feet or $\frac{1}{2}$ mile. The horizontal distance covered is 5 miles. Thus, the slope of the hill is $\frac{1}{2}$ mile/5 miles = 1/10 = 0.10.   ■

To explain this notion further, consider the line segment whose end points are A and B with coordinates (x_1, y_1) and (x_2, y_2), respectively. (See Figure 3.2.) Clearly, the coordinates of P are (x_2, y_1). The change in height is

$$PB = NB - NP$$
$$= NB - MA = y_2 - y_1$$

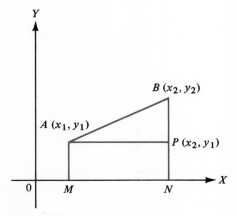

Figure 3.2

whereas the corresponding change in horizontal distance is

$$AP = MN$$
$$= 0N - 0M = x_2 - x_1$$

Thus,

$$\text{slope of } AB = \frac{PB}{AP} = \frac{y_2 - y_1}{x_2 - x_1}$$

This suggests the following definition.

Definition 3.2.1: The slope of the line segment joining two distinct points A and B with coordinates (x_1, y_1) and (x_2, y_2), respectively, is

(3.1) $\quad \dfrac{y_2 - y_1}{x_2 - x_1} \qquad x_2 \neq x_1$

and is denoted by the letter m.

Note that had we used (x_2, y_2) and (x_1, y_1) as coordinates of A and B, respectively, the resulting slope m would be the same.

An immediate consequence of this definition is that if a line rises sharply to the right, the difference in y coordinates of two points is large as compared to the difference in x coordinates. This yields a large value of m. If a line segment slopes downward from left to right, the differences in x and y coordinates of any two points on this line segment have opposite signs; consequently, the slope of such a line segment is negative. If the line segment is parallel to the x axis, then all points on this horizontal line, say AB (see Figure 3.3) have the same y coordinates, that is, $y_1 = y_2$. This means that the difference in y coordinates of all points on this line segment is zero; consequently, the slope is zero. A vertical line, on the other hand, does not have slope. This is clear from the fact that the x coordinates of any two points on, say, line CD in Figure 3.4, are the same; that is, $x_1 = x_2$; hence, the denominator in $(y_2 - y_1)/(x_2 - x_1)$ is zero and the slope m of this vertical line is not defined. We wish to emphasize that a horizontal line has slope zero whereas a vertical line does not have any slope.

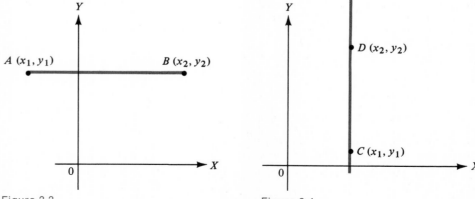

Figure 3.3

Figure 3.4

Example 3.2

Find the slopes of the line segments determined by

  a. A (3, 2), B (5, 8)
  b. A (8, -7), B (3, -2)
  c. A (4, 3), B (8, 3)

SOLUTION

  a. Let

$$x_1 = 3, y_1 = 2 \qquad x_2 = 5, y_2 = 8$$

then,

$$m = \frac{y_2 - y_1}{x_2 - x_1} = \frac{8 - 2}{5 - 3} = \frac{6}{2} = 3$$

We wish to remark that had we used B (5, 8) as (x_1, y_1) and A (3, 2) as (x_2, y_2), the resulting slope m would be the same.

  b. Let

$$x_1 = 8, y_1 = -7 \qquad x_2 = 3, y_2 = -2$$

then

$$m = \frac{y_2 - y_1}{x_2 - x_1} = \frac{-2 - (-7)}{3 - 8} = -\frac{5}{5} = -1$$

  c. The y coordinates of the two points are equal, hence the slope of this line segment is zero.

  We advise the reader to demonstrate graphically that the line AB slopes upward from left to right in part a, slopes downward from right to left in part b, and is horizontal in part c. ■

Definition 3.2.2: Two line segments are said to be parallel if and only if they have equal slopes.

Example 3.3

Determine whether or not the following line segments are parallel to each other:

  a. A (2, 3), B (5, 4) and C (-8, 6), D (-5, 7)
  b. A (-5, 4), B (4, 1) and C (0, 1), D (3, 2)

SOLUTION

  a. The slope m of the line segment AB is

$$m_1 = \frac{4 - 3}{5 - 2} = \frac{1}{3}$$

Similarly, the slope m_2 of the line segment CD is

$$m_2 = \frac{7 - 6}{-5 - (-8)} = \frac{1}{3}$$

Thus, $m_1 = m_2$ and the line segments are parallel.

b. The slope m_1 of AB is

$$m_1 = \frac{1 - 4}{4 - (-5)} = -\frac{1}{3}$$

and slope m_2 of CD is

$$m_2 = \frac{2 - 1}{3 - 0} = \frac{1}{3}$$

Here $m_1 \neq m_2$. Thus, the line segments are not parallel.   ∎

Definition 3.2.3: Two line segments with slopes m_1 and m_2 are perpendicular to each other if and only if $m_1 m_2 = -1$ ($m_1 \neq 0$, $m_2 \neq 0$).

Example 3.4

Determine whether or not the following line segments are perpendicular to each other.
   a. A (3, 5), B (8, 1) and C (6, 2) and D (10, 7)
   b. A (0, 4), B (3, 10) and C (3, -1) and D (5, 0)

SOLUTION

   a. The slope of line segment AB is

$$m_1 = \frac{1 - 5}{8 - 3} = -\frac{4}{5}$$

whereas the slope of line segment CD is

$$m_2 = \frac{7 - 2}{10 - 6} = \frac{5}{4}$$

Because $m_1 m_2 = (-\frac{4}{5})(\frac{5}{4}) = -1$, it follows that the line segments AB and CD are perpendicular to each other.

   b. The slope m_1 of the line segment AB is

$$m_1 = \frac{10 - 4}{3 - 0} = 2$$

and the slope m_2 of the line segment CD is

$$m_2 = \frac{0 - (-1)}{5 - 3} = \frac{1}{2}$$

$$m_1 m_2 = 2(\tfrac{1}{2}) = 1$$

Thus, the line segments are not perpendicular to each other.   ∎

Slope of a Straight Line

Having defined the slope of a line segment, it seems natural to extend this concept and define the slope of a straight line. Note that a line segment is only part of a straight line.

We must demonstrate that all segments of a nonvertical straight line have the same slope. Let AB and BC be two line segments of the same straight line. (See Figure 3.5.) Draw AL, BM, and CN perpendicular to x axis and AP and BQ perpendicular to MB and NC, respectively. The right triangles APB and BQC so constructed are similar. (Why?) Thus, the corresponding sides have the same ratio. Hence,

$$\frac{PB}{AP} = \frac{QC}{BQ}$$

Now

$$PB = MB - MP$$
$$= MB - LA = y_2 - y_1$$
$$AP = LM = 0M - 0L = x_2 - x_1$$
$$QC = NC - NQ$$
$$= NC - MB = y_3 - y_2$$
$$BQ = MN = 0N - 0M = x_3 - x_2$$

Thus,

$$\frac{y_2 - y_1}{x_2 - x_1} = \frac{y_3 - y_2}{x_3 - x_2}$$

and the slopes of AB and BC are equal. This suggests the following definition.

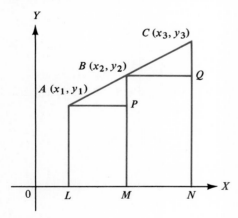

Figure 3.5

Definition 3.2.4: The slope of a nonvertical straight line AB is equal to the slope of any one of its segments.

Example 3.5

Show that the points

$$A\ (0, 2),\quad B\ (3, 4),\quad \text{and}\quad C\ (9, 8)$$

lie on the same straight line.

SOLUTION

The slope of line segment AB is

$$AB = \frac{4 - 2}{3 - 0} = \frac{2}{3}$$

the slope of line segment BC is

$$BC = \frac{8 - 4}{9 - 3} = \frac{4}{6} = \frac{2}{3}$$

and the slope of line segment AC is

$$AC = \frac{8 - 2}{9 - 0} = \frac{6}{9} = \frac{2}{3}$$

Because the slopes of AB, BC, and AC are equal (see Figure 3.6), it follows that the points A, B, and C lie on the same straight line.

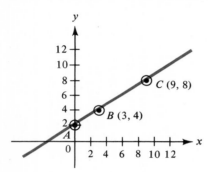

Figure 3.6

EXERCISE 3.1

1. Find the slopes of the line determined by the points A and B.
   a. A (3, 4), B (4, 3)   **b.** A (4, 5), B (8, 13)
   c. A (−2, 2), B (5, 5)   **d.** A (3, 2), B (6, 8)
   e. A (−5, 2), B (5, 6)

2. Determine whether or not the following lines are parallel to each other.
   a. A (3, 3), B (5, 7) and C (0, 0), D (2, 4)
   b. A (0, 0), B (1, 3) and C (1, 2), D (4, 6)
   c. A (−1, 2), B (4, 8) and C (2, 3), D (14, 13)
   d. A (−3, −3), B (−7, 6) and C (1, 0), D (−3, 9)
   e. A (5, 8), B (1, 5) and C (6, 8), D (10, 11)

3. Determine whether or not the following line segments are perpendicular to each other.
   a. A (3, 1), B (4, 3) and C (1, −3), D (0, −2)
   b. A (−1, 2), B (4, 5) and C (2, −5), D (0, 0)
   c. A (4, −5), B (0, −2) and C (0, 0), D (3, 4)
   d. A (0, 2), B (4, 4) and C (4, −3), D (0, 3)
   e. A (−2, 0), B (10, 8) and C (2, 3), D (6, −3)

4. Determine whether or not the following sets of points lie on a straight line.
   a. A (2, -1), B (5, 3), and C (-4, -9)
   b. A (7, 5), B (-1, 1), and C (-5, -1)
   c. A (1, 4), B (3, -2), and C (-3, 16)
   d. A (-5, 1), B (5, 5), and C (10, 7)
   e. A (5, 0), B (4, 1), and C (3, 2)

3.3 EQUATION OF A STRAIGHT LINE

The simplest position in which a straight line can be displayed on a coordinate system is that in which it is parallel to one of the axes. It is, therefore, reasonable that we begin with lines in these positions and find the corresponding algebraic equations.

Proposition 3.3.1: The equation of a straight line parallel to the x axis and $|b|$* units from it is $y = b$. ▪

Consider a straight line AB drawn parallel to the x axis that meets the y axis in a point C so that $0C = b$. (See Figure 3.7.) D (x, y) is any arbitrary point on AB and DM is perpendicular to the x axis. Because $MD = 0C$, it follows that $y = b$ is the required equation.

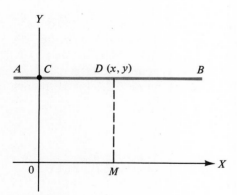

Figure 3.7

If b is positive, the line is above the x axis; and if b is negative, the line is below the x axis.

Lines parallel to the y axis are treated in the same manner. The equation $x = 2$ represents a line parallel to the y axis and two units to the right of it. Similarly, the equation $x = -2$ is a line parallel also to the y axis but two units to the left of it (Figure 3.8).

* See Definition A.3.1 in Appendix A.

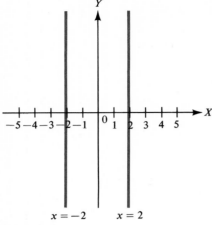

Figure 3.8

In general, we have the following proposition.

Proposition 3.3.2: The equation of a straight line parallel to the y axis and $|a|$ units from it is $x = a$. ■

If the line is to the right of the y axis, a is positive; and if it is to the left, a is negative.

Next, we determine an equation of a line not parallel to the axes. Obviously, this line meets the y axis in some point, the abscissa of which is zero. (See Figure 3.9.) The ordinate of this point is called the y intercept of the line and is denoted by b. Thus, the coordinates of the point C are $(0, b)$. If $D(x, y)$ is any arbitrary point on this line, then the slope m is obtained by applying Definition 3.2.1 to the points $C(0, b)$ and $D(x, y)$. Thus,

$$m = \frac{y - b}{x - 0}$$

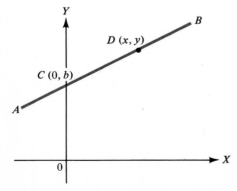

Figure 3.9

that is,

$$y - b = mx$$

or

$$y = mx + b$$

Conversely, suppose that we are given any point (x_1, y_1) satisfying the equation $y = mx + b$. Observe that $(0, b)$ also satisfies the equation and that the slope of the line connecting $(0, b)$ and (x_1, y_1) is

$$\frac{y_1 - b}{x_1 - 0} = \frac{(mx_1 + b) - b}{x_1 - 0} = m$$

Because any other point (x_2, y_2) satisfying $y = mx + b$ will also lie on the line of slope m through $(0, b)$, we conclude that all points satisfying $y = mx + b$ lie on the straight line with slope m and y intercept b. Thus, we have established the following proposition.

Proposition 3.3.3: Any point (x, y) belongs to a straight line that has an intercept b on the y axis and has slope m if and only if it satisfies the equation

(3.2) $y = mx + b$ ∎

Note that for any particular line not perpendicular to the x axis, the slope m and the intercept b assume finite values. Thus, the equation of the line passing through $(0, 3)$ with slope 4 (that is, $m = 4$ and $b = 3$) is given by

$$y = 4x + 3$$

Equation (3.2) is called the slope-intercept form of the equation of the straight line. Observe that if the line passes through the origin, then $b = 0$ and Eq. (3.2) becomes $y = mx$.

Example 3.6
Determine the slope and y intercept of the line

$$3y = 2x + 6$$

SOLUTION
Rewriting this equation in the slope-intercept form (3.2), we have

$$y = \tfrac{2}{3}x + 2$$

Comparing this equation with (3.2), we see that the slope is $\tfrac{2}{3}$ and this line intersects the y axis at the point $(0, 2)$. Thus, $m = \tfrac{2}{3}$ and $b = 2$.   ∎

Proposition 3.3.4: Two distinct (nonvertical) lines are parallel if and only if their slopes are equal.   ∎

Let us illustrate this proposition in the following example.

Example 3.7

Determine whether or not the following lines are parallel:
  a. $2x + 3y - 4 = 0; 3x + y - 7 = 0$
  b. $3x - 2y + 8 = 0; 6x - 4y + 12 = 0$

SOLUTION

a. Rewriting $2x + 3y - 4 = 0$ and $3x + y - 7 = 0$ in the slope-intercept form (3.2), we have

$$y = -\tfrac{2}{3}x + \tfrac{4}{3} \quad \text{and} \quad y = -3x + 7$$

respectively. These lines have slopes $-\tfrac{2}{3}$ and -3, respectively. Because the slopes are not equal, we conclude that the lines are not parallel.

b. Expressing $3x - 2y + 8 = 0$ in the form (3.2), we have

$$y = \tfrac{3}{2}x + 4$$

which implies that the slope of this line is $m_1 = \tfrac{3}{2}$. Similarly, solving $6x - 4y + 12 = 0$ for y, we obtain

$$y = \tfrac{3}{2}x + 3$$

We note that $m_2 = \tfrac{3}{2}$. Because the slopes of the lines are equal, we conclude that the lines $3x - 2y + 8 = 0$ and $6x - 4y + 12 = 0$ are parallel. ∎

Next, we state (without proof) the following proposition.

Proposition 3.3.5: Two distinct (nonvertical) lines are perpendicular to each other if and only if the product of their slopes equals -1. ∎

Example 3.8

Determine whether or not the following pairs of lines are perpendicular:
  a. $3x + 2y + 7 = 0$ and $2x - 3y + 1 = 0$
  b. $10x - 6y + 2 = 0$ and $6x + 2y + 1 = 0$

SOLUTION

a. Solving $3x + 2y + 7 = 0$ for y, we have

$$y = -\tfrac{3}{2}x - \tfrac{7}{2}$$

Thus, this line has slope $m_1 = -\tfrac{3}{2}$. Similarly, the line $2x - 3y + 1 = 0$ is equivalent to

$$y = \tfrac{2}{3}x + \tfrac{1}{3}$$

so that $m_2 = \tfrac{2}{3}$. Because $m_1 m_2 = (-\tfrac{3}{2})(\tfrac{2}{3}) = -1$, it follows that the lines are perpendicular to each other.

b. The lines $10x - 6y + 2 = 0$ and $6x + 2y + 1 = 0$ expressed in the slope-intercept form are

$$y = \tfrac{5}{3}x + \tfrac{1}{3} \quad \text{and} \quad y = -3x - \tfrac{1}{2}$$

The slopes of the lines are $\tfrac{5}{3}$ and -3, respectively. Because the product of the slopes of these lines does not equal -1, we conclude that the lines are not perpendicular. ∎

Suppose that the slope m of a straight line and a point (x_1, y_1) on the line are known. If (x, y) is any other point on the line, then using (3.1), we have

$$\frac{y - y_1}{x - x_1} = m \qquad x \neq x_1$$

and

$$y - y_1 = m(x - x_1)$$

Thus, we have established the following proposition.

Proposition 3.3.6: The equation of a straight line passing through the point (x_1, y_1) and the slope m is

(3.3) $\quad y - y_1 = m(x - x_1)$ ∎

Because Eq. (3.3) uses a given point (x_1, y_1) and the slope m of the line, it is called the point-slope form of the equation of the line.

Example 3.9

Find the equation of the line that passes through the point $(3, 5)$ and has the slope $m = 2$.

SOLUTION
Note that

$$x_1 = 3, \quad y_1 = 5, \quad \text{and} \quad m = 2$$

Hence, the required equation of the line is

$$y - 5 = 2(x - 3)$$

that is,

$$y = 2x - 1$$

∎

Example 3.10

Find the equation of the line that has the same slope as $3x - 2y + 12 = 0$, but passes through the point $(5, -3)$.

SOLUTION

Solving $3x - 2y + 12 = 0$, we have

$$y = \tfrac{3}{2}x + 6$$

Thus, the slope of this line is $m = \tfrac{3}{2}$. Because the required line passes through $(5, -3)$, the equation of the line is obtained by substituting $x_1 = 5$ and $y_1 = -3$ in (3.3). That is,

$$y - (-3) = \tfrac{3}{2}(x - 5)$$

which on simplification yields

$$3x - 2y - 21 = 0$$ ■

Example 3.11

Find the equation of the line passing through $A\,(5, 6)$ and $B\,(3, 2)$.

SOLUTION

The slope of the line joining the two points $A\,(5, 6)$ and $B\,(3, 2)$ is

$$m = \frac{2 - 6}{3 - 5} = \frac{-4}{-2} = 2$$

Choosing one of the given points as (x_1, y_1), say $(5, 6)$, we use (3.3) and obtain

$$y - 6 = 2(x - 5)$$

that is,

$$y = 2x - 4$$

Note that had we used $(3, 2)$ as (x_1, y_1) instead, the resulting equation would be the same.   ■

Recall that we can determine the slope of a line by selecting any two points (x_1, y_1) and (x_2, y_2) and then use (3.1). Thus,

$$m = \frac{y_2 - y_1}{x_2 - x_1} \qquad x_1 \neq x_2$$

Note that the equation of a straight line passing through a given point (x_1, y_1) and the slope m, by Proposition 3.3.6, is

$$y - y_1 = m(x - x_1)$$

Substituting the value of m, we obtain

$$y - y_1 = \frac{y_2 - y_1}{x_2 - x_1}(x - x_1)$$

Thus, we have established the following proposition.

Proposition 3.3.7: The equation of the line joining the points (x_2, y_1) and (x_1, y_2) is

(3.4) $\quad y - y_1 = \dfrac{y_2 - y_1}{x_2 - x_1}(x - x_1) \qquad x_1 \neq x_2$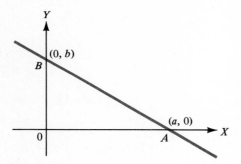

This is called the two-point form of the equation of the straight line.

Next, we determine the equation of a straight line that has given intercepts a and b on the x and y axes, respectively.

Proposition 3.3.8: The equation of a line that has intercepts a and b on the x axis and y axis, respectively, is

(3.5) $\quad \dfrac{x}{a} + \dfrac{y}{b} = 1 \qquad (a \neq 0, b \neq 0)$

Note that the coordinates of A and B are $(a, 0)$ and $(0, b)$, respectively (Figure 3.10). Here

$$x_1 = a, y_1 = 0; x_2 = 0, y_2 = b \text{ such that } a \neq 0, b \neq 0$$

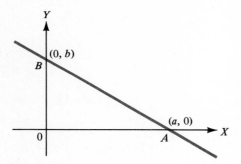

Figure 3.10

Substituting these values in (3.4), we have

$$y - 0 = \frac{b - 0}{0 - a}(x - a)$$

or

$$y = -\frac{b}{a}(x - a)$$

or

$$bx + ay = ab$$

Dividing both sides by ab, we have

$$\frac{x}{a} + \frac{y}{b} = 1$$

which proves our assertion.

Example 3.12

Find the equation of the line that makes intercepts 5 and 3 on the x and y axes, respectively.

SOLUTION

Here, $a = 5$ and $b = 3$. Using (3.5), we obtain

$$\frac{x}{5} + \frac{y}{3} = 1$$

or

$$3x + 5y - 15 = 0 \qquad \blacksquare$$

Example 3.13

Find the equation of the line passing through the point $(3, 4)$ that makes equal intercepts on the axes.

SOLUTION

Because the intercepts are equal, we have

$$\frac{x}{a} + \frac{y}{a} = 1$$

that is,

$$(3.6) \quad x + y = a$$

Further, because the point $(3, 4)$ lies on this line, its coordinates must satisfy (3.6). Thus,

$$3 + 4 = a \quad \text{or} \quad a = 7$$

Hence, the required equation is

$$x + y = 7 \qquad \blacksquare$$

We have considered equations of a straight line in all possible positions. We observed earlier that a line is either parallel to the x axis or parallel to the y axis or it meets the axes at fixed points. In the first case, its equation is of the form $y = b$ (Proposition 3.3.1); in the second case, its equation is of the form $x = a$ (Proposition 3.3.2); and in the third case, it is represented by $y = mx + b$, where m and b assume any finite values (Proposition 3.3.3). Thus, all equations are of the most general form $Ax + By + C = 0$, where A, B, and C are any real numbers and A and B cannot both be zero. Note that the first equation is in y alone, the second is in x alone, and the third contains both x and y.

Next, we reverse the procedure and start out with an equation $Ax + By + C = 0$ and show that every equation of this form represents a straight line.

Proposition 3.3.9: Every equation of the form

$$(3.7) \quad Ax + By + C = 0 \qquad A \neq 0 \quad \text{or} \quad B \neq 0$$

where A, B, and C have fixed values, represents a straight line.

PROOF

We consider two possible cases.

(a) $B \neq 0$. Solving (3.7) for y, we have

$$y = -\frac{A}{B}x - \frac{C}{B}$$

which is the equation of the straight line in the slope-intercept form (3.2) with $m = -A/B$ and $b = -C/B$. If $A = 0$, then

$$By + C = 0 \quad \text{or} \quad y = -\frac{C}{B}, \qquad B \neq 0$$

and this represents an equation of the straight line parallel to the x axis.

(b) $B = 0$ and $A \neq 0$. Then

$$Ax + C = 0 \quad \text{or} \quad x = -\frac{C}{A}$$

which represents an equation of the straight line parallel to the y axis.

Hence, $Ax + By + C = 0$ represents a straight line. ∎

EXERCISE 3.2

1. Find the equation of the line:

a. parallel to the x axis and 3 units above it

b. parallel to the x axis and 2 units below it

c. parallel to the y axis and 4 units to the right of it

d. parallel to the y axis and 3 units to the left of it

2. Find the slope of each of the following lines.

a. $x = 4$ **b.** $y = x + 2$

c. $2x - 3y = 5$ **d.** $y = 5$

e. $y = 2x + 3$ **f.** $4x + 5y = 0$

3. Determine whether or not the following lines are parallel.

a. $2x - 3y + 2 = 0; 4x - 6y = 0$

b. $3x + y + 4 = 0; 6x - 2y + 8 = 0$

c. $x + 2y - 3 = 0; 3x - 6y + 18 = 0$

d. $3x + 2y + 6 = 0; 9x + 6y + 20 = 0$

4. Using slopes, show that the points $P(2, -1)$, $Q(4, 5)$, $R(1, 8)$, and $S(-1, 2)$ are the vertices of a parallelogram.

5. Find the slope of the sides of the triangle whose vertices are $P(-4, 0)$, $Q(1, 1)$, and $R(3, -1)$.

6. Write the following equations in the slope-intercept form.

a. $2x - 3y - 6 = 0$ **b.** $3x - 4y = 9$

c. $3x + 4y + 1 = 0$ **d.** $6x - 14y = 21$

e. $ax + by + c = 0$

7. Find the slope and the y intercept in each of the following lines.

a. $3x - 2y + 12 = 0$ **b.** $x - y = 0$

c. $x + 5y - 10 = 0$ **d.** $2x - 5y + 10 = 0$

e. $3x + 2y - 15 = 0$ **f.** $-3x + 4y = 8$

8. Find the slope-intercept form of the line that passes through the point:
   a. $P(0, 3)$ and has a slope $m = 2$
   b. $P(0, -3)$ and has a slope $m = -\frac{2}{3}$
   c. $P(3, 4)$ and has a slope $m = 0$
   d. $P(1, 2)$ and has a slope $m = \frac{1}{4}$

9. Find the slope-intercept form of the line that passes through the point:
   a. $P(-2, -3)$ and has a slope $m = -2$
   b. $P(3, -4)$ and has a slope $m = \frac{3}{4}$
   c. $P(4, 5)$ and parallel to the line $2x - 3y - 3 = 0$
   d. $P(1, 2)$ and parallel to the line $3x + 5y - 12 = 0$
   e. $P(0, 3)$ and parallel to the line $3x - 9y + 11 = 0$

10. Find the equation of the line that passes through:
    a. the points $P(5, 2)$ and $Q(4, -1)$
    b. the points $P(5, 6)$ and $Q(3, 2)$
    c. the points $P(2, 3)$ and $Q(5, 6)$
    d. the points $P(-1, 2)$ and $Q(3, 8)$
    e. the origin and parallel to the line joining $P(5, 2)$ and $Q(4, -1)$
    f. the point $(3, 4)$ and parallel to the line joining $P(1, 1)$ and $Q(4, 5)$.

11. Find the slope and y intercept of the line that passes through the points P and Q:
    a. $P(2, 4)$, $Q(1, -1)$ **b.** $P(0, 5)$, $Q(2, 3)$
    c. $P(4, 3)$, $Q(3, 1)$

12. Find the equation of the line whose intercepts on the x axis and y axis are
    a. $3, 4$ **b.** $3, -4$
    c. $\frac{1}{2}, \frac{1}{3}$ **d.** $\frac{1}{2}, -\frac{1}{3}$
    e. $-\frac{1}{3}, 2$ **f.** $3, -\frac{1}{2}$
    respectively.

13. Find the equation of the line that passes through the point $P(2, 3)$ and makes equal intercepts on the coordinate axis.

14. Find the equation of the line that passes through the point $(1, -1)$ and makes intercepts on the axes equal in magnitude but opposite in sign.

15. Show that the lines

$$a_1x + b_1y + c_1 = 0$$

and

$$a_2x + b_2y + c_2 = 0$$

are parallel if and only if $a_1b_2 - b_1a_2 = 0$.

16. Show that the lines

$$a_1x + b_1y + c_1 = 0$$

and

$$a_2x + b_2y + c_2 = 0$$

are perpendicular to each other if and only if $a_1a_2 + b_1b_2 = 0$.

3.4 APPLICATIONS

Linear functions play a dominant role in the cost analysis in which business firms exercise careful control over the cost of production. The cost function is generally expressed by an equation of a straight line

$$C(x) = mx + b$$

where b is the fixed cost and generally includes rent, executive salaries, interest on investments, taxes, insurance, advertising, and allowances for equipment and its depreciation, and m refers to the costs that can be charged directly to the products a firm produces. These costs, referred to as variable costs, include the cost of raw materials, fuel, supplies, packaging, freight, and direct labor. Consider, for instance, that the cost of making x dining tables in a furniture company is approximated by a linear function

$$C(x) = \$100x + \$5000$$

Note that $5000 is the overhead cost of the plant and $100 represents the cost of the raw material, labor, and so on, used in the production of each table. Thus, the total cost of producing 50 dining tables is given by

$$C(50) = \$(100)(50) + \$5000$$
$$= \$10,000$$

whereas the cost of producing 60 tables is

$$C(60) = \$(100)(60) + \$5000$$
$$= \$11,000$$

As another illustration, consider a car rental company at an international airport that leases automobiles and charges $15 a day plus $0.12 a mile. Clearly, $15 is a fixed charge and $0.12 a mile is a variable cost related directly to the number of miles the car is driven. If x represents the distance traveled in a day, then the cost function may be expressed as

$$C(x) = \$15 + \$0.12x$$

Thus, if a customer drives 50 miles in a day, he is charged $(0.12)50 + 15 = \$21$ and if he travels 70 miles in one day, he must pay $23.40 for the day he rented the automobile.

Linear Depreciation

Apartment buildings, automobiles, office equipment, furniture, machines, and other business assets depreciate in value over a number of years. This loss in value is computed generally by using the linear depreciation method approved by the Internal Revenue Service. As the name suggests, the method assumes that business property with n years of its life loses $1/n$ of its original cost every year. Thus, if C is the original cost of an asset depreciated linearly over n years, then the total depreciation after m

years is $(C/n)m$. The value V of this asset at the end of m years is

$$V = C - \frac{C}{n} \cdot m$$

(3.8)

$$= C\left(1 - \frac{m}{n}\right) \qquad 0 \le m \le n$$

Example 3.14

A business property sold for \$80,000 in 1965 is assumed to depreciate linearly over 20 years of its life. Determine the value in (a) 1971, and (b) 1976.

SOLUTION

Here,

$$C = \$80,000 \qquad n = 20 \text{ years}$$

The value V of the property in 1971 is obtained by letting $m = 6$ in (3.8). Thus,

$$V_{1971} = \$80,000(1 - \tfrac{6}{20}) = \$56,000$$

Similarly, the value of the asset in 1976 is obtained by substituting $m = 11$ in (3.8). This yields

$$V_{1976} = \$80,000(1 - \tfrac{11}{20}) = \$36,000 \qquad\qquad \blacksquare$$

We wish to remark that the linear depreciation method does not reflect the actual rate at which various business assets depreciate in value. Some assets, such as automobiles, lose value more rapidly in the first few years as compared to the later part of their life. For this reason some nonlinear methods, which we shall discuss in Chapter 15, are also used for depreciating business property.

Some other applications of linear functions involve determining trend lines, which are useful in forecasting sales, inventory in business, or growth in population.

Example 3.15

The sales of a certain department store are approximated by a linear function. The sales were \$45,000 in 1965 and \$75,000 in 1971. Determine the linear function representing this increase in sales.

Assuming that this linear trend continues, estimate the sales in 1974.

SOLUTION

Let x represent the number of years past 1965. Then $x = 6$ represents the year 1971. Because sales are linearly related to time, we need to determine an equation of the straight line passing through $(0, 45000)$ and $(6, 75000)$. The slope of this line is

$$m = \frac{75,000 - 45,000}{6 - 0} = \frac{30,000}{6} = 5000$$

Thus, the equation of the straight line is

$$y - 45,000 = 5000(x - 0)$$

That is,

$$y = 45,000 + 5000x$$

where y denotes the sales in year x.

To find the estimated sales in 1974, we substitute $x = 9$ in the above equation. Then

$$y = 45,000 + 5000(9)$$
$$= \$90,000$$

Example 3.16

The population of a small town is approximately linearly related to time. The population was 2000 in 1960 and 2800 in 1970. Determine the linear function representing this increase in population. Estimate the population in 1975 and 1980.

SOLUTION

Let $x = 0$ represent 1960. Then $x = 10$ represents the year 1970. Clearly, the two points $(0, 2000)$ and $(10, 2800)$ need to be used to find the equation of the trend line. The slope of this line is

$$m = \frac{2800 - 2000}{10 - 0} = 80$$

Using (3.3), we have

$$y - 2000 = 80(x - 0)$$
$$y = 2000 + 80x$$

where y denotes the size of the population in the year x. To find the population in 1975, we let $x = 15$ in the above equation and obtain

$$y = 2000 + 80(15) = 3200$$

Similarly, the population in 1980 is obtained by letting $x = 20$. Thus,

$$y = 2000 + 80(20) = 3600$$

EXERCISE 3.3

1. A community college is offering a course in principles of accounting. The operating cost for this course is $750 plus $15 for each student registered. Determine the cost function. What is the operating cost if 30 students are enrolled in this course?
2. A local newspaper is planning to conduct a survey to study the voting habits of the residents in a certain community. The operating cost is $1000 plus $2 for each family polled.
   a. Determine the cost function.
   b. What is the total cost if 2450 families are to be polled?
   c. How many families will be polled if there is $5000 available in the budget?

3. A truck rental agency in a town leases trucks and charges $20 a day plus $0.50 a mile.
   a. Determine the cost function.
   b. What is the total charge if the truck is used for 38 miles?
4. A manufacturer uses special gears in his line of production. He installed new machines at an expense of $50,000. Determine the cost function if the variable cost per gear is $20.
5. A new machine was installed in the plant in 1970 at an expense of $100,000. If this machine is depreciated linearly over 25 years, determine its value in
   a. 1978
   b. 1984
6. An apartment building worth $300,000 built in 1965 is being depreciated linearly over 50 years. Determine the value of this building in 1984.
7. An electric typewriter purchased on December 1, 1974 for $480 is being depreciated linearly over a period of 5 years. Determine the undepreciated value of this typewriter on June 30, 1976.
8. A new machine purchased for $50,000 in 1965 had a scrap value of $3000 at the end of 1975.
   a. Determine the linear equation that expresses the value of the machine at the end of n years.
   b. What was the value of the machine at the end of 1968?
9. An investment of $10,000 in a certain stock yields an annual income of $1000, and an investment of $50,000 in a similar stock yields an income of $7000. Assuming that the income y is a linear function of the investment x, determine the linear equation $y = mx + b$ that expresses the annual income in terms of an investment.
10. The Hill Publishing Company must set a price for a new book. The past sales experience of the company on similar books reveals the following information:

Number of Copies Sold	Price of the Book
40,000	$8
60,000	$6

Assuming that the relationship is linear, determine the equation of the line that expresses the price of the book in terms of the number of copies sold. What price should be set for the book if management expects to sell 75,000 copies?

4

Systems of Linear Equations and Linear Inequalities

4.1 INTRODUCTION

In this chapter, we shall be concerned exclusively with systems of linear equations and linear inequalities—an important topic in mathematics with wide applications in many areas. Most readers are probably familiar with the process of solving two linear equations in two variables from high school algebra, using graphs, elimination, or substitution techniques. We shall exploit these relatively simple but powerful methods. Later, in Chapter 6, we shall examine the solution of linear equations by utilizing matrix theory.

4.2 LINEAR EQUATIONS IN TWO VARIABLES

Many business, economics, and management problems involve several conditions expressed in the form of linear equations in two variables that must be satisfied simultaneously. Suppose, for example, that a salesman tells one of his customers that the total price of a color television and a black-and-white television is $650 but that the color set costs $350 more than the black-and-white set. Can you guess the price of each set? Perhaps, after some trial and error, you come to the conclusion that a black-and-white set costs $150 and a color set costs $500, because the sum of these prices is $650 and their difference is $350. How did you arrive at this solution? Did you use some technique that you learned in high school algebra, or was it a good guess? Suppose that 1000 teachers from secondary schools attended a professional convention in New York last summer. If the number of male teachers is 80 less than twice the number of female teachers, can you determine the number of male and female teachers who attended the convention? If you have organized your thinking and your answer is that 640 male teachers and 360 female teachers attended the conference, you have some insight into solving similar problems. Many times, however, we are faced with problems too complicated to solve by trial and error without using any mathematical model. Consider, for example, that a dairy has

45 gallons of milk containing 4 percent butterfat and 20 gallons of cream containing 24 percent butterfat. Can you determine the number of gallons of milk that should be mixed with the cream to obtain "half-and-half" containing 12 percent butterfat? (Note that half-and-half is not strictly equal parts of milk and cream.) Obviously, guess work is not helpful in problems of this nature, and we must seek a systematic procedure that expresses the relevant information in the form of linear equations that may be solved by graphing, substitution, or elimination methods we encountered in high school algebra.

   To introduce formally a procedure that helps us to find a solution of the type of problems discussed, we recall from Chapter 3 that $Ax + By + C = 0$ is a linear equation that describes a particular kind of relationship between two unknown quantities. For example, the equation $3x + 4y = 24$ is a linear equation in two variables, x and y. A solution of this equation is an ordered pair of numbers (x, y) that when substituted for x and y in this equation converts it into a true statement. The pair $(4, 3)$, for example, is one such solution, because

$$4(3) + 3(4) = 24$$

Similarly, many other ordered pairs, such as $(0, 6)$, $(8, 0)$, $(12, -3)$, $(16, -6)$, are all solutions of the linear equation $3x + 4y = 24$. In fact, a linear equation in more than one unknown has an infinite number of solutions, commonly referred to as the solution set.

   Now consider the following pair of linear equations:

(4.1)
$$3x + 4y = 24$$
$$2x - y = 5$$

We have two equations in two unknowns and we wish to determine a solution set. Adding the first equation to four times the second equation eliminates y and we obtain $11x = 44$ so that $x = 4$. Substituting this value of x in either of two original equations, we obtain $y = 3$. Thus, the solution to the system of linear equations (4.1) is the ordered pair $(4, 3)$ that satisfies both equations. Had we wanted to eliminate x instead of y, we could have multiplied the first equation by 2, the second equation by 3, and then would have obtained

(4.2)
$$6x + 8y = 48$$
$$6x - 3y = 15$$

Subtracting the second equation from the first equation in (4.2), we would have $11y = 33$ or $y = 3$ as before. Note that the method of elimination that we have used here assumes that we can multiply "equals by equals," add "equals to equals," and subtract "equals from equals."

   As another approach, we can solve each of the two linear equations for x. The first equation in (4.1) gives

$$x = \frac{24 - 4y}{3}$$

and the second equation yields

$$x = \frac{y + 5}{2}$$

Equating these two expressions, we have

$$\frac{24 - 4y}{3} = \frac{y + 5}{2}$$

that is,

$$48 - 8y = 3y + 15$$

which yields

$$11y = 33 \quad \text{or} \quad y = 3$$

The corresponding value of $x = 4$ is obtained by substituting $y = 3$ in either of the two equations. If we wanted to solve each of the original equations for y instead of x, we would have obtained

$$y = \frac{24 - 3x}{4} \quad \text{and} \quad y = 2x - 5$$

Equating these expressions, we obtain

$$\frac{24 - 3x}{4} = 2x - 5$$

or

$$24 - 3x = 8x - 20$$

which yields $11x = 44$ or $x = 4$. Because $y = 2x - 5$ is one of the original equations, we substitute the value of x and obtain

$$y = 2(4) - 5 = 3$$

as before.

Another method of finding the solution set is that of graphs. To represent a linear equation graphically, we choose two distinct points whose coordinates satisfy the linear equation. Note that the points $P\,(8, 0)$ and $Q\,(0, 6)$ lie on $3x + 4y = 24$; the straight line joining these two points P and Q represents the graph of this linear equation. (See Figure 4.1.)

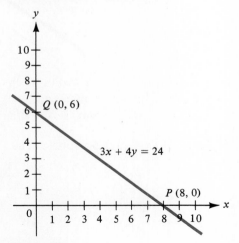

Figure 4.1

The second equation, $2x - y = 5$, is satisfied by infinitely many points, some of which are $A\,(3, 1)$, $B\,(4, 3)$, $C\,(5, 5)$, and $D\,(7, 9)$. The line joining any of these points determines the graph of the linear equation $2x - y = 5$ (Figure 4.2).

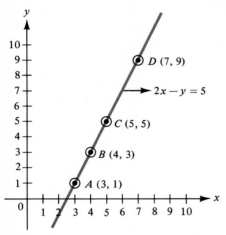

Figure 4.2

Because the solution set of a linear equation is the set of all ordered pairs (x, y) that satisfy the equation, our interest lies only in those ordered pairs that satisfy both the equations simultaneously. Consequently, the solution set of (4.1) is the intersection of the solution sets of the individual equations. Having plotted the graphs of the equations, we simply read off the coordinates of the point of intersection of the two straight lines. The solution set consists of the ordered pair (4, 3), as shown in Figure 4.3.

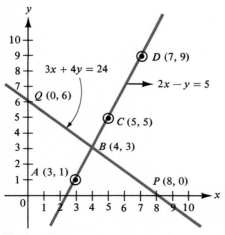

Figure 4.3

We consider it worth our while to warn the reader that the graphical method of finding the point of intersection of two lines has serious practical limitations, because we can only read off an approximation of the solution from the graph. Unless there are reasons to the contrary, we suggest that the reader avoid the use of graphical methods for solving simultaneous linear equations.

The graphical representation of a system of two linear equations in two variables may result in one of three possibilities:

(a) the lines intersect; or
(b) the lines are parallel; or
(c) the lines coincide.

We have provided an illustration of (a) in Figure 4.3. Each of the remaining possibilities is illustrated in the following example.

Example 4.1

Solve the following sets of linear equations graphically.

a. $2x - 3y = 6$
   $6x - 9y = 54$

b. $x - 2y = 5$
   $2x - 4y = 10$

SOLUTION

a. The ordered pairs $(-3, -4)$, $(0, -2)$, $(3, 0)$, $(6, 2)$, $(9, 4)$ and infinitely many more ordered pairs are all solutions of the linear equation $2x - 3y = 6$. Some of the ordered pairs that satisfy the linear equation $6x - 9y = 54$ are $(3, -4)$, $(6, -2)$, $(9, 0)$, $(12, 2)$. The graph of these equations is shown in Figure 4.4. Note that the linear equation $2x - 3y = 6$, when expressed in the slope-intercept form (3.2), yields

$$y = \tfrac{2}{3}x - 2$$

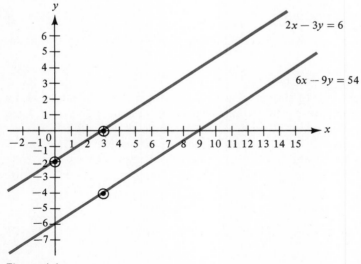

Figure 4.4

and this implies that the slope of this line is $m_1 = \frac{2}{3}$. Similarly, solving $6x - 9y = 54$ for y, we have

$$y = \frac{2}{3}x - 6$$

Thus, $m_2 = \frac{2}{3}$. Because the slopes m_1 and m_2 are equal, we conclude that $2x - 3y = 6$ and $6x - 9y = 54$ are distinct parallel lines and have, therefore, no common point of intersection. Thus, the solution is the null set.

b. Note that because $x - 2y = 5$ and $2x - 4y = 10$ is the equation of the same straight line (Why?), the ordered pairs $(1, -2)$, $(3, -1)$, $(5, 0)$, and infinitely many more that satisfy the linear equation $x - 2y = 5$ also satisfy the equation

$$2x - 4y = 10.$$

Hence, the lines coincide (see Figure 4.5). Because every ordered pair that is a solution of one linear equation is also a solution of the other linear equation, it follows that the system has an infinite number of solutions.

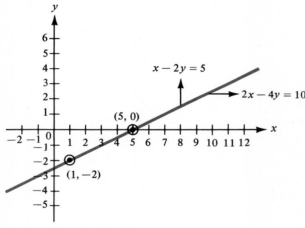

Figure 4.5

The following examples provide practical illustrations of solutions of two equations in two unknowns.

Example 4.2

A company makes two kinds of electric pencil sharpeners, a standard model and a deluxe model. Each model must pass through two assembly points, A and B. Each unit of standard model requires 10 minutes on machine A and 15 minutes on machine B, whereas each unit of deluxe model requires 20 minutes on machine A and 5 minutes on machine B. If both machines operate for $7\frac{1}{2}$ hours a day, how many pencil sharpeners of each type are produced daily, assuming that most efficient use is made of the machines?

SOLUTION

The following table summarizes the information furnished in the problem:

	Machine A	Machine B
Standard model	10 minutes	15 minutes
Deluxe model	20 minutes	5 minutes

Let x and y be the number of units of standard and deluxe models, respectively. Then we have the following system of linear equations to solve:

$$10x + 20y = 450$$
$$15x + 5y = 450$$

Subtracting the first equation from the second, we have

$$5x - 15y = 0$$

that is,

$$x = 3y$$

Substituting this expression in either of the original equations, we obtain $y = 9$. Thus, $x = 27$. ∎

Example 4.3

A solution A of liquids contains 30 percent alcohol and 70 percent water. A second solution B contains 45 percent alcohol and 55 percent water. How much of solution A must be mixed with 30 quarts of solution B to produce another solution containing 35 percent alcohol?

SOLUTION

Let x represent the number of quarts of solution A that needs to be mixed with 30 quarts of solution B to produce y quarts of the mixed solution. Then,

$$(4.3) \quad y = x + 30$$

The alcoholic content in x quarts of solution A is $(0.30)x$, in 30 quarts of solution B the alcoholic content is $30(0.45)$, and y quarts of the mixture contains $(0.35)y$ alcohol. This gives us another linear equation,

$$(0.35)y = (0.30)x + (0.45)(30)$$

that is,

$$(4.4) \quad 35y = 30x + 1350$$

Solving (4.3) and (4.4), we have $x = 60$. Thus, 60 quarts of solution A must be mixed with 30 quarts of solution B to produce a solution containing 35 percent alcoholic content. ∎

EXERCISE 4.1

1. Determine the solution set of the following systems of linear equations.

   a. $x + y = 1$
      $x - y = 1$

   b. $x + 2y = 5$
      $2x + 3y = 8$

   c. $2x - 3y = 13$
      $4x + y = 5$

   d. $2x - y = 4$
      $5x - y = 13$

   e. $x + y = 5$
      $2x + 3y = 12$

   f. $x - 3y = 7$
      $2x + y = 7$

   g. $3x - 2y = 6$
      $x + y = 4$

   h. $2x - 3y = 5$
      $3x - 2y = -4$

2. Determine whether the following sets of linear equations represent parallel lines, coincident lines, or intersecting lines.

a. $x + y = 3$
$3x + 3y = 12$

b. $3x - y = 4$
$3x - y = 8$

c. $3x - y = 8$
$2x + 3y = 9$

d. $x - y = 0$
$x + 3y = 8$

e. $x + y = 3$
$2x + 2y = 6$

f. $x - 2y = 0$
$3x + 2y = 8$

3. Solve graphically the following systems of linear equations.

a. $x - y = 2$
$2x + 3y = 9$

b. $2x + y = 5$
$x + 2y = 4$

c. $x - y = 0$
$x + 3y = 8$

d. $x + 2y = 2$
$x - 2y = 2$

e. $x + 3y = 9$
$3x + 2y = 13$

f. $x - y = -1$
$3x + 2y = 12$

4. The sum of two numbers is 52. If one of the numbers is 6 more than the other number, find the two numbers.

5. Three shirts and two ties cost $32 in a department store, but if one buys five shirts and three ties, the total cost is $52. Determine the price of each shirt and tie.

6. A total of 3640 votes were cast in a mayoral election with two candidates. Three times the number of votes received by one candidate was 720 more than twice the number received by the other. How many votes did each candidate receive?

7. At an Ice Capades performance, an adult paid $2.50 whereas children were charged $1.50. There were 800 more adult tickets sold than children's tickets. If the total receipts for the show were $4400, how many of each type of admission ticket were sold?

8. At a theater performance, children were charged $0.50 whereas an adult paid $1.25 for an admission ticket. There were 600 fewer children's tickets sold than adult tickets. If the total receipts for the performance were $2500, how many of each type of admission tickets were sold?

9. Gary deposited $10,000 in a savings bank, some at an annual interest of 5 percent and the rest at an annual rate of 6 percent. If the interest collected at the end of 1 year is $560, how much money was deposited at 5 percent and 6 percent, respectively?

10. A total of $8000 is invested in two savings plans, some at an annual rate of interest of $5\frac{1}{2}$ percent and the rest at 7 percent. If $485 is collected as interest at the end of a year, how much money is invested at $5\frac{1}{2}$ percent?

11. The manager of a grocery store wishes to mix peanuts that sell for $0.60 a pound with pecans that sell for $1.20 a pound. How many pounds of peanuts should be mixed with 50 pounds of pecans to produce a mixture selling for $0.90 a pound?

12. How many pounds of nuts worth $0.80 a pound should be mixed with nuts worth $0.60 a pound to produce a mixture of 50 pounds that will sell at $0.70 a pound?

13. A grocer wants to market a new brand of mixed nuts by mixing cashews that sell for $1.50 a pound and peanuts that sell for $0.80 a pound. How many pounds of peanuts should be mixed with 30 pounds of cashews to get a mixture selling for $1.20 a pound?

14. The manager of a grocery store wishes to mix peanuts that sell for $0.80 a pound with pecans that sell for $1.40 a pound. How many pounds of peanuts should be mixed with 20 pounds of pecans to produce a mixture selling for $1.00 a pound?

15. A solution A of liquids contains 26 percent alcohol and 74 percent water. A second solution B contains 42 percent alcohol and 58 percent water. How much of each solution must be mixed to make 120 quarts of solution containing 30 percent alcohol?

16. A solution A of liquids contains 40 percent alcohol and 60 percent water. A second solution B contains 30 percent alcohol and 70 percent water. How much of each solution must be mixed to make 100 quarts of a solution containing 32 percent alcohol?

17. A dairy has a quantity of milk containing 3 percent butterfat and 15 gallons of cream containing 30 percent butterfat. How many gallons of milk should be mixed with the cream to obtain a mixture containing 9 percent butterfat?

4.3 BREAK-EVEN ANALYSIS

Many situations in a successful business require that management is able to determine, in advance and with some degree of accuracy, the effects that certain decisions may have on the sales of its products and the total costs of their production. An important consideration for the firm is to estimate its revenue derived from the sales forecast during the year and then build enough safety valves to assure itself that this revenue is large enough to cover not only the cost of production but also the costs of transporting the goods and advertising costs necessary to make the goods marketable. Generally, the revenue from sales is expressed as a linear function of the number of units x the firm expects to sell during the year. The total costs of production can be expressed in the form of

$$y = b + mx$$

where b is the fixed cost and m refers to variable costs that can be charged directly and specifically to the products a firm produces.

When the total receipt from sales just equals the total costs, the firm has neither made nor lost any money—the firm has just broken even. The break-even point is thus the volume or level of production at which total revenue from sales is just enough to cover the total costs of the entire production. If the firm has operated at a level higher (lower) than this point, the firm would have shown a profit (loss).

Let

$x =$ number of units produced

$p =$ selling price per unit

Then R, the total receipts in dollars, is

$$R = px$$

Further, let

$m =$ variable cost per unit

$b =$ fixed costs

Then the total costs of production C (in dollars) is given by

$$C = b + mx$$

The graph of the revenue and cost functions is shown in Figure 4.6.

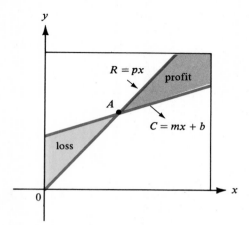

Figure 4.6

The point A, where the lines $R = px$ and $C = mx + b$ intersect, represents the break-even point.

To determine the break-even point algebraically, we must find the value of x at which the revenue from sales (R) equals the cost of production (C). That is,

$$px = b + mx$$
$$px - mx = b$$
$$(p - m)x = b$$

Thus, solving for x, we have

$$x = \frac{b}{p - m}$$

Example 4.4

The Johnson and Johnson Company publishes college textbooks. An analysis of their last audit report provides the following information:

Capacity	50,000 books per year
Variable cost	$4 per book
Fixed costs	$200,000 per year
Selling price	$12 per book

Determine the break-even point.

SOLUTION

Here, $b = \$200,000$, $p = \$12$, and $m = \$4$. Thus, the number of books that the company must publish to break even is given by

$$x = \frac{200,000}{12 - 4}$$

$$= 25,000$$

Thus, if less than 25,000 copies are published, a loss is incurred; and if more than 25,000 are published and sold, a profit results. ∎

Example 4.5

A motel on an interstate highway contains 60 rooms as follows:

Type of Room	Number of Rooms	Rate per Night
Single	40	$12
Double	20	$18

The operating cost is $444 per day. The variable cost is $3 for each single room and $4 for each double room per night. What percentage of rooms should be occupied if the management wishes to make a profit of $100 per day?

SOLUTION

Because the variable cost is $3 for a single room and $4 for a double room per night, it is clear that the occupancy of a single room contributes $12 − $3 = $9 and an occupied double room contributes $18 − $4 = $14 per night toward the fixed costs and the profits. If all rooms are occupied, then the total contribution is as follows:

$$40 \text{ single rooms} \times \$9 = \$360$$
$$20 \text{ double rooms} \times \$14 = \$280$$
$$\text{total} = \$640$$
$$\text{fixed costs and profits} = \$444 + \$100$$
$$= \$544$$

If x represents the percentage of occupancy, then the net contribution is $640x$, which must equal the operating cost and the accrued profit. Thus,

$$640x = 544$$

$$x = \frac{544}{640} = 0.85 \quad \text{or} \quad 85\%$$ ∎

EXERCISE 4.2

1. A firm manufactures its products at a cost of $10 per unit and sells it in the market for $25 per unit. The management has established that the overhead cost of its operation is $300. Determine the number of units the firm must sell to break even.

2. A college is offering a course in marine biology. The operating cost is $900 plus $45 for each student who registers for this course. If tuition is $105, determine the number of students who must register for the course if the college is to break even.

3. The Washington Motor Company currently buys exhaust pipes for its motors at $7.50 each. The company is planning to set up its own plant to manufacture these pipes at a fixed cost of $5000. Assuming that the variable cost is $6.25 for each pipe, determine the number of units the company must produce to break even.

4. The ABC Company is planning an advertising program at an additional expense of $8000. Their product, now selling at $12, has a variable cost of $4. If the current fixed costs are $40,000, how many additional units must be sold in order to justify the advertising? Determine also the new break-even point in units.

5. The Puritan Furniture Company manufactures lawn chairs for the summer. An analysis of their last audit reveals the following information.

Capacity	8000 chairs
Variable cost	$3
Fixed costs	$54,000
Selling price	$12

At what percent of its capacity should the company operate to break even? How many chairs must be sold to show a profit of $4500?

6. A hotel in Chicago has 45 rooms to rent as follows:

Type of Room	Number	Rent per Night
Single	20	$18
Double	20	$28
Suites	5	$55

The operating cost is $600 per day plus a variable cost of $3 per night for each single and double room and $5 per night for each suite, which covers linen, soap, and other supplies. What should be the overall percentage of occupied rooms if the management wishes to make a profit of $240 per day?

4.4 SYSTEMS OF LINEAR INEQUALITIES IN TWO VARIABLES

There are many problems in education, marketing, and management fields in which several conditions expressed in the form of linear inequalities must be satisfied simultaneously. The funds allocated for the faculty limits the number of new teachers that can be hired for the next fall; the number of teachers available limits the enrollment of the college; the number of hours a student studies limits the possible grade he can get in a course; the size of the parking lot limits the number of automobiles that can be parked at a given time; the amount people earn limits their expenditures on entertainment; the production capacity of a factory limits the quantity of goods that can be shipped to warehouses; the number of workers on the job in a third shift limits the production in that shift, and so on.

Linear equalities are of the form

$$Ax + By + C = 0$$

where A, B, and C are real numbers and A and B are not both zero. If the equality sign is replaced by $<$, $\leq$, $>$, or $\geq$, the resulting inequality is called a linear inequality. Thus,

$$3x + 4y \geq 12$$

and

$$2x - 3y \leq 6$$

are examples of linear inequalities.

As shown in Figure 4.7, a line divides a plane into three parts, the line itself and two half-planes on either side of the line. The line does not belong to either of the half-planes, and the half-planes I and II are themselves disjoint. Just as the points on the line can be described by means of linear equations, the points in the half-planes can be described by linear inequalities.

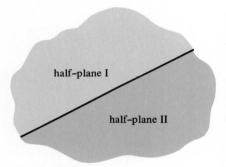

half–plane I

half–plane II

Figure 4.7

To plot the graph of a linear inequality in two unknowns, we first graph the line by choosing any two points that satisfy the linear equation and connecting them with a straight line. To plot $3x + 4y \geq 12$, for example, we need to determine which of the two half-planes satisfy the linear inequality $3x + 4y > 12$. The proper half-plane can be determined by choosing an arbitrary point in one of the half-planes that is not on the line. If its coordinates satisfy the inequality, then the half-plane that contains that point is the graph of the inequality. If the coordinates of the point do not satisfy the inequality, then the other half-plane is the desired graph. The origin $(0, 0)$ is often a good choice for the test because the resulting arithmetic is obviously simplified.

Thus, if we substitute $x = 0$, $y = 0$ into the linear inequality $3x + 4y > 12$, we obtain

$$3(0) + 4(0) > 12$$

that is,

$$0 > 12$$

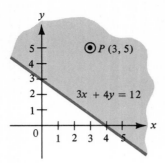

Figure 4.8

which is a false statement. This means that the point $(0, 0)$ is not a part of the half-plane determined by $3x + 4y > 12$. The shaded region in Figure 4.8 together with the line $3x + 4y = 12$ is the desired graph of the linear inequality $3x + 4y \geq 12$. Note that the point $P (3, 5)$ is a part of the graph because if we substitute $x = 3$, $y = 5$ into the linear inequality $3x + 4y > 12$, we have

$$3(3) + 4(5) > 12$$
$$29 > 12$$

which is a true statement. ■

Example 4.6

Sketch the graph of the linear inequality

$$x + 2y > 4$$

SOLUTION

The region we want to sketch is one of the half-planes determined by the linear equality $x + 2y = 4$ given in Figure 4.9(a). Now choose an arbitrary point, say the origin $(0, 0)$, as a testing point. Substituting $x = 0$, $y = 0$ in the inequality $x + 2y > 4$, we obtain

$$0 + 2(0) > 4$$

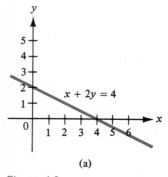

(a)

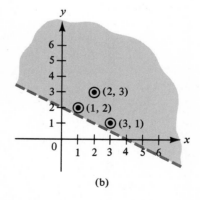

(b)

Figure 4.9

that is,

$$0 > 4$$

which is false. This implies that the origin is not located in the desired half-plane. The reader can verify that the points $(1, 2)$, $(2, 3)$, and $(3, 1)$ are parts of the desired graph and lie on the same side of $x + 2y = 4$, whereas the points $(-1, -1)$ and $(1, 1)$ lie on the other side of the line [see Figure 4.9(b)]. The fact that the line representing the equation is dotted shows that it is not part of the graph of the inequality. ■

We shall now consider systems of linear inequalities in two variables x and y such as

$$\begin{array}{cc} 2x + y \geq 200 \\ 10x + 3y \geq 750 \end{array} \quad \text{or} \quad \begin{array}{c} 6x + 56 \leq 30 \\ x - 2y \leq 2 \\ 4x + 8y \leq 32 \\ x \geq 0, y \geq 0 \end{array}$$

and determine values of x and y that satisfy all the linear inequalities simultaneously. The set of ordered pairs (x, y) so obtained is called the solution set of the system of linear inequalities.

Example 4.7

Determine the region satisfying the linear inequalities

$$x \geq 0, y \geq 0$$

SOLUTION

The linear inequality $y \geq 0$ corresponds to the upper-half of the plane and includes the line $y = 0$ (Figure 4.10). Similarly, the inequality $x \geq 0$ refers to the right-half of the plane in Figure 4.11, and this region includes the line $x = 0$. Thus, the linear inequalities $x \geq 0$ and $y \geq 0$ refer to the first quadrant and this region includes the axes as shown in Figure 4.12.

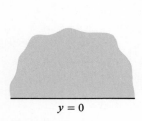

$y = 0$

Figure 4.10

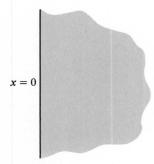

$x = 0$

Figure 4.11

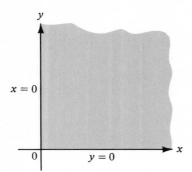

Figure 4.12

These inequalities play a very important role in essentially all linear programming problems, which we shall consider in Chapter 7.

Example 4.8

Determine the region satisfying the linear inequalities

$$2x + y \le 2$$
$$2x - 3y \ge 6$$

SOLUTION

First, we draw the graph of the linear equation $2x + y = 2$. Using $(0, 0)$ as a test point, we determine the half-plane that corresponds to the linear inequality $2x + y < 2$. The shaded region in Figure 4.13 together with the line $2x + y = 2$ represents the graph of $2x + y \le 2$. Similarly, the linear inequality $2x - 3y \ge 6$ is represented by the shaded region in Figure 4.14. The solution set of the inequalities $2x + y \le 2$ and $2x - 3y \ge 6$ is the intersection of the solution sets of the two inequalities and is given by the shaded region in Figure 4.15. We suggest that you consider a sample point in the shaded region and convince yourself that the sample point satisfies the linear inequalities simultaneously.

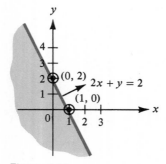

Figure 4.13

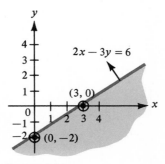

Figure 4.14

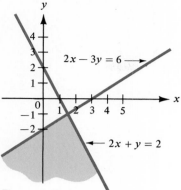

Figure 4.15

Example 4.9

Determine the region satisfying the following linear inequalities:

$$x - y \geq 1$$
$$x + y \geq 5$$
$$x < 7$$

SOLUTION

We have a system of three linear inequalities in two unknowns. First, we draw the graph of the line $x - y = 1$ and shade the region that corresponds to the linear inequality $x - y \geq 1$ (see Figure 4.16). Then, draw the line $x + y = 5$ and shade the region that corresponds to the intersection of linear inequalities $x - y \geq 1$ and $x + y \geq 5$ as shown in Figure 4.17. Finally, we graph the line $x = 7$ and shade the triangle *CDE* as in Figure 4.18. This region is the intersection of the three linear inequalities $x - y \geq 1$, $x + y \geq 5$, and $x < 7$. Note that the vertical line $x = 7$ does not form the part of the solution set.

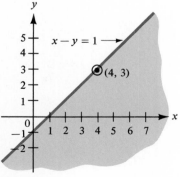

Figure 4.16

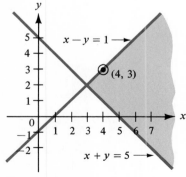

Figure 4.17

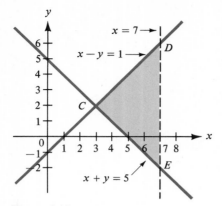

Figure 4.18

Example 4.10

Draw the graph of the following linear inequalities and determine the solution set:

$$5x + 3y \leq 150$$
$$x + y \leq 40$$
$$x \geq 0, y \geq 0$$

SOLUTION

We have a system of four linear inequalities in the two unknowns x and y. As in Example 4.7, the linear inequalities $x \geq 0$ and $y \geq 0$ refer to the right half and the upper half of the plane respectively, that is, the first quadrant, and this region includes the axes. As far as the other inequalities are concerned, we simply graph the lines $5x + 3y = 150$ and $x + y = 40$ and find that the solution set of the system of four linear inequalities is given by the shaded region of Figure 4.19.

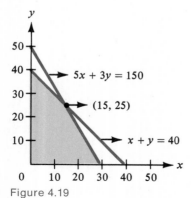

Figure 4.19

Example 4.11

Draw graphs of the following linear inequalities and determine the solution set:

$$2x + y \geq 100$$
$$x + y \geq 80$$
$$x \geq 0, y \geq 0$$

SOLUTION

The graph of the inequalities is shown in Figure 4.20.

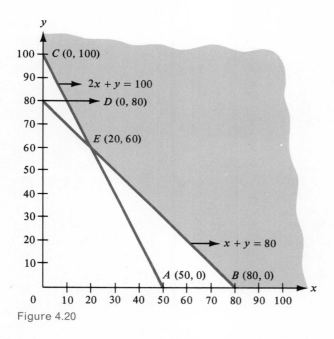

Figure 4.20

The solution set is represented by the shaded region, which is understood to extend indefinitely upward and to the right. ■

Example 4.12

Sketch the following linear inequalities and determine the solution set:

$$x + y \geq 60$$
$$x + 2y \leq 50$$
$$x \geq 0, y \geq 0$$

SOLUTION

The graph of the four inequalities is shown in Figure 4.21. Because there is no common region, we conclude that this system of linear inequalities has no solution.

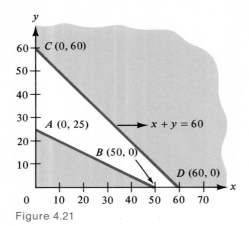

Figure 4.21

EXERCISE 4.3

Draw graphs of the following linear inequalities:

1. $x + 6y \geq 10$ **2.** $4x + 3y \geq 12$

3. $3x + 2y < 6$ **4.** $3x - 4y \leq 12$

5. $x + 3y \geq 8$ **6.** $8x + 7y \leq 28$

Shade the area consisting of points (if any) that satisfy the system of linear inequalities in each of the following problems.

7. $x + 6y \geq 11$ and $3x - 4y + 11 > 0$

8. $2x - 3y > 3$ and $3x + 4y \leq 30$

9. $x \geq 0$, $y \geq 0$, and $3x + 4y \leq 12$

10. $x \geq 0$, $y \geq 0$, and $x + 2y \leq 8$

11. $x - y \geq 0$, $x + y \leq 4$, and $y \leq 8$

12. $x \geq 0$, $y \geq 0$, $2x + 5y \leq 30$, and $4x + 5y \leq 40$

Determine the region, if any, satisfied by each of the following systems of inequalities.

13. $x + 6y \geq 11$, $3x - 4y + 11 \geq 0$, and $2x + y < 11$

14. $x \geq 0$, $y \geq 0$, $x + y \leq 6$, and $x + 4y \leq 12$

15. $x \geq 0$, $y \geq 0$, $2x + y \leq 100$, and $x + y \leq 75$

16. $x \geq 0$, $y \geq 0$, $2x + y \leq 200$, and $10x + 3y \leq 750$

17. $x \geq 0$, $y \geq 0$, $x \geq y + 4$, and $3x + 4y \geq 24$

18. $x \geq 0$, $y \geq 1$, $x - 2y + 4 \geq 0$, $x - 3y + 4 \geq 0$, and $x + y - 7 \leq 0$

19. $x \geq 0$, $y \geq 0$, $x - y + 1 \geq 0$, $x + y - 5 \leq 0$, and $3x + y - 8 \leq 0$

20. $x \geq 2$, $x \leq 6$, $y \leq 4$, $x + y \geq 3$, and $8x + 7y \geq 56$

CHAPTER 5
Vectors and Matrices

5.1 INTRODUCTION

In this chapter, we discuss basic arithmetic of vectors and matrices. Historically, the theory of matrices originated in the famous works of William R. Hamilton (1804–1865) and was developed by Cayley (1821–1895), Sylvester (1814–1897), and many other leading mathematicians and physicists. Since the introduction of high-speed electronic computers, vectors and matrices have found increasing applications in almost all areas of pure and applied mathematics. Matrices are frequently used in solving systems of linear equations, in linear programming, in Markov processes, in queuing (waiting-line) theory, in regression analysis, in game theory, and have interesting applications in business and economics.

5.2 VECTORS

Suppose that a political scientist has conducted a survey in his home town and wishes to report whether or not a person's political party has any effect on his views toward an amendment to a bill in the state legislature. The survey might reveal that of the total residents interviewed, 48 percent approve the amendment, 37 percent oppose it, and the remaining 15 percent have no opinion. In abbreviated form, this information can be presented as

In favor   Opposed   No opinion
(48   37   15   )

As another example, suppose that an automobile dealer wishes to report his sales to his regional office for April 1976. The dealer might report that he sold 8 Granadas, 12 Mavericks, 23 Mustangs, and 41 Pintos during April 1976. This information to the regional office may be expressed as

Granada   Maverick   Mustang   Pinto
(8   12   23   41)

Arrays of numbers like this are called row vectors; similarly numbers presented in a column are referred to as column vectors.

Definition 5.2.1: **A row (column) vector** is an ordered collection of real numbers written in a row (column).

Examples of row vectors are

$$(2 \quad 3), \quad (1 \quad -1 \quad 5), \quad (4 \quad -2 \quad 7 \quad -1)$$

Similarly, column vectors may be represented as

$$\begin{pmatrix} 1 \\ 2 \end{pmatrix}, \quad \begin{pmatrix} 15 \\ 22 \\ 34 \end{pmatrix}, \quad \begin{pmatrix} 451 \\ 345 \\ 273 \\ 161 \end{pmatrix}, \quad \text{or} \quad \begin{pmatrix} 20 \\ -15 \\ 32 \\ 18 \\ -7 \end{pmatrix}$$

The individual numbers in a vector are called components or elements. If a vector has n components, it is called an n-dimensional vector. Thus, the first row vector in the above example is two-dimensional, the second is three-dimensional, and the third is four-dimensional. Similarly, the first column vector is two-dimensional, the second is three-dimensional, and so on.

The geometrical interpretation of vectors plays a significant role in many basic concepts of physics. A vector in physics is a physical quantity, such as force, that has magnitude as well as direction. In a plane or in three dimensions, a vector is represented by an arrow; the length of the line segment represents the magnitude, and the direction of the arrow indicates the direction in which the quantity acts. Thus, a row vector (5, 4) in a plane (see Figure 5.1) is uniquely determined by a line segment starting from the origin (0, 0) and terminating at a point (5, 4).

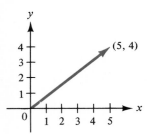

Figure 5.1

Definition 5.2.2: Two row (column) vectors are equal if and only if they are of same dimensions and their corresponding components are equal.

Thus, if $\mathbf{a} = (a_1 \ a_2 \cdots a_n)$ and $\mathbf{b} = (b_1 \ b_2 \cdots b_n)$, where the a's and b's are real numbers, then $\mathbf{a} = \mathbf{b}$ if and only if

$$a_i = b_i \qquad \text{for } i = 1, 2, 3, \ldots, n$$

Specifically, if $\mathbf{a} = (1 \ 2 \ x \ 5)$ and $\mathbf{b} = (1 \ y \ 6 \ 5)$, then $\mathbf{a} = \mathbf{b}$ if and only if $x = 6$ and $y = 2$. Note that $\mathbf{a}$ and $\mathbf{b}$ have the same dimensions.

Now that we have defined a physical quantity called a vector, we may wonder whether or not it is possible to add two vectors, or subtract one vector from another vector, or multiply a vector by a real number and, if so, what is their geometrical significance? To add two vectors in a plane, we place the vectors so that their initial points coincide as in Figure 5.2. Then, their sum is represented by the diagonal of the parallelogram formed with the two vectors as sides. Note that because the figure is a parallelogram, the opposite sides are equal in measure and parallel.

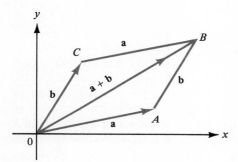

Figure 5.2

Thus, if 8 boys 5 girls enrolled in seminar I and 6 boys and 4 girls enrolled in seminar II are represented by $\mathbf{a} = (8\ 5)$ and $\mathbf{b} = (6\ 4)$, respectively, then

$$\mathbf{a} + \mathbf{b} = (8\quad 5) + (6\quad 4)$$
$$= (8 + 6\quad 5 + 4)$$
$$= (14\quad 9)$$

represents the combined enrollment of 14 boys and 9 girls in both the seminars. This suggests the following definition.

Definition 5.2.3: The sum of two row (column) vectors of n components each is obtained by adding their corresponding components.

Thus, if $\mathbf{a} = (a_1\ a_2 \cdots a_n)$ and $\mathbf{b} = (b_1\ b_2 \cdots b_n)$ where the a's and b's are real numbers, then

$$\mathbf{a} + \mathbf{b} = (a_1 + b_1\quad a_2 + b_2 \cdots a_n + b_n)$$

For example,

$$(2\quad 1\quad 5) + (6\quad 4\quad 3) = (2 + 6\quad 1 + 4\quad 5 + 3)$$
$$= (8\quad 5\quad 8)$$

and

$$\begin{pmatrix} 2 \\ 3 \\ 4 \end{pmatrix} + \begin{pmatrix} -4 \\ 0 \\ 1 \end{pmatrix} = \begin{pmatrix} 2 - 4 \\ 3 + 0 \\ 4 + 1 \end{pmatrix} = \begin{pmatrix} -2 \\ 3 \\ 5 \end{pmatrix}$$

Note that the addition of two vectors is defined only when they are both row or both column vectors and each vector has the same number of components.

Definition 5.2.4: Let $\mathbf{a} = (a_1\ a_2 \cdots a_n)$ be a row vector and k be any real number, then

$$ k\mathbf{a} = (ka_1 \quad ka_2 \cdots ka_n) $$

Thus, if $\mathbf{a} = (1\ 4\ -5\ 3)$, then $3\mathbf{a} = (3\ 12\ -15\ 9)$ and if

$$ \mathbf{a} = \begin{pmatrix} 2 \\ 4 \\ 3 \end{pmatrix}, \quad \text{then} \quad 4\mathbf{a} = \begin{pmatrix} 8 \\ 16 \\ 12 \end{pmatrix} $$

Note that the multiplication of a row (column) vector by a real number is performed by multiplying each component of the vector by that real number.

A scalar multiple of a vector $\mathbf{a}$ in a plane also has a geometrical interpretation, as shown in Figure 5.3(a). Thus, if $\mathbf{a} = (x\ y)$, then $2\mathbf{a} = (2x\ 2y)$ and $(-1)\mathbf{a} = (-x\ -y)$. This means that the new vector retains the direction of the old vector $\mathbf{a}$ if the scalar k is a positive number, but its length increases to k times that of the old vector. If the scalar k is negative, then the direction of the new vector is reversed, as shown in Figure 5.3(b).

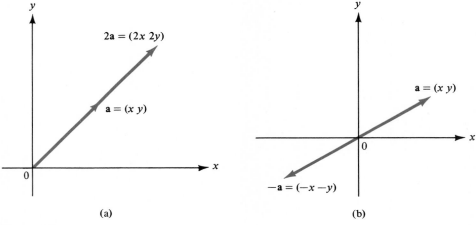

(a)   (b)

Figure 5.3

We have seen so far how row (column) vectors having the same number of components are added. We have also examined the scalar multiples of a row (column) vector. It seems reasonable to ask why it is necessary to have two means of representing vectors, particularly when there is no real difference in the properties of row and column vectors. The answer lies in the product of two vectors, where two kinds of quantities are studied simultaneously and it becomes necessary to represent one as a row vector and the other as a column vector.

Suppose that a manager of a Cinema I, II, III, and IV reports that in a particular show 1320 tickets were sold for Cinema I, 1540 persons bought tickets for Cinema II, 1430 tickets were sold for Cinema III, and 986 persons purchased tickets for Cinema IV. These figures are represented by a row vector

$$\mathbf{a} = (1320 \quad 1540 \quad 1430 \quad 986)$$

Suppose further that a ticket in Cinema I costs \$3.50, that an admission in Cinema II costs \$3.25, one in Cinema III costs \$3.00, and one in Cinema IV costs \$2.50. This information can be represented in a column vector

$$\mathbf{b} = \begin{bmatrix} \$3.50 \\ \$3.25 \\ \$3.00 \\ \$2.50 \end{bmatrix}$$

What are the total receipts for this show?

We must multiply the number of tickets sold by the corresponding price in each Cinema and then add these amounts to get the total receipts. Clearly, the multiplication should have the form

$$\mathbf{a} \cdot \mathbf{b} = (1320 \quad 1540 \quad 1430 \quad 986) \begin{pmatrix} \$3.50 \\ \$3.25 \\ \$3.00 \\ \$2.50 \end{pmatrix}$$

$$= 1320(\$3.50) + 1540(\$3.25) + 1430(\$3.00) + 986(\$2.50)$$

$$= \$16,380$$

Definition 5.2.5: Let $\mathbf{a} = (a_1 \ a_2 \ \cdots \ a_n)$ be a row vector with n elements and

$$\mathbf{b} = \begin{pmatrix} b_1 \\ b_2 \\ \vdots \\ b_n \end{pmatrix}$$

be a column vector also of n components. Then

$$\mathbf{a} \cdot \mathbf{b} = (a_1 \quad a_2 \quad \cdots \quad a_n) \begin{pmatrix} b_1 \\ b_2 \\ \vdots \\ b_n \end{pmatrix}$$

$$= a_1 b_1 + a_2 b_2 + \cdots + a_n b_n$$

Note that we write the row vector first and the column vector second; the vector multiplication is a row-by-column operation and is defined if and only if both the row and column vectors have the same number of components, and the vector multiplication thus performed always yields a real number.

Example 5.1

Consider the following shopping list with unit prices given for each item:

6 cans of soup	$0.34 each
3 cans of frozen juice	$0.79 each
1 dozen eggs	$0.99 per dozen
2 gallons of milk	$1.29 per gallon
3 pounds of hamburger meat	$1.39 per pound

Determine the total bill.

SOLUTION

The purchases can be represented by the row vector

$$
\begin{array}{cccccc}
 & \text{soup} & \begin{array}{c}\text{orange}\\\text{juice}\end{array} & \begin{array}{c}\text{eggs}\\\text{(dozens)}\end{array} & \begin{array}{c}\text{milk}\\\text{(gallons)}\end{array} & \begin{array}{c}\text{meat}\\\text{(pounds)}\end{array} \\
\mathbf{a} = (& 6 & 3 & 1 & 2 & 3 &)
\end{array}
$$

The prices of these items are represented by the column vector

$$
\mathbf{b} = \begin{pmatrix} \$0.34 \\ \$0.79 \\ \$0.99 \\ \$1.29 \\ \$1.39 \end{pmatrix}
$$

The multiplication that the cashier performs to obtain the correct bill is

$$
\mathbf{a} \cdot \mathbf{b} = (6 \quad 3 \quad 1 \quad 2 \quad 3) \begin{pmatrix} \$0.34 \\ \$0.79 \\ \$0.99 \\ \$1.29 \\ \$1.39 \end{pmatrix}
$$

$$
= (6)(\$0.34) + (3)(\$0.79) + (1)(\$0.99) + (2)(\$1.29) + (3)(\$1.39)
$$

$$
= \$12.15 \qquad\qquad \blacksquare
$$

EXERCISE 5.1

1. Let $\mathbf{a} = (2\ 1\ 4)$, $\mathbf{b} = (-1\ 0\ 5)$, and $\mathbf{c} = (3\ 2\ 6)$. Compute the following.

   a. $\mathbf{a} + \mathbf{b}$ b. $\mathbf{b} + \mathbf{c}$ c. $2\mathbf{a} + 3\mathbf{b} + 5\mathbf{c}$

2. Find $\mathbf{a} + \mathbf{b}$ and $\mathbf{a} - \mathbf{b}$ for each of the following pairs of vectors, if possible.

   a. $\mathbf{a} = (5\ 2\ 3\ 4)$, $\mathbf{b} = (1\ 3\ 6\ 8)$

   b. $\mathbf{a} = \begin{pmatrix} 1 \\ 2 \\ 3 \end{pmatrix}$, $\mathbf{b} = \begin{pmatrix} -7 \\ 1 \\ 8 \end{pmatrix}$

   c. $\mathbf{a} = \begin{pmatrix} 1 \\ 2 \\ 3 \end{pmatrix}$, $\mathbf{b} = (-7\ 1\ 8)$

3. Find x, y, and z in each of the following.
   a. $2(1\ 2\ 3) + (x\ y\ z) = (3\ 6\ 5)$
   b. $(-1\ 2\ 3) + 3(x\ y\ z) = (5\ 8\ 3)$
   c. $(3\ 2\ 4) + 2(x\ y\ z) = (7\ 2\ 10)$

   d. $\begin{pmatrix} -1 \\ 2 \\ 3 \end{pmatrix} + 2\begin{pmatrix} x \\ y \\ z \end{pmatrix} = \begin{pmatrix} 4 \\ -3 \\ 5 \end{pmatrix}$

4. Let $\mathbf{a} = (1\ 2\ 3)$, $\mathbf{b} = (5\ 2\ -1)$, and $\mathbf{c} = \begin{pmatrix} 2 \\ -1 \\ 3 \end{pmatrix}$. Compute the following.

   a. $\mathbf{a}\,\mathbf{c}$ **b.** $\mathbf{b}\,\mathbf{c}$
   c. $(\mathbf{a} + \mathbf{b})\mathbf{c}$ **d.** $(\mathbf{a} - \mathbf{b})\mathbf{c}$

5. Solve for x.

   a. $(1 \quad 2 \quad 3 \quad x)\begin{pmatrix} 3 \\ -1 \\ 1 \\ 2 \end{pmatrix} = 8$ **b.** $(-1 \quad x \quad 2 \quad 3)\begin{pmatrix} 1 \\ 5 \\ 3 \\ -4 \end{pmatrix} = 18$

6. Given that

   $$\mathbf{a} = (x\ y), \quad \mathbf{b} = \begin{pmatrix} 2 \\ 3 \end{pmatrix}, \quad \text{and} \quad \mathbf{c} = \begin{pmatrix} 3 \\ 2 \end{pmatrix}$$

   If $\mathbf{a} \cdot \mathbf{b} = 13$ and $\mathbf{a} \cdot \mathbf{c} = 12$, find x and y.

7. Given that

   $$\mathbf{a} = (x\ y), \quad \mathbf{b} = \begin{pmatrix} 1 \\ -2 \end{pmatrix}, \quad \text{and} \quad \mathbf{c} = \begin{pmatrix} 5 \\ 3 \end{pmatrix}$$

   If $\mathbf{a} \cdot \mathbf{b} = 0$ and $\mathbf{a}\,\mathbf{c} = 13$, find x and y.

8. Anita goes to a grocery store and purchases three apples, four oranges, and five pears. Write a row vector $\mathbf{a}$ expressing these purchases. If an apple costs \$0.10, an orange \$0.08, and a pear \$0.07, express these prices as a column vector $\mathbf{b}$. What does $\mathbf{a} \cdot \mathbf{b}$ represent?

9. Mrs. Young purchased five cans of soup, two cans of orange juice, one dozen eggs, two chickens, and one gallon of milk. Write a row vector $\mathbf{a}$ expressing these purchases. Suppose that a can of soup costs \$0.31, a can of frozen orange juice costs \$0.73, one dozen eggs costs \$0.95, a chicken costs \$0.79, and a gallon of milk costs \$1.53. Write a column vector $\mathbf{b}$ indicating the prices. Determine the total amount Mrs. Young must pay at the check-out counter.

10. Roger goes to a package store and buys some liquor for a party he is throwing to honor Jeannie after her graduation. He purchases two quarts of scotch whiskey, three quarts of blended whiskey, two quarts of gin, three quarts of vodka, one keg of beer, and five bottles of wine. Write a row vector $\mathbf{a}$ expressing these purchases. Suppose further that scotch costs \$9.00 per quart; blended whiskey, \$7.00 per quart; gin, \$6.50 per quart; vodka, \$7.25 per quart; a keg of beer, \$17.30; and a bottle of wine \$3.75. Express these prices as a column vector $\mathbf{b}$. Determine the total amount Roger must pay for his purchases.

11. Mr. Hawkins has purchased 40 shares of stock 1, 50 shares of stock 2, 75 shares of stock 3, and 80 shares of stock 4 in the American Stock Exchange. Write a row vector **a** expressing these purchases. Suppose further that stock 1 costs $12 per share, stock 2 costs $10 per share, stock 3 costs $15 per share, and stock 4 costs $20 per share. Write a column vector **b** indicating these prices. Determine the total amount Mr. Hawkins has invested in the stocks.

12. A business manager of the baseball team reports that 1200 persons bought box seats, 4500 bought reserved seats, and 6800 bought general admissions. Write a row vector **a** whose components represent this information. Suppose that a box seat costs $10.00, a reserved seat costs $7.50, and a general admission costs $5.00. Write a column vector **b** with three components representing admission costs. Determine the total receipts for the game.

5.3 WHAT IS A MATRIX?

Any rectangular array of numbers arranged in rows and columns is called a matrix. As such, it is a useful device for presenting numerical data in a condensed form. Suppose, for example, that a contractor of two housing projects needs 50 units of steel, 80 units of wood, 60 units of glass, and 120 units of labor for project I. The requirements for project II are 60 units of steel, 75 units of wood, 90 units of glass, and 130 units of labor. This information can be presented by means of a rectangular array as follows:

	Steel	Wood	Glass	Labor
Project I	50	80	60	120
Project II	60	75	90	130

The numbers in the first row indicate the requirements for project I and those in the second row pertain to the material required for project II. This rectangular array, which is a simple example of a matrix, has two rows and four columns and is called a (2×4) matrix. Thus, a matrix is a collection of row vectors of the same size placed one under the other. It can also be considered as a set of column vectors of the same size placed side by side.

As another example, consider a manufacturer who operates three plants, P_1, P_2, and P_3, and ships his product to four warehouses W_1, W_2, W_3, and W_4. The information presented below in a rectangular form indicates the capacities of the plants and the quantity of product shipped to each of the four warehouses.

Warehouses

	W_1	W_2	W_3	W_4
P_1	155	185	160	120
P_2	160	75	90	55
P_3	95	65	125	95

Plants

The numbers in the first row indicate the quantity of products shipped from plant P_1 to warehouses W_1, W_2, W_3, W_4 in different locations, and those in the second and third rows pertain to the quantity shipped to the warehouses from plants P_2 and P_3, respectively. This rectangular array has three rows and four columns; we call this array a (3×4) matrix.

Definition 5.3.1: A *matrix* is a rectangular array of numbers arranged in rows and columns.

What does this mean? It means simply that a matrix is a set of numbers arranged in a pattern that suggests the geometric form of a rectangle. Some simple examples are given below.

$$\begin{bmatrix} 1 & 2 & -1 & 4 \\ 3 & 0 & 5 & 6 \end{bmatrix} \qquad \begin{bmatrix} 1 & 2 \\ 3 & 4 \\ 5 & 6 \\ 7 & 8 \end{bmatrix} \qquad \begin{bmatrix} 1 & 2 & 3 \\ 4 & 5 & 6 \\ 7 & 8 & 9 \end{bmatrix}$$

The first example is a 2×4 matrix, the second is a 4×2 matrix, and the third example is a square matrix with three rows and three columns.

It is necessary sometimes to refer to the general matrix; in that event, it is assumed that the matrix A consists of mn numbers arranged in m rows and n columns. The individual numbers in the matrix A are denoted by a_{ij}, where i denotes the row in which the element is located and j refers to the column. Thus, for example, in the matrix A,

$$A = \begin{bmatrix} a_{11} & a_{12} & a_{13} & a_{14} \\ a_{21} & a_{22} & a_{23} & a_{24} \\ a_{31} & a_{32} & a_{33} & a_{34} \end{bmatrix}_{(3 \times 4)}$$

a_{11} is the element in the first row and first column, a_{34} is the element in the third row and fourth column, a_{22} is the element in the second row and second column, a_{31} is the element in the third row and first column, and so on.

Definition 5.3.2: A matrix with m rows and n columns is called an $m \times n$ matrix, and is read as "m by n matrix."

Definition 5.3.3: The dimensions of a matrix are given in the form $m \times n$ where m represents the number of rows and n the number of columns.

Thus, a matrix

$$A = \begin{bmatrix} 2 & 0 & 1 \\ 1 & 4 & 3 \end{bmatrix}$$

with two rows and three columns is of dimensions 2×3. Note that in stating the dimensions of the matrix, we always list the number of rows first and the number of columns second.

We consider it worthwhile to point out that a row vector with n components is a $1 \times n$ matrix, and a column vector with m components is a $m \times 1$ matrix. Thus, an $m \times n$ matrix is simply a set of m row vectors, each with n elements placed one under the other, or a set of n column vectors, each with m elements placed from left to right.

Definition 5.3.4: An $m \times n$ matrix A is called a zero matrix if all its elements are zero.

The matrix

$$A = \begin{bmatrix} 0 & 0 & 0 & 0 \\ 0 & 0 & 0 & 0 \\ 0 & 0 & 0 & 0 \end{bmatrix}$$

is a zero matrix of dimensions 3×4.

It is important that we distinguish a zero matrix from the real number 0. Generally, it is clear from the context whether the symbol 0 is to be interpreted as a zero matrix or an ordinary number. We shall represent a zero matrix by the symbol **0.**

Definition 5.3.5: **A** matrix with n rows and n columns is called a square matrix of order n.

Thus, for example,

$$A = \begin{bmatrix} a_{11} & a_{12} & \cdots & a_{1n} \\ a_{21} & a_{22} & \cdots & a_{2n} \\ \vdots & & & \\ a_{n1} & a_{n2} & \cdots & a_{nn} \end{bmatrix}$$

is a square matrix of order n.

Definition 5.3.6: **The elements** $a_{11}, a_{22}, \ldots, a_{nn}$ are said to constitute the main diagonal of the square matrix A.

Definition 5.3.7: **A** square matrix of order n that has 1's along the main diagonal and 0's elsewhere is called the identity matrix and is denoted by I.

Thus,

$$I = \begin{bmatrix} 1 & 0 \\ 0 & 1 \end{bmatrix}$$

is the identity matrix of order 2, and

$$I = \begin{bmatrix} 1 & 0 & 0 \\ 0 & 1 & 0 \\ 0 & 0 & 1 \end{bmatrix}$$

is the identity matrix of order 3. In general,

$$I = \begin{bmatrix} 1 & 0 & 0 & \cdots & 0 \\ 0 & 1 & 0 & \cdots & 0 \\ 0 & 0 & 1 & \cdots & 0 \\ \vdots & & & & \\ 0 & 0 & 0 & \cdots & 1 \end{bmatrix}$$

is the identity matrix of order n.

Definition 5.3.8: Two matrices A and B are equal if and only if they have the same dimensions, and their corresponding elements are equal.

Thus, if

$$A = \begin{bmatrix} a_{11} & a_{12} & a_{13} \\ a_{21} & a_{22} & a_{23} \end{bmatrix} \quad \text{and} \quad B = \begin{bmatrix} b_{11} & b_{12} & b_{13} \\ b_{21} & b_{22} & b_{23} \end{bmatrix}$$

then $A = B$ implies that $a_{11} = b_{11}, a_{12} = b_{12}, a_{13} = b_{13}$, and so on.

Example 5.2

Given that

$$\begin{bmatrix} x & 3 & 2 \\ 5 & y & 4 \end{bmatrix} = \begin{bmatrix} 1 & 3 & z \\ 5 & 6 & 4 \end{bmatrix}$$

then $x = 1$, $y = 6$, and $z = 2$. ∎

Example 5.3

Consider the matrices

$$A = \begin{bmatrix} 1 & 2 & -1 \\ 2 & 3 & 0 \end{bmatrix} \quad \text{and} \quad B = \begin{bmatrix} 1 & 2 & -1 \\ 2 & 3 & 4 \end{bmatrix}$$

Here $A \neq B$ because some of the corresponding elements are not equal. The matrices

$$C = \begin{bmatrix} 1 \\ 2 \end{bmatrix} \quad \text{and} \quad D = \begin{bmatrix} 1 & 0 \\ 2 & 1 \end{bmatrix}$$

are not equal because they are of different dimensions. ∎

Having defined vectors and matrices, we shall devote the next few sections to the rules according to which matrices are combined. As we shall see that matrices can be added (subtracted) if and only if they are of same dimensions, matrix addition (subtraction) reduces to the vector addition (subtraction) when matrices under consideration are, in fact, row or column vectors. We shall show that multiplication of a matrix by a scalar is the natural extension of multiplication of a vector by a scalar, and the rules that apply to vector multiplication can be extended to matrix multiplication, but that some fundamental properties of ordinary algebra do not extend themselves to matrix algebra.

5.4 ADDITION AND SUBTRACTION OF MATRICES

Definition 5.4.1: If A and B are two matrices each of dimensions $(m \times n)$, then their sum (difference) is defined to be another matrix C also of dimensions $m \times n$ such that every element of the matrix C is the sum (difference) of the corresponding elements of the matrices A and B.

Definition 5.4.2: Two matrices A and B are said to be conformable for addition (or subtraction) if and only if they have the same dimensions.

Example 5.4

If

$$A = \begin{bmatrix} 8 & 4 & 2 \\ 9 & 5 & 3 \end{bmatrix}_{(2 \times 3)}$$

and

$$B = \begin{bmatrix} 5 & 1 & 0 \\ 3 & 2 & 4 \end{bmatrix}_{(2 \times 3)}$$

then A and B are conformable for addition and subtraction. Clearly,

$$A + B = \begin{bmatrix} 8 + 5 & 4 + 1 & 2 + 0 \\ 9 + 3 & 5 + 2 & 3 + 4 \end{bmatrix} = \begin{bmatrix} 13 & 5 & 2 \\ 12 & 7 & 7 \end{bmatrix}$$

and

$$A - B = \begin{bmatrix} 8 - 5 & 4 - 1 & 2 - 0 \\ 9 - 3 & 5 - 2 & 3 - 4 \end{bmatrix} = \begin{bmatrix} 3 & 3 & 2 \\ 6 & 3 & -1 \end{bmatrix} \qquad \blacksquare$$

Thus, two matrices are conformable for addition (or subtraction) if and only if they have the same number of rows and the same number of columns. To illustrate further the concept of addition of two matrices, consider the following example.

Example 5.5

The distribution of a product shipped from three plants P_1, P_2, and P_3 to four warehouses in different locations during January 1975 is as follows:

Warehouses

		W_1	W_2	W_3	W_4
	P_1	130	75	49	51
Plants	P_2	125	58	61	57
	P_3	110	52	73	48

The shipment of the product from the plants to the warehouses during February 1975 is given below:

	W_1	W_2	W_3	W_4
P_1	120	73	55	69
P_2	145	52	69	58
P_3	95	59	71	49

Then over the two months, the combined shipment of the product to these warehouses is the sum of the corresponding elements in the above matrices; that is,

$$\begin{array}{c} P_1 \\ P_2 \\ P_3 \end{array} \begin{bmatrix} 130 + 120 & 75 + 73 & 49 + 55 & 51 + 69 \\ 125 + 145 & 58 + 52 & 61 + 69 & 57 + 58 \\ 110 + 95 & 52 + 59 & 73 + 71 & 48 + 49 \end{bmatrix} = \begin{bmatrix} 250 & 148 & 104 & 120 \\ 270 & 110 & 130 & 115 \\ 205 & 111 & 144 & 97 \end{bmatrix} \qquad \blacksquare$$

Proposition 5.4.1: If A, B, and C are three matrices conformable for addition, then

(i) $A + B = B + A$
(ii) $A + 0 = 0 + A = A$
(iii) $A + (B + C) = (A + B) + C$
(iv) $A + C = B + C$ if and only if $A = B$ ∎

We advise readers to write out the details in full for matrices of some particular order and convince themselves as to the validity of the above proposition.

5.5 SCALAR MULTIPLES OF MATRICES

Suppose that

$$A = \begin{bmatrix} 1 & 4 \\ 3 & 2 \end{bmatrix}$$

then

(i) $A + A = \begin{bmatrix} 1 & 4 \\ 3 & 2 \end{bmatrix} + \begin{bmatrix} 1 & 4 \\ 3 & 2 \end{bmatrix} = \begin{bmatrix} 1+1 & 4+4 \\ 3+3 & 2+2 \end{bmatrix} = \begin{bmatrix} 2 & 8 \\ 6 & 4 \end{bmatrix} = 2A$

(ii) $A + A + A = \begin{bmatrix} 1 & 4 \\ 3 & 2 \end{bmatrix} + \begin{bmatrix} 1 & 4 \\ 3 & 2 \end{bmatrix} + \begin{bmatrix} 1 & 4 \\ 3 & 2 \end{bmatrix} = \begin{bmatrix} 1+1+1 & 4+4+4 \\ 3+3+3 & 2+2+2 \end{bmatrix}$

$$= \begin{bmatrix} 3 & 12 \\ 9 & 6 \end{bmatrix} = 3A$$

This example illustrates that if we add k matrices each equal to A, we obtain another matrix whose elements are those of A each multiplied by the number k. This leads us to the following definition.

Definition 5.5.1: Let A be an $m \times n$ matrix and k be a scalar, then kA is another matrix B of order $m \times n$, where

$$b_{ij} = k \cdot a_{ij} \qquad \text{for every } (i, j)$$

Example 5.6

If

$$A = \begin{bmatrix} 2 & 1 & 4 \\ 3 & 5 & 7 \end{bmatrix}$$

then

(i) $(-1) \cdot A = \begin{bmatrix} -2 & -1 & -4 \\ -3 & -5 & -7 \end{bmatrix}$

(ii) $7A = \begin{bmatrix} 14 & 7 & 28 \\ 21 & 35 & 49 \end{bmatrix}$

In general, if k is a scalar, then

$$kA = \begin{bmatrix} 2k & k & 4k \\ 3k & 5k & 7k \end{bmatrix}$$ ∎

Example 5.7

If

$$A = \begin{bmatrix} 3 & 2 \\ 4 & 1 \end{bmatrix}$$

and

$$B = \begin{bmatrix} -1 & 1 \\ 2 & -3 \end{bmatrix}$$

then

$$3A + 2B = \begin{bmatrix} 9 & 6 \\ 12 & 3 \end{bmatrix} + \begin{bmatrix} -2 & 2 \\ 4 & -6 \end{bmatrix} = \begin{bmatrix} 7 & 8 \\ 16 & -3 \end{bmatrix}$$ ∎

Proposition 5.5.1: Let A and B be two $m \times n$ matrices. If k_1 and k_2 are scalars, then

(i) $(k_1 + k_2)A = k_1 A + k_2 A$
(ii) $k_1(k_2 A) = (k_1 k_2)A$
(iii) $k_1(A + B) = k_1 A + k_1 B$ ∎

EXERCISE 5.2

1. Given that

$$\begin{bmatrix} -2 & x & 4 & 0 \\ 3 & 2 & y & 3 \end{bmatrix} = \begin{bmatrix} -2 & 3 & z & 0 \\ 3 & 2 & 1 & u \end{bmatrix}$$

Find the values of x, y, z, and u.

2. Given that

$$\begin{bmatrix} x & 3 & -1 \\ 4 & -1 & 0 \\ 2 & z & -3 \end{bmatrix} = \begin{bmatrix} 5 & 3 & -1 \\ 4 & y & 0 \\ 2 & 0 & -3 \end{bmatrix}$$

Find the values of x, y, and z.

3. Find $A + B$ and $A - B$ in each of the following.

a. $A = \begin{bmatrix} 1 & 2 \\ 3 & 4 \end{bmatrix}$, $B = \begin{bmatrix} 2 & -1 \\ -1 & 3 \end{bmatrix}$

b. $A = \begin{bmatrix} 1 & 2 & 3 \\ 3 & 1 & 2 \end{bmatrix}$, $B = \begin{bmatrix} -2 & -1 & -4 \\ 1 & 3 & 2 \end{bmatrix}$

c. $A = \begin{bmatrix} 2 & -1 & 1 \\ 2 & 3 & 4 \\ 5 & -1 & 1 \\ 1 & 7 & 3 \end{bmatrix}$, $B = \begin{bmatrix} 4 & -2 & 3 \\ 5 & -1 & 2 \\ 2 & 1 & -3 \\ -1 & 2 & 1 \end{bmatrix}$

d. $A = \begin{bmatrix} 2 & 1 & 3 & 4 \\ 4 & -1 & 2 & 3 \end{bmatrix}$, $B = \begin{bmatrix} -1 & 2 & -1 & 3 \\ 3 & -1 & 2 & -5 \end{bmatrix}$

4. Given that

$$A = \begin{bmatrix} 5 & 8 \\ 7 & 9 \end{bmatrix}, \quad B = \begin{bmatrix} 1 & 2 \\ 3 & 4 \end{bmatrix}, \quad \text{and} \quad C = \begin{bmatrix} 7 & 5 \\ 6 & 9 \end{bmatrix}$$

Calculate the following.

a. $3A + 2B$ **b.** $A + 2B + 3C$

c. $A + (B + C)$ **d.** $(A + B) + C$

5. Given that

$$A = \begin{bmatrix} 2 & 1 & 3 \\ 4 & -1 & 2 \end{bmatrix}, \quad B = \begin{bmatrix} -3 & 2 & 0 \\ 1 & 5 & 2 \end{bmatrix}, \quad C = \begin{bmatrix} -2 & 5 & 4 \\ 2 & 1 & 3 \end{bmatrix}$$

Verify that $A + (B + C) = (A + B) + C$.

5.6 MULTIPLICATION OF MATRICES

Suppose that the retail unit sales of products I, II, III, and IV in a given month were 63, 50, 35, and 43, respectively. These figures may be represented by a row vector (1×4 matrix)

$$\mathbf{a} = (63 \quad 50 \quad 35 \quad 43)$$

Assuming that the selling prices of the products for that month were $13.00, $12.50, $12.00 and $10.75, respectively, and representing this information in a column vector (4×1 matrix)

$$\mathbf{b} = \begin{bmatrix} \$13.00 \\ \$12.50 \\ \$12.00 \\ \$10.75 \end{bmatrix}$$

we observe that sales revenue for all the products for the month is given by

(5.1)
$$\mathbf{ab} = 63(\$13.00) + 50(\$12.50) + 35(\$12.00) + 43(\$10.75)$$
$$= \$2304.75$$

Note that the product of two vectors is defined only if both row and column vectors have the same number of elements. This is precisely the Definition 5.2.5 we discussed earlier. We shall now show that this definition can, in fact, be extended to matrix multiplication.

Suppose that the company has three stores located in different regions. The retail unit sales of the products in these stores is given in the following matrix A,

$$
\begin{array}{c}
\qquad\qquad\quad \text{Products} \\
\begin{array}{cccc}
\text{I} & \text{II} & \text{III} & \text{IV}
\end{array} \\
\begin{array}{c}
\text{Store 1} \\
\text{Store 2} \\
\text{Store 3}
\end{array}
\begin{bmatrix}
63 & 50 & 35 & 43 \\
81 & 66 & 51 & 48 \\
85 & 60 & 48 & 32
\end{bmatrix}
\end{array}
$$

where the first row of the matrix A shows the number of products sold in store 1 and the second and third rows reflect the unit sales in store 2 and store 3, respectively.

The sales revenue matrix is

$$A\mathbf{b} = \begin{bmatrix} 63 & 50 & 35 & 43 \\ 81 & 66 & 51 & 48 \\ 85 & 60 & 48 & 32 \end{bmatrix} \begin{bmatrix} \$13.00 \\ \$12.50 \\ \$12.00 \\ \$10.75 \end{bmatrix}$$

The sales revenue for store 1 is given by (5.1). The sales revenue for store 2 is

(5.2) $81(\$13.00) + 66(\$12.50) + 51(\$12.00) + 48(\$10.75) = \$3006.00$

whereas the sales revenue for store 3 is

(5.3) $(85)(\$13.00) + 60(\$12.50) + 48(\$12.00) + 32(\$10.75) = \$2775.00$

Thus,

$$A\mathbf{b} = \begin{bmatrix} 63 & 50 & 35 & 43 \\ 81 & 66 & 51 & 48 \\ 85 & 60 & 48 & 32 \end{bmatrix} \begin{bmatrix} \$13.00 \\ \$12.50 \\ \$10.75 \end{bmatrix}$$

$$= \begin{bmatrix} \$2,304.75 \\ \$3,006.00 \\ \$2,775.00 \end{bmatrix}$$

If we are interested in the sales revenue of all three stores, then the product matrix $A\mathbf{b}$ is to be premultiplied by the row vector (1 1 1), that is,

$$(1 \quad 1 \quad 1) \begin{bmatrix} \$2,304.75 \\ \$3,006.00 \\ \$2,775.00 \end{bmatrix} = \$2,304.75 + \$3,006.00 + \$2,775.00$$

$$= \$8,085.75$$

If the interest lies only in the number of products sold in each store, then the matrix A is premultiplied by the row vector (1 1 1). Thus,

$$(1 \quad 1 \quad 1) \begin{bmatrix} 63 & 50 & 35 & 43 \\ 80 & 66 & 51 & 48 \\ 85 & 60 & 48 & 32 \end{bmatrix} = (228 \quad 176 \quad 134 \quad 123)$$

These examples suggest the following definition.

Definition 5.6.1: Let A be an $m \times n$ matrix and $\mathbf{b}$ be an n-component column vector. Then the matrix-vector product $A\mathbf{b}$ is defined to be an m-component column vector whose ith element is the sum of the products of the elements in the ith row of A and the corresponding elements of $\mathbf{b}$.

In other words,

$$\begin{bmatrix} a_{11} & a_{12} & \cdots & a_{1n} \\ a_{21} & a_{22} & \cdots & a_{2n} \\ \vdots & & & \\ a_{i1} & a_{i2} & \cdots & a_{in} \\ \vdots & & & \\ a_{m1} & a_{m2} & \cdots & a_{mn} \end{bmatrix} \begin{bmatrix} b_1 \\ b_2 \\ \vdots \\ b_i \\ \vdots \\ b_n \end{bmatrix} = \begin{bmatrix} u_1 \\ u_2 \\ \vdots \\ u_i \\ \vdots \\ u_m \end{bmatrix}$$

where

$$u_i = a_{i1}b_1 + a_{i2}b_2 + \cdots + a_{in}u_n$$

Example 5.8

Let

$$A = \begin{bmatrix} 2 & 4 & 5 \\ 1 & 3 & 7 \end{bmatrix}_{(2 \times 3)} \qquad \mathbf{b} = \begin{bmatrix} 3 \\ 5 \\ 8 \end{bmatrix}_{(3 \times 1)}$$

Then,

$$A\mathbf{b} = \begin{bmatrix} 2 & 4 & 5 \\ 1 & 3 & 7 \end{bmatrix} \begin{bmatrix} 3 \\ 5 \\ 8 \end{bmatrix} = \begin{bmatrix} 2(3) + 4(5) + 5(8) \\ 1(3) + 3(5) + 7(8) \end{bmatrix} = \begin{bmatrix} 6 + 20 + 40 \\ 3 + 15 + 56 \end{bmatrix} = \begin{bmatrix} 66 \\ 74 \end{bmatrix} \qquad ■$$

Definition 5.6.2: Let A be an $m \times n$ matrix and $\mathbf{c}$ be an m-component row vector. Then the vector-matrix product $\mathbf{c}A$ is defined to be an n-component row vector whose jth element is the sum of the products of the elements of $\mathbf{c}$ and the corresponding elements of ith column of A.

In other words,

$$(c_1 \quad c_2 \quad \cdots \quad c_m) \begin{bmatrix} a_{11} & a_{12} & \cdots & a_{1j} & \cdots & a_{1n} \\ a_{21} & a_{22} & \cdots & a_{2j} & \cdots & a_{2n} \\ \vdots & & & & & \\ a_{i1} & a_{i2} & \cdots & a_{ij} & \cdots & a_{in} \\ \vdots & & & & & \\ a_{m1} & a_{m2} & \cdots & a_{mj} & \cdots & a_{mn} \end{bmatrix} = (v_1 \quad v_2 \quad \cdots \quad v_j \quad \cdots \quad v_n)$$

where

$$v_j = c_1 a_{1j} + c_2 a_{2j} + \cdots + c_m a_{mj}$$

Example 5.9

Let

$$\mathbf{c} = (7 \quad 4 \quad 2)_{(1 \times 3)} \qquad A = \begin{bmatrix} 2 & 1 & 3 \\ 5 & 6 & -1 \\ 7 & 8 & 4 \end{bmatrix}_{(3 \times 3)}$$

Then,

$$\mathbf{c}A = (7 \quad 4 \quad 2) \begin{bmatrix} 2 & 1 & 3 \\ 5 & 6 & -1 \\ 7 & 8 & 4 \end{bmatrix}$$

$$= (7(2) + 4(5) + 2(7) \quad 7(1) + 4(6) + 2(8) \quad 7(3) + 4(-1) + 2(4))$$

$$= (14 + 20 + 14 \quad 7 + 24 + 16 \quad 21 - 4 + 8)$$

$$= (48 \quad 47 \quad 25) \qquad \blacksquare$$

This discussion leads us to the following definition.

Definition 5.6.3: Let A be an $m \times n$ matrix and B be an $n \times p$ matrix. The product AB is then defined to be the $m \times p$ matrix whose element in the ith row and jth column is the sum of the products of the elements in ith row of A and the corresponding elements of the jth column of B.

In other words,

$$\begin{bmatrix} a_{11} & a_{12} & \cdots & a_{1n} \\ a_{21} & a_{22} & \cdots & a_{2n} \\ \vdots & & & \\ a_{i1} & a_{i2} & \cdots & a_{in} \\ \vdots & & & \\ a_{m1} & a_{m2} & \cdots & a_{mn} \end{bmatrix} \begin{bmatrix} b_{11} & b_{12} & \cdots & b_{1j} & \cdots & b_{1p} \\ b_{21} & b_{22} & \cdots & b_{2j} & \cdots & b_{2p} \\ \vdots & & & & & \\ b_{n1} & b_{n2} & \cdots & b_{nj} & \cdots & b_{np} \end{bmatrix} = \begin{bmatrix} c_{11} & c_{12} & \cdots & c_{ij} & \cdots & c_{1p} \\ c_{21} & c_{22} & \cdots & c_{2j} & \cdots & c_{2p} \\ \vdots & & & & & \\ c_{i1} & c_{i2} & \cdots & c_{ij} & \cdots & c_{ip} \\ \vdots & & & & & \\ c_{m1} & c_{m2} & \cdots & c_{mj} & \cdots & c_{mp} \end{bmatrix}$$

where

$$c_{ij} = (a_{i1} \quad a_{i2} \quad \cdots \quad a_{in}) \begin{bmatrix} b_{1j} \\ b_{2j} \\ \vdots \\ b_{nj} \end{bmatrix}$$

$$= a_{i1} b_{1j} + a_{i2} b_{2j} + \cdots + a_{in} b_{nj}$$

Let $i = 1, j = 1$, then

$$c_{11} = a_{11} b_{11} + a_{12} b_{21} + \cdots + a_{1n} b_{n1}$$

Note that this is the direct result of multiplying the elements in the first row of matrix A by the corresponding elements in the first column of matrix B.

If $i = 2, j = 3$, then

$$c_{23} = a_{21} b_{13} + a_{22} b_{23} + \cdots + a_{2n} b_{n3}$$

Again, this is the sum of the products of the elements in the second row of matrix A and the corresponding elements of the third column of matrix B.

It is important to observe that the product matrix AB is defined or A is comformable to B for multiplication if and only if the number of columns of the first matrix A equals the number of rows of the second matrix B. Further, the product matrix AB

has the same number of rows as the matrix A and the same number of columns as the matrix B. Thus,

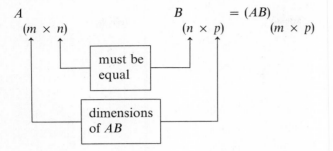

$$
\begin{array}{ccc}
A & B & = (AB) \\
(m \times n) & (n \times p) & (m \times p)
\end{array}
$$

must be equal

dimensions of AB

Notice that matrix multiplication is merely an extension of vector-matrix or matrix-vector multiplication which, in turn, extends the concept of vector multiplication.

Example 5.10

Let

$$
A = \begin{bmatrix} 1 & 3 & 2 \\ -4 & 5 & 4 \end{bmatrix} \qquad B = \begin{bmatrix} 5 & 7 \\ 2 & 3 \\ 1 & -2 \end{bmatrix}
$$

(2×3) (3×2)

Do they match?

If so, then the dimension of AB is (2×2).

The matrix AB is defined because the number of columns of the matrix A is the same as the number of rows of the matrix B. The product matrix $C = AB$ will have two rows and two columns. Thus,

$$
\begin{bmatrix} 1 & 3 & 2 \\ -4 & 5 & 4 \end{bmatrix} \begin{bmatrix} 5 & 7 \\ 2 & 3 \\ 1 & -2 \end{bmatrix} = \begin{bmatrix} c_{11} & c_{12} \\ c_{21} & c_{22} \end{bmatrix}
$$

To obtain c_{11}, we multiply the elements in the first row of the matrix A by the corresponding elements in the first column of the matrix B and then add. Thus,

$$
c_{11} = (1 \quad 3 \quad 2) \begin{bmatrix} 5 \\ 2 \\ 1 \end{bmatrix} = 1(5) + 3(2) + 2(1) = 13
$$

Similarly,

$$c_{12} = (1 \quad 3 \quad 2) \begin{bmatrix} 7 \\ 3 \\ -2 \end{bmatrix} = 1(7) + 3(3) + 2(-2) = 12$$

$$c_{21} = (-4 \quad 5 \quad 4) \begin{bmatrix} 5 \\ 2 \\ 1 \end{bmatrix} = (-4)(5) + 5(2) + 4(1) = -6$$

and

$$c_{22} = (-4 \quad 5 \quad 4) \begin{bmatrix} 7 \\ 3 \\ -2 \end{bmatrix} = (-4)(7) + (5)(3) + (4)(-2) = -21$$

Thus,

$$C = AB = \begin{bmatrix} 13 & 12 \\ -6 & -21 \end{bmatrix}$$

∎

Example 5.11

Mrs. Berman wishes to purchase five cans of soup, two cans of frozen orange juice, one dozen eggs, two chickens, and two gallons of milk. Mrs. Carlson needs seven cans of soup, four cans of orange juice, two dozen eggs, one chicken, and one gallon of milk. There are two supermarkets close by that sell these items. Each store's price list is given below:

Store

	I	II
can of soup	$0.31	$0.32
orange juice	$0.73	$0.71
$B =$ dozen eggs	$0.95	$0.89
chicken	$0.79	$0.81
milk	$0.97	$0.99

At what store will Mrs. Berman expect her grocery bill to be the minimum? Should Mrs. Carlson also buy at this store?

SOLUTION

First, we summarize the grocery needs of Mrs. Berman and Mrs. Carlson in the following matrix A.

	soup	juice	eggs	chicken	milk
Mrs. Berman	5	2	1	2	2
Mrs. Carlson	7	4	2	1	1

$$A = \begin{bmatrix} 5 & 2 & 1 & 2 & 2 \\ 7 & 4 & 2 & 1 & 1 \end{bmatrix}_{(2 \times 5)}$$

If we multiply the 2×5 matrix A by the 5×2 price matrix B, we obtain a 2×2 matrix. Thus,

$$A \cdot B = \begin{bmatrix} 5 & 2 & 1 & 2 & 2 \\ 7 & 4 & 2 & 1 & 1 \end{bmatrix} \begin{bmatrix} \$0.31 & \$0.32 \\ \$0.73 & \$0.71 \\ \$0.95 & \$0.89 \\ \$0.79 & \$0.81 \\ \$0.97 & \$0.99 \end{bmatrix} = \begin{bmatrix} c_{11} & c_{12} \\ c_{21} & c_{22} \end{bmatrix}$$

where

$$c_{11} = 5(0.31) + 2(0.73) + 1(0.95) + 2(0.79) + 2(0.97) = \$7.48$$
$$c_{12} = 5(0.32) + 2(0.71) + 1(0.89) + 2(0.81) + 2(0.99) = \$7.51$$
$$c_{21} = 7(0.31) + 4(0.73) + 2(0.95) + 1(0.79) + 1(0.97) = \$8.75$$

and

$$c_{22} = 7(0.32) + 4(0.71) + 2(0.89) + 1(0.81) + 1(0.99) = \$8.66$$

Thus, the product matrix AB is given as follows:

	Store I	Store II
Mrs. Berman	$7.48	$7.51
Mrs. Carlson	$8.75	$8.66

The first row in the product matrix provides the information as to what it would cost Mrs. Berman to buy her groceries in store I and store II, respectively. Similarly, the elements in the second row reflect what it would cost Mrs. Carlson to buy in stores I and II, respectively. If the stores are conveniently located, Mrs. Berman and Mrs. Carlson should shop at store I and II, respectively. ■

5.7 PROPERTIES OF MATRIX MULTIPLICATION

We recall that the product of two matrices AB is defined or A is conformable to B for multiplication if and only if the number of columns of A equals the number of rows of B. The product matrix AB has the same number of rows as A and the same number of columns as B. Thus, if

$$A = \begin{bmatrix} 1 & 2 & -1 \\ 2 & 3 & 0 \end{bmatrix}_{(2 \times 3)} \quad \text{and} \quad B = \begin{bmatrix} 5 & 7 & 1 \\ 2 & 3 & 4 \\ 1 & -2 & 5 \end{bmatrix}_{(3 \times 3)}$$

then product AB is defined because A has three columns and B has three rows. The resulting product matrix has two rows and three columns. Further, in the product AB, we say that B is premultiplied by A and that A is postmultiplied by B.

The product BA is, however, not defined in the above example, because the number of columns in B is not equal to the number of rows in A. Even if the products AB and BA are defined, AB may not, in general, be equal to BA.

Example 5.12

Let

$$A = \begin{bmatrix} 1 & 2 \\ 4 & 3 \\ 0 & 1 \end{bmatrix}_{(3 \times 2)} \quad \text{and} \quad B = \begin{bmatrix} 5 & 1 \\ 2 & 4 \end{bmatrix}_{(2 \times 2)}$$

Then

$$AB = \begin{bmatrix} 1 & 2 \\ 4 & 3 \\ 0 & 1 \end{bmatrix} \begin{bmatrix} 5 & 1 \\ 2 & 4 \end{bmatrix} = \begin{bmatrix} 9 & 9 \\ 26 & 16 \\ 2 & 4 \end{bmatrix}$$

Note that the product BA is not defined. ∎

Example 5.13

Let

$$A = \begin{bmatrix} 3 & 5 \\ 1 & -2 \\ 2 & 4 \end{bmatrix} \quad \text{and} \quad I = \begin{bmatrix} 1 & 0 \\ 0 & 1 \end{bmatrix}$$

Then

$$AI = \begin{bmatrix} 3 & 5 \\ 1 & -2 \\ 2 & 4 \end{bmatrix} \begin{bmatrix} 1 & 0 \\ 0 & 1 \end{bmatrix} = \begin{bmatrix} 3 & 5 \\ 1 & -2 \\ 2 & 4 \end{bmatrix}$$

Note that $AI = A$ but IA is not defined. ∎

Example 5.14

Let

$$A = \begin{bmatrix} 1 & 2 & 4 \\ 2 & 3 & 0 \end{bmatrix} \quad \text{and} \quad B = \begin{bmatrix} 5 & 7 \\ 2 & 1 \\ 1 & 3 \end{bmatrix}$$

Then

$$AB = \begin{bmatrix} 1 & 2 & 4 \\ 2 & 3 & 0 \end{bmatrix} \begin{bmatrix} 5 & 7 \\ 2 & 1 \\ 1 & 3 \end{bmatrix} = \begin{bmatrix} 13 & 21 \\ 16 & 17 \end{bmatrix}$$

$$BA = \begin{bmatrix} 5 & 7 \\ 2 & 1 \\ 1 & 3 \end{bmatrix} \begin{bmatrix} 1 & 2 & 4 \\ 2 & 3 & 0 \end{bmatrix} = \begin{bmatrix} 19 & 31 & 20 \\ 4 & 7 & 8 \\ 7 & 11 & 4 \end{bmatrix}$$

Note that AB and BA are both defined, but AB is of dimensions 2×2 whereas BA is of dimensions 3×3. ∎

Example 5.15
Let

$$A = \begin{bmatrix} 1 & 2 \\ 4 & 5 \end{bmatrix} \quad \text{and} \quad B = \begin{bmatrix} 3 & 1 \\ 2 & 7 \end{bmatrix}$$

Then

$$AB = \begin{bmatrix} 1 & 2 \\ 4 & 5 \end{bmatrix} \begin{bmatrix} 3 & 1 \\ 2 & 7 \end{bmatrix} = \begin{bmatrix} 7 & 15 \\ 22 & 39 \end{bmatrix}$$

whereas

$$BA = \begin{bmatrix} 3 & 1 \\ 2 & 7 \end{bmatrix} \begin{bmatrix} 1 & 2 \\ 4 & 5 \end{bmatrix} = \begin{bmatrix} 7 & 11 \\ 30 & 39 \end{bmatrix}$$

Thus, AB and BA are both defined, but they are not equal. ∎

Example 5.16
Let

$$A = \begin{bmatrix} 2 & 3 & 4 \\ 1 & 5 & 2 \\ 0 & 6 & 1 \end{bmatrix} \quad \text{and} \quad I = \begin{bmatrix} 1 & 0 & 0 \\ 0 & 1 & 0 \\ 0 & 0 & 1 \end{bmatrix}$$

Then

$$AI = \begin{bmatrix} 2 & 3 & 4 \\ 1 & 5 & 2 \\ 0 & 6 & 1 \end{bmatrix} \begin{bmatrix} 1 & 0 & 0 \\ 0 & 1 & 0 \\ 0 & 0 & 1 \end{bmatrix} = \begin{bmatrix} 2 & 3 & 4 \\ 1 & 5 & 2 \\ 0 & 6 & 1 \end{bmatrix}$$

and

$$IA = \begin{bmatrix} 1 & 0 & 0 \\ 0 & 1 & 0 \\ 0 & 0 & 1 \end{bmatrix} \begin{bmatrix} 2 & 3 & 4 \\ 1 & 5 & 2 \\ 0 & 6 & 1 \end{bmatrix} = \begin{bmatrix} 2 & 3 & 4 \\ 1 & 5 & 2 \\ 0 & 6 & 1 \end{bmatrix}$$

Note that AI and IA are both defined and $AI = IA = A$. ∎

We shall now show that the familiar rule in ordinary arithmetic that if $ab = ac$, then $b = c$, also breaks down in the multiplication of matrices. This is illustrated by the following example.

Example 5.17
Let

$$A = \begin{bmatrix} 1 & 3 & 0 \\ 2 & 1 & 0 \\ -3 & 4 & 0 \end{bmatrix} \quad B = \begin{bmatrix} 1 & 3 & 2 \\ 2 & 1 & 3 \\ 1 & 1 & 1 \end{bmatrix} \quad C = \begin{bmatrix} 1 & 3 & 2 \\ 2 & 1 & 3 \\ 2 & 2 & 2 \end{bmatrix}$$

Then

$$AB = \begin{bmatrix} 7 & 6 & 11 \\ 4 & 7 & 7 \\ 5 & -5 & 6 \end{bmatrix} = AC$$

Thus, $AB = AC$ although $B \neq C$. In other words, the cancellation property in the real number system does not carry over to arithmetic of matrices. However, the cancellation law holds in a special case, which we shall explore later. ∎

Another important rule in ordinary arithmetic is that if the product of two numbers a and b is zero, then at least one of them must be zero. This rule also fails to hold for matrix multiplication. This is illustrated by the following example.

Example 5.18

Form the product AB, where

$$A = \begin{bmatrix} 1 & 0 \\ 4 & 0 \end{bmatrix} \quad \text{and} \quad B = \begin{bmatrix} 0 & 0 \\ 2 & -1 \end{bmatrix}$$

The product is

$$AB = \begin{bmatrix} 1 & 0 \\ 4 & 0 \end{bmatrix} \begin{bmatrix} 0 & 0 \\ 2 & -1 \end{bmatrix} = \begin{bmatrix} 0 & 0 \\ 0 & 0 \end{bmatrix}$$

The reader may observe that BA is not a zero matrix. ∎

In summary, we wish to emphasize that three fundamental properties of ordinary multiplication do not extend themselves to matrix multiplication.

1. The commutative law, $AB = BA$, does not, in general, hold.
2. If $AB = AC$ or $BA = CA$, we cannot, in general, cancel A from both sides, even if A is not a zero matrix.
3. If $AB = 0$, it does not necessarily follow that at least one of the matrices is a zero matrix.

The fact that some fundamental properties of ordinary arithmetic do not, in general, hold for matrix arithmetic might make one believe that matrix multiplication is nearly a worthless operation. That is, of course, not true, because some of the vital properties, associative and distributive laws, still remain to be verified in matrix multiplication.

We shall now state (without proof) the property of "associativity" in matrix multiplication. If A, B, and C are three matrices whose dimensions are properly related, then multiplication is associative; that is, $A(BC) = (AB)C$. Consider, for instance, the following example.

Example 5.19

Let

$$A = \begin{bmatrix} 2 & 1 \\ 4 & 3 \end{bmatrix} \qquad B = \begin{bmatrix} 3 & 5 \\ 1 & 7 \end{bmatrix} \qquad C = \begin{bmatrix} -1 \\ 2 \end{bmatrix}$$

Then

$$(AB)C = \begin{bmatrix} 7 & 17 \\ 15 & 41 \end{bmatrix}\begin{bmatrix} -1 \\ 2 \end{bmatrix} = \begin{bmatrix} 27 \\ 67 \end{bmatrix} \quad \text{and} \quad A(BC) = \begin{bmatrix} 2 & 1 \\ 4 & 3 \end{bmatrix}\begin{bmatrix} 7 \\ 13 \end{bmatrix} = \begin{bmatrix} 27 \\ 67 \end{bmatrix}$$

Thus,

$$A(BC) = (AB)C$$

■

The next property we state (without proof) is that of the "distributive law." The property in the number system that $a(b + c) = ab + ac$ can be extended for matrices of proper dimension and

$$A(B + C) = AB + AC$$

The matrices B and C must be of the same dimensions for matrix addition. If B and C are two matrices both with n rows and p columns, then A must have n columns so that the products AB and AC can be formed. Under these conditions a distributive law in the real number system is carried over to arithmetic of matrices.

Example 5.20

Let

$$A = \begin{bmatrix} 2 & 3 \\ 1 & 4 \end{bmatrix} \qquad B = \begin{bmatrix} -1 & -2 \\ 3 & 5 \end{bmatrix} \qquad C = \begin{bmatrix} 1 & 2 \\ 2 & 5 \end{bmatrix}$$

Then

$$B + C = \begin{bmatrix} 0 & 0 \\ 5 & 10 \end{bmatrix}$$

$$A(B + C) = \begin{bmatrix} 2 & 3 \\ 1 & 4 \end{bmatrix}\begin{bmatrix} 0 & 0 \\ 5 & 10 \end{bmatrix} = \begin{bmatrix} 15 & 30 \\ 20 & 40 \end{bmatrix}$$

$$AB = \begin{bmatrix} 2 & 3 \\ 1 & 4 \end{bmatrix}\begin{bmatrix} -1 & -1 \\ 3 & 5 \end{bmatrix} = \begin{bmatrix} 7 & 11 \\ 11 & 18 \end{bmatrix}$$

$$AC = \begin{bmatrix} 2 & 3 \\ 1 & 4 \end{bmatrix}\begin{bmatrix} 1 & 2 \\ 2 & 5 \end{bmatrix} = \begin{bmatrix} 8 & 19 \\ 9 & 22 \end{bmatrix}$$

$$AB + AC = \begin{bmatrix} 7 & 11 \\ 11 & 18 \end{bmatrix} + \begin{bmatrix} 8 & 19 \\ 9 & 22 \end{bmatrix} = \begin{bmatrix} 15 & 30 \\ 20 & 40 \end{bmatrix}$$

Thus,

$$A(B + C) = AB + AC$$

■

EXERCISE 5.3

1. For each of the following matrices, determine the size of the product matrix AB.
a. A is a 3×3 matrix and B is a 3×5 matrix
b. A is a 5×3 matrix and B is a 3×5 matrix
c. A is a 3×5 matrix and B is a 5×3 matrix
d. A is a 2×7 matrix and B is a 7×4 matrix
e. A is a 3×2 matrix and B is a 2×4 matrix

2. For the following pairs of matrices, determine whether it is possible to compute AB, BA, both, or neither.
a. A is a 3×5 matrix and B is a 5×2 matrix
b. A is a 2×4 matrix and B is a 4×2 matrix
c. A is a 5×7 matrix and B is a 3×5 matrix
d. A is a 5×6 matrix and B is a 3×4 matrix

3. Consider the following matrices:

$$A = \begin{bmatrix} 3 & -2 & 4 \\ 2 & 1 & 6 \end{bmatrix} \qquad B = \begin{bmatrix} 4 & 1 \\ 3 & -5 \\ 1 & 2 \end{bmatrix}$$

Compute:
a. the first row of AB
b. the second column of BA
c. the third row of BA

4. Given that

$$A = \begin{bmatrix} 1 & 2 & 3 \\ 4 & 5 & 6 \end{bmatrix} \qquad B = \begin{bmatrix} 2 & -1 & 0 \\ 3 & 2 & 4 \\ 1 & 3 & 7 \end{bmatrix} \qquad C = \begin{bmatrix} 3 & 1 & 2 \\ 1 & 2 & 4 \\ 4 & 0 & 5 \end{bmatrix}$$

Compute the following:
a. AB **b.** AC **c.** BC

5. Given that

$$A = \begin{bmatrix} 1 & 0 & 3 \\ 2 & 3 & 5 \\ 3 & 1 & 8 \end{bmatrix} \qquad B = \begin{bmatrix} -1 & 1 & 2 & 4 & 3 \\ 2 & 3 & 1 & 6 & 5 \\ 4 & 2 & 5 & 7 & 8 \end{bmatrix}$$

Compute AB.

6. Consider the following matrices:

$$A = \begin{bmatrix} 4 & 5 \\ 2 & 1 \end{bmatrix} \qquad B = \begin{bmatrix} -1 & 3 \\ 2 & 5 \end{bmatrix} \qquad C = \begin{bmatrix} 5 & -3 \\ 2 & 5 \end{bmatrix}$$

Compute the following:
a. AB **b.** BA **c.** AC
d. BC **e.** CA **f.** CB

7. Let A, B, and C be the matrices defined in Exercise 6. Verify the following:
a. $A(BC) = (AB)C$
b. $A(B + C) = AB + AC$
c. $(B + C)A = BA + CA$

8. Given that

$$A = \begin{bmatrix} 2 & 6 \\ 3 & 9 \end{bmatrix} \quad \text{and} \quad B = \begin{bmatrix} -6 & 15 \\ 2 & -5 \end{bmatrix}$$

Is AB a zero matrix? If so, can you conclude that if $AB = 0$, then either A or B or both are zero matrices?

9. Given that

$$A = \begin{bmatrix} 3 & 2 \\ 1 & 0 \end{bmatrix} \quad B = \begin{bmatrix} 2 & 4 \\ 1 & 2 \end{bmatrix} \quad C = \begin{bmatrix} 1 & 6 \\ 3 & -4 \end{bmatrix}$$

   a. Compare the products AB and CB. Is $AB = CB$? If so, does $AB = CB$ imply that $A = C$?

   b. Verify that $(AB)C = A(BC)$.

10. In a grocery store, Susan purchased five cans of soup, two cans of frozen orange juice, one dozen eggs, two chickens, and two gallons of milk. Judy bought seven cans of soup, four cans of frozen orange juice, two dozen eggs, one chicken, one gallon of milk, and one half-gallon of ice cream. The respective costs of these purchases per unit are: a can of soup, \$0.31; a can of frozen orange juice, \$0.79; a dozen eggs, \$0.95; chicken, \$0.73; a gallon of milk, \$1.39; and a half-gallon of ice cream, \$1.50.

    a. Represent these purchases in a (2×6) matrix.

    b. Write the price vector of these purchases as a (6×1) matrix.

    c. Determine the amount Susan spent on her groceries. Compute the total amount Judy spent on her purchases.

11. Mrs. Hawkes wishes to purchase the following items of groceries: 16 cans of soup, 8 cans of frozen orange juice, 3 dozen eggs, 4 chickens, 4 pounds of hamburger meat, 2 gallons of milk, 1 half-gallon of ice cream, and 2 packs of cigarettes. There are three supermarkets close by that sell these items. Each store's price list for the respective items is given below:

    Store 1: \$0.32, \$0.79, \$0.95, \$0.73, \$1.39, \$1.29, \$1.59, \$0.43
    Store 2: \$0.29, \$0.75, \$0.93, \$0.77, \$1.43, \$1.35, \$1.58, \$0.45
    Store 3: \$0.36, \$0.74, \$0.99, \$0.79, \$1.25, \$1.23, \$1.49, \$0.44

    At which store should she expect her grocery bill to be the minimum?

12. An automobile manufacturer offers five pollution-free models, A, B, C, D, and E, and expects orders for 1 million, 3 million, 2 million, 1 million, and 4 million, respectively. The following matrix gives the amount of raw material needed for each model expressed in conveniently chosen units:

	Steel	Chromium	Glass	Rubber	Paint
A	8	1	7	6	5
B	5	2	6	7	4
C	4	2	5	6	4
D	3	1	6	6	5
E	4	2	5	5	3

The respective costs of material per unit are $15.00 for steel, $5.00 for chromium, $4.00 for glass, $3.00 for rubber, and $2.00 for paint.

a. Express the expected demand for the various models as a 1×5 matrix.

b. Using matrix multiplication, determine the total amounts of raw material needed.

c. Express the price vector as 5×1 matrix.

d. Using matrix multiplication, determine the total cost of material per car for each model.

e. Determine the total investment as a 1×1 matrix.

6

Matrices and Linear Systems

6.1 INTRODUCTION

In Chapter 4, we considered equations in two variables x_1 and x_2 that have a linear relationship and we noticed that if one of the unknowns in $ax_1 + bx_2 = c$, say x_1, is assigned an arbitrary value, the value of the other unknown x_2 is readily determined. There are, however, many problems in business, economics, and management in which the value of one unknown depends on more than one variable. For example, the supply of a product may depend on its demand in the market as well as its retail price. The sale of air conditioners in summer depends on the size of the community, prices charged by competing manufacturers, the humidity, and the number of hot days in a particular summer. The attendance at a theater depends not only on the quality of the performance but also on the other attractions available on the same evening. We therefore consider in this chapter systems of linear equations in more than two variables and use matrix theory in providing numerical solutions. Input-output analysis developed by Leontiff (1936) for analyzing the interdependence of the various sectors of the economy is also discussed later in the chapter.

6.2 SOLUTION OF LINEAR EQUATIONS: GAUSS-JORDAN ELIMINATION METHOD

When a system of linear equations involves n equations in n unknowns, $n > 2$, solving the system by means of graphs or substitution methods is hardly a pleasant experience. We therefore illustrate here a method of elimination that is not only useful for machine calculations but is also fundamental to the understanding of the basic concepts involved.

Consider, for example, the following set of three equations in three unknowns:

$$(6.1) \quad \begin{aligned} 3x_1 - 5x_2 + 4x_3 &= 67 \\ x_1 + 2x_2 + 3x_3 &= 21 \\ 5x_1 + 8x_2 + 11x_3 &= 81 \end{aligned}$$

Our objective is first to transform this set of equations into a triangular system,

$$x_1 + b_{12}x_2 + b_{13}x_3 = c_1$$
$$x_2 + b_{23}x_3 = c_2$$
$$x_3 = c_3$$

and then reduce it subsequently to the form

$$x_1 + 0 \cdot x_2 + 0 \cdot x_3 = c_1{}^*$$
$$0 \cdot x_1 + x_2 + 0 \cdot x_3 = c_2{}^*$$
$$0 \cdot x_1 + 0 \cdot x_2 + x_3 = c_3$$

so that $x_1 = c_1{}^*$, $x_2 = c_2{}^*$, and $x_3 = c_3$ is the obvious solution to the original set of equations (6.1). An interchange in the first two equations in (6.1) yields

$$x_1 + 2x_2 + 3x_3 = 21$$
(6.2) $$3x_1 - 5x_2 + 4x_3 = 67$$
$$5x_1 + 8x_2 + 11x_3 = 81$$

The first equation in (6.2) has 1 as its leading coefficient and can therefore be used to eliminate the variable x_1 from the second and third equations in (6.2). Subtracting three times the first equation from the second and five times the first equation from the third equation, we obtain

$$x_1 + 2x_2 + 3x_3 = 21$$
(6.3) $$-11x_2 - 5x_3 = 4$$
$$-2x_2 - 4x_3 = -24$$

Now we divide the third equation by (-2) so as to have 1 as its leading coefficient and then interchange the equation so obtained with the second equation. This yields the following system:

$$x_1 + 2x_2 + 3x_3 = 21$$
(6.4) $$x_2 + 2x_3 = 12$$
$$-11x_2 - 5x_3 = 4$$

Adding 11 times the second equation in (6.4) to the third equation results in the elimination of the variable x_2 from the third equation, and we obtain

$$x_1 + 2x_2 + 3x_3 = 21$$
(6.5) $$x_2 + 2x_3 = 12$$
$$17x_3 = 136$$

Dividing the third equation by the coefficient of x_3, we have the following system in triangular form:

$$x_1 + 2x_2 + 3x_3 = 21$$
(6.6) $$x_2 + 2x_3 = 12$$
$$x_3 = 8$$

To eliminate x_3 from the first two equations, we add (-2) times the third equation to the second equation and (-3) times the third equation to the first equation. Thus, we get

$$
\begin{aligned}
x_1 + 2x_2 \qquad &= -3 \\
x_2 \qquad &= -4 \\
x_3 &= 8
\end{aligned}
$$
(6.7)

Adding (-2) times the second equation to the first equation, we obtain

$$
\begin{aligned}
x_1 \qquad\qquad &= 5 \\
x_2 \qquad &= -4 \\
x_3 &= 8
\end{aligned}
$$
(6.8)

We leave it for the reader to verify by substitution in the original set of equations (6.1) that this is, in fact, a solution of the three linear equations in three unknowns.

Definition 6.2.1: Two systems of linear equations in the variables $x_1, x_2, \ldots, x_n$ are said to be equivalent if and only if every solution of one system is also a solution of the other.

The elimination process of solving a system of equations reduces the given set of linear equations to an equivalent set of equations from which the existence of solutions can be read easily. Thus, (6.1), (6.2), and (6.3) are equivalent. Similarly, the system of equations (6.3), (6.4), (6.5), and (6.6) are also equivalent, as are (6.7) and (6.8).

Observe that in finding the solution to the original set of equations (6.1), we used operations of the following form:

1. The interchange of any two equations of a system
2. The addition of an arbitrary multiple of one equation to another equation of the system
3. The multiplication of an equation of a system by a constant

It is easy to show that the above operations preserve the solution of the set of equations.

In reducing the given system of linear equations to equivalent systems, we actually operate on the coefficients and the corresponding constants. The variables serve simply to keep their coefficients properly aligned in columns. Thus, a good deal of needless writing is saved by operating on the matrix representation of the system of linear equations and performing the same operations that are actually used on the set of equations.

The system of equations (6.1) can be written in matrix form as

$$
\begin{bmatrix} 3 & -5 & 4 \\ 1 & 2 & 3 \\ 5 & 8 & 11 \end{bmatrix} \begin{bmatrix} x_1 \\ x_2 \\ x_3 \end{bmatrix} = \begin{bmatrix} 67 \\ 21 \\ 81 \end{bmatrix}
$$

or more precisely, as

$$ AX = B $$

where A is the coefficient matrix and B is the vector of constants.

Definition 6.2.2: The augmented matrix for the system $AX = B$ is the matrix $[A:B]$, formed by adjoining the column vector B of constants to the right of the coefficient matrix A.

Thus, the augmented matrix of the system of equations (6.1) is

$$[A:B] = \begin{bmatrix} 3 & -5 & 4 & 67 \\ 1 & 2 & 3 & 21 \\ 5 & 8 & 11 & 81 \end{bmatrix}$$

Each row vector of the augmented matrix contains the coefficients of the unknowns and the constant term of the corresponding equation.

The technique of solving linear equations using matrices involves first obtaining a 1 in the a_{11} position either by dividing the first row by its leading term or by interchanging the first row with another row having 1 as its leading term. Suitable multiples of the new first row are then added to the remaining rows to obtain 0's in the a_{21} and a_{31} positions. The process is repeated by selecting a new row amongst the altered rows, dividing it by its leading nonzero term, if necessary, to locate a 1 in the a_{22} position. The new second row thus obtained is then used to obtain 0 in the a_{32} position. The process is continued until we obtain an equivalent augmented matrix in the triangular form as follows.

$$[A^*:B^*] = \begin{bmatrix} 1 & b_{12} & b_{13} & c_1 \\ 0 & 1 & b_{23} & c_2 \\ 0 & 0 & 1 & c_3 \end{bmatrix}$$

Adding suitable multiples of the last row to the remaining rows yields zeros in b_{13} and b_{23} positions. Again, adding a suitable multiple of the second row to the first row places a zero in the b_{12} position. Thus, we have

$$\begin{bmatrix} 1 & 0 & 0 & c_1^* \\ 0 & 1 & 0 & c_2^* \\ 0 & 0 & 1 & c_3 \end{bmatrix}$$

so that $x_1 = c_1^*$, $x_2 = c_2^*$, and $x_3 = c_3$ is a solution to the original set of equations (6.1).

The operations we performed on the system of linear equations (6.1) correspond exactly to those we perform now on the rows of the augmented matrix $[A:B]$. The augmented matrix is

	Rows	x_1	x_2	x_3	Constant
	R_1	3	-5	4	67
(6.1a)	R_2	1	2	3	21
	R_3	5	8	11	81

Because 1 happens to be in the a_{21} position, we begin by interchanging the first two rows of the above matrix so as to obtain 1 in the a_{11} position as shown:

$$
\begin{array}{cc}
\text{Row Operations} & \begin{array}{ccc} x_1 & x_2 & x_3 \end{array} \qquad \text{Constant} \\[4pt]
\begin{array}{c} R_1' = R_2 \\ R_2' = R_1 \\ R_3 \end{array} &
\left[\begin{array}{ccc|c}
1 & 2 & 3 & 21 \\
3 & -5 & 4 & 67 \\
5 & 8 & 11 & 81
\end{array}\right]
\end{array}
$$

(6.2a)

Next, we need to obtain 0's in the a_{21} and a_{31} positions. This can be accomplished simply by multiplying the elements of the new first row R_1' by (-3) and (-5) and then adding the results to the corresponding elements of the new second row R_2' and R_3, respectively. The new matrix along with the symbolic representation of the operations involved is given below:

$$
\begin{array}{cc}
\text{Row Operations} & \begin{array}{ccc} x_1 & x_2 & x_3 \end{array} \qquad \text{Constant} \\[4pt]
\begin{array}{c} R_1' \\ R_2'' = R_2' + (-3)R_1' \\ R_3' = R_3 + (-5)R_1' \end{array} &
\left[\begin{array}{ccc|c}
1 & 2 & 3 & 21 \\
0 & -11 & -5 & 4 \\
0 & -2 & -4 & -24
\end{array}\right]
\end{array}
$$

(6.3a)

Now we need to get 1 in the a_{22} position. This can be accomplished by multiplying the elements of the second row R_2'' by $(-\frac{1}{11})$, or we can divide the elements of the third row R_3' by (-2) and then interchange the new third row so obtained with R_2''. Thus, we obtain

$$
\begin{array}{cc}
\text{Row Operations} & \begin{array}{ccc} x_1 & x_2 & x_3 \end{array} \qquad \text{Constant} \\[4pt]
\begin{array}{c} R_1' \\ R_2''' = (-\frac{1}{2})R_3' \\ R_3'' = R_2'' \end{array} &
\left[\begin{array}{ccc|c}
1 & 2 & 3 & 21 \\
0 & 1 & 2 & 12 \\
0 & -11 & -5 & 4
\end{array}\right]
\end{array}
$$

(6.4a)

To obtain 0 in the a_{32} position, we multiply the elements of the second row R_2''' by 11 and add the results to the corresponding elements of third row R_3''. The resulting matrix along with the symbolic representation of the operations involved is

$$
\begin{array}{cc}
\text{Row Operations} & \begin{array}{ccc} x_1 & x_2 & x_3 \end{array} \quad \text{Constant} \\[4pt]
\begin{array}{c} R_1' \\ R_2''' \\ R_3''' = R_3'' + 11R_2''' \end{array} &
\left[\begin{array}{ccc|c}
1 & 2 & 3 & 21 \\
0 & 1 & 2 & 12 \\
0 & 0 & 17 & 136
\end{array}\right]
\end{array}
$$

(6.5a)

Dividing the elements of third row R_3''' by 17, the above matrix becomes

$$
\begin{array}{cc}
\text{Row Operations} & \begin{array}{ccc} x_1 & x_2 & x_3 \end{array} \qquad \text{Constant} \\[4pt]
\begin{array}{c} R_1' \\ R_2''' \\ R_3^{IV} = (\frac{1}{17})R_3''' \end{array} &
\left[\begin{array}{ccc|c}
1 & 2 & 3 & 21 \\
0 & 1 & 2 & 12 \\
0 & 0 & 1 & 8
\end{array}\right]
\end{array}
$$

(6.6a)

Now we use the last row $R_3{}^{IV}$ to obtain 0's in the a_{13} and a_{23} positions. Adding (-3) and (-2) times the elements of $R_3{}^{IV}$ to the corresponding elements of the first and second row of the preceding matrix yields

$$\begin{array}{c} \text{Row Operations} \\ R_1{}'' = R_1{}' + (-3)R_3{}^{IV} \\ (6.7a) \quad R_2{}^{IV} = R_2{}''' + (-2)R_3{}^{IV} \\ R_3{}^{IV} \end{array} \quad \begin{array}{ccc} x_1 & x_2 & x_3 \\ \end{array} \quad \text{Constant} \\ \left[\begin{array}{ccc|c} 1 & 2 & 0 & -3 \\ 0 & 1 & 0 & -4 \\ 0 & 0 & 1 & 8 \end{array} \right]$$

Finally, we multiply the elements of the second row $R_2{}^{IV}$ in the preceding matrix by (-2) and add the results to the corresponding elements of the first row $R_1{}''$. The resulting matrix is

$$\begin{array}{c} \text{Row Operations} \\ R_1{}''' = R_1{}'' + (-2)R_2{}^{IV} \\ (6.8a) \quad R_2{}^{IV} \\ R_3{}^{IV} \end{array} \quad \begin{array}{ccc} x_1 & x_2 & x_3 \\ \end{array} \quad \text{Constant} \\ \left[\begin{array}{ccc|c} 1 & 0 & 0 & 5 \\ 0 & 1 & 0 & -4 \\ 0 & 0 & 1 & 8 \end{array} \right]$$

Thus,

$$x_1 = 5 \qquad x_2 = -4 \qquad x_3 = 8$$

is the solution to the system of linear equations.

We wish to remark that the sequence of operations used to obtain an identity matrix on the left and a solution vector on the right is arranged in each case simply to take full advantage of any obvious circumstances and is by no means unique. Note carefully that each equation in the final matrix involves one unknown with a 1 as its coefficient so that the corresponding constant term is a solution for that unknown.

To apply these operations on the augmented matrix, we give a definition for the corresponding operations on the rows of this matrix, because these rows correspond precisely to the set of simultaneous equations. These are referred to as elementary operations.

Definition 6.2.3: The elementary operations on the rows of a matrix are of the following form:

Type 1. Multiplying the elements of any row, say, R_i, by a constant k and then replacing it by $R_i{}'$. Symbolically, we may express this operation as

$$R_i{}' = k \cdot R_i$$

Type 2. Interchanging any two rows R_i and R_j. In symbols, we may write

$$R_j{}' = R_i$$

and

$$R_i{}' = R_j$$

Type 3. Multiplying the elements of any row, say, R_i, by a scalar k and adding the results to the corresponding elements of another row, say, R_j. This operation replaces the original row R_j by the new row R_j', where

$$R_j' = R_j + k \cdot R_i$$

To apply these operations to the augmented matrix $[A:B]$, we first check the first column to find a nonzero element that could be easily changed to 1. The row with the selected element is then interchanged with the first row by using an elementary operation of type 2. The new first row is divided, if necessary, by its first component to obtain a 1 in the a_{11} position. This is elementary row operation of type 1. Then, using an elementary row operation of type 3, suitable multiples of this new first row are added to the other rows to obtain 0's in the rest of the first column. The process is then repeated on the second column with the exception that the first row is no longer available for searching the nonzero element. Using elementary operation of type 2, the row containing the selected element is then interchanged with the second row. The new second row is then divided by the element in the a_{22} position so as to obtain a 1 in that place. Suitable multiples of the second row are then added to the remaining rows to obtain zeros in the rest of the second column, including the first row. This is an elementary row operation of type 3. The process is continued until we have an identity matrix on the left augmented by the solution vector on the right. This process is called the Gauss-Jordan elimination method.

The following examples will further illustrate the above discussion.

Example 6.1

Using the Gauss-Jordan elimination method, solve the following system of linear equations:

$$\begin{aligned}
x_1 + x_2 + x_3 + x_4 &= 6 \\
2x_1 + 4x_2 - 3x_3 + 2x_4 &= 0 \\
3x_1 - 4x_2 - 2x_3 - x_4 &= 3 \\
4x_1 + 3x_2 - 5x_3 + 4x_4 &= 7
\end{aligned}$$

SOLUTION

The augmented matrix is

	x_1	x_2	x_3	x_4	Constant
R_1	1	1	1	1	6
R_2	2	4	-3	2	0
R_3	3	-4	-2	-1	3
R_4	4	3	-5	4	7

Because 1 happens to be in the a_{11} position, we perform the following row operations in the order specified:

1. $R_2' = R_2 + (-2)R_1$
2. $R_3' = R_3 + (-3)R_1$
3. $R_4' = R_4 + (-4)R_1$

These operations transform the preceding matrix into

$$
\begin{array}{c}
\\
R_1 \\
R_2' \\
R_3' \\
R_4'
\end{array}
\begin{array}{cccc}
x_1 & x_2 & x_3 & x_4 & \text{Constant} \\
\left[\begin{array}{cccc|c}
1 & 1 & 1 & 1 & 6 \\
0 & 2 & -5 & 0 & -12 \\
0 & -7 & -5 & -4 & -15 \\
0 & -1 & -9 & 0 & -17
\end{array}\right]
\end{array}
$$

Next, we may multiply the elements of R_4' by (-1) and then interchange the row so obtained with the second row R_2'. Symbolically,

1. $R_2'' = (-1)R_4'$
2. $R_4'' = R_2'$

Thus, we obtain the matrix

$$
\begin{array}{c}
\\
R_1 \\
R_2'' \\
R_3' \\
R_4''
\end{array}
\begin{array}{cccc}
x_1 & x_2 & x_3 & x_4 & \text{Constant} \\
\left[\begin{array}{cccc|c}
1 & 1 & 1 & 1 & 6 \\
0 & 1 & 9 & 0 & 17 \\
0 & -7 & -5 & -4 & -15 \\
0 & 2 & -5 & 0 & -12
\end{array}\right]
\end{array}
$$

We now add the suitable multiples of R_2'' to the remaining rows to obtain zeros in the rest of the second column including the first row. Thus, we perform the following operations:

1. $R_1' = R_1 + (-1)R_2''$
2. $R_3'' = R_3 + 7R_2''$
3. $R_4''' = R_4'' + (-2)R_2''$

which transforms the preceding matrix into

$$
\begin{array}{c}
\\
R_1' \\
R_2'' \\
R_3'' \\
R_4'''
\end{array}
\begin{array}{cccc}
x_1 & x_2 & x_3 & x_4 & \text{Constant} \\
\left[\begin{array}{cccc|c}
1 & 0 & -8 & 1 & -11 \\
0 & 1 & 9 & 0 & 17 \\
0 & 0 & 58 & -4 & 104 \\
0 & 0 & -23 & 0 & -46
\end{array}\right]
\end{array}
$$

Because we need to get 1 in the a_{33} position now, we divide the elements of R_4''' by (-23) and then interchange the row so obtained with R_3''. Symbolically,

1. $R_3''' = (-\frac{1}{23})R_4''$
2. $R_4^{IV} = R_3''$

These transformations yield the matrix

$$
\begin{array}{c}
\\
R_1' \\
R_2'' \\
R_3''' \\
R_4^{IV}
\end{array}
\begin{array}{cccc}
x_1 & x_2 & x_3 & x_4 & \text{Constant} \\
\left[\begin{array}{cccc|c}
1 & 0 & -8 & 1 & -11 \\
0 & 1 & 9 & 0 & 17 \\
0 & 0 & 1 & 0 & 2 \\
0 & 0 & 58 & -4 & 104
\end{array}\right]
\end{array}
$$

Finally, we perform the following row operations in the order specified.

1. $R_1'' = R_1' + 8R_3'''$
2. $R_2''' = R_2'' + (-9)R_3'''$
3. $R_4{}^V = (-\frac{1}{4})[R_4{}^{IV} + (-58)R_3''']$
4. $R_1''' = R_1'' + (-1)R_4{}^V$

and thus obtain the matrix

$$
\begin{array}{c}
\\
R_1''' \\
R_2''' \\
R_3''' \\
R_4{}^V
\end{array}
\begin{array}{cccc}
x_1 & x_2 & x_3 & x_4 \\
\end{array}
\qquad \text{Constant}
$$

$$
\begin{array}{c}
R_1''' \\
R_2''' \\
R_3''' \\
R_4{}^V
\end{array}
\left[
\begin{array}{cccc|c}
1 & 0 & 0 & 0 & 2 \\
0 & 1 & 0 & 0 & -1 \\
0 & 0 & 1 & 0 & 2 \\
0 & 0 & 0 & 1 & 3
\end{array}
\right]
$$

Thus,

$$x_1 = 2, \quad x_2 = -1, \quad x_3 = 2, \quad \text{and} \quad x_4 = 3$$

is the solution of the system of the linear equations. ∎

The Gauss-Jordan elimination method can also be used for solving simultaneously the systems of linear equations

$$AX_1 = B_1, AX_2 = B_2, \ldots, AX_n = B_n$$

all of which have the same coefficient matrix. We illustrate this in the following example.

Example 6.2

Solve the following sets of linear equations using the Gauss-Jordan elimination method.

a.
$$
\begin{aligned}
x_2 + 2x_3 - 3x_4 &= 7 \\
2x_1 - x_2 - 3x_3 + x_4 &= -2 \\
-2x_1 + 3x_2 + 2x_3 - 2x_4 &= 1 \\
x_1 + 2x_2 + 3x_3 - x_4 &= 4
\end{aligned}
$$

b.
$$
\begin{aligned}
x_2 + 2x_3 - 3x_4 &= -5 \\
2x_1 - x_2 - 3x_3 + x_4 &= 12 \\
-2x_1 + 3x_2 + 2x_3 - 2x_4 &= -7 \\
x_1 + 2x_2 + 3x_3 - x_4 &= -5
\end{aligned}
$$

c.
$$
\begin{aligned}
x_2 + 2x_3 - 3x_4 &= 1 \\
2x_1 - x_2 - 3x_3 + x_4 &= -2 \\
-2x_1 + 3x_2 + 2x_3 - 2x_4 &= -6 \\
x_1 + 2x_2 + 3x_3 - x_4 &= 6
\end{aligned}
$$

SOLUTION

The three systems of linear equations have the same coefficient matrix and differ only in their constant values. Because the calculations on the coefficient matrix are precisely the same for all the three systems, we shall solve three sets of linear equations at the same time. This system has an augmented matrix,

Row	x_1	x_2	x_3	x_4	Constant	Column	Vectors
R_1	0	1	2	-3	7	-5	1
R_2	2	-1	-3	1	-2	12	-2
R_3	-2	3	2	-2	1	-7	-6
R_4	1	2	3	-1	4	-5	6

that can be simplified by the series of row operations as shown in Table 6.1.

Table 6.1

Row Operations	x_1	x_2	x_3	x_4	Constant Column Vectors		
					a	b	c
R_1	0	1	2	-3	7	-5	1
R_2	2	-1	-3	1	-2	12	-2
R_3	-2	3	2	-2	1	-7	-6
R_4	1	2	3	-1	4	-5	6
$R_1' = R_4$	1	2	3	-1	4	-5	6
R_2	2	-1	-3	1	-2	12	-2
R_3	-2	3	2	-2	1	-7	-6
$R_4' = R_1$	0	1	2	-3	7	-5	1
R_1'	1	2	3	-1	4	-5	6
$R_2' = R_2 + (-2)R_1'$	0	-5	-9	3	-10	22	-14
$R_3' = R_3 + 2R_1'$	0	7	8	-4	9	-17	6
R_4'	0	1	2	-3	7	-5	1
R_1'	1	2	3	-1	4	-5	6
$R_2'' = R_4'$	0	1	2	-3	7	-5	1
R_3'	0	7	8	-4	9	-17	6
$R_4'' = R_2'$	0	-5	-9	3	-10	22	-14
$R_1'' = R_1' + (-2)R_2''$	1	0	-1	5	-10	5	4
R_2''	0	1	2	-3	7	-5	1
$R_3'' = R_3' + (-7)R_2''$	0	0	-6	17	-40	18	-1
$R_4''' = R_4 + 5R_2''$	0	0	1	-12	25	-3	-9
R_1''	1	0	-1	5	-10	5	4
R_2''	0	1	2	-3	7	-5	1
$R_3''' = R_4'''$	0	0	1	-12	25	-3	-9
$R_4^{IV} = R_3''$	0	0	-6	17	-40	18	-1
$R_1''' = R_1'' + R_3'''$	1	0	0	-7	15	2	-5
$R_2''' = R_2'' + (-2)R_3'''$	0	1	0	21	-43	1	19
R_3'''	0	0	1	-12	25	-3	-9
$R_4^V = (-\frac{1}{55})[R_4^{IV} + 6R_3''']$	0	0	0	1	-2	0	1
$R_1^{IV} = R_1''' + 7R_4^V$	1	0	0	0	1	2	2
$R_2^{IV} = R_2''' + (-21)R_4'''$	0	1	0	0	-1	1	-2
$R_3^{IV} = R_3''' + 12R_2'''$	0	0	1	0	1	-3	3
R_4^V	0	0	0	1	-2	0	1

We leave it for the reader to verify that $x_1 = 1$, $x_2 = -1$, $x_3 = 1$, and $x_4 = -2$ is the solution of the system of equations in part a, $x_1 = 2$, $x_2 = 1$, $x_3 = -3$, and $x_4 = 0$ is the solution to the linear equations in part b, and $x_1 = 2, x_2 = -2, x_3 = 3$, and $x_4 = 1$ is the solution to the set of equations in part c. ∎

EXERCISE 6.1

Solve the following system of linear equations by using elementary row operations.

1. $2x_1 + 3x_2 = 13$
$\quad x_1 + 2x_2 = 8$

2. $\quad 3x_1 + 4x_2 = 25$
$\quad -2x_1 + 5x_2 = 14$

3. $\quad x_1 + x_2 + 5x_3 = 8$
$\quad 2x_1 + x_2 - x_3 = 3$
$\quad 3x_1 + 2x_2 + 5x_3 = 12$

4. $\quad x_1 - 5x_2 - x_3 = 6$
$\quad x_1 - x_2 - x_3 = -2$
$\quad 2x_1 - 2x_2 + x_3 = 17$

5. $\quad x_1 - 2x_2 + 3x_3 = 11$
$\quad 3x_1 - x_2 - 2x_3 = 0$
$\quad 6x_1 + 3x_2 - x_3 = 9$

6. $\quad x_1 + 2x_2 + 3x_3 = 6$
$\quad 2x_1 - 2x_2 + 5x_3 = 5$
$\quad 4x_1 - x_2 - 3x_3 = 0$

7. $\quad x_1 + x_2 - x_3 = 0$
$\quad 2x_1 + x_2 + 3x_3 = 9$
$\quad x_1 + 3x_2 + x_3 = 6$

8. $\quad x_1 + 2x_2 + 3x_3 = 14$
$\quad -x_1 + x_2 + 2x_3 = 7$
$\quad 3x_1 - x_2 + 5x_3 = 16$

9. $\quad x_1 - x_2 + x_3 = -2$
$\quad 2x_1 - 4x_2 + 3x_3 = -3$
$\quad -2x_2 + 3x_3 = 7$

10. $\quad 2x_1 + x_2 + 3x_3 + 6x_4 = 11$
$\quad 3x_1 - x_2 + x_3 + 3x_4 = 6$
$\quad -x_1 - 2x_2 + 3x_3 = 8$
$\quad x_1 + 4x_2 + 2x_3 + 7x_4 = 7$

11. $\quad x_1 + x_3 + 3x_4 = 5$
$\quad 2x_1 + x_2 + 5x_3 + 7x_4 = 15$
$\quad 3x_1 - x_2 + x_3 + 8x_4 = 11$
$\quad 4x_1 + 2x_2 + 8x_3 + 14x_4 = 28$

12. $\quad x_1 + x_2 + x_3 - x_4 = 1$
$\quad 2x_1 - 3x_2 - 2x_3 + 2x_4 = 4$
$\quad 2x_1 - x_2 + x_3 + 2x_4 = 3$
$\quad 5x_1 + 2x_2 + 7x_3 + 3x_4 = 5$

Solve the following set of linear equations simultaneously.

13. a. $x_1 + 2x_2 + 3x_3 = 5$
$\quad 3x_1 - 5x_2 + 4x_3 = 16$
$\quad 5x_1 + 8x_2 + 11x_3 = 19$

b. $x_1 + 2x_2 + 3x_3 = 14$
$\quad 3x_1 - 5x_2 + 4x_3 = 5$
$\quad 5x_1 + 8x_2 + 11x_3 = 54$

14. a. $x_1 + 2x_2 + x_3 = 4$
$\quad 2x_1 + 3x_2 + 4x_3 = 19$
$\quad 3x_1 - x_2 + x_3 = 9$

b. $x_1 + 2x_2 + x_3 = 4$
$\quad 2x_1 + 3x_2 + 4x_3 = 4$
$\quad 3x_1 - x_2 + x_3 = 0$

15. a. $2x_1 - x_2 + x_3 + x_4 = 3$
$\quad -x_1 + x_2 + 2x_3 + 3x_4 = 21$
$\quad x_1 - 2x_2 + 3x_3 + 4x_4 = 20$
$\quad -3x_1 - 3x_2 + x_3 + x_4 = 4$

b. $2x_1 - x_2 + x_3 + x_4 = -4$
$\quad -x_1 + x_2 + 2x_3 + 3x_4 = 4$
$\quad x_1 - 2x_2 + 3x_3 + 4x_4 = -2$
$\quad -3x_1 - 3x_2 + x_3 + x_4 = 4$

c. $2x_1 - x_2 + x_3 + x_4 = 3$
$\quad -x_1 + x_2 + 2x_3 + 3x_4 = 0$
$\quad x_1 - 2x_2 + 3x_3 + 4x_4 = 3$
$\quad -3x_1 - 3x_2 + x_3 + x_4 = -2$

6.3 SOME SPECIAL CASES OF THE MATRIX SOLUTION

We have so far investigated the Gauss-Jordan elimination method for solving n linear equations in n variables in which the system of equations possesses a solution and the solution is unique. We shall now consider systems of linear equations in which it is simply not possible to obtain the identity matrix augmented by the unique solution vector. In some of the cases we shall find that no solution of the system exists. In others we shall find that there are infinitely many solutions to the system.

Example 6.3

Find all solutions of the following system of simultaneous equations:

$$
\begin{aligned}
x_1 + 2x_2 - x_3 &= 6 \\
-x_1 - x_2 + 4x_3 &= -7 \\
2x_1 - x_2 + x_3 &= -1 \\
3x_1 - 4x_2 + 2x_3 &= -7
\end{aligned}
$$

SOLUTION

Note that this system has four linear equations in three unknowns and as such the coefficient matrix is not a square matrix. The augmented matrix

$$
\begin{array}{c}
\begin{array}{cccc} \quad\quad x_1 & x_2 & x_3 & \text{Constant} \end{array} \\
\begin{array}{c} R_1 \\ R_2 \\ R_3 \\ R_4 \end{array}
\left[
\begin{array}{ccc|c}
1 & 2 & -1 & 6 \\
-1 & -1 & 4 & -7 \\
2 & -1 & 1 & -1 \\
3 & -4 & 2 & -7
\end{array}
\right]
\end{array}
$$

can be simplified by the series of elementary row operations as shown in Table 6.2.

Table 6.2

Row Operations	x_1	x_2	x_3	Constant Column Vector
R_1	1	2	-1	6
R_2	-1	-1	4	-7
R_3	2	-1	1	-1
R_4	3	-4	2	-7
R_1	1	2	-1	6
$R_2' = R_2 + R_1$	0	1	3	-1
$R_3' = R_3 + (-2)R_1$	0	-5	3	-13
$R_4' = R_4 + (-3)R_1$	0	-10	5	-25
$R_1' = R_1 + (-2)R_2'$	1	0	-7	8
R_2'	0	1	3	-1
$R_3'' = \frac{1}{18}[R_3' + 5R_2']$	0	0	1	-1
$R_4'' = \frac{1}{35}[R_4' + 10R_2']$	0	0	1	-1
$R_1'' = R_1' + 7R_3''$	1	0	0	1
$R_2'' = R_2' + (-3)R_3''$	0	1	0	2
R_3''	0	0	1	-1
$R_4''' = R_4'' + (-1)R_3''$	0	0	0	0

The last row of 0's is indicative of the fact that the first three equations in the linear system possesses a unique solution

$$ x_1 = 1, \quad x_2 = 2, \quad \text{and} \quad x_3 = -1 $$

whereas the fourth equation in the system is simply a combination of the first three equations. ■

Sometimes it is possible that at the certain step in our reduction process a nonzero element in the ith column does not appear in the ith row. Because there is then no way that we can obtain a nonzero element for the ith column in the ith row, we can go no further in finding an identity matrix. Consider, for instance, the following example.

Example 6.4

Find all solutions for the following set of linear equations:

$$\begin{aligned}
x_1 - x_2 + x_3 &= 5 \\
3x_1 + 5x_2 - 13x_3 &= -9 \\
5x_1 + 3x_2 - 11x_3 &= 1
\end{aligned}$$

SOLUTION

The augmented matrix, in this case, is reduced by a series of elementary row operations as shown in Table 6.3.

Table 6.3

Row Operations	x_1	x_2	x_3	Constant Column Vector
R_1	1	-1	1	5
R_2	3	5	-13	-9
R_3	5	3	-11	1
R_1	1	-1	1	5
$R_2' = \frac{1}{8}[R_2 + (-3)R_1]$	0	1	-2	-3
$R_3' = \frac{1}{8}[R_3 + (-5)R_1]$	0	1	-2	-3
$R_1' = R_1 + R_2'$	1	0	-1	2
R_2'	0	1	-2	-3
$R_3'' = R_3' + (-1)R_2'$	0	0	0	0

The last matrix corresponds to the linear equations

$$\begin{aligned}
x_1 \quad - x_3 &= 2 \\
x_2 - 2x_3 &= -3
\end{aligned}$$

Expressing x_1 and x_2 in terms of x_3, we have

$$\begin{aligned}
x_1 &= 2 + x_3 \\
x_2 &= -3 + 2x_3
\end{aligned}$$

Clearly, x_3 can take any arbitrary value. Thus, if $x_3 = c$, then

$$\begin{aligned}
x_1 &= 2 + c \\
x_2 &= -3 + 2c
\end{aligned}$$

We leave it for the reader to verify by substituting $x_1 = 2 + c$, $x_2 = -3 + 2c$, and $x_3 = c$ in the original set of equations that this is, in fact, a solution of the three linear equations in three unknowns.

Note that for each value of c we obtain a solution. Because c can assume any value, we conclude that the system has an infinite number of solutions. ∎

Another special case is illustrated by the following example.

Example 6.5

Solve the following set of simultaneous equations:

$$x_1 + 3x_2 - 4x_3 = 5$$
$$2x_1 - x_2 + 5x_3 = 7$$
$$7x_1 + 7x_2 - 2x_3 = 31$$

SOLUTION

The augmented matrix is simplified by a series of row operations as shown in Table 6.4.

Table 6.4

Row Operations	x_1	x_2	x_3	Constant Column Vectors
R_1	1	3	-4	5
R_2	2	-1	5	7
R_3	7	7	-2	31
R_1	1	3	-4	5
$R_2' = R_2 + (-2)R_1$	0	-7	13	-3
$R_3' = R_3 + (-7)R_1$	0	-14	26	-4
R_1	1	3	-4	5
R_2'	0	-7	13	-3
$R_3'' = R_3' + (-2)R_2'$	0	0	0	2

The last row determines the equation

$$0 \cdot x_1 + 0 \cdot x_2 + 0 \cdot x_3 = 2$$

Because there are no values of x_1, x_2, and x_3 for which this equation holds, we conclude that the system of equations has no solution. ■

These examples illustrate that a given system of equations may have no solution, one solution, or an infinite number of solutions.

EXERCISE 6.2

Find the solution or solutions, if they exist, for the following sets of equations.

1. $x_1 + x_2 - x_3 = 4$
   $2x_1 + x_2 + 3x_3 = 10$
   $3x_1 + 2x_2 - 2x_3 = 10$

2. $x_1 + x_2 - x_3 = 5$
   $2x_1 + x_2 + 3x_3 = 3$
   $5x_1 + 4x_2 = 18$

3. $x_1 + 2x_2 + 3x_3 = 6$
   $2x_1 + 4x_2 - x_3 = 5$
   $4x_1 + 8x_2 + 3x_3 = 15$

4. $x_1 + 2x_2 - 3x_3 = 7$
   $2x_1 - x_2 + x_3 = 5$
   $3x_1 + x_2 - 2x_3 = 12$

5. $x_1 + 2x_2 - x_3 = 6$
   $3x_1 - x_2 + 2x_3 = 9$
   $5x_1 + 3x_2 = 21$

6. $-x_1 + 2x_2 + x_3 = 2$
   $4x_1 - x_2 + 6x_3 = -4$
   $2x_1 + 3x_2 + 8x_3 = 2$

7. $\begin{aligned} x_1 - x_2 + x_3 &= 3 \\ 2x_1 + 3x_2 - x_3 &= -5 \\ 4x_1 + x_2 + x_3 &= 1 \end{aligned}$

8. $\begin{aligned} x_1 + 2x_2 - x_3 &= 5 \\ 2x_1 + 4x_2 + 4x_3 &= 22 \\ 4x_1 + 8x_2 + 3x_3 &= 34 \end{aligned}$

9. $\begin{aligned} x_1 - x_2 - x_3 &= 0 \\ 2x_1 + x_2 + 2x_3 &= 11 \\ -x_1 + 3x_2 + x_3 &= 2 \end{aligned}$

10. $\begin{aligned} x_1 - x_2 + 2x_3 &= 2 \\ -2x_1 + 3x_2 - 2x_3 &= -1 \\ 4x_1 - 7x_2 + 2x_3 &= -4 \end{aligned}$

6.4 GEOMETRIC INTERPRETATIONS*

Recall from Section 4.2 that an equation of the form $ax_1 + bx_2 = c$ is a linear equation in two variables that can be represented by a straight line in a plane. A solution of this equation is an ordered pair (x_1, x_2) of numbers which when substituted for x_1 and x_2 converts the linear equation into a true statement. The pair $(4, -3)$, for example, is one solution of the linear equation $5x_1 + 4x_2 = 8$, because $5(4) + 4(-3) = 8$. Similarly, many other ordered pairs, for example, $(0, 2)$, $(-4, 7)$, $(8, -8)$, are all solutions of the linear equation $5x_1 + 4x_2 = 8$. Thus, a linear equation may have an infinite number of solutions. Further, if there are two lines in a plane, they intersect or they are coincident or they are parallel. If the lines intersect, they intersect in a point the coordinates of which represent the solution to the system of two linear equations in two variables. If the lines are parallel, they do not intersect and consequently their equations have no solution. Such a system of linear equations is called inconsistent. If the lines coincide, then the set of points on one line are also points on the other line. Thus, the equations of coincident lines have an infinite number of solutions. If there are three or more equations in two variables x_1 and x_2, the system will have a solution if and only if the corresponding lines pass through a common point of intersection.

A linear equation in three unknowns x_1, x_2, and x_3,

$$ax_1 + bx_2 + cx_3 = d$$

represents an equation of a plane in three dimensions. If there are two planes, they intersect in a common line or they are coincident or they are parallel. If the planes are parallel, the system does not have any solution, but if the planes coincide, then the set of points (x_1, x_2, x_3) that lie on one plane are also points on the other plane and the system has an infinite number of solutions. If there are three planes intersecting at a single point, the coordinates (x_1, x_2, x_3) of that point determine the solution for the corresponding system of linear equations. If there are more than three planes, the system will have a unique solution if and only if all the planes pass through a common point of intersection. The coordinates of this point constitute the solution for the system of equations.

Similar interpretations for equations involving more than three unknowns can be formulated. Such equations represent hyperplanes in four or more dimensions.

---

* This section may be omitted, if necessary, without any loss of continuity.

6.5 INVERSE OF A SQUARE MATRIX

In elementary algebra, the equation

$$ax = b$$

can be solved for the unknown x by dividing both sides of the equation by a, thus obtaining

$$x = \frac{b}{a} \quad \text{where} \quad a \neq 0$$

Alternatively, we can multiply both sides of the equation by the multiplicative inverse of a, namely $1/a$ or a^{-1}. This yields

$$a^{-1}(ax) = a^{-1}b$$
$$(a^{-1}a)x = a^{-1}b$$

Because $a^{-1}a = 1$, we have

$$x = a^{-1}b$$

as the solution to the equation $ax = b$. This concept of the multiplicative inverse can be extended to matrix multiplication, and then used effectively for solving a set of linear equations.

Definition 6.5.1: If A is a square matrix of order n and B is another square matrix also of order n such that

$$AB = BA = I$$

then B is called an inverse of the matrix A.

Example 6.6
Let

$$A = \begin{bmatrix} 7 & 3 \\ 9 & 4 \end{bmatrix} \quad \text{and} \quad B = \begin{bmatrix} 4 & -3 \\ -9 & 7 \end{bmatrix}$$

Then

$$AB = \begin{bmatrix} 7 & 3 \\ 9 & 4 \end{bmatrix}\begin{bmatrix} 4 & -3 \\ -9 & 7 \end{bmatrix} = \begin{bmatrix} 1 & 0 \\ 0 & 1 \end{bmatrix}$$

and

$$BA = \begin{bmatrix} 4 & -3 \\ -9 & 7 \end{bmatrix}\begin{bmatrix} 7 & 3 \\ 9 & 4 \end{bmatrix} = \begin{bmatrix} 1 & 0 \\ 0 & 1 \end{bmatrix}$$

Thus, B is an inverse of the matrix A.

Example 6.7

Let A and B be the following 3×3 matrices:

$$A = \begin{bmatrix} 3 & 1 & 2 \\ 1 & -4 & 1 \\ 2 & 3 & 0 \end{bmatrix} \quad \text{and} \quad B = \tfrac{1}{15} \begin{bmatrix} -3 & 6 & 9 \\ 2 & -4 & -1 \\ 11 & -7 & -13 \end{bmatrix}$$

Then, we have

$$AB = \begin{bmatrix} 3 & 1 & 2 \\ 1 & -4 & 1 \\ 2 & 3 & 0 \end{bmatrix} \cdot \left(\tfrac{1}{15}\right) \begin{bmatrix} -3 & 6 & 9 \\ 2 & -4 & -1 \\ 11 & -7 & -13 \end{bmatrix} = \begin{bmatrix} 1 & 0 & 0 \\ 0 & 1 & 0 \\ 0 & 0 & 1 \end{bmatrix}$$

and

$$BA = \tfrac{1}{15} \begin{bmatrix} -3 & 6 & 9 \\ 2 & -4 & -1 \\ 11 & -7 & -13 \end{bmatrix} \begin{bmatrix} 3 & 1 & 2 \\ 1 & -4 & 1 \\ 2 & 3 & 0 \end{bmatrix} = \begin{bmatrix} 1 & 0 & 0 \\ 0 & 1 & 0 \\ 0 & 0 & 1 \end{bmatrix}$$

Consequently, matrix B is an inverse of matrix A and matrix A is an inverse of matrix B. ■

We do not wish to leave an impression that all nonzero square matrices have inverses. Consider, for example, the matrix

$$A = \begin{bmatrix} 1 & 0 \\ 0 & 0 \end{bmatrix}$$

and suppose that

$$B = \begin{bmatrix} a & b \\ c & d \end{bmatrix}$$

is an inverse of A. Then $AB = I$. That is,

$$\begin{bmatrix} 1 & 0 \\ 0 & 0 \end{bmatrix} \begin{bmatrix} a & b \\ c & d \end{bmatrix} = \begin{bmatrix} 1 & 0 \\ 0 & 1 \end{bmatrix}$$

$$\begin{bmatrix} a & b \\ 0 & \boxed{0} \end{bmatrix} \quad \begin{bmatrix} 1 & 0 \\ 0 & \boxed{1} \end{bmatrix}$$

Because the matrices are equal, we have, by Definition 5.3.8, that

$$0 = 1$$

which is false. Hence, we conclude that the matrix A does not have an inverse.

Later, we shall use the Gauss-Jordan elimination method to determine whether or not the inverse of a given square matrix exists.

Proposition 6.5.1: The inverse of a square matrix, if it exists, is unique.

PROOF

Let A be a matrix with A^{-1} as its inverse. Suppose that B is another matrix that is also an inverse of A. Then

$$AA^{-1} = A^{-1}A = I$$

and

$$AB = BA = I$$

Then, premultiplying both sides of $AB = I$ by A^{-1}, we have

$$A^{-1}(AB) = A^{-1}I = A^{-1}$$

Also,

$$A^{-1}(AB) = (A^{-1}A)B = IB = B$$

Hence,

$$B = A^{-1}$$

In view of this result, we shall henceforth denote the inverse of a matrix A by the symbol A^{-1}. ■

EXERCISE 6.3

1. Show that the inverse of

$$A = \begin{bmatrix} 4 & 7 \\ 1 & 2 \end{bmatrix} \quad \text{is} \quad A^{-1} = \begin{bmatrix} 2 & -7 \\ -1 & 4 \end{bmatrix}$$

by verifying that $AA^{-1} = A^{-1}A = I$.

2. Show that the inverse of

$$A = \begin{bmatrix} a & b \\ c & d \end{bmatrix} \quad \text{is} \quad A^{-1} = \frac{1}{(ad - bc)} \begin{bmatrix} d & -b \\ -c & a \end{bmatrix}$$

if and only if $ad - bc \neq 0$.

3. Show that the inverse of

$$A = \begin{bmatrix} 1 & 0 & 2 \\ 3 & 1 & 2 \\ 1 & -1 & 0 \end{bmatrix} \quad \text{is} \quad A^{-1} = \tfrac{1}{6} \begin{bmatrix} -2 & 2 & 2 \\ -2 & 2 & -4 \\ 4 & -1 & -1 \end{bmatrix}$$

by verifying that $AA^{-1} = A^{-1}A = I$.

4. Show that the inverse of

$$A = \begin{bmatrix} 1 & 1 & 1 \\ 3 & 4 & -1 \\ 2 & -5 & 3 \end{bmatrix} \quad \text{is} \quad A^{-1} = \tfrac{1}{27} \begin{bmatrix} -7 & 8 & 5 \\ 11 & -1 & -4 \\ 23 & -7 & -1 \end{bmatrix}$$

by verifying that $AA^{-1} = A^{-1}A = I$.

5. Prove that if A is a matrix with A^{-1} as its inverse and $AB = AC$, then $B = C$.

Solution of Linear Equations Using A^{-1}

We shall now illustrate how A^{-1}, if it exists, is used to solve a system of n linear equations in n unknowns. Consider, for instance, the following example.

Example 6.8

Solve the following:

(6.9)
$$x_1 + 2x_2 = 4$$
$$2x_1 + 3x_2 = 7$$

SOLUTION

Expressed in matrix notation, we have

(6.10)
$$\begin{bmatrix} 1 & 2 \\ 2 & 3 \end{bmatrix} \begin{bmatrix} x_1 \\ x_2 \end{bmatrix} = \begin{bmatrix} 4 \\ 7 \end{bmatrix}$$

or $$AX = B$$

where

$$A = \begin{bmatrix} 1 & 2 \\ 2 & 3 \end{bmatrix} \qquad X = \begin{bmatrix} x_1 \\ x_2 \end{bmatrix} \qquad B = \begin{bmatrix} 4 \\ 7 \end{bmatrix}$$

Assuming that we can find A^{-1} such that $AA^{-1} = A^{-1}A = I$, we premultiply both sides of Eq. (6.10) by A^{-1} and obtain

(6.11) $\quad A^{-1}(AX) = A^{-1}B$

Using the associative property in matrix multiplication, we get

(6.12) $\quad (A^{-1}A)X = A^{-1}B$

Because $A^{-1}A = I$, we obtain the solution

(6.13) $\quad X = A^{-1}B$

In the specific example,

$$A^{-1} = \begin{bmatrix} -3 & 2 \\ 2 & -1 \end{bmatrix}$$

since

$$A^{-1}A = \begin{bmatrix} -3 & 2 \\ 2 & -1 \end{bmatrix} \begin{bmatrix} 1 & 2 \\ 2 & 3 \end{bmatrix} = \begin{bmatrix} 1 & 0 \\ 0 & 1 \end{bmatrix}$$

$$AA^{-1} = \begin{bmatrix} 1 & 2 \\ 2 & 3 \end{bmatrix} \begin{bmatrix} -3 & 2 \\ 2 & -1 \end{bmatrix} = \begin{bmatrix} 1 & 0 \\ 0 & 1 \end{bmatrix}$$

Thus,

$$X = A^{-1}B = \begin{bmatrix} -3 & 2 \\ 2 & -1 \end{bmatrix} \begin{bmatrix} 4 \\ 7 \end{bmatrix} = \begin{bmatrix} 2 \\ 1 \end{bmatrix}$$

Hence, $x_1 = 2$ and $x_2 = 1$ are the solutions to the linear equations (6.9). ∎

The problem now remains as how to compute A^{-1}. The Gauss-Jordan elimination procedure that we have used in solving a system of linear equations can also be applied to compute the inverse of the coefficient matrix.

To compute A^{-1}, we set up the equations

$$AX = E_1, AX = E_2, \ldots, AX = E_n$$

where E_i is a column vector with a 1 in the ith row and 0's elsewhere. Then the augmented matrix is

$$[A:E_1, E_2, \ldots, E_n] = [A:I_n]$$

If A^{-1} exists, we can reduce $[A:I_n]$ to $[I_n:A^{-1}]$ by repeatedly using elementary row operations. The following examples will illustrate the above discussion.

Example 6.9

Find the inverse of

$$A = \begin{bmatrix} 1 & 2 \\ 3 & 7 \end{bmatrix}$$

SOLUTION

The elementary operations are performed in the order specified in Table 6.5.

Table 6.5

Row Operations	a_1	a_2	E_1	E_2
R_1	1	2	1	0
R_2	3	7	0	1
R_1	1	2	1	0
$R_2' = R_2 + (-3)R_1$	0	1	-3	1
$R_1' = R_1 + (-2)R_2'$	1	0	7	-2
R_2'	0	1	-3	1

The augmented matrix $[A:I_2]$ is reduced to $[I_2:A^{-1}]$, where

$$A^{-1} = \begin{bmatrix} 7 & -2 \\ -3 & 1 \end{bmatrix}$$

∎

Example 6.10

Find the inverse of the matrix

$$A = \begin{bmatrix} 1 & 1 & 1 \\ 3 & 4 & -1 \\ 2 & -5 & 3 \end{bmatrix}$$

and use A^{-1} to solve the following linear equations:

$$\begin{aligned} x_1 + x_2 + x_3 &= 9 \\ 3x_1 + 4x_2 - x_3 &= 13 \\ 2x_1 - 5x_2 + 3x_3 &= 8 \end{aligned}$$

SOLUTION

The elementary row operations are performed in the order specified in Table 6.6.

Table 6.6

Row Operations	a_1	a_2	a_3	E_1	E_2	E_3
R_1	1	1	1	1	0	0
R_2	3	4	-1	0	1	0
R_3	2	-5	3	0	0	1
R_1	1	1	1	1	0	0
$R_2' = R_2 + (-3)R_1$	0	1	-4	-3	1	0
$R_3' = R_3 + (-2)R_1$	0	-7	1	-2	0	1
$R_1' = R_1 + (-1)R_2'$	1	0	5	4	-1	0
R_2'	0	1	-4	-3	1	0
$R_3'' = (-\frac{1}{27})(R_3' + 7R_2')$	0	0	1	$\frac{23}{27}$	$-\frac{7}{27}$	$-\frac{1}{27}$
$R_1'' = R_1' + (-5)R_3''$	1	0	0	$-\frac{7}{27}$	$\frac{8}{27}$	$\frac{5}{27}$
$R_2'' = R_2' + 4R_3''$	0	1	0	$\frac{11}{27}$	$-\frac{1}{27}$	$-\frac{4}{27}$
R_3''	0	0	1	$\frac{23}{27}$	$-\frac{7}{27}$	$-\frac{1}{27}$

so that

$$A^{-1} = \tfrac{1}{27} \begin{bmatrix} -7 & 8 & 5 \\ 11 & -1 & -4 \\ 23 & -7 & -1 \end{bmatrix}$$

Thus,

$$\begin{bmatrix} x_1 \\ x_2 \\ x_3 \end{bmatrix} = A^{-1} \begin{bmatrix} 9 \\ 13 \\ 8 \end{bmatrix} = \tfrac{1}{27} \begin{bmatrix} -7 & 8 & 5 \\ 11 & -1 & -4 \\ 23 & -7 & -1 \end{bmatrix} \begin{bmatrix} 9 \\ 13 \\ 8 \end{bmatrix} = \begin{bmatrix} 3 \\ 2 \\ 4 \end{bmatrix}$$

so that $x_1 = 3$, $x_2 = 2$, and $x_3 = 4$ is the unique solution to the system of linear equations. ∎

We have observed earlier that not all nonzero square matrices have inverses. Consider, for instance, the following square matrix:

$$A = \begin{bmatrix} 1 & -1 & 2 \\ -2 & 3 & -2 \\ 4 & -7 & 2 \end{bmatrix}$$

Recall that in order for A^{-1} to exist, we must be able to reduce the augmented matrix

$$[A:E_1, E_2, E_3] = [A:I_3]$$

to the form $[I_3:A^{-1}]$ by repeatedly using elementary row operations. Let us perform the elementary operations in the order specified as shown in Table 6.7.

Table 6.7

Row Operations	a_1	a_2	a_3	E_1	E_2	E_3
R_1	1	-1	2	1	0	0
R_2	-2	3	-2	0	1	0
R_3	4	-7	2	0	0	1
R_1	1	-1	2	1	0	0
$R_2' = R_2 + 2R_1$	0	1	2	2	1	0
$R_3' = R_3 + (-4)R_1$	0	-3	-6	-4	0	1
$R_1' = R_1 + R_2'$	1	0	4	3	1	0
R_2'	0	1	2	2	1	0
$R_3'' = R_3' + 3R_2'$	0	0	0	2	3	1

Because we have a row of zeros in the first three columns, there is no way that we can reduce the coefficient matrix A to the identity matrix I. Hence, we conclude that A^{-1} does not exist. Further, note that it is impossible to solve the equations

$$\begin{bmatrix} 1 & -1 & 2 \\ -2 & 3 & -2 \\ 4 & -7 & 2 \end{bmatrix} \begin{bmatrix} x_1 \\ x_2 \\ x_3 \end{bmatrix} = \begin{bmatrix} 1 \\ 0 \\ 0 \end{bmatrix}$$

because these equations are equivalent to the set of equations

$$\begin{bmatrix} 1 & 0 & 4 \\ 0 & 1 & 2 \\ 0 & 0 & 0 \end{bmatrix} \begin{bmatrix} x_1 \\ x_2 \\ x_3 \end{bmatrix} = \begin{bmatrix} 3 \\ 2 \\ 2 \end{bmatrix}$$

and these equations are inconsistent. Specifically, the last row corresponds to the equation

$$0 \cdot x_1 + 0 \cdot x_2 + 0 \cdot x_3 = 2$$

and there are no values of x_1, x_2, x_3 for which this equation holds.

Frequently, we wish to treat simultaneously the systems of equations

$$AX = B_1, AX = B_2, \ldots, AX = B_n$$

all of which have the same coefficient matrix A. We observed earlier that these systems can be solved simultaneously by using the Gauss-Jordan elimination method. Alternatively, we may observe that if the square matrix A has an inverse, then we can premultiply the augmented matrix

$$[A:B_1, B_2, \ldots, B_n]$$

by A^{-1} and obtain

$$[I_n:A^{-1}B_1, A^{-1}B_2, \ldots, A^{-1}B_n]$$

Note that $A^{-1}B_1, A^{-1}B_2, \ldots, A^{-1}B_n$ are the solutions to the systems of equations $AX = B_1, AX = B_2, \ldots, AX = B_n$, respectively.

Example 6.11

Find the inverse of the matrix

$$A = \begin{bmatrix} 1 & 1 & 5 \\ 2 & 1 & -1 \\ 3 & 2 & 5 \end{bmatrix}$$

and use it to solve the following systems of linear equations:

a. $x_1 + x_2 + 5x_3 = 0$
$2x_1 + x_2 - x_3 = 8$
$3x_1 + 2x_2 + 5x_3 = 7$

b. $x_1 + x_2 + 5x_3 = 26$
$2x_1 + x_2 - x_3 = -1$
$3x_1 + 2x_2 + 5x_3 = 30$

c. $x_1 + x_2 + 5x_3 = 41$
$2x_1 + x_2 - x_3 = 1$
$3x_1 + 2x_2 + 5x_3 = 49$

d. $x_1 + x_2 + 5x_3 = 7$
$2x_1 + x_2 - x_3 = 1$
$3x_1 + 2x_2 + 5x_3 = 9$

SOLUTION

We leave it for the reader to show that

$$A^{-1} = \begin{bmatrix} -7 & -5 & 6 \\ 13 & 10 & -11 \\ -1 & -1 & 1 \end{bmatrix}$$

Note that the four systems of linear equations, which have the same coefficient matrix, differ only in the constant values. The augmented matrix associated with these systems is

Constant Column
Vectors

$$[A:B_1, B_2, B_3, B_4] = \begin{bmatrix} 1 & 1 & 5 & | & 0 & 26 & 41 & 7 \\ 2 & 1 & -1 & | & 8 & -1 & 1 & 1 \\ 3 & 2 & 5 & | & 7 & 30 & 49 & 9 \end{bmatrix} \begin{matrix} \mathbf{a} & \mathbf{b} & \mathbf{c} & \mathbf{d} \\ \\ \\ \end{matrix}$$

Now we premultiply the augmented matrix $[A:B_1, B_2, B_3, B_4]$ by A^{-1} and obtain

$$\begin{bmatrix} -7 & -5 & 6 \\ 13 & 10 & -11 \\ -1 & -1 & 1 \end{bmatrix} \begin{bmatrix} 1 & 1 & 5 & | & 0 & 26 & 41 & 7 \\ 2 & 1 & -1 & | & 8 & -1 & 1 & 1 \\ 3 & 2 & 5 & | & 7 & 30 & 49 & 9 \end{bmatrix} = \begin{bmatrix} 1 & 0 & 0 & | & 2 & 3 & 2 & 0 \\ 0 & 1 & 0 & | & 3 & -2 & 4 & 2 \\ 0 & 0 & 1 & | & -1 & 5 & 7 & 1 \end{bmatrix}$$

Hence, $x_1 = 2, x_2 = 3, x_3 = -1$ is the solution to the system of equations in part **a**, $x_1 = 3, x_2 = -2, x_3 = 5$ is the solution to the linear equations in part **b**, $x_1 = 2, x_2 = 4, x_3 = 7$ is the solution to the system of equations in part **c**, and $x_1 = 0, x_2 = 2,$ and $x_3 = 1$ is the solution to the set of linear equations in part **d**. ∎

As an application of the system of linear equations, consider a shipping company that has n different types of cargo ships which it uses to transport n different types of cargo.

Let

x_i = number of cargo ships of type i available at a given time

b_j = amount of goods of type j to be transported

a_{ij} = number of cargo ships of type i required to transport an amount of goods j; $i, j = 1, 2, 3, \ldots, n$

Then the number of cargo ships $x_1, x_2, \ldots, x_n$ required to ship b_i units of cargo i is given by the solution of the equations

$$a_{i1}x_1 + a_{i2}x_2 + \cdots + a_{in}x_n = b_i$$

which, in matrix notation, may be represented as

$$AX = B$$

Because the amount of cargo b_j of type j to be transported varies periodically, the shipping company must solve a different system of linear equations every time and determine the number of ships of type i required to ship the amount of cargo b_j of type j. A great deal of time and labor will be saved if A^{-1} is known, because the company would then have to compute $A^{-1}B^*$ periodically for the new column vector B^* rather than solving $AX = B^*$ afresh.

Example 6.12

A shipping company has three different types of cargo ships, S_1, S_2, and S_3, which can transport the number of units of heavy machinery M_1, M_2, and M_3 as given in the following matrix.

Machinery

		M_1	M_2	M_3
	S_1	3	2	4
Cargo Ships	S_2	4	6	8
	S_3	1	7	9

An international organization requests 44 units of M_1, 92 units of M_2, and 91 units of M_3 for delivery in April 1976. How many cargo ships of each type are required to fill this order?

How many ships are needed to deliver 29 units of M_1, 56 units of M_2, and 53 units of M_3 in May 1976?

SOLUTION

Suppose that x_i, $i = 1, 2, 3$ is the number of cargo ships of type S_i required to deliver the needed equipment. We therefore need to solve the following system of linear equations:

$$AX = B_1 \quad \text{and} \quad AX = B_2$$

where

$$A = \begin{bmatrix} 3 & 2 & 4 \\ 4 & 6 & 8 \\ 1 & 7 & 9 \end{bmatrix}, \quad X = \begin{bmatrix} x_1 \\ x_2 \\ x_3 \end{bmatrix}, \quad B_1 = \begin{bmatrix} 44 \\ 92 \\ 91 \end{bmatrix}, \quad \text{and} \quad B_2 = \begin{bmatrix} 29 \\ 56 \\ 53 \end{bmatrix}$$

In order to determine the number of ships to make deliveries in the future, we compute A^{-1} once and then calculate $X = A^{-1}B$ instead of repeating the elimination method for each new column vector. The augmented matrix

$$[A:E_1, E_2, E_3] = [A:I_3]$$

is reduced to

$$[I_3:A^{-1}]$$

by using elementary row operations in the order specified in Table 6.8.

Table 6.8

Row Operations	a_1	a_2	a_3	E_1	E_2	E_3
R_1	3	2	4	1	0	0
R_2	4	6	8	0	1	0
R_3	1	7	9	0	0	1
$R_1' = R_3$	1	7	9	0	0	1
R_2	4	6	8	0	1	0
$R_3' = R_1$	3	2	4	1	0	0
R_1'	1	7	9	0	0	1
$R_2' = (-\frac{1}{22})[R_2 + (-4)R_1']$	0	1	$\frac{14}{11}$	0	$-\frac{1}{22}$	$\frac{22}{11}$
$R_3'' = R_3' + (-3)R_1'$	0	-19	-23	1	0	-3
$R_1'' = R_1' + (-7)R_2'$	1	0	$\frac{1}{11}$	0	$\frac{7}{22}$	$-\frac{3}{11}$
R_2'	0	1	$\frac{14}{11}$	0	$-\frac{1}{22}$	$\frac{2}{11}$
$R_3''' = \frac{11}{13}(R_3'' + 19R_2')$	0	0	1	$\frac{11}{13}$	$-\frac{19}{26}$	$\frac{5}{13}$
$R_1''' = R_1'' + (-\frac{1}{11})R_3'''$	1	0	0	$-\frac{1}{13}$	$\frac{5}{13}$	$-\frac{4}{13}$
$R_2'' = R_2' + (-\frac{14}{11})R_3'''$	0	1	0	$-\frac{14}{13}$	$\frac{23}{26}$	$-\frac{4}{13}$
R_3'''	0	0	1	$\frac{11}{13}$	$-\frac{19}{26}$	$\frac{5}{13}$

Thus,

$$A^{-1} = \tfrac{1}{26} \begin{bmatrix} -2 & 10 & -8 \\ -28 & 23 & -8 \\ 22 & -19 & 10 \end{bmatrix}$$

and

$$\begin{bmatrix} x_1 \\ x_2 \\ x_3 \end{bmatrix} = \tfrac{1}{26} \begin{bmatrix} -2 & 10 & -8 \\ -28 & 23 & -8 \\ 22 & -19 & 10 \end{bmatrix} \begin{bmatrix} 44 \\ 92 \\ 91 \end{bmatrix} = \begin{bmatrix} 4 \\ 6 \\ 5 \end{bmatrix}$$

This shows that the shipping company needs to requisition four ships of type S_1, six ships of type S_2, and five ships of type S_3 to deliver the supplies in April 1976. Similarly, for another delivery in May 1976, we must compute

$$
\begin{bmatrix} x_1 \\ x_2 \\ x_3 \end{bmatrix} = \tfrac{1}{26} \begin{bmatrix} -2 & 10 & -8 \\ -28 & 23 & -8 \\ 22 & -19 & 10 \end{bmatrix} \begin{bmatrix} 29 \\ 56 \\ 53 \end{bmatrix} = \begin{bmatrix} 3 \\ 2 \\ 4 \end{bmatrix}
$$

Thus, the shipping company needs three ships of type S_1, two ships of type S_2, and four ships of type S_3. ■

EXERCISE 6.4

1. Find, if possible, the inverse of the following matrices:

a. $\begin{bmatrix} 3 & 2 \\ 5 & 4 \end{bmatrix}$

b. $\begin{bmatrix} 4 & 1 \\ 5 & 2 \end{bmatrix}$

c. $\begin{bmatrix} -8 & 10 \\ 6 & -7 \end{bmatrix}$

d. $\begin{bmatrix} 1 & -1 \\ 4 & 5 \end{bmatrix}$

e. $\begin{bmatrix} -1 & 3 & 0 \\ 0 & 2 & 1 \\ 1 & 0 & 4 \end{bmatrix}$

f. $\begin{bmatrix} 1 & 2 & 0 \\ -1 & 1 & 1 \\ 2 & 3 & 1 \end{bmatrix}$

g. $\begin{bmatrix} 1 & 2 & 2 \\ 2 & 2 & 1 \\ 5 & 4 & -3 \end{bmatrix}$

h. $\begin{bmatrix} -3 & 6 & 9 \\ 2 & -4 & -1 \\ 11 & -7 & 13 \end{bmatrix}$

i. $\begin{bmatrix} 1 & 1 & 2 \\ 2 & 1 & 0 \\ 1 & 2 & 2 \end{bmatrix}$

j. $\begin{bmatrix} 2 & 3 & -1 \\ 1 & 1 & 1 \\ 0 & 2 & -1 \end{bmatrix}$

2. Find the inverse of the matrix

$$
A = \begin{bmatrix} 3 & 2 \\ 4 & 1 \end{bmatrix}
$$

and use A^{-1} to solve the following systems of linear equations:

a. $3x_1 + 2x_2 = 12$
$4x_1 + x_2 = 11$
c. $3x_1 + 2x_2 = 11$
$4x_1 + x_2 = -2$

b. $3x_1 + 2x_2 = 6$
$4x_1 + x_2 = 13$
d. $3x_1 + 2x_2 = 1$
$4x_1 + x_2 = 3$

3. Find the inverse of the matrix

$$
\begin{bmatrix} 1 & 1 & 1 \\ 2 & 5 & -3 \\ 3 & 4 & -7 \end{bmatrix}
$$

and use A^{-1} to solve the following systems of linear equations:

a. $\begin{aligned} x_1 + x_2 + x_3 &= 3 \\ 2x_1 + 5x_2 - 3x_3 &= 4 \\ 3x_1 + 4x_2 - 7x_2 &= 0 \end{aligned}$

b. $\begin{aligned} x_1 + x_2 + x_3 &= 6 \\ 2x_1 + 5x_2 - 3x_3 &= 3 \\ 3x_1 + 4x_3 - 7x_3 &= -10 \end{aligned}$

c. $\begin{aligned} x_1 + x_2 + x_3 &= -1 \\ 2x_1 + 5x_2 - 3x_3 &= 13 \\ 3x_1 + 4x_2 - 7x_3 &= 27 \end{aligned}$

d. $\begin{aligned} x_1 + x_2 + x_3 &= 6 \\ 2x_1 + 5x_2 - 3x_3 &= 13 \\ 3x_1 + 4x_2 - 7x_3 &= 10 \end{aligned}$

4. Find the inverse of the matrix

$$\begin{bmatrix} 1 & -1 & 0 & 2 \\ 0 & 1 & 1 & -1 \\ 2 & 1 & 2 & 1 \\ 3 & -2 & 1 & 6 \end{bmatrix}$$

and use A^{-1} to solve the following systems of linear equations:

a. $\begin{aligned} x_1 - x_2 \qquad\quad + 2x_4 &= 2 \\ x_2 + x_3 - x_4 &= 1 \\ 2x_1 + x_2 + 2x_3 + x_4 &= 6 \\ 3x_1 - 2x_2 + x_3 + 6x_4 &= 8 \end{aligned}$

b. $\begin{aligned} x_1 - x_2 \qquad\quad + 2x_4 &= 6 \\ x_2 + x_3 - x_4 &= -2 \\ 2x_1 + x_2 + 2x_3 + x_4 &= 5 \\ 3x_1 - 2x_2 + x_3 + 6x_4 &= 18 \end{aligned}$

5. Solve the following systems of linear equations by using the inverse of the coefficient matrix:

a. $\begin{aligned} x_1 + 3x_2 + 2x_3 &= 5 \\ 2x_1 + 7x_2 + 4x_3 &= 12 \\ 3x_1 + 10x_2 + 7x_3 &= 16 \end{aligned}$

b. $\begin{aligned} x_1 + 3x_2 + 2x_3 &= 8 \\ 2x_1 + 7x_2 + 4x_3 &= 16 \\ 3x_1 + 10x_2 + 7x_3 &= 27 \end{aligned}$

c. $\begin{aligned} x_1 + 3x_2 + 2x_2 &= 0 \\ 2x_1 + 7x_2 + 4x_3 &= -1 \\ 3x_1 + 10x_2 + 7x_3 &= 0 \end{aligned}$

d. $\begin{aligned} x_1 + 3x_2 + 2x_3 &= -1 \\ 2x_1 + 7x_2 + 4x_3 &= -1 \\ 3x_1 + 10x_3 + 7x_3 &= -5 \end{aligned}$

6. A department store has 90 men's suits of three different types, which it must sell this spring. If it sells type I suits for \$50, type II suits for \$60, and type III suits for \$75, the net sales amounts to \$5800, but if these are sold at \$45, \$55, and \$60, respectively, total revenue in sales is \$4950 only. Determine the number of suits of each type the store has in stock.

7. An automobile manufacturer uses three different types of trucks, T_1, T_2, and T_3, to transport the number of station wagons, full-size, and intermediate-size cars as shown in the following matrix:

		Station Wagons	Full-Size Cars	Intermediate-Size Cars
	T_1	2	6	9
Trucks	T_2	3	7	12
	T_3	6	6	8

Using the inverse of the matrix, determine the number of trucks of each type required to supply 58 station wagons, 75 full-size, and 62 intermediate-size cars to a dealer in Chicago.

If a dealer in Cleveland orders 46 station wagons, 60 full-size, and 64 intermediate-size cars, how many trucks of each type does the factory need to make this delivery?

8. A shipping company has four different types of cargo ships, S_1, S_2, S_3, and S_4, which can transport the number of units of heavy machinery M_1, M_2, M_3, and M_4 as given in the matrix below:

Machinery

$$
\begin{array}{c}
\text{Cargo} \\
\text{Ships}
\end{array}
\begin{array}{c}
\\
S_1 \\
S_2 \\
S_3 \\
S_4
\end{array}
\begin{array}{cccc}
M_1 & M_2 & M_3 & M_4 \\
\left[\begin{array}{cccc}
3 & 2 & 4 & 1 \\
4 & 6 & 8 & 3 \\
1 & 7 & 9 & 10 \\
8 & 5 & 12 & 14
\end{array}\right]
\end{array}
$$

If an order is received for 46 units of M_1, 98 units of M_2, 111 units of M_3, and 150 units for M_4, how many ships of each different type are required to make this delivery?

6.6 INPUT-OUTPUT MODEL

In this section we shall discuss the inverse matrix in relation to the Leontief's input-output model, which deals with the interdependencies of the various sectors of the economy. Consider an economy with n interdependent industries, each producing a single commodity. The output of any industry, say, the steel industry, is needed as an input in the other $(n - 1)$ industries and even for that industry itself because some of its output is used to meet the demand of an open sector. Some electricity is consumed, for example, in the process of generating electricity, some oil is used by the oil refinery itself, some automobiles are used both by management and labor in the production of automobiles and some are used by automobile dealers in promoting the sales of these automobiles, and so on. Thus, the correct level of the output of any industry depends not only on the input requirements of the n industries but also on the demand of the open sector. What level of output should, therefore, each of the n industries produce to satisfy the total demand for their products?

Let a_{ij} denote the amount of input of an industry i required to produce one unit of commodity j. Specifically, each unit of jth commodity needs the amount a_{1j} of the first industry, a_{2j} of the second industry, a_{3j} of the third industry, and so on. However, we shall interpret a_{ij} to represent the cost of the material of the ith industry needed to produce a dollar's worth of commodity j. Thus, the statement that $a_{43} = 0.25$ means that $0.25 worth of material of the fourth industry is required as an input to produce $1.00 worth of the third commodity.

Assuming that the market is in equilibrium, and the total output x_i of an industry i is just sufficient to meet the input requirements of the n industries as well as the demands of the open sector, the output level must satisfy the following linear equation

$$x_i = a_{i1}x_1 + a_{i2}x_2 + \cdots + a_{in}x_n + d_i$$

where $a_{ij}x_j$ represents the input requirements for producing x_j products in the jth industry and d_i denotes the final demand of the product i in the open sector. Thus, the output levels of the n industries are represented by the following system of n linear equations in n variables:

(6.14)
$$\begin{aligned}
x_1 &= a_{11}x_1 + a_{12}x_2 + \cdots + a_{1n}x_n + d_i \\
x_2 &= a_{21}x_1 + a_{22}x_2 + \cdots + a_{2n}x_n + d_2 \\
&\vdots \\
x_n &= a_{n1}x_1 + a_{n2}x_2 + \cdots + a_{nn}x_n + d_n
\end{aligned}$$

Expressed in matrix notation, we have

$$\begin{bmatrix} x_1 \\ x_2 \\ \vdots \\ x_n \end{bmatrix} = \begin{bmatrix} a_{11} & a_{12} & \cdots & a_{1n} \\ a_{21} & a_{22} & \cdots & a_{2n} \\ \vdots & & & \\ a_{n1} & a_{n2} & \cdots & a_{nn} \end{bmatrix} \begin{bmatrix} x_1 \\ x_2 \\ \vdots \\ x_n \end{bmatrix} + \begin{bmatrix} d_1 \\ d_2 \\ \vdots \\ d_n \end{bmatrix}$$

or

$$X = AX + D$$
$$IX = AX + D$$
(6.15) $$(I - A)X = D$$

where

$$X = \begin{bmatrix} x_1 \\ x_2 \\ \vdots \\ x_n \end{bmatrix} \qquad A = \begin{bmatrix} a_{11} & a_{12} & \cdots & a_{1n} \\ a_{21} & a_{22} & \cdots & a_{2n} \\ \vdots & & & \\ a_{n1} & a_{n2} & \cdots & a_{nn} \end{bmatrix} \qquad D = \begin{bmatrix} d_1 \\ d_2 \\ \vdots \\ d_n \end{bmatrix}$$

and I is the identity matrix of order n. The matrix A, called the input coefficient matrix, defines the interdependencies of the n industries involved in the economy. Note that all elements of the matrix A are non-negative and the sum of the elements in each column, say j, represents the input cost incurred in producing a dollar's worth of commodity j. It is clear that if the sum of the elements in column j is greater or equal to $1.00, the production of the commodity j is not economically feasible. Symbolically, the condition that

$$a_{1j} + a_{2j} + \cdots + a_{nj} < 1$$

must be satisfied for the production of commodity j.

Assuming that a_{ij} remains constant over a period of time, we can determine the total output of each industry necessary to meet the total demand of n industries as well as that of the open sector. If $(I - A)^{-1}$ exists and all its elements are non-negative, we can premultiply both sides of (6.15) by $(I - A)^{-1}$ and obtain

(6.16) $\quad X = (I - A)^{-1}D$

Example 6.13

Consider an oversimplified two-sector economy in which there are two industries, each producing a single commodity. The production of $1.00 worth of the first industry's product requires material worth $0.30 of the first industry and $0.20 of the second industry. The production of the second industry's product worth $1.00 requires $0.10 and $0.30 material of the first and second industries, respectively. Determine the output levels of each industry necessary to meet the open sector demand of $12 million and $5 million worth of goods of the first and second industries, respectively.

SOLUTION
The input coefficient matrix is given by

$$A = \begin{bmatrix} 0.30 & 0.20 \\ 0.10 & 0.30 \end{bmatrix}$$

Note that each column sum is less than $1. Next,

$$I - A = \begin{bmatrix} 1 & 0 \\ 0 & 1 \end{bmatrix} - \begin{bmatrix} 0.30 & 0.20 \\ 0.10 & 0.30 \end{bmatrix}$$

$$= \begin{bmatrix} 0.7 & -0.2 \\ -0.1 & 0.7 \end{bmatrix}$$

We leave it for the reader to verify that

$$(I - A)^{-1} = \frac{1}{0.47} \begin{bmatrix} 0.7 & 0.2 \\ 0.1 & 0.7 \end{bmatrix}$$

The demand in the open sector is given by

$$D = \begin{bmatrix} 12 \\ 5 \end{bmatrix}$$

Using (6.16), we have

$$\begin{bmatrix} x_1 \\ x_2 \end{bmatrix} = \frac{1}{0.47} \begin{bmatrix} 0.7 & 0.2 \\ 0.1 & 0.7 \end{bmatrix} \begin{bmatrix} 12 \\ 5 \end{bmatrix} = \begin{bmatrix} 20 \\ 10 \end{bmatrix}$$

Thus, industries 1 and 2 must produce goods worth $20 million and $10 million, respectively, to meet the nonindustrial demands. ∎

Example 6.14

Consider the input coefficient matrix A and the open sector demand vector D (in millions of dollars) given below. Determine the output level required of each industry necessary to meet the demand.

$$A = \begin{bmatrix} 0.3 & 0.1 & 0.2 \\ 0.2 & 0.4 & 0.1 \\ 0.1 & 0.2 & 0.5 \end{bmatrix} \qquad D = \begin{bmatrix} 6.6 \\ 13.2 \\ 9.9 \end{bmatrix}$$

SOLUTION

With the matrix A above, the input-output system can be expressed in the form (6.15) as follows:

$$(I - A)X = D$$

that is,

$$\begin{bmatrix} 0.7 & -0.1 & -0.2 \\ -0.2 & 0.6 & -0.1 \\ -0.1 & -0.2 & 0.5 \end{bmatrix} \begin{bmatrix} x_1 \\ x_2 \\ x_3 \end{bmatrix} = \begin{bmatrix} 6.6 \\ 13.2 \\ 9.9 \end{bmatrix}$$

where x_i, $i = 1, 2, 3$, represents the output level of ith industry necessary to meet the demand. Finding the inverse of the matrix $(I - A)$, we have

$$(I - A)^{-1} = \frac{1}{0.165} \begin{bmatrix} 0.28 & 0.09 & 0.13 \\ 0.11 & 0.33 & 0.11 \\ 0.10 & 0.15 & 0.40 \end{bmatrix}$$

Using (6.16), we obtain

$$\begin{bmatrix} x_1 \\ x_2 \\ x_3 \end{bmatrix} = \frac{1}{0.165} \begin{bmatrix} 0.28 & 0.09 & 0.13 \\ 0.11 & 0.33 & 0.11 \\ 0.10 & 0.15 & 0.40 \end{bmatrix} \begin{bmatrix} 6.6 \\ 13.2 \\ 9.9 \end{bmatrix} = \begin{bmatrix} 26.2 \\ 35.4 \\ 40.0 \end{bmatrix}$$

Thus, in order to meet the demand levels of the open sector, industries 1, 2, and 3 will have to produce goods worth \$26.2 million, \$35.4 million, and \$40 million, respectively. ∎

EXERCISE 6.5

Determine the output levels required of each industry necessary to meet the demand (in millions of dollars) of the open sector in each of the following problems.

1. $A = \begin{bmatrix} 0.20 & 0.10 \\ 0.25 & 0.20 \end{bmatrix}, D = \begin{bmatrix} 61.5 \\ 123.0 \end{bmatrix}$

2. $A = \begin{bmatrix} 0.50 & 0.20 \\ 0.30 & 0.40 \end{bmatrix}, D = \begin{bmatrix} 10 \\ 6 \end{bmatrix}$

3. $A = \begin{bmatrix} 0.60 & 0.40 \\ 0.20 & 0.30 \end{bmatrix}, D = \begin{bmatrix} 12 \\ 5 \end{bmatrix}$

4. $A = \begin{bmatrix} 0.20 & 0.30 & 0.20 \\ 0.40 & 0.10 & 0.20 \\ 0.10 & 0.30 & 0.20 \end{bmatrix}, D = \begin{bmatrix} 12 \\ 8 \\ 6 \end{bmatrix}$

5. $A = \begin{bmatrix} 0.30 & 0.40 & 0.20 \\ 0.20 & 0.0 & 0.50 \\ 0.10 & 0.30 & 0.10 \end{bmatrix}, D = \begin{bmatrix} 10 \\ 12 \\ 5 \end{bmatrix}$

7

Introduction to Linear Programming

7.1 INTRODUCTION

Linear programming deals with the allocation of limited resources to meet a clearly stated objective when both the objective and the associated constraints can be translated into the form of linear equations or linear inequalities. The adjective linear describes a relationship between two or more variables; the term programming refers to the use of mathematical techniques to obtain the best possible allocation of resources. Although the subject had its origin in the 1920s, its present development in business and industry stems from the work of George B. Dantzig, who collaborated with Marshall Wood, Alex Ordin, and many other scientists while working for the U.S. Air Force.

Business firms continue to expand their operation both in size and complexity which, in turn, gives rise to new dimensions to their problems and creates new uncertainties in the highly competitive market. Management constantly faces the problem of efficiency in all its operations whenever scarce resources of capital, labor, equipment, raw material, time, and space are to be allocated either to achieve optimal profits or to minimize the cost of operations. Business executives must, therefore, continue to explore in a systematic manner such problems as how a certain job can be done most efficiently with the available personnel, how goods can be produced most economically with given material and equipment, how food costs can be minimized while meeting certain caloric and nutritional demands, how airlines should coordinate their flights for different routes to minimize the number of unfilled seats, how crude oil should be allocated among refineries to obtain the optimal production, how products can be shipped from various plants to retail outlets at a minimum cost, what route a salesperson should take to minimize the distance and still cover the specified territory, and so on.

Consider, for example, a manufacturing firm that produces a number of fairly similar products. Each product requires a number of operations to be performed by different personnel on a number of different machines with each machine requiring varying lengths of time for each operation. Suppose that information is available regarding the process time per product, per operation, per machine, per worker, hours of machine availability, quantity of raw material available, and many other factors that may or may not have any appreciable effect on the finished product. The problem for management is to determine the best possible allocation of its limited resources so as to yield the highest return on its investment. The theory of linear programming provides the optimal solutions to certain types of such problems having certain common characteristics. The fact that scarce resources are allocated with the preciseness inherent in linear programming makes it a powerful tool for assisting management in planning its activities.

7.2 GRAPHICAL SOLUTIONS TO LINEAR PROGRAMMING PROBLEMS

Consider a manufacturer who produces two items, bookcases and library tables. Past experience indicates that it requires 2 worker hours to manufacture a bookcase, whereas a library table requires 3 worker hours to complete. Assuming that there are 40 worker hours available, we seek the possible combination of the two products that can be produced within the available time. As a first step toward finding the solution, we must reformulate the problem into mathematical language. Let x_1 and x_2 represent the number of bookcases and tables, respectively, that the firm can manufacture. Evidently,

(7.1) $x_1 \geq 0$ and $x_2 \geq 0$

because production of a negative number of bookcases and tables has no physical interpretation. Further, the worker hours used in manufacturing these products cannot exceed the total worker hours available. It therefore follows that

(7.2) $2x_1 + 3x_2 \leq 40$

The linear inequalities (7.1) and (7.2) are represented in Figure 7.1.

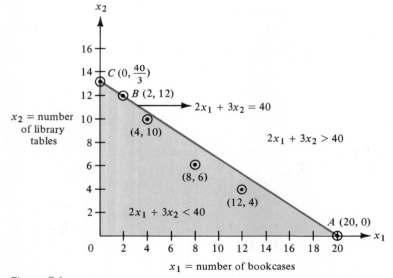

Figure 7.1

If all the available time is spent in manufacturing bookcases, the firm could have at most 20 such products. This determines the point A (20, 0). Similarly, if the firm needs two bookcases, it could use the remaining time in producing at most 12 tables. Thus, $x_2 = 0$ implies that $x_1 \leq 20$ and $x_1 = 2$ implies that $x_2 \leq 12$. These two points A (20, 0) and B (2, 12) determine the line representing $2x_1 + 3x_2 = 40$ as shown in the figure. Several other points can be located on this line, and each such point represents a combination of the products that will utilize all the worker hours available. We leave it for the reader to verify that the points (5, 10), (8, 8), (11, 6), and (14, 4) also lie on the line. However, if the company decides to produce 4 bookcases, it will be left with 32 worker hours during which at most 10 tables can be produced, and if the company decides to spend all the available time in producing tables only, it could complete at most 13 tables. This combination will apparently leave 1 worker hour that cannot be used. Alternatively, one may express this statement by saying that the point (0, 13) does not lie on the line $2x_1 + 3x_2 = 40$. (Why?) Similarly, any other combination of x_1 bookcases and x_2 tables that lies within the region bounded by the triangle $0AC$ can be produced without exceeding the available time limit. Thus, the solution set of this problem is represented by the triangular region $0AC$ bounded by the lines $x_1 = 0$, $x_2 = 0$, and $2x_1 + 3x_2 = 40$.

Now we introduce another variable. Suppose that each product goes through two different departments of the company. Each bookcase requires 2 worker hours in department 1 and 4 worker hours in department 2. Each library table requires 3 worker hours in department 1 and 2 worker hours in department 2. Assuming that there are 40 worker hours available in department 1, as before, and 48 worker hours available in department 2, we seek the different combinations of bookcases and library tables that can be produced within the time available in both departments. If each bookcase brings in a profit of $20 and each table yields $25, what is the optimal combination of these products that will maximize the profit?

Table 7.1

	Worker Hours Required for		Total Worker Hours
	Bookcase	Table	Available
Department 1	2	3	40
Department 2	4	2	48
Profit	$20	$25	

Table 7.1 presents the above information in a mathematical format. Because the worker hours required in producing these products cannot exceed the time available in department 2, we have an additional linear constraint:

(7.3) $4x_1 + 2x_2 \leq 48$

How about the profit? The firm makes $20 on each bookcase and $25 on each table. If P denotes the profit, we ask for the best combination of bookcases and tables that will maximize

(7.4) $P = 20x_1 + 25x_2$

This equation (7.4) is called the objective function. We summarize the above problem in the following manner:

> Determine the non-negative numbers x_1 and x_2 that will maximize the objective function

(7.5) $P = 20x_1 + 25x_2$

> subject to the linear constraints

> 1. $2x_1 + 3x_2 \leq 40$
> 2. $4x_1 + 2x_2 \leq 48$

The inequalities (7.1) and (7.2) were represented by the triangular region $0AC$ in Figure 7.1. If the linear constraint (7.2) is replaced by the linear inequality (7.3), the region bounded by the triangle $D0E$ in Figure 7.2 is obtained. The line DE represents all possible combinations of bookcases and library tables that will use all the worker hours available in department 2. Because the products go through both departments 1 and 2, we must look for the solution set determined by the intersection of the individual linear constraints (7.1), (7.2), and (7.3). This means that we are interested only in those combinations of products that fall simultaneously in both the triangles

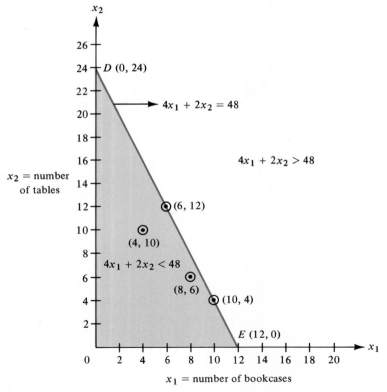

Figure 7.2

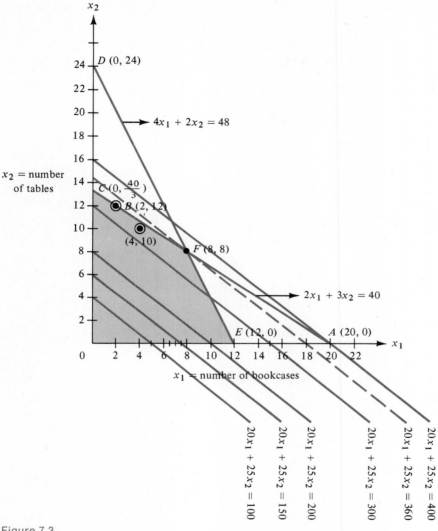

Figure 7.3

$A0C$ and $D0E$ as shown in Figure 7.3. The solution thus lies in the region bounded by the quadrilateral with corner points $(0, 0)$, $(0, \frac{40}{3})$, $(8, 8)$, and $(12, 0)$. These corner points in the solution set are called vertices or extreme points. The problem now reduces to finding the point(s) (x_1, x_2) in the solution set at which the objective function $P = 20x_1 + 25x_2$ attains the maximum value. Let us therefore evaluate P at some of the points in the solution set, as shown in Table 7.2. Because the evaluation of $P = 20x_1 + 25x_2$ at each possible point in the solution set and then choosing the point(s) at which the function attains its maximum value is hardly a rewarding experience, we must develop an efficient procedure by examining the objective function closely.

Table 7.2

(x_1, x_2)	$(0, 0)$	$(0, \frac{40}{3})$	$(2, 12)$	$(4, 10)$	$(8, 6)$	$(8, 8)$	$(9, 7)$	$(10, 3)$	$(12, 0)$
P	$0	$333.33	$340	$330	$310	$360	$355	$275	$240

Before we begin to locate a production level of bookcases and tables that will yield the maximum profit, let us examine if there is any possible combination(s) of the products that will yield a profit of, say, $100. This implies that we look for a point (x_1, x_2) in the solution set that lies on the line

$$20x_1 + 25x_2 = 100$$

Certainly, the points $(5, 0)$ and $(0, 4)$ lie on this line. These two points represent, respectively, the company forgetting about library tables and concentrating only on the production of 5 bookcases, or scheduling the production of 4 library tables only. Either of these combinations (or any other combination of x_1 and x_2 on the above line) thus yields a profit of $100. Similarly, we can also determine combinations of the products that will yield a profit of, say, $150, $200, $300, and $400. Accordingly, we draw the graphs of

$$20x_1 + 25x_2 = 150$$
$$20x_1 + 25x_2 = 200$$
$$20x_1 + 25x_2 = 300$$

and

$$20x_1 + 25x_2 = 400$$

Note that these lines are parallel to the line $20x_1 + 25x_2 = 100$. Further, because the profit increases as the corresponding profit line moves away from the origin, it appears that the maximum profit line must meet three conditions:

1. It must be parallel to the line $20x_1 + 25x_2 = 100$.
2. It must lie at a maximum distance from the origin.
3. It must pass through at least one point in the solution set.

Thus, the lines representing a total profit of $150, $200, or $300 fail to meet condition 2 because they are not as far from the origin as possible, whereas the profit line of $400 fails to meet condition 3. However, the line $20x_1 + 25x_2 = 360$, which passes through the point $F (8, 8)$ of the solution set, is parallel to $20x_1 + 25x_2 = 100$, is farthest away from the origin, and yields a maximum profit of $360. This is the line of maximum possible profit that satisfies all the linear constraints.

Having obtained the optimal solution in the problem, we now introduce some basic ideas.

Definition 7.2.1: The set of vertices (extreme points) determined by the intersection of a finite number of linear inequalities is called a polyhedral set.

This polyhedral set of points is convex; that is, it has the property that if P and Q are any pair of points in the set, then the entire line segment joining PQ lies entirely in that set. This leads us to the following definition.

Definition 7.2.2: **A polyhedral convex set is a set of points such that the line segment joining any pair of points in the set lies entirely in that set.**

In a plane, these are sets bounded by the segments of straight lines. Thus, triangles, rectangles, quadrilaterals, pentagons, and so on, are all examples of polyhedral convex sets. Specifically, Figures 7.4(d) and (e) are examples of a polyhedral convex set, whereas Figures 7.4(a), (b), and (c) are not.

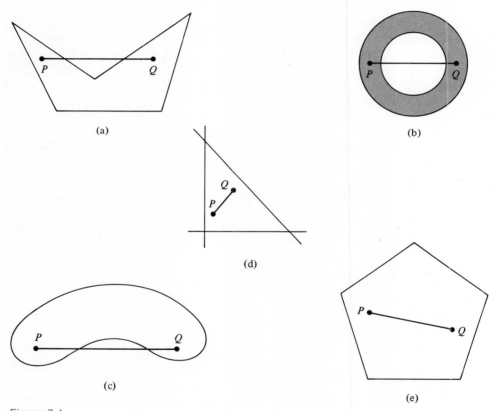

Figure 7.4

Definition 7.2.3: **Any point in the polyhedral convex set is called a** feasible solution.

We now state (without proof) the following propositions that are of significance in linear programming problems.

Proposition 7.2.1: **A set of points obtained by graphing a system of linear inequalities is a polyhedral convex set.** ∎

Proposition 7.2.2: **A linear function defined over a polyhedral convex set takes on its optimal value at a vertex.** ∎

Let us now consider the following examples.

Example 7.1

Find the maximum value of $P = 3x_1 + 5x_2$ subject to the linear constraints:

$$x_1 \geq 0, x_2 \geq 0, x_1 \leq 4, x_2 \leq 5, \text{ and } 5x_1 + 4x_2 \leq 30$$

SOLUTION

The graph of the linear inequalities is shown in Figure 7.5. The shaded area represents the polyhedral convex set of points with vertices at $(0, 0), (4, 0), (4, 2.5), (2, 5),$ and $(0, 5)$. Evaluating the objective function $P = 3x_1 + 5x_2$ at each of the extreme points, we have

Point 0 $(0, 0)$ $= 3(0) + 5(0) = 0$
Point A $(4, 0)$ $= 3(4) + 5(0) = 12$
Point B $(4, 2.5) = 3(4) + 5(2.5) = 24.5$
Point C $(2, 5)$ $= 3(2) + 5(5) = 31$
Point D $(0, 5)$ $= 3(0) + 5(5) = 25$

Note that the maximum value of the objective function P occurs at the vertex C $(2, 5)$ which lies on the line $3x_1 + 5x_2 = 31$. This is the farthest possible line away from the origin that passes through a vertex of the polyhedral convex set of feasible solutions.

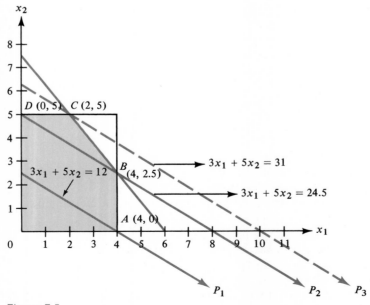

Figure 7.5

Example 7.2

Find the maximum value of $P = 8x_1 + 7x_2$ subject to the linear constraints:

$$2x_1 + 3x_2 \leq 24$$
$$2x_1 + x_2 \leq 16$$
$$x_1 \geq 0 \qquad x_2 \geq 0$$

SOLUTION

The graph of the linear inequalities is shown in Figure 7.6. The shaded area represents the polyhedral convex set of points with vertices at A (0, 0), B (8, 0), D (0, 8), and E (6, 4). Evaluating $P = 8x_1 + 7x_2$ at the vertices, we obtain

$$A\,(0, 0) = 8(0) + 7(0) = 0$$
$$B\,(8, 0) = 8(8) + 7(0) = 64$$
$$D\,(0, 8) = 8(0) + 7(8) = 56$$
$$E\,(6, 4) = 8(6) + 7(4) = 76$$

The maximum value of the objective function P occurs at the vertex E (6,4). This point lies on the line $8x_1 + 7x_2 = 76$ and is farthest from the origin yet passes through an extreme point of the polyhedral convex set of feasible solutions.

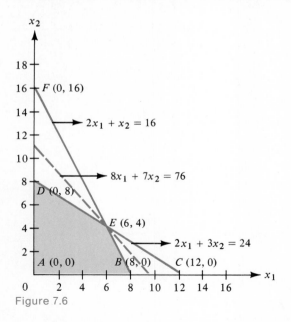

Figure 7.6

Note that in each of the examples the solution that maximizes the objective function is unique and is located at a vertex of the polyhedral convex set. However, if the linear programming problem has more than one optimal solution, then at least one of them is located at a vertex of the polyhedral convex set. We illustrate this possibility in the following example.

Example 7.3

Determine the maximum value of $P = 6x_1 + 9x_2$ subject to the linear constraints:

$$2x_1 + 5x_2 \leq 50$$
$$x_1 + x_2 \leq 11$$
$$2x_1 + x_2 \leq 20$$
$$x_1 \geq 0 \qquad x_2 \geq 0$$

SOLUTION

We have a system of five linear inequalities in the two unknowns x_1 and x_2. The graph of these inequalities is shown in Figure 7.7. The shaded area indicates the polyhedral convex set of points with vertices $0\ (0, 0)$, $A\ (0, 10)$, $B\ (\frac{5}{3}, \frac{28}{3})$, $C\ (9, 2)$, and $D\ (10, 0)$. Next, we consider the value of the objective function, $P = 6x_1 + 9x_2$, at each vertex in the shaded region.

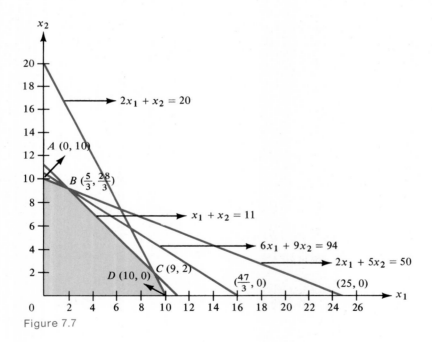

Figure 7.7

At $x_1 = 0$, $x_2 = 0$, the value of the objective function is

$$P = 6(0) + 9(0) = 0$$

At $x_1 = 0$, $x_2 = 10$, the value of the function is

$$P = 6(0) + 9(10) = 90$$

Evaluating $P = 6x_1 + 9x_2$ at the remaining vertices, we obtain

$B\left(\frac{5}{3}, \frac{28}{3}\right)$: $6\left(\frac{5}{3}\right) + 9\left(\frac{28}{3}\right) = 94$

$C\,(9, 2)$: $6(9) + 9(2) = 72$

$D\,(10, 0)$: $6(10) + 4(0) = 60$

Thus, the values of x_1 and x_2 that maximize the objective function lie on the line $6x_1 + 9x_2 = 94$ and this line passes through the vertex $B\left(\frac{5}{3}, \frac{28}{3}\right)$. ∎

This example serves essentially to dispel the common notion that the solution to a linear programming problem will necessarily yield results that are in whole numbers. If the units x_1 and x_2 are indivisible so that x_1 and x_2 must be positive integers and the solution is not in whole numbers, we must modify the corner(s) to round them off to the next lower numbers with the inherent risk of obtaining a solution that may not be optimal. These decisions depend largely on the nature of the problem under consideration: for example, the number of units in question, the cost per unit, and so on.

Let us return to the corner $B\left(\frac{5}{3}, \frac{28}{3}\right)$ in Example 7.3 and round it off to the next lower whole numbers assuming that x_1 and x_2 are indivisible units. Thus, $\left(\frac{5}{3}, \frac{28}{3}\right)$ rounds off to $(1, 9)$ with the value of the objective function given by

$$P = 6(1) + 9(9) = 87$$

This solution can obviously be improved by evaluating the objective function at a vertex $A\,(0, 10)$ of the polyhedral convex set. Thus, if the units x_1 and x_2 are not divisible and the solution in whole numbers is our major concern, we may have to opt for the solution $x_1 = 0$, $x_2 = 10$. In other words, it is simply not profitable to produce the item represented by x_1.

If we replace the linear constraint $x_1 + x_2 \leq 11$ by $x_1 + x_2 \leq 12$, the reader will observe that the polyhedral convex set of points has its vertices $B\left(\frac{10}{3}, \frac{26}{3}\right)$ and $C\,(8, 4)$ in addition to the $0\,(0, 0)$, $A\,(0, 10)$, and $D\,(10, 0)$ as before. Note that the vertex $B\left(\frac{10}{3}, \frac{26}{3}\right)$ rounds off to $B^*\,(3, 8)$ and the value of the objective function $P = 6x_1 + 9x_2$ at the corner $A\,(0, 10)$ and at the point $B^*\,(3, 8)$ is precisely the same. Thus, we have two optimal solutions and one of them is located at a vertex of the polyhedral convex set.

As another illustration of a nonunique solution, we consider the following linear programming problem, in which the objective function is parallel to one of the linear constraints.

Example 7.4

Two products are manufactured by the ABC Company. Product 1 brings a profit of $48 and product 2 contributes $36. The production of both products requires consumption of raw material, the supply of which is limited to 120 pounds. One unit of product 1 requires 4 pounds of raw material and one unit of product 2 requires 3 pounds. Furthermore, each unit of product 1 requires 4 hours of machine time and 2 hours of assembly line time, whereas each unit of product 2 needs 1 hour of machine time and 4 hours of assembly line time. Assuming that 80 hours of machine time and 120 hours of assembly line time are available, what is the best combination of the two products for the firm to produce so as to maximize profit?

SOLUTION

The information in the problem is summarized in Table 7.3.

Table 7.3

	Product 1	Product 2	Resources
Raw material	4 pounds	3 pounds	120 pounds
Machine time	4 hours	1 hour	80 hours
Assembly line time	2 hours	4 hours	120 hours
Profit	$48	$36	

Let x_1 and x_2 represent the number of units of products 1 and 2, respectively. This means that

$$x_1 \geq 0 \qquad x_2 \geq 0$$

These variables must satisfy the following linear inequalities:

$$4x_1 + 3x_2 \leq 120$$
$$4x_1 + x_2 \leq 80$$
$$2x_1 + 4x_2 \leq 120$$

Because the company makes $48 on each unit of product 1 and $36 on each unit of product 2, the objective function to be maximized subject to the above constraints is

$$P = 48x_1 + 36x_2$$

The region of feasible solution shown in Figure 7.8 is bounded by the graphs of the linear equalities $4x_1 + 3x_2 = 120$, $4x_1 + x_2 = 80$, and $2x_1 + 4x_2 = 120$, and by the coordinate axes x_1 and x_2.

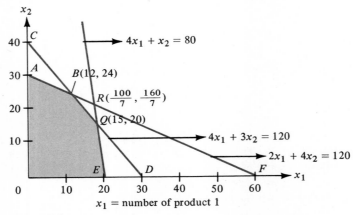

Figure 7.8

The objective function $P = 48x_1 + 36x_2$ is clearly parallel to the linear equality $4x_1 + 3x_2 = 120$. It appears that any point on the line BQ is a feasible solution, because it satisfies all the linear constraints. The points B and Q determined by solving the corresponding linear equations are given by $B(12, 24)$ and $Q(15, 20)$. One can verify that the production of 13 units of product 1 leaves enough worker hours for at most 22 units of product 2. This means that if $x_1 = 13$, then $x_2 \leq 22$. Similarly, $x_1 = 14$ implies that $x_2 \leq 21$. Both these points, though within the feasible solution set, do not lie on BQ; thus, production of these combinations does not give the highest yield. This leaves $x_1 = 12$, $x_2 = 24$ and $x_1 = 15$, $x_2 = 20$ as the only combinations that give a maximum profit of \$1440. We leave it for the reader to verify that there exist no other combinations of x_1 and x_2 that gives a profit exceeding \$1440. ∎

We wish to emphasize that in each of the examples, at least one of the solutions that maximized the objective function is located at a vertex of the polyhedral convex set of feasible solutions. The fact that an optimal solution that minimizes the objective function is also located at a vertex is illustrated in the following examples.

Example 7.5

Mrs. Hawkins needs a diet that will supply her with at least 1250 calories and at least 700 units of vitamin C per day. This requirement can be met from two types of food. Each unit of food 1 contains 20 calories and 10 units of vitamin C and costs 9 cents; each unit of food 2 contains 15 calories and 10 units of vitamin C and costs 7 cents. Determine the best possible combinations of the two types of food that will minimize cost while meeting the dietary requirements.

SOLUTION

Let x_1 and x_2 represent the number of units of type 1 and type 2 foods, respectively. The total calories provided by x_1 units of food 1 and x_2 units of food 2 is given by $20x_1 + 15x_2$; the total vitamin C contained in x_1 units of food 1 and x_2 units of food 2 is given by $10x_1 + 10x_2$. The minimum daily requirement of calorie and vitamin C can be expressed as:

$$20x_1 + 15x_2 \geq 1250$$
$$10x_1 + 10x_2 \geq 700$$

Further, x_1 units of food 1 and x_2 units of food 2 costs $9x_1 + 7x_2$. The problem asks for the best possible combination of x_1 and x_2 units of foods 1 and 2, respectively, that would minimize the objective function

$$C = 9x_1 + 7x_2$$

subject to the linear constraints

$$x_1 \geq 0 \qquad x_2 \geq 0$$
$$20x_1 + 15x_2 \geq 1250$$
$$10x_1 + 10x_2 \geq 700$$

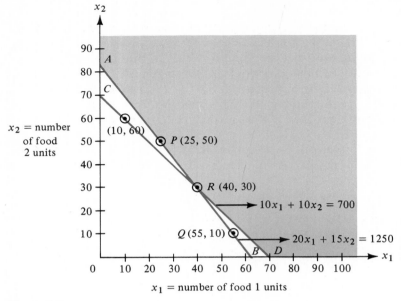

Figure 7.9

To determine the region of feasible solution, we graph the linear constraints as shown in Figure 7.9.

The points on line AB whose coordinates (x_1, x_2) satisfy the linear equality

$$20x_1 + 15x_2 = 1250$$

represent the combinations of the two types of food that yield exactly 1250 calories. Similarly, the points on the line

$$10x_1 + 10x_2 = 700$$

are combinations of foods that provide exactly 700 units of vitamin C. The area of feasible solutions consists of all points falling on or to the right of the line segments AR and RD. To determine the minimum cost combination, we test each vertex of the feasible solutions. The point R in the above Figure 7.9 can also be determined by solving the two linear equations in two unknowns. The values of the objective function $C = 9x_1 + 7x_2$ at different vertices are as follows.

Point A (0, 83): $9(0) + 7(83) = \$5.81$
Point R (40, 30): $9(40) + 7(30) = \$5.70$
Point D (70, 0): $9(70) + 7(0) = \$6.30$

The points A and D can be dropped from further consideration because of the higher costs. The optimum solution is, therefore, at the vertex R (40, 30). This means that the specified requirements of calories and vitamin C is met at a minimum cost of $\$5.70$ if we supply 40 units of food 1 and 30 units of food 2. ∎

Example 7.6

A small-scale manufacturer has production facilities for producing two different products. Each of the products requires three different operations: grinding, assembling, and testing. Product 1 requires 30, 40, and 20 minutes to grind, assemble, and test, respectively; product 2 requires 15, 80, and 90 minutes for grinding, assembling, and testing. The production run calls for at least 15 hours of grinding time, at least 40 hours of assembling time, and at least 30 hours of testing time. If product 1 costs $10 and product 2 costs $15 to manufacture, we seek the number of units of each product the firm should produce in order to minimize the cost of operations.

SOLUTION

Let x_1 and x_2 be the number of units of product 1 and product 2, respectively. These units are associated with the objective function

$$C = 10x_1 + 15x_2$$

to be minimized subject to the following linear constraints:

$$30x_1 + 15x_2 \geq 900$$
$$40x_1 + 80x_2 \geq 2400$$
$$20x_1 + 90x_2 \geq 1800$$
$$x_1 \geq 0 \quad \text{and} \quad x_2 \geq 0$$

Using the procedure previously established, we graph the linear constraints (see Figure 7.10) and determine the region of feasible solutions, which consists of all points falling on and to the right of the line segments AP, PQ, and QF. Each corner in this feasible solution is to be tested to determine the minimum cost combination. As before, points P and Q are obtained by solving simultaneously linear equations in two unknowns.

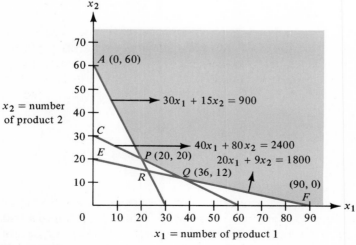

Figure 7.10

The value of the objective function for the different vertices in the feasible solution area are as follows:

Point A (0, 60): $\quad C = 10(0) + 15(60) = \$900$

Point P (20, 20): $\quad C = 10(20) + 15(20) = \$500$

Point Q (36, 12): $\quad C = 10(36) + 15(12) = \$540$

Point F (90, 0): $\quad C = 10(90) + 15(0) = \$900$

The optimum solution is at the point P (20, 20), because the production of 20 units each of products 1 and 2 minimizes the cost. ∎

EXERCISE 7.1

Determine graphically the values of x_1 and x_2 that maximize each of the following objective functions subject to the given linear constraints.

1. $P = 5x_1 + 3x_2$
$2x_1 + 4x_2 \le 80$
$5x_1 + 2x_2 \le 80$
$x_1 \ge 0, x_2 \ge 0$

2. $P = 8x_1 + 6x_2$
$x_1 + 2x_2 \le 150$
$x_1 + x_2 \le 100$
$x_1 \ge 0, x_2 \ge 0$

3. $P = 15x_1 + 10x_2$
$3x_1 + 2x_2 \le 80$
$2x_1 + 3x_2 \le 70$
$x_1 \ge 0, x_2 \ge 0$

4. $P = 16x_1 + 20x_2$
$10x_1 + 20x_2 \le 360$
$20x_1 + 10x_2 \le 360$
$x_1 \ge 0, x_2 \ge 0$

5. $P = 6x_1 + 4x_2$
$x_1 + 2x_2 \le 240$
$3x_1 + 2x_2 \le 300$
$x_1 \ge 0, x_2 \ge 0$

6. $P = 4x_1 + 5x_2$
$2x_1 + 3x_2 \le 24$
$2x_1 + x_2 \le 16$
$x_1 \ge 0, x_2 \ge 0$

7. $P = 16x_1 + 8x_2$
$6x_1 + 4x_2 \ge 24$
$4x_1 + 2x_2 \le 16$
$3.5x_1 + 3x_2 \le 21$
$x_1 \ge 0, x_2 \ge 3$

8. $P = 2x_1 + 3x_2$
$x_1 + x_2 \ge 4$
$5x_1 + 2x_2 \le 25$
$x_1 \le 5, x_2 \le 5$
$x_1 \ge 0, x_2 \ge 0$

Determine graphically the values of x_1 and x_2 that minimize each of the following cost functions subject to the given linear restrictions.

9. $C = 3x_1 + 4x_2$
$x_1 \le 4, x_2 \le 3$
$x_1 + x_2 \ge 6$
$x_1 \ge 0, x_2 \ge 0$

10. $C = 28x_1 + 35x_2$
$2x_1 + x_2 \ge 110$
$2x_1 + 3x_2 \ge 170$
$x_1 \ge 0, x_2 \ge 0$

11. $C = 9x_1 + 15x_2$
$3x_1 + 4x_2 \ge 25$
$x_1 + 3x_2 \ge 15$
$x_1 \ge 0, x_2 \ge 0$

12. $C = 6x_1 + 7x_2$
$3x_1 + 9x_2 \ge 36$
$6x_1 + 2x_2 \ge 24$
$2x_1 + 2x_2 \ge 16$
$x_1 \ge 0, x_2 \ge 0$

13. A company manufactures two products. Each product must pass through two assembly points, A_1 and A_2. Each unit of product 1 requires 4 hours in A_1 and 4 hours in A_2. Product 2 requires 3 hours in A_1 and 1 hour in A_2. There are

110 hours available in A_1 and 90 hours available in A_2. The net profit on each unit of product 1 and 2 is \$10 and \$6, respectively. Using graphical linear programming, determine the optimal combination of the products 1 and 2 that will maximize the profit.

14. The Alexander Manufacturing Company produces glass doors and glass windows. Each glass door requires 6 worker hours in department 1 and 2 worker hours in department 2; each glass window requires 4 worker hours in department 1 and 3 worker hours in department 2. The profits on each glass door and glass window are \$25 and \$20, respectively. There are 60 worker hours available in department 1 and 30 worker hours available in department 2. Using graphical linear programming, determine the optimal combination of glass doors and glass windows that will maximize the profit.

15. A manufacturer makes two kinds of radios, model 1 and model 2. The process requires 2 hours in department A, 2 hours in department B, and 1 hour in department C. Model 2, however, requires 1.5 hours in department A, 0.5 hour in department B, and 2 hours in department C. The profit on each unit of model 1 and model 2 are \$45 and \$20, respectively. If there are 60 hours available in department A, 40 hours in department B, and 60 hours in department C, determine graphically the optimal combination of the products that will maximize the profit.

16. Mrs. Hawkes needs to prepare breakfast that will supply her with at least 7 units of vitamin A and at least 11 units of vitamin B. This requirement can be met from two types of food. Each unit of food 1 contains 1 unit of vitamin A and 2 units of vitamin B and costs 8 cents; each unit of food 2 contains 2 units of vitamin A and 1 unit of vitamin B and costs 12 cents. Determine graphically the best possible combination of the two types of food that will minimize the cost while meeting the nutritional requirements.

7.3 ALGEBRAIC SOLUTIONS TO LINEAR PROGRAMMING PROBLEMS

The graphical analysis of a linear programming problem involves inspecting each vertex in the region of feasible solutions and choosing the points that maximize or minimize the objective function. This method, which was meant only to enhance intuitive understanding, becomes impractical in many applications of linear programming, which generally involve more than two variables and as many or more constraints expressed in the form of linear inequalities. Even for two variables, the graphical methods are cumbersome, inefficient, and sometimes inaccurate, particularly if the extreme points are to be located by visual inspection. Ultimately, business and management executives must find more efficient nongraphical methods of solution if linear programming is to be employed as an effective tool in decision making.

To illustrate the algebraic method, let us return to Examples 7.4 and 7.5 of the previous section and demonstrate how the extreme points can be identified without graphing the linear inequalities. If x_1 and x_2 are the number of products 1 and 2, respectively, then in the problem of Example 7.4, we must maximize the objective function

$$P = 48x_1 + 36x_2$$

subject to the linear constraints

$$4x_1 + 3x_2 \leq 120$$
$$4x_1 + x_2 \leq 80$$
$$2x_1 + 4x_2 \leq 120$$

where x_1 and x_2 must be non-negative. The first step in the algebraic method is to convert each of the linear inequalities into equalities by adding slack variables that take up the slack of the raw material, assembly line time, or machine time not used in the plant. Note that if the quantity of raw material, $4x_1 + 3x_2$, is less than 120, then there exists a non-negative number x_3 such that

$$4x_1 + 3x_2 + x_3 = 120$$

If $4x_1 + 3x_2$ equals 120, then there is no slack and $x_3 = 0$ in this equation. Thus, it follows that $x_3 \geq 0$. Similarly, the second inequality dealing with machine time is converted into an equality by introducing another slack variable x_4 such that

$$4x_1 + x_2 + x_4 = 80$$

where x_4 refers to the unused machine time. If all the available machine time is used in the production of the products 1 and 2, then $x_4 = 0$, but if $4x_1 + x_2$ is actually less than 80, then x_4 must be a positive quantity. Thus, $x_4 \geq 0$. Again, the third inequality is converted into the linear equality

$$2x_1 + 4x_2 + x_5 = 120$$

where the slack variable x_5 is positive if $2x_1 + 4x_2 < 120$ and is zero if

$$2x_1 + 4x_2 = 120,$$

so that $x_5 \geq 0$.

The problem now reduces to finding the values of x_1, x_2, x_3, x_4, and x_5 that maximize the objective function

$$P = 48x_1 + 36x_2 + 0 \cdot x_3 + 0 \cdot x_4 + 0 \cdot x_5$$

subject to the linear constraints

$$\begin{aligned}
4x_1 + 3x_2 + x_3 &= 120 \\
(7.6) \quad 4x_1 + x_2 + x_4 &= 80 \\
2x_1 + 4x_2 + x_5 &= 120
\end{aligned}$$

where $x_i \geq 0$ for $i = 1, 2, 3, 4,$ and 5.

Let us now apply the same procedures to Example 7.5. In this problem we must minimize the cost function

$$C = 9x_1 + 7x_2$$

where x_1 and x_2 are the number of units of type 1 and type 2 foods, respectively. These non-negative variables must satisfy the dietary constraints

$$20x_1 + 15x_2 \geq 1250$$
$$10x_1 + 10x_2 \geq 700$$

This problem is different from the preceding in the sense that the direction of the inequality is $\geq$ instead of $\leq$. This necessitates introduction of "surplus variables." Observe that if the expression $20x_1 + 15x_2$ is greater than 1250, then there exists a positive number x_3 that must be subtracted from the left side of the inequality so that

$$20x_1 + 15x_2 - x_3 = 1250$$

If $20x_1 + 15x_2$ equals 1250, then x_3 must be zero. Thus, in either case, $x_3 \geq 0$. Similarly, the second inequality can be converted into an equality by introducing a non-negative surplus variable x_4 such that

$$10x_1 + 10x_2 - x_4 = 700$$

The dietary interpretation of the surplus variables is that x_3 represents calories supplied from x_1 units of food 1 and x_2 units of food 2 in excess of the daily requirements and x_4 represents vitamins supplied in excess of the daily requirements of 700 units. Because Mrs. Hawkins is not willing to pay anything for these excess quantities, the coefficients of x_3 and x_4 in the cost function are zero.

The problem now asks for the non-negative values of x_1, x_2, x_3, and x_4 that minimize the objective function

$$C = 9x_1 + 7x_2 + 0 \cdot x_3 + 0 \cdot x_4$$

subject to the linear constraints

$$
\begin{aligned}
(7.7) \quad & 20x_1 + 15x_2 - x_3 && = 1250 \\
& 10x_1 + 10x_2 && - x_4 = 700
\end{aligned}
$$

Finally, we return to Example 7.6, in which products are made that require the three different operations of grinding, assembling, and testing. The cost function to be minimized in this problem is

$$C = 10x_1 + 15x_2$$

subject to

$$
\begin{aligned}
30x_1 + 15x_2 &\geq 900 \\
40x_1 + 80x_2 &\geq 2400 \\
20x_1 + 90x_2 &\geq 1800
\end{aligned}
$$

Using the procedure explained above, we introduce three non-negative surplus variables x_3, x_4, and x_5 such that

$$
\begin{aligned}
(7.8) \quad & 30x_1 + 15x_2 - x_3 && = 900 \\
& 40x_1 + 80x_2 && - x_4 && = 2400 \\
& 20x_1 + 90x_2 && && - x_5 = 1800
\end{aligned}
$$

The variable x_3 represents grinding time in excess of 15 hours. Similarly, the variables x_4 and x_5 are interpreted to mean assembling time and testing time in excess of 40 hours and 30 hours, respectively.

Identification of Basic Feasible Solutions

In the preceding discussion, we introduced non-negative slack or surplus variables to convert linear inequalities into linear equations. This generated more variables than the number of linear equations. In the first example, we have five variables but only three equations (7.6); in the dietary problem there are four variables and two equations (7.7); and in the third example, we again have five variables in three equations (7.8). At first, these equations appear impossible to solve, at least to obtain a unique solution. In fact, there are many solutions. We may recall from our discussion in Chapter 6 that there are infinitely many solutions to a system of linear equations whenever the number of variables exceeds the number of linear equations. Thus, the system of three equations in five variables in the first example, two equations in four variables in the second example, and three equations in five variables in the third example each have a number of solutions. Which of the solutions on the graphs are feasible solutions?

Let us pursue further the problem in Example 7.4. The system of three equations in five variables has many solutions. Of these solutions, the solutions that contain negative values for any of the variables are dropped. This leaves only those feasible solutions where two of the five variables are zero and the other three are non-negative. These feasible solutions are called the basic feasible solutions. Graphically, the basic feasible solutions correspond to the vertices of the feasible region. Thus, if two variables are equal to zero and the system of three equations in three unknowns yields non-negative values with respect to these remaining variables, the solution thus obtained will be a basic feasible solution. In carrying out this process to identify basic feasible solutions, we must recognize that if two of the unknowns are equal to zero, then there are 10 cases to be examined. Let us now consider these cases:

Case 1. $x_1 = 0$, $x_2 = 0$ Case 2. $x_1 = 0$, $x_3 = 0$
Case 3. $x_1 = 0$, $x_4 = 0$ Case 4. $x_1 = 0$, $x_5 = 0$
Case 5. $x_2 = 0$, $x_3 = 0$ Case 6. $x_2 = 0$, $x_4 = 0$
Case 7. $x_2 = 0$, $x_5 = 0$ Case 8. $x_3 = 0$, $x_4 = 0$
Case 9. $x_3 = 0$, $x_5 = 0$ Case 10. $x_4 = 0$, $x_5 = 0$

Case 1

If $x_1 = 0$ and $x_2 = 0$, then substituting these values in the linear equations (7.6) yields

$$x_3 = 120 \qquad x_4 = 80 \qquad x_5 = 120$$

Thus, the values of the variables that satisfy the linear equations (7.6) are found to be $(x_1, x_2, x_3, x_4, x_5) = (0, 0, 120, 80, 120)$. This is a basic feasible solution which corresponds to the point 0 in Figure 7.8. This, in turn, implies that the raw material, machine time, and assembly line time are unused, that no products are manufactured and that, therefore, there is no profit. Obviously, this situation can be improved.

Case 2

Let $x_1 = 0$ and $x_3 = 0$. These values, when substituted in (7.6), give

$$x_2 = 40 \qquad x_4 = 40 \qquad x_5 = -40$$

Thus, $(x_1, x_2, x_3, x_4, x_5) = (0, 40, 0, 40, -40)$ is a solution. It is interpreted to mean that production of 40 units of product 2 uses up the raw material, but 40 hours of machine time is not used and the assembly line time is in short supply by 40 hours. The fact that x_5 is negative makes it an unfeasible solution and it must, therefore, be discarded.

Case 3

If $x_1 = 0$ and $x_4 = 0$, then solving the linear equations (7.6), we have

$$x_2 = 80 \qquad x_3 = -120 \qquad x_5 = -200$$

Thus, $(x_1, x_2, x_3, x_4, x_5) = (0, 80, -120, 0, -200)$ is another solution where some of the variables assume negative values. Again, this solution is not feasible.

Case 4

If $x_1 = 0$ and $x_5 = 0$, it follows by solving the linear equations (7.6) that

$$x_2 = 30 \qquad x_3 = 30 \qquad x_4 = 50$$

Thus, the solution $(x_1, x_2, x_3, x_4, x_5) = (0, 30, 30, 50, 0)$ is a basic feasible solution and corresponds to point A in Figure 7.8. The production of 30 units of product 2 leaves 30 pounds of unused raw material and 50 hours of unused machine time. This combination of products brings in a profit of \$1080.

Case 5

When $x_2 = 0$ and $x_3 = 0$, (7.6) has the unique solution determined by

$$x_1 = 30 \qquad x_4 = -40 \qquad x_5 = 60$$

The values of the variables that satisfy the linear equalities are found to be

$$(x_1, x_2, x_3, x_4, x_5) = (30, 0, 0, -40, 60)$$

This means that the production of 30 units of product 1 will use all the raw material but that the machine time will be in short supply by 40 hours, whereas 60 hours of assembly line time will remain unused. This solution is unfeasible.

For the remaining cases, we apply the same procedure to locate basic feasible solutions. The analysis of the 10 cases is presented in Table 7.4. Cases 1, 4, 6, 8, and 9 are identified as basic feasible solutions. The values of the objective function for each of the basic feasible solutions is as follows:

Point 0 $(0, 0)$ $48x_1 + 36x_2 = 48(0) + 36(0) = \$0$

Point A $(0, 30)$ $48x_1 + 36x_2 = 48(0) + 36(30) = \$1080$

Point E $(20, 0)$ $48x_1 + 36x_2 = 48(20) + 36(0) = \$960$

Point Q $(15, 20)$ $48x_1 + 36x_2 = 48(15) + 36(20) = \$1440$

Point B $(12, 24)$ $48x_1 + 36x_2 = 48(12) + 36(24) = \$1440$

The profits are maximum when $x_1 = 15$, $x_2 = 20$ or when $x_1 = 12$, $x_2 = 24$. These conclusions agree with those established by the graphical methods.

Table 7.4

Cases	Solutions to Linear Eq. (7.6)	Basic Feasible or Not	Points on the Graph
1	$x_1 = x_2 = 0$; $x_3 = 120$; $x_4 = 80$; $x_5 = 120$	Yes	0
2	$x_1 = x_3 = 0$; $x_2 = x_4 = 40$; $x_5 = -40$	No	C
3	$x_1 = x_4 = 0$; $x_2 = 80$; $x_3 = -120$; $x_5 = -200$	No	
4	$x_1 = x_5 = 0$; $x_2 = x_3 = 30$; $x_4 = 50$	Yes	A
5	$x_2 = x_3 = 0$; $x_1 = 30$; $x_4 = -40$; $x_5 = 60$	No	D
6	$x_2 = x_4 = 0$; $x_1 = 20$; $x_3 = 40$; $x_5 = 80$	Yes	E
7	$x_2 = x_5 = 0$; $x_1 = 60$; $x_2 = -160$; $x_3 = -120$	No	F
8	$x_3 = x_4 = 0$; $x_1 = 15$; $x_2 = 20$; $x_5 = 10$	Yes	Q
9	$x_3 = x_5 = 0$; $x_1 = 12$; $x_2 = 24$; $x_4 = 8$	Yes	B
10	$x_4 = x_5 = 0$; $x_3 = -\frac{40}{7}$; $x_1 = \frac{100}{7}$; $x_2 = \frac{160}{7}$	No	R

Let us now return to the cost minimization problem of Example 7.6. We must minimize the cost function

$$C = 10x_1 + 15x_2$$

subject to

$$(7.8) \quad \begin{aligned} 30x_1 + 15x_2 - x_3 &= 900 \\ 40x_1 + 80x_2 \quad\quad - x_4 &= 2400 \\ 20x_1 + 90x_2 \quad\quad\quad - x_5 &= 1800 \end{aligned}$$

where $x_i \geq 0$ for $i = 1, 2, 3, 4, 5$.

Again, the system of three equations in five unknowns has several solutions. The basic feasible solutions are the solutions where two of the five variables are zero and the remaining three variables are non-negative. Because there are 10 different cases, we examine each of these cases to identify the basic feasible solutions. An analysis is presented in Table 7.5. Cases 2, 7, 8, and 10 provide basic feasible solutions. When the cost is computed for each of these feasible solutions, the point P (20, 20) in case 8 emerges as the optimal basic feasible solution because production of 20 units each of product 1 and product 2 minimizes the cost.

Table 7.5

Cases	Solutions to Linear Eq. (7.8)	Basic Feasible or Not	Points on the Graph
1	$x_1 = x_2 = 0; x_3 = -900;$ $x_4 = -2400; x_5 = -1800$	No	0
2	$x_1 = x_3 = 0; x_2 = 60;$ $x_4 = 2400; x_5 = 3600$	Yes	A
3	$x_1 = x_4 = 0; x_2 = 30;$ $x_3 = -450; x_5 = 900$	No	C
4	$x_1 = x_5 = 0; x_2 = 20;$ $x_3 = -600; x_4 = -800$	No	E
5	$x_2 = x_3 = 0; x_1 = 30;$ $x_4 = -1200; x_5 = -1200$	No	B
6	$x_2 = x_4 = 0; x_1 = 60;$ $x_3 = 900; x_5 = -600$	No	D
7	$x_2 = x_5 = 0; x_1 = 90;$ $x_3 = 1800; x_4 = 1200$	Yes	F
8	$x_3 = x_4 = 0; x_1 = x_2 = 20;$ $x_5 = 400$	Yes	P
9	$x_3 = x_5 = 0; x_1 = 22.5;$ $x_2 = 15; x_4 = -300$	No	R
10	$x_1 = 36; x_2 = 12; x_3 = 60;$ $x_4 = x_5 = 0$	Yes	Q

EXERCISE 7.2

In Exercises 1 through 4, determine algebraically the values of x_1 and x_2 that maximize each of the following profit functions subject to the given linear constraints.

1. $P = 10x_1 + 20x_2$
$4x_1 + 2x_2 \le 16$
$3x_1 + 6x_2 \le 18$
$x_1 \ge 0, x_2 \ge 0$

2. $P = 3x_1 + 5x_2$
$4x_1 + 3x_2 \le 27$
$4x_1 + 5x_2 \le 37$
$x_1 \ge 0, x_2 \ge 0$

3. $P = 60x_1 + 80x_2$
$x_1 + x_2 \le 12$
$x_1 + 2x_2 \le 16$
$x_1 + 3x_2 \le 22$
$x_1 \ge 0, x_2 \ge 0$

4. $P = 8x_1 + 8x_2$
$x_1 + x_2 \le 24$
$x_1 + 2x_2 \le 40$
$x_1 + 3x_2 \le 60$
$x_1 \ge 3, x_2 \ge 0$

5. A manufacturer makes two products, each requiring time on three different machines. Each unit of product 1 requires 5 hours on machine 1, 2.5 hours on machine 2, and 2 hours on machine 3; each unit of product 2 requires 4 hours on machine 1, 2 hours on machine 2, and 3 hours on machine 3. Machine 1 is available for 110 hours, machine 2 for 55 hours, and machine 3 for 65 hours. The profits are $15 and $12 on products 1 and 2, respectively. Using both graphical and algebraic methods, determine the optimal combination of the products that will maximize profit.

6. ABC Company makes two products. Each unit of product 1 requires 1 hour on machine 1 and 1 hour on machine 2, whereas each unit of product 2 requires 2 hours on machine 1 and 1 hour on machine 2. The profits on products 1 and 2 are $25 and $20, respectively. If there are 40 hours available on machine 1 and 24 hours on machine 2, what is the optimal combination of products 1 and 2 that will maximize the profit? Use both graphical and algebraic methods.

7. A manufacturer makes two products, each requiring time on three different machines. Each unit of product 1 requires 10 minutes on machine 1, 6 minutes on machine 2, and 9 minutes on machine 3, whereas each unit of product 2 requires 5 minutes on machine 1, 12 minutes on machine 2, and 9 minutes on machine 3. Machine 1 and 3 each is available for 7.5 hours and machine 2 is available for 8 hours. The profits are $5 and $3 on products 1 and 2, respectively. Using both graphical and algebraic methods, determine the optimal combination of the products that will maximize profit.

8. Two products, A and B, are manufactured by Kathy and John Company. Each unit of product A requires 3 hours on machine 1, 2.5 hours on machine 2, and 1 hour on machine 3; each unit of product B requires 2 hours on each of the machines 1, 2, and 3. Machine 1 cannot be used for more than 20 hours; machine 2 is available for 18 hours, and machine 3 can be used for 12 hours. The product A brings a profit of $16 and product B contributes $14. Using both graphical and algebraic methods of linear programming, determine the optimal combination of the products the firm should schedule to maximize its profit.

9. There are two types of food available for breakfast. Each ounce of type 1 food contains 1 unit of vitamin A and 2 units of vitamin B and costs 1 cent, whereas each ounce of type 2 food contains 4 units of vitamin A and 3 units of vitamin B and costs 2 cents. How many ounces of each type of food should be purchased to meet minimim daily requirements of 10 units of vitamin A and 15 units of vitamin B at minimum cost? Use both graphical and algebraic methods.

10. Mrs. Hawkes needs to prepare two foods so as to provide herself with at least 750 grams of protein and 975 grams of carbohydrates. Each unit of food 1 contains 12 grams of protein and 15 grams of carbohydrates and costs 35 cents; each unit of food 2 contains 9 grams of protein and 12 grams of carbohydrates and costs 40 cents. How many grams of each food should be purchased to meet the daily requirements at minimum cost?

11. Marilyn must supplement her diet with at least 80 mg of calcium and 17 mg of iron. This requirement can be met from two types of vitamin tablets, P and Q. Each vitamin tablet P contains 5 mg of calcium and 1 mg of iron, whereas each vitamin tablet Q contains 8 mg of calcium and 2 mg of iron. The vitamin tablets P and Q cost 6 cents and 8 cents, respectively. How many tablets of each kind should she purchase to meet her daily requirements at a minimum cost?

12. Jeannie needs a diet that will supply her with at least 1400 calories, 165 units of vitamin B, and 240 units of calcium. This requirement can be met from two types of food. Each unit of food 1 contains 35 calories, 5 units of vitamin B, and 5 units of calcium and costs 5 cents, whereas each unit of food 2 contains 20 calories, 5 units of vitamin B, and 4 units of calcium and costs 4 cents. Determine both graphically and algebraically the optimal combination of the two types of food that Jeannie should buy to meet her daily requirements at a minimum cost.

13. A pound of fish contains 3 units of carbohydrates, 6 units of vitamins, and 12 units of proteins and costs $1.10, whereas a quart of milk contains 2 units of carbohydrates, 3 units of vitamins, and 4 units of proteins and costs 40 cents. If the minimum daily requirements are 12 units of carbohydrates, 15 units of vitamins, and 36 units of proteins, determine the least expensive diet.

7.4 THE SIMPLEX METHOD

The algebraic method of solving linear programming problems requires that each of the m linear inequalities in n variables be converted into linear equations by introducing m non-negative slack or surplus variables. The system of m linear equations in $m + n$ variables thus obtained has many solutions. Of these several solutions, the solutions that contain negative values for any of the $m + n$ variables are eliminated to leave the remaining solutions for further investigation. If any n of the variables is set equal to zero, then the system of m linear equations in m unknowns has a unique solution provided that the linear equations are independent and consistent. The solutions that contain non-negative values with respect to the m variables are basic feasible solutions. In identifying the basic feasible solutions, we must underscore the fact that if n of the unknowns are set equal to zero, then there are several candidates to be examined to locate these basic solutions—a task that may be too great even for high-speed electronic computers.

The algebraic method introduced in the preceding section is, therefore, inadequate for solving linear programming problems involving several linear inequalities and as many or more linear constraints. Instead, more efficient algorithms have been developed to solve multivariable and multiconstraint linear programming problems without having to identify and evaluate every basic feasible solution. One such method, known as the simplex method, was developed by George B. Dantzig in 1947 and has since gained increasing popularity because of its adaptability to high-speed computers, whose use is increasing in almost every field of human endeavor.

The General Linear Programming Problem

The basic concepts of the simplex algorithm are illustrated in the following linear programming problem in which we maximize

$$P = c_1 x_1 + c_2 x_2 + \cdots + c_n x_n$$

subject to the linear constraints

$$a_{11} x_1 + a_{12} x_2 + \cdots + a_{1n} x_n \le b_1$$
$$a_{21} x_1 + a_{22} x_2 + \cdots + a_{2n} x_n \le b_2$$
$$\vdots$$
$$a_{m1} x_1 + a_{m2} x_2 + \cdots + a_{mn} x_n \le b_m$$

where b_i and x_j are non-negative for $i = 1, 2, 3, \ldots, m$; $j = 1, 2, \ldots, n$. Because $P = c_1 x_1 + c_2 x_2 + \cdots + c_n x_n$, we can consider the linear equation

$$-c_1 x_1 - c_2 x_2 - \cdots - c_n x_n + P = 0$$

as another "constraint." Thus, the problem is to find non-negative values x_j that will maximize P using the system of linear equations

$$
\begin{aligned}
a_{11}x_1 + a_{12}x_2 + \cdots + a_{1n}x_n + x_{n+1} \phantom{+ x_{n+2}} &= b_1 \\
a_{21}x_1 + a_{22}x_2 + \cdots + a_{2n}x_n + x_{n+2} &= b_2 \\
\vdots & \\
a_{m1}x_1 + a_{m2}x_2 + \cdots + a_{mn}x_n + x_{n+m} &= b_m \\
-c_1x_1 - c_2x_2 - \cdots - c_nx_n + P &= 0
\end{aligned}
$$

where $x_{n+1}, x_{n+2}, \ldots, x_{n+m}$ are non-negative slack variables.

In matrix notation, we have

$$
\begin{bmatrix}
a_{11} & a_{12} & \cdots & a_{1n} & 1 & 0 & \cdots & 0 & 0 \\
a_{21} & a_{22} & \cdots & a_{2n} & 0 & 1 & \cdots & 0 & 0 \\
\vdots & & & & & & \vdots & & \\
a_{m1} & a_{m2} & \cdots & a_{mn} & 0 & 0 & \cdots & 1 & 0 \\
-c_1 & -c_2 & \cdots & -c_n & 0 & 0 & \cdots & 0 & 1
\end{bmatrix}
\begin{bmatrix}
x_1 \\ x_2 \\ \vdots \\ x_n \\ x_{n+1} \\ \vdots \\ x_{n+m} \\ P
\end{bmatrix}
=
\begin{bmatrix}
b_1 \\ b_2 \\ \vdots \\ b_m \\ 0
\end{bmatrix}
$$

which may be further abbreviated in the form of an initial simplex tableau as follows.

$$
\begin{array}{c}
\begin{array}{cccccccc}
x_1 & x_2 & & x_n & x_{n+1} & x_{n+2} & x_{n+m} & P
\end{array} \\
\begin{bmatrix}
a_{11} & a_{12} & \cdots & a_{1n} & 1 & 0 & \cdots & 0 & 0 & b_1 \\
a_{21} & a_{22} & \cdots & a_{2n} & 0 & 1 & \cdots & 0 & 0 & b_2 \\
\vdots & & & & & & \vdots & & & \vdots \\
a_{m1} & a_{m2} & \cdots & a_{mn} & 0 & 0 & \cdots & 1 & 0 & b_m \\
-c_1 & -c_2 & \cdots & -c_n & 0 & 0 & \cdots & 0 & 1 & 0
\end{bmatrix}
\end{array}
$$

Note that a_{ij} is the coefficient of x_j in the ith row of the $m \times n$ coefficient matrix. The problem is solved by following the procedure outlined below.

1. Set up the initial simplex tableau.
2. Choose one column with the most negative number in the objective function row (the last row). This column is called the pivotal column. If most negative number appears in more than one column, select either one.
3. Divide each positive number of the pivotal column into the corresponding number of the last column. Select the row with the smallest quotient. This row is called the pivotal row. The entry in the pivotal row and pivotal column is called the pivot element.
4. The pivot element is made equal to 1, if necessary, by dividing all the elements in the pivotal row by the pivot.
5. Using a procedure similar to the Gauss-Jordan elimination method, obtain 0's in the pivotal column by adding suitable multiples of the pivotal row to the remaining ones.

6. If a negative number remains in the last row, go to step 2. If none of the numbers in the last row are negative, the optimal solution has been reached and the problem is solved.

The maximum value of P, which appears in the last row and the last column of the final tableau, is attained by

$$x_j = b_i^* \qquad \text{for } a_{ij}^* = 1 \text{ and } a_{pj}^* = 0, i \neq p$$
$$\quad = 0 \quad \text{otherwise}$$

where $i, p = 1, 2, \ldots, m, j = 1, 2, \ldots, n$, a_{ij}^* and b_i^* are the elements in the $m \times n$ coefficient matrix on the left and the last column on the right, respectively, in the terminal tableau. In other words, if the column under x_j has a 1 in some position and 0's elsewhere, then the value of x_j that maximizes P is the last entry on the right of the row that has the 1 in it. If the column under x_j in the terminal tableau fails to consist of a 1 in some position with 0's elsewhere, then $x_j = 0$.

Note that if $m < n$, the number of variables x_j that assume positive values will not exceed the number of linear equations; but if $m > n$, then the number of variables x_j assuming positive values will be at most n.

The maximum value of P occurs at one and only one vertex provided that $m = n$ and the number of linear equations are independent and consistent. This means that the solution in terms of x_j that maximize P is unique.

We shall now amplify the above procedure in the following examples.

Example 7.7

Using the simplex method, maximize

$$P = 20x_1 + 25x_2$$

subject to the linear constraints

$$2x_1 + 3x_2 \leq 40$$
$$4x_1 + 2x_2 \leq 48$$
$$x_1 \geq 0 \qquad x_2 \geq 0$$

SOLUTION

To use the simplex method, we first introduce slack variables x_3 and x_4 such that

$$2x_1 + 3x_2 + x_3 \qquad = 40$$
$$4x_1 + 2x_2 \qquad + x_4 = 48$$

Step 1

The initial simplex tableau is

$$
\begin{array}{ccccc}
x_1 & x_2 & x_3 & x_4 & P \\
\end{array}
$$

$$
\left[
\begin{array}{ccc|ccc|c}
2 & 3 & 1 & 0 & 0 & 40 \\
4 & 2 & 0 & 1 & 0 & 48 \\
-20 & -25 & 0 & 0 & 1 & 0 \\
\end{array}
\right]
$$

Step 2

The second column in the tableau is the pivotal column because -25 is the most negative entry in the last row. Thus,

$$
\begin{array}{ccccccc}
 & x_1 & x_2 & x_3 & x_4 & P & \\
\left[\begin{array}{ccc|ccc|c}
2 & 3 & 1 & 0 & 0 & 40 \\
4 & 2 & 0 & 1 & 0 & 48 \\
-20 & -25 & 0 & 0 & 1 & 0
\end{array}\right]
\end{array}
$$

$$\uparrow$$
Pivotal
column

Step 3

Dividing each positive number in the second column into the corresponding numbers of the last column, we obtain $\frac{40}{3}$ in the first row and $\frac{48}{2} = 24$ in the second row. The smaller quotient of $\frac{40}{3}$ in the first row makes it a pivotal row. The element 3 in the pivotal row and the pivotal column is the pivot. Thus,

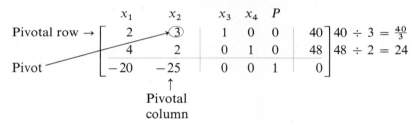

$$40 \div 3 = \frac{40}{3}$$
$$48 \div 2 = 24$$

$$\uparrow$$
Pivotal
column

Step 4

Dividing the elements in the first row by 3, we have

$$
\begin{array}{cccccc}
 & x_1 & x_2 & x_3 & x_4 & P \\
\left[\begin{array}{ccc|ccc|c}
\frac{2}{3} & 1 & \frac{1}{3} & 0 & 0 & \frac{40}{3} \\
4 & 2 & 0 & 1 & 0 & 48 \\
-20 & -25 & 0 & 0 & 1 & 0
\end{array}\right]
\end{array}
$$

Step 5

We now perform the following row operations in the order specified.

1. $R_2' = R_2 + (-2)R_1$
2. $R_3' = R_2 + 25R_1$

These operations transform the preceding matrix into

$$
\begin{array}{cccccc}
 & x_1 & x_2 & x_3 & x_4 & P \\
\left[\begin{array}{ccc|ccc|c}
\frac{2}{3} & 1 & \frac{1}{3} & 0 & 0 & \frac{40}{3} \\
\frac{8}{3} & 0 & -\frac{2}{3} & 1 & 0 & \frac{64}{3} \\
-\frac{10}{3} & 0 & \frac{25}{3} & 0 & 1 & \frac{1000}{3}
\end{array}\right]
\end{array}
$$

Because there is a negative element ($-\frac{10}{3}$ in column 1), we go back to step 2 and repeat the process with the first column as the pivotal column. The second row is the pivotal row, because we have $(\frac{40}{3}) \div (\frac{2}{3}) = 20$ in the first row and $(\frac{64}{3}) \div (\frac{8}{3}) = 8$ in the second row. The entry in the second row and first column is the new pivot:

$$
\begin{array}{c}
\\
\text{Pivotal row} \rightarrow
\end{array}
\begin{array}{ccccc|c}
x_1 & x_2 & x_3 & x_4 & P & \\
\frac{2}{3} & 1 & \frac{1}{3} & 0 & 0 & \frac{40}{3} \\
\boxed{\frac{8}{3}} & 0 & -\frac{2}{3} & 1 & 0 & \frac{64}{3} \\
-\frac{10}{3} & 0 & \frac{25}{3} & 0 & 1 & \frac{1000}{3}
\end{array}
\begin{array}{l}
\frac{40}{3} \div \frac{2}{3} = 20 \\
\frac{64}{3} \div \frac{8}{3} = 8 \\
\\
\end{array}
$$

$$
\begin{array}{c}
\uparrow \\
\text{Pivotal} \\
\text{column}
\end{array}
$$

The elimination process is completed by performing the following elementary row operations in the order specified.

1. $R_2'' = (\frac{3}{8})R_2'$
2. $R_1'' = R_1' + (-\frac{2}{3})R_2''$
3. $R_3'' = R_3' + (\frac{10}{3})R_2''$

These operations transform the preceding matrix into

$$
\begin{array}{ccccc|c}
x_1 & x_2 & x_3 & x_4 & P & \\
0 & 1 & \frac{1}{2} & -\frac{1}{4} & 0 & 8 \\
1 & 0 & -\frac{1}{4} & \frac{3}{8} & 0 & 8 \\
0 & 0 & \frac{15}{2} & \frac{5}{4} & 1 & 360
\end{array}
$$

Step 6

Because all the numbers in the last row are non-negative, the optimum solution is reached. The objective function $P = 20x_1 + 25x_2$ has a maximum value of 360.

Note that the column under the variable x_1 has a 1 in the second position and 0's elsewhere, thus $x_1 = 8$. This is the value of x_1 that maximizes P. Similarly, because the column under x_2 has a 1 in the first position and 0's elsewhere, we see that $x_2 = 8$:

$$
\begin{array}{ccccc|c}
x_1 & x_2 & x_3 & x_4 & P & \\
0 & \textcircled{1} & \frac{1}{2} & -\frac{1}{4} & 0 & \textcircled{8} \\
\textcircled{1} & 0 & -\frac{1}{4} & \frac{3}{8} & 0 & \textcircled{8} \\
0 & 0 & \frac{15}{2} & \frac{5}{4} & 1 & 360
\end{array}
$$

This solution agrees with the graphical solution we found earlier in Figure 7.3. ■

Example 7.8

Maximize

$$P = 48x_1 + 36x_2$$

subject to the linear constraints

$$4x_1 + 3x_2 \leq 120$$
$$4x_1 + x_2 \leq 80$$
$$2x_1 + 4x_2 \leq 120$$
$$x_1 \geq 0 \qquad x_2 \geq 0$$

SOLUTION

Introducing the slack variables, we have

$$4x_1 + 3x_2 + x_3 \qquad\qquad = 120$$
$$4x_1 + x_2 \qquad + x_4 \qquad = 80$$
$$2x_1 + 4x_2 \qquad\qquad + x_5 = 120$$

Step 1

The initial simplex tableau is

$$
\begin{array}{cccccc}
x_1 & x_2 & x_3 & x_4 & x_5 & P \\
\end{array}
$$

$$
\left[
\begin{array}{cccccc|c}
4 & 3 & 1 & 0 & 0 & 0 & 120 \\
4 & 1 & 0 & 1 & 0 & 0 & 80 \\
2 & 4 & 0 & 0 & 1 & 0 & 120 \\
\hline
-48 & -36 & 0 & 0 & 0 & 1 & 0 \\
\end{array}
\right]
$$

Step 2

The first column in the tableau becomes the pivotal column because -48 is the most negative entry in the last row. Thus,

$$
\begin{array}{cccccc}
x_1 & x_2 & x_3 & x_4 & x_5 & P \\
\end{array}
$$

$$
\left[
\begin{array}{cccccc|c}
4 & 3 & 1 & 0 & 0 & 0 & 120 \\
4 & 1 & 0 & 1 & 0 & 0 & 80 \\
2 & 4 & 0 & 0 & 1 & 0 & 120 \\
\hline
-48 & -36 & 0 & 0 & 0 & 1 & 0 \\
\end{array}
\right]
$$

↑
Pivotal
column

Step 3

Dividing each positive number in the first column into the corresponding elements of the last column, we obtain $\frac{120}{4} = 30$ in the first row, $\frac{80}{4} = 20$ in the second row, and $\frac{120}{2} = 60$ in the third row. The smallest quotient of 20 in the second row makes it the pivotal row. The circled element 4 in the pivotal row and the pivotal column is the pivotal element. That is,

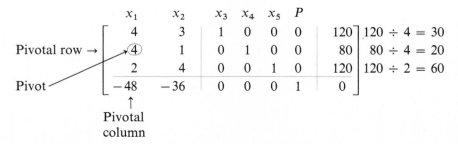

Step 4

If each element in the second row is divided by the pivotal element 4, the tableau becomes

$$
\begin{array}{ccccccc}
x_1 & x_2 & x_3 & x_4 & x_5 & P & \\
\left[\begin{array}{cccccc|c}
4 & 3 & 1 & 0 & 0 & 0 & 120 \\
1 & \frac{1}{4} & 0 & \frac{1}{4} & 0 & 0 & 20 \\
2 & 4 & 0 & 0 & 1 & 0 & 120 \\
\hline
-48 & -36 & 0 & 0 & 0 & 1 & 0
\end{array}\right]
\end{array}
$$

Step 5

To obtain 0's in the pivotal column, we perform the following elementary row operations.

1. $R_1' = R_1 + (-4)R_2$
2. $R_3' = R_3 + (-2)R_2$
3. $R_4' = R_4 + 48R_2$

These operations transform the preceding tableau into

$$
\begin{array}{ccccccc}
x_1 & x_2 & x_3 & x_4 & x_5 & P & \\
\left[\begin{array}{cccccc|c}
0 & 2 & 1 & -1 & 0 & 0 & 40 \\
1 & \frac{1}{4} & 0 & \frac{1}{4} & 0 & 0 & 20 \\
0 & \frac{7}{2} & 0 & -\frac{1}{2} & 1 & 0 & 80 \\
\hline
0 & -24 & 0 & 12 & 0 & 1 & 960
\end{array}\right]
\end{array}
$$

Because there is a negative element in the last row (-24 in column 2), we must go back to step 2 and repeat the process with the second column as the pivotal column. The first row is the pivotal row, because we have $\frac{40}{2} = 20$ in the first row, $20 \div \frac{1}{4} = 80$ in the second row, and $80 \times \frac{2}{7} = \frac{160}{7}$ in the third row. The entry 2 in the first row and the second column is the new pivot. Thus, we have

$$
\begin{array}{l}
\text{Pivotal row} \rightarrow \\
\\
\\
\\
\end{array}
\begin{array}{ccccccc}
x_1 & x_2 & x_3 & x_4 & x_5 & P & \\
\left[\begin{array}{cccccc|c}
0 & ② & 1 & -1 & 0 & 0 & 40 \\
1 & \frac{1}{4} & 0 & \frac{1}{4} & 0 & 0 & 20 \\
0 & \frac{7}{2} & 0 & -\frac{1}{2} & 1 & 0 & 80 \\
\hline
0 & -24 & 0 & 12 & 0 & 1 & 960
\end{array}\right]
\end{array}
\begin{array}{l}
40 \div 2 = 20 \\
20 \div \frac{1}{4} = 80 \\
80 \div \frac{7}{2} = \frac{160}{7} \\
\\
\end{array}
$$

$$\uparrow$$
$$\text{Pivotal column}$$

The elimination process is completed by performing the following elementary operations in the order specified.

1. $R_1'' = (\frac{1}{2})R_1'$
2. $R_2'' = R_2' + (-\frac{1}{4})R_1''$
3. $R_3'' = R_3' + (-\frac{7}{2})R_1''$
4. $R_4'' = R_4' + 24R_1''$

These operations transform the preceding tableau into

$$
\begin{array}{cc|ccccc|c}
x_1 & x_2 & x_3 & x_4 & x_5 & P & \\
\hline
0 & 1 & \frac{1}{2} & -\frac{1}{2} & 0 & 0 & 20 \\
1 & 0 & -\frac{1}{8} & \frac{3}{8} & 0 & 0 & 15 \\
0 & 0 & -\frac{7}{4} & \frac{5}{4} & 1 & 0 & 10 \\
\hline
0 & 0 & 12 & 0 & 0 & 1 & 1440
\end{array}
$$

Step 6

Because there are no more negative numbers in the last row, the problem is solved.

The maximizing value of each variable appears in the last column opposite the 1 in the column of that variable:

$$
\begin{array}{cc|ccccc|c}
x_1 & x_2 & x_3 & x_4 & x_5 & P & \\
\hline
0 & \boxed{1} & \frac{1}{2} & -\frac{1}{2} & 0 & 0 & \boxed{20} \\
\boxed{1} & 0 & -\frac{1}{8} & \frac{3}{8} & 0 & 0 & \boxed{15} \\
0 & 0 & -\frac{7}{4} & \frac{5}{4} & 1 & 0 & 10 \\
\hline
0 & 0 & 12 & 0 & 0 & 1 & 1440
\end{array}
$$

Thus, the maximum value of $P = 1440$ is attained for $x_1 = 15$ and $x_2 = 20$. Note that this solution corresponds to the point Q in the graphical solution (Figure 7.8). ■

This example illustrates that the algorithm fails to detect both the solutions B (12, 24) and Q (15, 20) that maximize the objective function P. Difficulties of this nature do arise occasionally in practical problems, but the simplex method has been studied in all its facets and ramifications and methods are available to treat such problems as they arise. Because a complete discussion of the simplex method requires considerably more space than we can devote here, we shall consider only those maximizing problems where the maximum of the objective function P occurs at only one vertex.

Problems in Three or More Variables

So far, we have restricted ourselves to problems in two variables. In both of our examples, the arithmetic was not excessively difficult and our conclusions agreed with those established earlier by graphical or algebraic methods. We shall now turn our attention to problems in three or more variables where graphing is virtually impossible and algebraic methods are exacting and hardly commensurate with the time and labor involved in the long string of calculations.

Example 7.9

Find the maximum value of

$$P = 2x_1 + 8x_2 + 3x_3$$

subject to the linear constraints

$$
\begin{aligned}
x_1 + x_2 & \leq 5 \\
3x_1 + 2x_2 + x_3 & \leq 14 \\
x_1 \geq 0 \qquad x_2 \geq 0 \qquad x_3 & \geq 0
\end{aligned}
$$

SOLUTION
Introducing the slack variables, we have

$$x_1 + x_2 \qquad + x_4 \qquad = 5$$
$$3x_1 + 2x_2 + x_3 \qquad + x_5 = 14$$

The initial simplex tableau is

$$
\begin{array}{ccc|ccc|c}
x_1 & x_2 & x_3 & x_4 & x_5 & P & \\
\hline
1 & 1 & 0 & 1 & 0 & 0 & 5 \\
3 & 2 & 1 & 0 & 1 & 0 & 14 \\
-2 & -8 & -3 & 0 & 0 & 1 & 0 \\
\end{array}
$$

The second column in the tableau is the pivotal column. (Why?) Dividing each positive number in the second column into the corresponding elements of the last column, we obtain $5 \div 1 = 5$ in the first row and $14 \div 2 = 7$ in the second row. The smaller quotient of 5 in the first row makes it the pivotal row. The element 1 in the pivotal row and the pivotal column is the pivot:

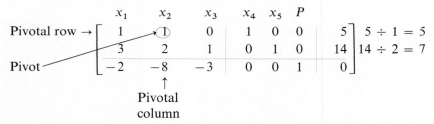

We now perform the following row operations in the order specified:

1. $R_2' = R_2 + (-2)R_1$
2. $R_3' = R_3 + 8R_1$

These operations transform the preceding matrix into

$$
\begin{array}{ccc|ccc|c}
x_1 & x_2 & x_3 & x_4 & x_5 & P & \\
\hline
1 & 1 & 0 & 1 & 0 & 0 & 5 \\
1 & 0 & 1 & -2 & 1 & 0 & 4 \\
6 & 0 & -3 & 8 & 0 & 1 & 40 \\
\end{array}
$$

Because there is a negative element (-3 in column 3), we repeat the procedure with the third column as the pivotal column. The second row is the pivotal row and the circled element 1 is the new pivot. Thus,

$$
\begin{array}{c}
\\
\\
\text{Pivotal row} \rightarrow \\
\\
\end{array}
\begin{array}{ccc|ccc|c}
x_1 & x_2 & x_3 & x_4 & x_5 & P & \\
\hline
1 & 1 & 0 & 1 & 0 & 0 & 5 \\
1 & 0 & \textcircled{1} & -2 & 1 & 0 & 4 \\
6 & 0 & -3 & 8 & 0 & 1 & 40 \\
\end{array}
$$

$$\uparrow$$
$$\text{Pivotal}$$
$$\text{column}$$

Adding 3 times the second row to the third row, we obtain

$$
\begin{array}{ccc|ccc|c}
x_1 & x_2 & x_3 & x_4 & x_5 & P & \\
1 & 1 & 0 & 1 & 0 & 0 & 5 \\
1 & 0 & 1 & -2 & 1 & 0 & 4 \\
9 & 0 & 0 & 2 & 3 & 1 & 52
\end{array}
$$

Because all the numbers in the last row are non-negative, the problem is solved. The columns under the variables x_2 and x_3 have a 1 in the first and second positions respectively and 0's elsewhere; thus, we conclude that $x_2 = 5$ and $x_3 = 4$ are the maximizing values of P. Because the column under x_1 fails to have a 1 in some position and 0's elsewhere, we set $x_1 = 0$. Thus, the maximum value of

$$P = 2x_1 + 8x_2 + 3x_3$$

is 52 attained for $x_1 = 0$, $x_2 = 5$, and $x_3 = 4$. ∎

Example 7.10

Using the simplex algorithm, maximize

$$P = 5x_1 + 6x_2 + 8x_3$$

subject to the linear constraints

$$
\begin{aligned}
x_1 + \quad x_2 + 2x_3 &\le 65 \\
x_1 + 2x_2 + 4x_3 &\le 120 \\
2x_1 + 2x_2 + \quad x_3 &\le 70 \\
x_1 \ge 0 \quad x_2 \ge 0 \quad & x_3 \ge 0
\end{aligned}
$$

SOLUTION

The initial simplex tableau is

$$
\begin{array}{ccc|cccc|c}
x_1 & x_2 & x_3 & x_4 & x_5 & x_6 & P & \\
1 & 1 & 2 & 1 & 0 & 0 & 0 & 65 \\
1 & 2 & 4 & 0 & 1 & 0 & 0 & 120 \\
2 & 2 & 1 & 0 & 0 & 1 & 0 & 70 \\
-5 & -6 & -8 & 0 & 0 & 0 & 1 & 0
\end{array}
$$

The third column in the tableau is the pivotal column because -8 is the most negative entry in the last row. Dividing each positive number in the third column into the corresponding element of the last column, we have $65 \div 2 = \frac{65}{2}$ in the first column, $120 \div 4 = 30$ in the second row, and $70 \div 1 = 70$ in the third row. The smallest quotient of 30 in the second row makes it a pivotal row. The element 4 is the pivot:

$$
\begin{array}{ccc|cccc|c}
x_1 & x_2 & x_3 & x_4 & x_5 & x_6 & P & \\
1 & 1 & 2 & 1 & 0 & 0 & 0 & 65 \\
1 & 2 & 4 & 0 & 1 & 0 & 0 & 120 \\
2 & 2 & 1 & 0 & 0 & 1 & 0 & 70 \\
-5 & -6 & -8 & 0 & 0 & 0 & 1 & 0
\end{array}
$$

Pivotal row →   Pivot

$65 \div 2 = \frac{65}{2}$
$120 \div 4 = 30$
$70 \div 1 = 70$

↑
Pivotal
column

The following operations performed in the specified order

1. $R_2' = \frac{1}{4}R_2$
2. $R_1' = R_1 + (-2)R_2'$
3. $R_3' = R_3 + (-1)R_2'$
4. $R_4' = R_4 + 8R_2'$
5. $R_1'' = 2R_1'$

transform the above tableau into

$$
\begin{array}{c}
\text{Pivotal row} \rightarrow \\
\\
\\
\\
\end{array}
\begin{array}{cc}
& \begin{array}{ccccccc} x_1 & x_2 & x_3 & x_4 & x_5 & x_6 & P \end{array} \\
\left[\begin{array}{ccc|cccc}
① & 0 & 0 & 2 & -1 & 0 & 0 \\
\frac{1}{4} & \frac{1}{2} & 1 & 0 & \frac{1}{4} & 0 & 0 \\
\frac{7}{4} & \frac{3}{2} & 0 & 0 & -\frac{1}{4} & 1 & 0 \\
-3 & -2 & 0 & 0 & 2 & 0 & 1
\end{array} \right. &
\left. \begin{array}{c}
10 \\ 30 \\ 40 \\ 240
\end{array} \right]
\begin{array}{l}
10 \div 1 = 10 \\
30 \div \frac{1}{4} = 120 \\
40 \div \frac{7}{4} = 70 \\
\\
\end{array}
\end{array}
$$

$$\begin{array}{c}\uparrow\\ \text{Pivotal}\\ \text{column}\end{array}$$

We now perform the following operations in the order specified.

1. $R_2'' = R_2' + (-\frac{1}{4})R_1''$
2. $R_3'' = R_3' + (-\frac{7}{4})R_1''$
3. $R_4'' = R_4' + 3R_1''$

These operations transform the preceding tableau into

$$
\begin{array}{c}
\\
\\
\text{Pivotal row} \rightarrow \\
\\
\end{array}
\begin{array}{c}
\begin{array}{ccccccc} x_1 & x_2 & x_3 & x_4 & x_5 & x_6 & P \end{array} \\
\left[\begin{array}{ccc|cccc|c}
1 & 0 & 0 & 2 & -1 & 0 & 0 & 10 \\
0 & \frac{1}{2} & 1 & -\frac{1}{2} & \frac{1}{2} & 0 & 0 & \frac{55}{2} \\
0 & ③\!\!\frac{3}{2} & 0 & -\frac{7}{2} & \frac{3}{2} & 1 & 0 & \frac{45}{2} \\
0 & -2 & 0 & 6 & -1 & 0 & 1 & 270
\end{array} \right]
\end{array}
$$

$$\begin{array}{c}\uparrow\\ \text{Pivotal}\\ \text{column}\end{array}$$

Because there remains a negative number $(-2$ in the second column), we must repeat the process. The element $\frac{3}{2}$ in the third row and the second column is the new pivot. (Why?) The pivot element is made 1 by dividing all the elements of the third row by $\frac{3}{2}$. The new third row is

$$
\begin{array}{ccccccc} x_1 & x_2 & x_3 & x_4 & x_5 & x_6 & P \end{array} \\
\left[\begin{array}{ccc|ccc|c} 0 & 1 & 0 & -\frac{7}{3} & 1 & \frac{2}{3} & 0 & 15 \end{array} \right]
$$

Adding suitable multiples of this row to second and fourth rows, we obtain

$$
\begin{array}{c}
\begin{array}{ccccccc} x_1 & x_2 & x_3 & x_4 & x_5 & x_6 & P \end{array} \\
\left[\begin{array}{ccc|cccc|c}
1 & 0 & 0 & 2 & -1 & 0 & 0 & 10 \\
0 & 0 & 1 & \frac{2}{3} & 0 & -\frac{1}{3} & 0 & 20 \\
0 & 1 & 0 & -\frac{7}{3} & 1 & \frac{2}{3} & 0 & 15 \\
0 & 0 & 0 & \frac{4}{3} & 1 & \frac{4}{3} & 1 & 300
\end{array} \right]
\end{array}
$$

Because none of the numbers in the last row is negative, the problem is solved. Note that the objective function $P = 5x_1 + 6x_2 + 8x_3$ attains the maximum value of 300 for $x_1 = 10$, $x_2 = 15$, and $x_3 = 20$:

$$
\begin{array}{ccccccc}
x_1 & x_2 & x_3 & x_4 & x_5 & x_6 & P \\
\end{array}
$$

$$
\begin{bmatrix}
1 & 0 & 0 & 2 & -1 & 0 & 0 & 10 \\
0 & 0 & 1 & \frac{2}{3} & 0 & -\frac{1}{3} & 0 & 20 \\
0 & 1 & 0 & -\frac{7}{3} & 1 & \frac{2}{3} & 0 & 15 \\
0 & 0 & 0 & \frac{4}{3} & 1 & \frac{4}{3} & 1 & 300
\end{bmatrix}
$$

EXERCISE 7.3

In Exercises 1 through 12, use the simplex algorithm to find the maximum value of P subject to the given linear constraints.

1. $P = 6x_1 + 4x_2$
$x_1 + 2x_2 \le 240$
$3x_1 + 2x_2 \le 300$
$x_1 \ge 0, x_2 \ge 0$

2. $P = 8x_1 + 6x_2$
$4x_1 + 2x_2 \le 60$
$2x_1 + 4x_2 \le 48$
$x_1 \ge 0, x_2 \ge 0$

3. $P = 6x_1 + 2x_2$
$3x_1 + 2x_2 \le 12$
$4x_1 + x_2 \le 20$
$x_1 \ge 0, x_2 \ge 0$

4. $P = 2x_1 + 6x_2$
$6x_1 + 2x_2 \le 12$
$4x_1 + x_2 \le 20$
$x_1 \ge 0, x_2 \ge 0$

5. $P = 30x_1 + 40x_2$
$x_1 + x_2 \le 12$
$x_1 + 2x_2 \le 16$
$x_1 + 3x_2 \le 22$
$x_1 \ge 0, x_2 \ge 0$

6. $P = 4x_1 + 5x_2$
$x_1 + 2x_2 \le 17$
$x_1 + 4x_2 \le 29$
$3x_1 + x_2 \le 21$
$x_1 \ge 0, x_2 \ge 0$

7. $P = 5x_1 + 3x_2 + 5x_3$
$x_1 + x_2 + 3x_3 \le 6$
$3x_1 + x_2 + x_3 \le 4$
$x_1 \ge 0, x_2 \ge 0, x_3 \ge 0$

8. $P = 2x_1 + 4x_2 + 3x_3$
$x_1 + 2x_2 + x_3 \le 40$
$5x_1 + 3x_2 + 4x_3 \le 68$
$x_1 \ge 0, x_2 \ge 0, x_3 \ge 0$

9. $P = 4x_1 + 8x_2 + 3x_3$
$2x_1 + x_2 \le 6$
$x_1 + 2x_2 + 4x_3 \le 32$
$x_1 \ge 0, x_2 \ge 0, x_3 \ge 0$

10. $P = 4x_1 + 2x_2 + 6x_3$
$x_1 + x_2 + 2x_3 \le 30$
$5x_1 + 4x_2 + 4x_3 \le 90$
$x_1 \ge 0, x_2 \ge 0, x_3 \ge 0$

11. $P = 4x_1 + 2x_2 + 5x_3$
$3x_1 + x_3 \le 21$
$x_1 + 2x_2 + 4x_3 \le 97$
$x_2 + 2x_3 \le 46$
$x_1 \ge 0, x_2 \ge 0, x_3 \ge 0$

12. $P = 6x_1 + 9x_2 + 8x_3$
$2x_1 + 6x_2 + 5x_3 \le 20$
$5x_1 + 2x_2 + 4x_3 \le 20$
$6x_1 + 12x_2 + 8x_3 \le 40$
$x_1 \ge 0, x_2 \ge 0, x_3 \ge 0$

13. Use the simplex method to solve Exercise 13 in Section 7.1.
14. Use the simplex method to solve Exercise 14 in Section 7.1.
15. Use the simplex algorithm to solve Exercise 6 in Section 7.2.
16. Use the simplex algorithm to solve Exercise 8 in Section 7.2.

7.5 THE DUAL PROBLEM

For every maximization problem, there is a unique minimization problem and conversely. One of these is called the primal problem, and the other is called the dual problem. The method of solution in the maximization problems determines the production of that combination of products which would maximize the profit or the market share subject to the given environmental constraints. In the minimization problems, we determine, for each unit of operation, the value that minimizes the costs, use of raw material or completion time, and at the same time does not violate the contribution to profit or overhead costs per unit of operation per product. Thus, the dual of a given maximum or minimum problem has important economic interpretations.

If the primal problem is to determine the non-negative numbers $x_1, x_2, \ldots, x_n$ that will maximize the objective function

$$P = c_1 x_1 + c_2 x_2 + \cdots + c_n x_n$$

subject to the linear constraints

$$\begin{bmatrix} a_{11} & a_{12} & \cdots & a_{1n} \\ a_{21} & a_{22} & \cdots & a_{2n} \\ \vdots & & & \\ a_{m1} & a_{m2} & \cdots & a_{mn} \end{bmatrix} \begin{bmatrix} x_1 \\ x_2 \\ \vdots \\ x_n \end{bmatrix} \leq \begin{bmatrix} b_1 \\ b_2 \\ \vdots \\ b_m \end{bmatrix}$$

then the corresponding dual problem is to determine the non-negative numbers $y_1, y_2, \ldots, y_n$ that will minimize the objective function

$$Q = b_1 y_1 + b_2 y_2 + \cdots + b_m y_m$$

subject to the linear constraints

$$\begin{bmatrix} a_{11} & a_{21} & \cdots & a_{m1} \\ a_{12} & a_{22} & \cdots & a_{m2} \\ \vdots & & & \\ a_{1n} & a_{2n} & \cdots & a_{mn} \end{bmatrix} \begin{bmatrix} y_1 \\ y_2 \\ \vdots \\ y_m \end{bmatrix} \geq \begin{bmatrix} c_1 \\ c_2 \\ \vdots \\ c_n \end{bmatrix}$$

Thus, the difference in setting up a maximum or a minimum problem, if the other is given, lies in row vectors being converted into column vectors while the coefficients $c_1, c_2, \ldots, c_n$ of the linear objective function in the primal problem become the bounding constants in the dual problem and the bounding constants $b_1, b_2, \ldots, b_m$ in the original problem become the coefficients of the linear objective function in the dual problem. Further, the value of the objective function is the same for the problem and its dual. This is a consequence of the fundamental theorem of linear programming, which we state without proof.

Theorem 7.5.1: If a linear programming problem has an optimal solution, then so does its dual, and the value of the objective function is the same for the problem and its dual.

Example 7.11

If the primal problem is to maximize

$$P = 48x_1 + 36x_2$$

subject to the linear constraints

$$4x_1 + 3x_2 \leq 120$$
$$4x_1 + x_2 \leq 80$$
$$2x_1 + 4x_2 \leq 120$$
$$x_1 \geq 0 \qquad x_2 \geq 0$$

then the dual problem is to minimize

$$Q = 120y_1 + 80y_2 + 120y_3$$

subject to the linear constraints

$$4y_1 + 4y_2 + 2y_3 \geq 48$$
$$3y_1 + y_2 + 4y_3 \geq 36$$
$$y_1 \geq 0 \qquad y_2 \geq 0 \qquad y_3 \geq 0$$

∎

Example 7.12

Minimize the function

$$Q = 45y_1 + 180y_2$$

subject to

$$y_1 + 5y_2 \geq 3$$
$$y_1 + 2y_2 \geq 2$$
$$y_1 \geq 0 \qquad y_2 \geq 0$$

by solving its dual by the simplex method.

SOLUTION

The corresponding dual problem is to maximize

$$P = 3x_1 + 2x_2$$

subject to the linear constraints

$$x_1 + 2x_2 \leq 45$$
$$5x_1 + 2x_2 \leq 180$$
$$x_1 \geq 0 \qquad x_2 \geq 0$$

The initial simplex tableau is

$$
\begin{array}{ccccc|c}
x_1 & x_2 & x_3 & x_4 & P & \\
\hline
1 & 1 & 1 & 0 & 0 & 45 \\
⑤ & 2 & 0 & 1 & 0 & 180 \\
-3 & -2 & 0 & 0 & 1 & 0 \\
\end{array}
$$

Pivotal row →

$45 \div 1 = 45$
$180 \div 5 = 36$

↑
Pivotal
column

The first column becomes the pivotal column because -3 is the most negative entry in the last row. If each positive number in the first column is divided into the corresponding element of the last column, we obtain 45 in the first row and 36 in the second row. The smallest quotient of 36 makes the second row as the pivotal row, and the element 5 is the pivot. Dividing the elements in the first row by 5, we obtain

$$
\begin{array}{ccccc}
x_1 & x_2 & x_3 & x_4 & P \\
\left[\begin{array}{ccccc|c}
1 & 1 & 1 & 0 & 0 & 45 \\
1 & \frac{2}{5} & 0 & \frac{1}{5} & 0 & 36 \\
-3 & -2 & 0 & 0 & 1 & 0
\end{array}\right]
\end{array}
$$

We now perform the following elementary row operations in the order specified.

1. $R_1' = R_1 + (-1)R_2$
2. $R_3' = R_1 + 3R_2$

These operations transform the preceding tableau into

$$
\begin{array}{ccccc}
& x_1 & x_2 & x_3 & x_4 & P \\
\text{Pivotal row} \rightarrow & \left[\begin{array}{ccccc|c}
0 & \textcircled{$\frac{3}{5}$} & 1 & -\frac{1}{5} & 0 & 9 \\
1 & \frac{2}{5} & 0 & \frac{1}{5} & 0 & 36 \\
0 & -\frac{4}{5} & 0 & \frac{3}{5} & 1 & 108
\end{array}\right]
\end{array}
\begin{array}{l}
9 \div \frac{3}{5} = 15 \\
36 \div \frac{2}{5} = 90
\end{array}
$$

$$
\underset{\substack{\text{Pivotal} \\ \text{column}}}{\uparrow}
$$

Because there is a negative element in the second column, we must repeat the process with the second column as the pivotal column. Dividing each positive number in the second column into the corresponding element of the last column, we obtain 15 in the first row and 90 in the second row. The smallest quotient of 15 makes the first row as the pivotal row, and the element $\frac{3}{5}$ is the pivot.

The following elementary row operations

1. $R_1'' = (\frac{5}{3})R_1'$
2. $R_2'' = R_2' + (-\frac{2}{5})R_1''$
3. $R_3'' = R_3' + (\frac{4}{5})R_1''$

transform the above matrix into

$$
\begin{array}{ccccc}
x_1 & x_2 & x_3 & x_4 & P \\
\left[\begin{array}{ccccc|c}
0 & 1 & \frac{5}{3} & -\frac{1}{3} & 0 & 15 \\
1 & 0 & -\frac{2}{3} & \frac{1}{3} & 0 & 30 \\
0 & 0 & \frac{4}{3} & \frac{1}{3} & 1 & 120
\end{array}\right]
\end{array}
$$

Because there are no more negative entries in the last row, the problem is solved. The maximum value of $P = 120$ attained for $x_1 = 30$ and $x_2 = 15$. Because the maximum value of P equals the minimum value of Q, we conclude that the minimum value of 120 is attained for $y_1 = \frac{4}{3}$ and $y_2 = \frac{1}{3}$. Note that these values of y_1 and y_2 appear as the third and fourth elements, respectively, of the last row in the terminal tableau. ∎

Let us now return to the minimization problem discussed in Example 7.6 and find the corresponding dual problem and then solve it by using simplex method.

Example 7.13

Minimize the cost function

$$C = 10y_1 + 15y_2$$

subject to the linear constraints

$$30y_1 + 15y_2 \geq 900$$
$$4y_1 + 80y_2 \geq 2400$$
$$20y_1 + 90y_2 \geq 1800$$
$$y_1 \geq 0 \qquad y_2 \geq 0$$

SOLUTION

The dual problem is to maximize

$$P = 900x_1 + 2400x_2 + 1800x_3$$

subject to

$$30x_1 + 40x_2 + 20x_3 \leq 10$$
$$15x_1 + 80x_2 + 90x_3 \leq 15$$
$$x_1 \geq 0 \qquad x_2 \geq 0 \qquad x_3 \geq 0$$

The initial simplex tableau is

	x_1	x_2	x_3	x_4	x_5	P	
	30	40	20	1	0	0	10
Pivotal row →	15	⑧⓪	90	0	1	0	15
	−900	−2400	−1800	0	0	1	0

↑
Pivotal
column

Because -2400 is the most negative entry, the second column becomes the pivotal column. Dividing each positive number in the second column into the corresponding element of the last column, we obtain $\frac{10}{40} = \frac{1}{4}$ in the first row and $\frac{15}{80} = \frac{3}{16}$ in the second row. The smallest quotient of $\frac{3}{16}$ in the second row makes this row as a pivotal row. If each element in the second row is divided by the pivotal element 80, the tableau becomes

	x_1	x_2	x_3	x_4	x_5	P	
	30	40	20	1	0	0	10
	$\frac{3}{16}$	1	$\frac{9}{8}$	0	$\frac{1}{80}$	0	$\frac{3}{16}$
	−900	−2400	−1800	0	0	1	0

The following elementary row operations

1. $R_1' = R_1 + (-40)R_2$
2. $R_3' = R_3 + 2400R_3$

transform the above tableau into

$$\text{Pivotal row} \rightarrow \begin{array}{ccccccc} & x_1 & x_2 & x_3 & x_4 & x_5 & P \\ \left[\begin{array}{ccc|ccc|c} \frac{45}{2} & 0 & -25 & 1 & -\frac{1}{2} & 0 & \frac{5}{2} \\ \frac{3}{16} & 1 & \frac{9}{8} & 0 & \frac{1}{80} & 0 & \frac{3}{16} \\ -450 & 0 & 900 & 0 & 30 & 1 & 450 \end{array}\right] \end{array}$$

$$\underset{\substack{\uparrow \\ \text{Pivotal} \\ \text{column}}}{}$$

There is a negative entry in column 1. We must, therefore, repeat the process with column 1 as a pivotal column. The first row is the pivotal row. (Why?) Dividing the elements in the pivotal row by $\frac{45}{2}$, we have

$$\begin{array}{ccccccc} x_1 & x_2 & x_3 & x_4 & x_5 & P \\ \left[\begin{array}{ccc|ccc|c} 1 & 0 & -\frac{10}{9} & \frac{2}{45} & -\frac{1}{45} & 0 & \frac{1}{9} \\ \frac{3}{16} & 1 & \frac{9}{8} & 0 & \frac{1}{80} & 0 & \frac{3}{16} \\ -450 & 0 & 900 & 0 & 30 & 1 & 450 \end{array}\right] \end{array}$$

Adding suitable multiples of the first row to the remaining rows, we obtain the terminal tableau

$$\begin{array}{ccccccc} x_1 & x_2 & x_3 & x_4 & x_5 & P \\ \left[\begin{array}{ccc|ccc|c} ① & 0 & -\frac{10}{9} & \frac{2}{45} & -\frac{1}{45} & 0 & \frac{1}{9} \\ 0 & ① & \frac{4}{3} & -\frac{1}{120} & \frac{1}{60} & 0 & \frac{1}{6} \\ 0 & 0 & 400 & 20 & 20 & 1 & 500 \end{array}\right] \end{array}$$

The objective function $P = 900x_1 + 2400x_2 + 1800x_3$ attains the maximum value of 500 for $x_1 = \frac{1}{9}$, $x_2 = \frac{1}{6}$, and $x_3 = 0$. Note that the maximum value of P equals the minimum value of C, attained for $y_1 = 20$, $y_2 = 20$, that we determined earlier by graphing (Figure 7.8).

We can thus always find a solution to the minimization problem by solving its dual through simplex methods. Observe that the values in the last row under the slack variables columns correspond to the solution of the variables in the original minimization problem. This is always the case.   ■

EXERCISE 7.4

For Exercises 1 through 12, use the simplex algorithm to determine the minimum value of C subject to the given linear constraints.

1. $C = 12y_1 + 20y_2$
   $6y_1 + 4y_2 \geq 2$
   $2y_1 + y_2 \geq 6$
   $y_1 \geq 0, y_2 \geq 0$

2. $C = 14y_1 + 10y_2$
   $5y_1 + 11y_2 \geq 4$
   $4y_1 + 8y_2 \geq 2$
   $y_1 \geq 0, y_2 \geq 0$

3. $C = 6y_1 + 5y_2$
$2y_1 + 3y_2 \geq 6$
$5y_1 + 2y_2 \geq 10$
$y_1 \geq 0, y_2 \geq 0$

4. $C = 60y_1 + 30y_2$
$6y_1 + 2y_2 \geq 25$
$4y_1 + 3y_2 \geq 20$
$y_1 \geq 0, y_2 \geq 0$

5. $C = 40y_1 + 48y_2$
$2y_1 + 4y_2 \geq 20$
$3y_1 + 2y_2 \geq 25$
$y_1 \geq 0, y_2 \geq 0$

6. $C = 30y_1 + 90y_2$
$y_1 + 5y_2 \geq 4$
$y_1 + 4y_2 \geq 2$
$2y_1 + 4y_2 \geq 6$
$y_1 \geq 0, y_2 \geq 0$

7. $C = 15y_1 + 60y_2$
$y_1 + 3y_2 \geq 12$
$y_1 + 4y_2 \geq 7$
$3y_1 + 10y_2 \geq 8$
$y_1 \geq 0, y_2 \geq 0$

8. $C = y_1 + 3y_2 + 4y_3$
$2y_1 + y_2 + 4y_3 \geq 18$
$y_1 + 2y_2 + 3y_3 \geq 24$
$y_1 \geq 0, y_2 \geq 0, y_3 \geq 0$

9. $C = 12y_1 + 16y_2 + 22y_3$
$y_1 + y_2 + y_3 \geq 30$
$y_1 + 2y_2 + 3y_3 \geq 40$
$y_1 \geq 0, y_2 \geq 0, y_3 \geq 0$

10. $C = 2y_1 + 3y_2 + 4y_3$
$2y_1 + y_2 + 3y_3 \geq 12$
$y_1 + 2y_2 + y_3 \geq 18$
$y_1 \geq 0, y_2 \geq 0, y_3 \geq 0$

11. $C = 20y_1 + 20y_2 + 40y_3$
$2y_1 + 5y_2 + 6y_3 \geq 6$
$6y_1 + 2y_2 + 12y_3 \geq 9$
$5y_1 + 4y_3 + 8y_3 \geq 8$
$y_1 \geq 0, y_2 \geq 0, y_3 \geq 0$

12. $C = 7y_1 + 20y_2 + 6y_3$
$y_1 + 4y_2 + y_3 \geq 8$
$2y_1 + 4y_2 + y_3 \geq 10$
$2y_1 + 3y_2 + y_3 \geq 6$
$y_1 \geq 0, y_2 \geq 0, y_3 \geq 0$

13. Use the simplex method to solve Exercise 16 in Section 7.1.
14. Use the simplex method to solve Exercise 9 in Section 7.2.
15. Use the simplex method to solve Exercise 10 in Section 7.2.
16. Use the simplex method to solve Exercise 11 in Section 7.2.
17. Use the simplex method to solve Exercise 12 in Section 7.2.
18. Use the simplex method to solve Exercise 13 in Section 7.2.

8

Special Types of Linear Programming Problems

8.1 INTRODUCTION

In Chapter 7, we introduced the general nature of a linear programming problem and discussed its solution by graphical, algebraic, and the simplex method. Within the general linear programming models, there are many important types, such as the transportation and assignment models, net work, and flow models. These models appear in a variety of contexts, such as scheduling, production, investment, personnel allotment problems, and so forth, and involve such a large number of variables and linear constraints that a direct application of the simplex method may be prohibitive even for high-speed electronic computers. Fortunately, most of the coefficients of the linear constraints in these problems are zero, and the few nonzero coefficients remaining appear in a definite pattern. Consequently, modified versions of the simplex method have recently been developed so as to exploit the special structure of such problems. These methods result in considerable savings in otherwise exacting and time-consuming numerical calculations.

One of the most useful special types of linear programming problem is the transportation model, which we shall discuss in this chapter. Later in the chapter we present the assignment model, where the "resources" are allocated to the "destinations" on a one-to-one basis to minimize the cost.

8.2 THE TRANSPORTATION PROBLEM

The transportation model first presented by F. L. Hitchcock in 1941 and later expanded by T. C. Koopmans deals with shipping a homogeneous product from several plants of a company to its warehouses at minimum cost. Each plant has a certain production capacity, and each warehouse has a definite requirement. The unit cost of shipping from each plant to each warehouse is known. The objective is to minimize the shipping cost and still satisfy the warehouse demand within the framework of plant production capacity.

To formulate the problem mathematically, consider an arbitrary transportation problem with m plants, $P_1, P_2, \ldots, P_m$, and n warehouses, $W_1, W_2, \ldots, W_n$. Each source P_i, $i = 1, 2, \ldots, m$, has a supply of s_i units to distribute to the warehouses and each warehouse W_j, $j = 1, 2, \ldots, n$, has a requirement of d_j units to be received from the plants. This information is presented in the following tableau.

Warehouses

From \ To	W_1	W_2	$\cdots$	W_j	$\cdots$	W_n	Supply
P_1	x_{11}	x_{12}	$\cdots$	x_{1j}	$\cdots$	x_{1n}	s_1
P_2	x_{21}	x_{22}	$\cdots$	x_{2j}	$\cdots$	x_{2n}	s_2
$\vdots$							
P_i	x_{i1}	x_{i2}	$\cdots$	x_{ij}	$\cdots$	x_{in}	s_i
$\vdots$							
P_m	x_{m1}	x_{m2}	$\cdots$	x_{mj}	$\cdots$	x_{mn}	s_m
Demand	d_1	d_2	$\cdots$	d_j	$\cdots$	d_n	

Plants (row label for P rows)

Note that x_{ij} is the number of units to be shipped from plant P_i, $i = 1, 2, \ldots, m$, to warehouse W_j, $j = 1, 2, \ldots, n$. If c_{ij} represents the shipping cost per unit from plant P_i to warehouse W_j, then the associated cost of shipping x_{ij} units is $c_{ij}x_{ij}$. Also, the total amount of goods shipped from plant P_i is

$$x_{i1} + x_{i2} + \cdots + x_{in} = s_i \qquad i = 1, 2, \ldots, m$$

and the total amount received by warehouse W_j is

$$x_{1j} + x_{2j} + \cdots + x_{mj} = d_j \qquad j = 1, 2, \ldots, n$$

The problem is to determine x_{ij} that would minimize the total transportation cost

$$
\begin{aligned}
(8.1) \quad Z = \quad & x_{11}c_{11} + x_{12}c_{12} + \cdots + x_{1n}c_{1n} \\
& + x_{21}c_{21} + x_{22}c_{22} + \cdots + x_{2n}c_{2n} \\
& + x_{31}c_{31} + x_{32}c_{32} + \cdots + x_{3n}c_{3n} \\
& \quad \vdots \\
& + x_{i1}c_{i1} + x_{i2}c_{i2} + \cdots + x_{in}c_{in} \\
& \quad \vdots \\
& + x_{m1}c_{m1} + x_{m2}c_{m2} + \cdots + x_{mn}c_{mn}
\end{aligned}
$$

subject to the linear constraints

$$(8.2) \quad \sum_{j=1}^{n*} x_{ij} = s_i \qquad i = 1, 2, \ldots, m$$

$$(8.3) \quad \sum_{i=1}^{m} x_{ij} = d_j \qquad j = 1, 2, \ldots, n$$

* A discussion of summation notation appears in Appendix B.

Note that

(8.4) $x_{ij} \geq 0$ for all i and j

The quantities s_i and d_j are called the rim conditions whereas the matrix C with entries

$$C = \begin{bmatrix} c_{11} & c_{12} & \cdots & c_{ij} & \cdots & c_{1n} \\ c_{21} & c_{22} & \cdots & c_{2j} & \cdots & c_{2n} \\ \vdots \\ c_{i1} & c_{i2} & \cdots & c_{ij} & \cdots & c_{in} \\ \vdots \\ c_{m1} & c_{m2} & \cdots & c_{mj} & \cdots & c_{mn} \end{bmatrix}$$

is called the cost matrix.

Definition 8.2.1: A set of non-negative values x_{ij}, $i = 1, 2, \ldots, m$; $j = 1, 2, \ldots, n$, that satisfies (8.2), (8.3), and (8.4) is called a feasible solution to the transportation problem.

We assume that the total demand of all the warehouses equals the amount produced in all the plants. This means that

(8.5) $$\sum_{j=1}^{n} d_j = \sum_{i=1}^{m} s_i$$

A balanced condition is said to exist if (8.5) holds. The problem is solved, in general, by using the following procedure.

1. Define the objective function Z to be minimized with the rim conditions imposed on the problem.
2. Set up the $m \times n$ matrix with m rows representing the sources (plants, factories, etc.) and n columns representing the destinations (stores, warehouses, markets, customers, etc.).
3. Develop an initial feasible solution to the problem.
4. Examine whether moving the shipment through any of the cell (i, j) not used in the initial feasible solution would reduce the shipping cost.
5. Modify the shipping schedule by including that cell (i, j) whose inclusion in the program results in largest savings.
6. Repeat steps 4 and 5 until an optimal solution is obtained.

Let us formulate a typical transportation problem involving three plants and three warehouses. A manufacturing concern operates plants P_1, P_2, and P_3 in different regions. The weekly production of these plants is as follows:

Plants	Weekly Production
P_1	100
P_2	80
P_3	45
Total	225

The total supply of the firm is absorbed by warehouses W_1, W_2, and W_3. Their weekly requirement is as follows:

Warehouses	Weekly Requirements
W_1	90
W_2	60
W_3	75
Total	225

The transportation cost from each plant to each warehouse is given below:

	Warehouses		
From \ To	W_1	W_2	W_3
P_1	$8	$10	$6
P_2	$7	$4	$9
P_3	$13	$12	$8

(Plants)

Clearly, the deliveries can be arranged from the plants to the warehouses in several possible ways at varying costs. The problem is to determine the shipment x_{ij} from plant P_i, $i = 1, 2, 3$ to warehouse W_j, $j = 1, 2, 3$ in a manner that would minimize the delivery cost subject to the production capacity of the plants and the warehouse requirements.

As a first step, we present the relevant information in Table 8.1, in which each row represents the source (plant) and each column represents the destination (warehouse). The last row and the last column in the matrix, which represent, respectively, the demand of the warehouses and the supply from the plants, are referred to as the rim requirements.

Table 8.1

	Warehouses			
From \ To	W_1	W_2	W_3	Supply
P_1	8 x_{11}	10 x_{12}	6 x_{13}	100
P_2	7 x_{21}	4 x_{22}	9 x_{23}	80
P_3	13 x_{31}	12 x_{32}	8 x_{33}	45
Demand	90	60	75	225

(Plants)

The objective is to choose x_{ij} so as to minimize Z, where

$$Z = 8x_{11} + 10x_{12} + 6x_{13} + 7x_{21} + 4x_{22} + 9x_{23} + 13x_{31} + 12x_{32} + 8x_{33}$$

subject to the linear constraints

$$
\begin{aligned}
x_{11} + x_{12} + x_{13} && && &= 100 \\
& x_{21} + x_{22} + x_{23} && &= 80 \\
&& x_{31} + x_{32} + x_{33} &= 45 \\
x_{11} && + x_{21} && + x_{31} &= 90 \\
x_{12} && + x_{22} && + x_{32} &= 60 \\
x_{13} && + x_{23} && + x_{33} &= 75
\end{aligned}
$$

and

$$x_{ij} \geq 0 \qquad i, j = 1, 2, 3$$

We shall show that the optimal solution for this problem is

$$
\begin{aligned}
x_{11} &= 70, & x_{12} &= 0, & x_{13} &= 30 \\
x_{21} &= 20, & x_{22} &= 60, & x_{23} &= 0 \\
x_{31} &= 0, & x_{32} &= 0, & x_{33} &= 45
\end{aligned}
$$

and the minimum cost is \$1480.

8.3 THE INITIAL BASIC FEASIBLE SOLUTION

Before we outline the procedure, we consider it worth our while to point out that it suffices to specify only five of the six linear constraints. Because the total demand of the warehouses equals the total production of the plants, any solution satisfying any five of the six linear constraints will also satisfy the remaining constraint. In general, if m is the number of sources and n is the number of warehouses, we can specify the initial feasible solution with $m + n - 1$ linear equations. This means that the set of $m + n$ linear equations has one redundant constraint and can, therefore, be deleted without affecting the initial solution. This leads to the following definition.

Definition 8.3.1: An initial feasible solution with an allocation of $(m + n - 1)$ number of variables, x_{ij}, $i = 1, 2, \ldots, m$; $j = 1, 2, \ldots, n$, is called a basic feasible solution.

An initial basic feasible solution can be constructed by selecting the $(m + n - 1)$ variables x_{ij} one at a time. After each selection, we assign a value to that variable so as to satisfy a linear constraint. After $(m + n - 1)$ selections, an entire basic feasible solution has been constructed in such a manner that rim requirements are satisfied. We shall discuss here three methods:

1. The northwest-corner rule
2. The minimum entry method, and
3. Vogel's approximation method

for finding an initial basic feasible solution.

1. The northwest-corner rule provides that the allocation of the shipment from the plants to the warehouses begin in cell (1, 1) in the northwest (upper left-hand) corner of the matrix. This allocation is of a magnitude that exhausts either the production at plant P_1 or the requirement of warehouse W_1 or both. If this allocation exhausts the production of plant P_1, then we move down to cell (2, 1) in the first column and assign the quantity that exhausts the production of plant P_2 or satisfies the requirement of warehouse W_1. If the allocation of cell (1, 1) satisfies the demand of warehouse W_1, we move to cell (1, 2) in the first row and make the second allocation that either exhausts the remaining capacity of plant P_1 or satisfies the requirement of warehouse W_2, and so on. Thus, in general, if x_{ij} was the last variable selected for an assignment, we move to cell $(i, j + 1)$ in the ith row if plant P_i has any supply remaining, otherwise we move down to cell $(i + 1, j)$ in the jth column and make an allocation that exhausts either the capacity of plant P_{i+1} or satisfies the requirement of warehouse W_j. This procedure is continued until all the linear constraints are satisfied.

Let us illustrate this procedure with the problem in Section 8.2. Because $m = n = 3$, we need to find an initial basic feasible solution with $m + n - 1 = 5$ variables x_{ij}. If the number of occupied cells is less than $m + n - 1$, the solution is degenerate and will be handled by a method that we explain later in the chapter.

Because the rim values of the first row and the first column are 100 and 90, respectively, we allocate 90 units to the cell (1, 1). This assignment, while satisfying the requirements of warehouse W_1, leaves 10 units to be allocated to cell (1, 2) in the first row. Recall that warehouse W_2 requires 60 units of which 10 have been supplied by plant P_1. Thus, we assign 50 units from plant P_2 to cell (2, 2), leaving the excess of P_2's capacity to be assigned to cell (2, 3). Because W_3 requires 75 units, we move down to cell (3, 3) in the third row to pick up the supply of 45 units from plant P_3. Thus, we develop the initial basic feasible solution shown in Table 8.2, where the arrows simply represent the order in which the variables have been selected.

Table 8.2

Clearly, the initial solution consists of five cells and

$$x_{11} = 90, \quad x_{12} = 10, \quad x_{13} = 0$$
$$x_{21} = 0, \quad x_{22} = 50, \quad x_{23} = 30$$
$$x_{31} = 0, \quad x_{23} = 0, \quad x_{33} = 45$$

The transportation costs associated with this initial solution is

$$(90)(\$8) + (10)(\$10) + (50)(\$4) + (30)(\$9) + (45)(\$8) = \$1650$$

Note that this method of assignment did not take into consideration the shipping cost; consequently, the initial solution obtained by this method usually requires several iterations before an optimal solution is obtained. The "minimum entry method" that we discuss next requires fewer iterations than the northwest-corner rule and develops a basic feasible solution based on the cost information.

2. The minimum entry method provides that the first allocation begins in the cell with the smallest available cost in the cost matrix. The initial basic feasible solution is obtained by following the steps outlined below:

M1. Choose the cell with the lowest available cost c_{ij} and allocate the shipment so as to exhaust either the production of plant P_i or meet the requirements of warehouse W_j or both.

M2. Delete the ith row or the jth column, depending on whether the allocation exhausts the supply at source P_i or meets the requirement of warehouse W_j. If both of these occur simultaneously (degenerate case), delete the ith row unless it is the only row remaining, in which case delete the jth column.

M3. Adjust the supply remaining at plant P_i or the unfilled demand of warehouse W_j.

M4. If there remains two or more rows or columns not yet deleted, go to step M1. Otherwise, the initial basic feasible solution is obtained.

We shall now use the problem in the preceding section to illustrate this method. The lowest cost is $4, which appears in cell $(2, 2)$. Because production at plant P_2 and warehouse requirement of W_2 are 80 and 60 units, respectively, we assign $x_{22} = 60$. This allocation meets the requirements of warehouse W_2 and still leaves a supply of 20 units at plant P_2. Consequently, we delete the second column, adjust the supply remaining at the source, and reduce the requirements of warehouse W_2 to zero as shown in Table 8.3.

Table 8.3

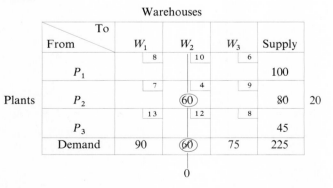

Because all three rows and the first and third columns are not yet crossed out, we return to step M1 and repeat the process. The lowest cost in the remaining matrix is 6 in cell (1, 3). Because the capacity of plant P_1 is 100 units and the requirement of warehouse W_3 is 75 units, we allocate $x_{13} = 75$ and cross out the first column. The supply remaining at plant P_1 and the requirement of warehouse W_1 not yet met is shown in Table 8.4.

Table 8.4

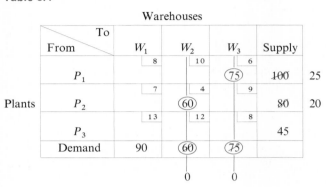

Because there are more than two rows and columns not yet crossed out, we go back to step M1. The smallest entry in the remaining cost matrix is \$7 in cell (2, 1) located in the middle left-hand corner. Recall that the supply remaining at plant P_2 is 20 units; thus, we assign $x_{21} = 20$. Obviously, this allocation exhausts the supply at plant P_2 and we cross out the second row. This algorithm requires two more steps to choose successively the cost entry 8 and then the cost entry 13 in the first column. The completed solution, along with the original rim condition, is presented in Table 8.5.

Table 8.5

	To				
		Warehouses			
From		W_1	W_2	W_3	Supply
Plants	P_1	⑧ 25	10	⑥ 75	100
	P_2	⑦ 20	④ 60	9	80
	P_3	⑬ 45	12	8	45
	Demand	90	60	75	225

The cost associated with this solution is

$$(25)(\$8) + (75)(\$6) + (20)(\$7) + (60)(\$4) + (45)(\$13) = \$1615$$

This is certainly an improvement over the solution developed earlier through the northwest-corner rule, but is not yet the lowest possible shipping schedule.

3. Vogel's approximation method also attempts to obtain the basic feasible solution based on the cost information. The necessary steps are outlined below:

V1. Compute the difference between the costs of two cheapest routes for each origin and each destination. Each individual difference is interpreted as a penalty for not choosing the cheapest route and is marked opposite each row and column.

V2. Identify the row or column with the largest difference. Allocate the shipment to the lowest-cost cell in that row or column so as to exhaust either the supply at a particular source or satisfy the demand at a warehouse.

V3. Drop the ith row or the jth column, depending on whether the allocation exhausts the supply at plant P_i or meets the requirements of warehouse W_j. If both of these occur simultaneously (degenerate case), delete the ith row unless it is the only row remaining, in which case drop the jth column.

V4. Adjust the supply remaining at source P_i or the demand of the warehouse not yet met.

V5. Go to step V1 and repeat the procedure until an initial assignment using $m + n - 1$ cells is obtained.

Let us return to the example in the preceding section and obtain the initial assignment by Vogel's approximation method. The row and column difference of the two cheapest routes are indicated against each row and each column as shown in Table 8.6.

Table 8.6

From \ To	W_1	W_2	W_3	Supply	Column Difference
P_1	8	10	6	100	2
P_2	7	4	9	80	3
P_3	13	12	8	45	4
Demand	90	60	75	225	
Row Difference	1	6	2		

The highest difference or penalty rating of 6 falls under column W_2. Because the first allocation is to be made to the lowest-cost cell under column W_2, we assign $x_{22} = 60$. This allocation meets the requirement of W_2 and leaves a supply of 20 units at plant P_2. Removing the column under W_2 temporarily, we recompute the difference between two cheapest routes for each origin and the remaining destinations as shown in Table 8.7.

Table 8.7

From \ To	W_1	W_2	W_3	Supply	Column Difference
P_1	8	10	6	100	2
P_2	7	4 (60)	9	20 (80)	2
P_3	13	12	8	45	5
Demand	90	(60) 0	75	225	
Row Difference	1		2		

Now the highest penalty rating of 5 falls in the third row. We therefore make an allocation of 45 units to the lowest-cost cell that exhausts the supply of plant P_3 and meets partially the demand of warehouse W_3. Removing the third row from the matrix, we make suitable adjustments in the supply remaining at source P_3 and the demand at warehouse W_3. The differences for the remaining origins and the destinations are recomputed. The result is shown in Table 8.8.

Table 8.8

From \ To	W_1	W_2	W_3	Supply	Column Difference
P_1	8	10	6	100	2
P_2	7	4 (60)	9	20 (80)	2
P_3	13	12	8 (45)	(45) 0	
Demand	90	(60) 0	(75) 30	225	
Row Difference	1		3		

Because the maximum difference occurs in the column for W_3, we make an allocation of 30 units to the lowest-cost cell under that column. This assignment of $x_{13} = 30$ satisfies the demand of warehouse W_3 and reduces the supply at plant P_1 accordingly. This yields the result shown in Table 8.9.

Table 8.9

From \ To	W_1	W_2	W_3	Supply	Column Difference
P_1	8	10	6 (30)	70 (100)	
P_2	7	4 (60)	9	20 (80)	
P_3	13	12	8 (45)	0 (45)	
Demand	90	(60) 0	(75) 0	225	
Row Difference					

The next step brings in the cost $7 in cell (2, 1) followed by the entry $8 in cell (1, 1). This calls for an assignment of $x_{11} = 70$ and $x_{21} = 20$ units, which certainly satisfies the demand of warehouse W_1. The initial basic feasible solution thus obtained is

$$x_{11} = 70, \quad x_{12} = 0, \quad x_{13} = 30$$
$$x_{21} = 20, \quad x_{22} = 60, \quad x_{23} = 0$$
$$x_{31} = 0, \quad x_{32} = 0, \quad x_{33} = 45$$

and the cost of this assignment is

$$(70)(\$8) + (30)(\$6) + (20)(\$7) + (60)(\$4) + (45)(\$8) = \$1480$$

which is considerably less than the cost associated with the initial solutions developed through the northwest-corner rule and the minimum entry method.

Let us now compare these three criteria we have used to develop the initial basic feasible solution to the problem. The northwest-corner rule is quick and straightforward, but disregards the unit shipping cost from the origin to the destination and hence the initial solution requires several iterations before reaching optimality. The minimum entry method develops the initial assignment by choosing the smallest available cost at each step and thus reduces the number of iterations required to reach an optimal solution. This method is improved further by basing the cell selection on the difference in the shipping cost between the two cheapest available routes for each origin and each destination. This measure makes effective use of the cost information, and the solution obtained is more near optimal than the ones obtained by the other two methods.

EXERCISE 8.1

Determine the initial basic feasible solution to each of the following transportation problems using the northwest-corner rule.

1.

Warehouses

From \ To	W_1	W_2	W_3	Supply
Plants P_1				85
P_2				65
Demand	45	75	30	150

2.

Warehouses

From \ To	W_1	W_2	W_3	Supply
Plants P_1				175
P_2				145
Demand	80	150	90	320

3.

Warehouses

From \ To	W_1	W_2	W_3	Supply
P_1				225
P_2				140
P_3				135
Demand	120	170	210	500

(Plants)

4.

Warehouses

From \ To	W_1	W_2	W_3	Supply
P_1				365
P_2				410
P_3				225
Demand	395	475	130	1000

(Plants)

5.

Warehouses

From \ To	W_1	W_2	W_3	W_4	Supply
P_1					115
P_2					235
P_3					310
Demand	145	170	240	105	660

(Plants)

6.

Warehouses

From \ To	W_1	W_2	W_3	W_4	Supply
P_1					365
P_2					225
P_3					295
Demand	270	245	210	160	885

(Plants)

Describe the initial basic feasible solution to each of the following transportation problems using
a. The minimum entry method
b. Vogel's approximation method

7.

Warehouses

From \ To	W_1	W_2	Supply
P_1	$1.30	$1.75	80
P_2	$2.25	$2.00	60
Demand	75	65	140

(Plants)

8.

Warehouses

From \ To	W_1	W_2	Supply
Plants			
P_1	$1.30	$1.50	80
P_2	$1.80	$2.25	45
Demand	70	55	125

9.

Warehouses

From \ To	W_1	W_2	W_3	Supply
Plants				
P_1	$1.20	$1.30	$1.05	115
P_2	$1.00	$0.90	$1.25	85
Demand	75	50	75	200

10.

Warehouses

From \ To	W_1	W_2	W_3	W_4	Supply
Plants					
P_1	$2.30	$2.50	$1.80	$1.40	47
P_2	$1.60	$2.00	$2.10	$2.00	35
Demand	27	17	18	20	82

11.

Warehouses

From \ To	W_1	W_2	W_3	Supply
Plants				
P_1	$13	$14	$10	95
P_2	$12	$11	$12	50
P_3	$12	$13	$14	70
Demand	75	60	80	215

12.

Warehouses

From \ To	W_1	W_2	W_3	Supply
Plants				
P_1	$12	$14	$16	110
P_2	$15	$12	$7	55
P_3	$17	$10	$13	70
Demand	65	90	80	235

13. Determine the initial basic feasible solution to the following problem by using
   a. The northwest-corner rule
   b. The minimum entry method
   c. Vogel's approximation method

From \ To	W_1	W_2	W_3	Supply
P_1	\$7	\$6	\$2	100
P_2	\$4	\$3	\$7	60
P_3	\$6	\$4	\$5	65
Demand	90	65	70	225

14. A corporation has three manufacturing plants that supply three warehouses. The daily production of the plants is

Plants	Products
P_1	55
P_2	50
P_3	45
	150

The daily requirements of the warehouses are as follows:

Warehouse	Requirements
W_1	40
W_2	55
W_3	55
	150

The freight rate per unit from each plant to each warehouse is

	W_1	W_2	W_3
P_1	\$0.90	\$1.00	\$1.00
P_2	\$1.00	\$1.40	\$0.80
P_3	\$1.20	\$1.00	\$0.90

Determine the initial basic feasible schedule using each of the following methods:
   a. The northwest-corner rule
   b. The minimum entry method
   c. Vogel's approximation method

15. A corporation XYZ has three factories shipping to three warehouses. The production of factories (in thousands of units), requirements of the warehouses (in thousands of units), and shipping cost per unit from each source to each warehouse is given on the next page:

Factories	Production	Warehouse	Requirements
F_1	80	W_1	90
F_2	60	W_2	70
F_3	55	W_3	35
	195		195

Freight Cost per Case

From \ To	W_1	W_2	W_3
F_1	$0.90	$0.70	$0.80
F_2	$1.00	$0.90	$1.30
F_3	$0.70	$0.60	$1.60

Determine the initial basic feasible schedule using each of the following methods:
a. The northwest-corner rule
b. The minimum entry method
c. Vogel's approximation method
and compare the costs.

Once an assignment is made using the northwest-corner rule, the minimum entry method, or Vogel's approximation method, the next step is to check whether or not the solution obtained can be improved. The evaluation procedure requires that each unused cell in the initial basic feasible solution be examined to determine whether or not moving a shipment into one of them reduces the delivery cost and then repeating this procedure until the lowest possible cost solution is obtained. There are, however, two methods for evaluating the unused cells:

1. The stepping-stone method
2. The modified distribution method, commonly referred to as MODI.

First, we discuss the stepping-stone method.

8.4 AN OPTIMAL SOLUTION—STEPPING-STONE METHOD

Recall that we obtained three initial basic feasible solutions for the transportation problem. Of these, let us consider the solution in Table 8.2 as the starting point for obtaining an optimal solution. There are nine cells in the matrix and our initial solution has used only five of them. Hence, we consider each of the remaining four cells

(1, 3), (2, 1), (3, 1), and (3, 2)

and examine if replacing any one of them with the one actually used would improve the initial solution. Let us evaluate cell (2, 1) as an illustration and assign x units to be supplied from plant P_2 to warehouse W_1. Note that an addition of a unit to cell (2, 1) adds $7 to the cost. Because the requirements of the warehouse must be satisfied, we must adjust the allocation of cell (1, 1) by subtracting x units from the initial assignment of 90 units. This clearly decreases the cost by $8 per unit. In order to make this adjustment and still satisfy the supply restriction at plants P_1 and P_2, we subtract x units from cell (2, 2) and then add x units to cell (2, 1). The closed path we follow in making these adjustments is given in Figure 8.1.

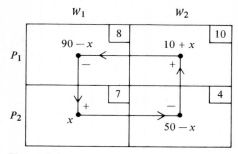

Figure 8.1

The net change in the cost is

$$-8 + 7 - 4 + 10 = \$5 \text{ per unit}$$

obtained by adding or subtracting a unit of the product on the route

$$(1, 1) \rightarrow (2, 1) \rightarrow (2, 2) \rightarrow (1, 2)$$

This means that each unit shipped from plant P_2 to cell $(2, 1)$ increases the distribution cost by \$5. Consequently, cell $(2, 1)$ is not included in the assignment. We still have three more cells and it is likely that using one of them may reduce the shipping cost. The evaluation of an unused cell proceeds as follows:

S1. Trace a closed path using the most direct route from the selected unused cell through at least three cells used in the solution and then back to the original unused cell.
S2. Use plus and minus signs alternately at each cell of the closed path, starting with a plus sign at the unused cell to be evaluated.
S3. Compute the net change in the cost along the closed path.
S4. Include the cell with the most negative value in the new solution.

Let us demonstrate the evaluation of one more unused cell $(3, 2)$. As before, we assign x units to cell $(3, 2)$ and make necessary adjustments in cells $(3, 3)$, $(2, 3)$, and $(2, 2)$. The shipping route associated with this assignment is shown in Figure 8.2.

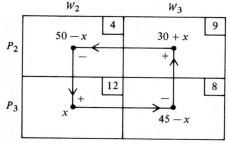

Figure 8.2

The net change in cost is

$$-4 + 12 - 8 + 9 = \$9 \text{ per unit}$$

obtained by adding or subtracting the cost of a unit on the route

$$(2, 2) \rightarrow (3, 2) \rightarrow (3, 3) \rightarrow (2, 3)$$

Because this route is more expensive than our initial solution, we shall not plan any changes based on this evaluation. Because it is likely that using any other unused cell might result in savings in the shipping cost, we return to step S1 and evaluate the remaining cells (1, 3) and (3, 1). The route suggested for each cell is given in Figures 8.3 and 8.4, respectively.

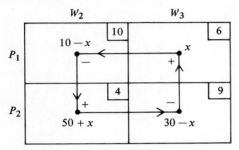

Figure 8.3

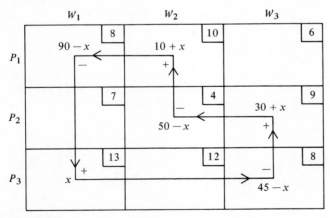

Figure 8.4

The closed path and the changes in cost for each of the unused cells are shown in Table 8.10. It is clear that every unit shipped from plant P_1 to warehouse W_3 results in savings of $9. Looking at Figure 8.3, we note that

$$10 - x \geq 0 \quad \text{and} \quad 30 - x \geq 0$$

Because x is to be made as large as possible, we choose $x = 10$. Thus, the second solution, which uses the five cells

$$(1, 1), (1, 3), (2, 2), (2, 3), (3, 3)$$

is given in Table 8.11.

Table 8.10

Unused Cell	Closed Route	Changes in Cost
(2, 1)	(1, 1)→(2, 1)→(2, 2)→(1, 2)	$-8+7-4+10=\$5$
(3, 2)	(2, 2)→(3, 2)→(3, 3)→(2, 3)	$-4+12-8+9=\$9$
(1, 3)	(3, 3)→(1, 3)→(1, 2)→(3, 2)	$-9+6-10+4=-\$9$
(3, 1)	(1, 1)→(3, 1)→(3, 3)→(2, 3)→(2, 2)→(1, 2)	$-8+13-8+9-4+10=\$12$

Table 8.11

From \ To	W_1	W_2	W_3	Supply
P_1	8 (90)	10	6 (10)	100
P_2	7	4 (60)	9 (20)	80
P_3	13	12	8 (45)	45
Demand	90	60	75	225

Thus,

$$x_{11} = 90, \quad x_{12} = 0, \quad x_{13} = 10$$
$$x_{21} = 0, \quad x_{22} = 60, \quad x_{23} = 20$$
$$x_{31} = 0, \quad x_{32} = 0, \quad x_{33} = 45$$

The cost associated with the solution is

$$90 \times \$8 + 10 \times \$6 + 60 \times \$4 + 20 \times \$9 + 45 \times \$8 = \$1560$$

We return to step S4 and examine if the delivery costs can be reduced further by replacing any of the unused cells with the one actually used in the second solution. Using the stepping-stone method, we compute the effect on the distribution cost for each of the unused cells

$$(1, 2), (2, 1), (3, 1), (3, 2)$$

The closed path for each of these cells is given in Figures 8.5, 8.6, 8.7, and 8.8, respectively. The changes in the delivery costs for each of the unused cells are shown in Table 8.12.

Cell (1, 2)

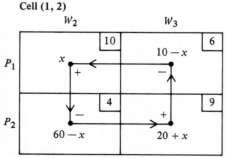

Figure 8.5

Cell (2, 1)

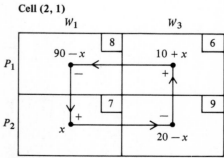

Figure 8.6

Cell (3, 1)

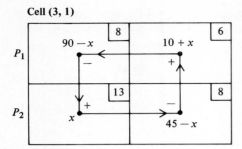

Figure 8.7

Cell (3, 2)

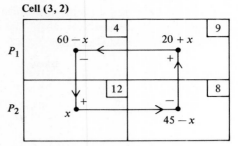

Figure 8.8

Table 8.12

Unused Cell	Closed Path	Changes in Cost
(1, 2)	(1, 3) → (1, 2) → (2, 2) → (2, 3)	$-6 + 10 - 4 + 9 = \$9$
(2, 1)	(1, 1) → (2, 1) → (2, 3) → (1, 3)	$-8 + 7 - 9 + 6 = -\$4$
(3, 1)	(1, 1) → (3, 1) → (3, 3) → (1, 3)	$-8 + 13 - 8 + 6 = \$3$
(3, 2)	(2, 2) → (3, 2) → (3, 3) → (2, 3)	$-4 + 12 - 8 + 9 = \$9$

The cell $(2, 1)$ with the negative value will be included in the new solution, because shipping one unit from point P_2 to warehouse W_1 reduces the delivery cost by \$4. Because $90 - x \geq 0$ and $20 - x \geq 0$ in Figure 8.6 and x is to be made as large as possible, we choose $x = 20$. The third solution, which uses the five cells

$$(1, 1), (1, 3), (2, 1), (2, 2), (3, 3)$$

is given in Table 8.13.

Table 8.13

To From	W_1	W_2	W_3	Supply
P_1	⑦⓪ 8	10	③⓪ 6	100
P_2	②⓪ 7	⑥⓪ 4	9	80
P_3	13	12	④⑤ 8	45
Demand	90	60	75	225

Thus,

$$x_{11} = 70, \quad x_{12} = 0, \quad x_{13} = 30$$
$$x_{21} = 20, \quad x_{22} = 60, \quad x_{23} = 0$$
$$x_{31} = 0, \quad x_{32} = 0, \quad x_{33} = 45$$

The corresponding shipping cost is

$$70 \times \$8 + 30 \times \$6 + 20 \times \$7 + 60 \times \$4 + 45 \times \$8 = \$1480$$

Note that this is exactly the same solution we obtained by using Vogel's approximation method. We go back to step S4 and examine each of the unused cells

$$(1, 2), (2, 3), (3, 1), (3, 2)$$

as to whether or not shipping products through any one of them results in further savings in the transportation cost. The analysis of the closed path for each of the unused cells is provided in Table 8.14.

Table 8.14

Unused Cell	Closed Path	Changes in Cost
$(1, 2)$	$(2, 2) \rightarrow (1, 2) \rightarrow (1, 1) \rightarrow (2, 1)$	$-4 + 10 - 8 + 7 = \$5$
$(2, 3)$	$(2, 1) \rightarrow (2, 3) \rightarrow (1, 3) \rightarrow (1, 1)$	$-7 + 9 - 6 + 8 = \$4$
$(3, 1)$	$(1, 1) \rightarrow (3, 1) \rightarrow (3, 3) \rightarrow (1, 3)$	$-8 + 13 - 8 + 6 = \$3$
$(3, 2)$	$(3, 3) \rightarrow (3, 2) \rightarrow (2, 2) \rightarrow (2, 1) \rightarrow (1, 1) \rightarrow (1, 3)$	$-8 + 12 - 4 + 7 - 8 + 6 = \$5$

Because none of the unused cells is associated with a negative value, we conclude that the solution in Table 8.13 is optimal and that the lowest cost is \$1480. The progress through the iterations is given below.

Iteration	Cost	Savings over Previous Solution
1	\$1650	
2	\$1560	\$90
3	\$1480	\$80

8.5 AN OPTIMAL SOLUTION—MODIFIED DISTRIBUTION METHOD

The modified distribution method has a pattern similar to that of the stepping-stone method except that it evaluates each of the unused cells in the process more efficiently. The main difference between these methods concerns that part of the solution at which the closed paths are drawn. In the stepping-stone method, a closed path is traced for each of the unused cells before the savings in respective costs, if any, can be calculated. The unused cell with the largest savings is identified as the one with the most negative value and then entered in the next solution. In the modified distribution method, however, the improvement costs of all the unused cells are calculated without having to trace their respective closed paths. In fact, we need to trace only one closed path in the modified distribution method after the unused cell with the most negative value has been identified.

We shall now illustrate the mechanics of the modified distribution method by solving the same problem. As discussed earlier, we may use the initial basic feasible solution as obtained by the northwest-corner rule, the minimum entry method, or Vogel's approximation method. We shall begin with the solution of Table 8.2 as obtained by the northwest-corner rule as our starting point.

As a first step, we determine a set of values for each row and each column. These values, which are by no means unique, depend on an initial basic feasible solution of the problem and are used to evaluate each of the cells not used in the solution. To compute u_i for each row and v_j for each column, we use the formula

$$c_{ij} = u_i + v_j$$

for each of the $m + n - 1$ cells used in the initial solution. Recall that c_{ij} is the shipping cost per unit from plant P_i to warehouse W_j. Note that there are $m + n - 1$

variables x_{ij} used in the initial solution and consequently there are $m + n - 1$ equations involving c_{ij}, u_i, and v_j. Because the number of unknowns u_i and v_j are $m + n$, we can assign an arbitrary value to one of the variables without violating the equations. Once one row or column number has been chosen arbitrarily, the rest of the rows and columns are determined by using the relation $c_{ij} = u_i + v_j$. To demonstrate, we give below each equation corresponding to $(m + n - 1)$ variables x_{ij} used in the initial basic feasible solution, as shown in Table 8.2. Thus,

$$8 = u_1 + v_1 \qquad 9 = u_2 + v_3$$
$$10 = u_1 + v_2 \qquad 8 = u_3 + v_3$$
$$4 = u_2 + v_2$$

Because there are six variables and five linear equations, we shall adopt the practice of setting $u_1 = 0$. Thus, we have

$$v_1 = 8, v_2 = 10, u_2 = -6, v_3 = 15, u_3 = -7$$

which together with the initial solution are shown in Table 8.15

Table 8.15

To From	W_1	W_2	W_3	Supply	Row Number
P_1	8 ⑨⓪	10 ⑩	6	100	$u_1 = 0$
P_2	7	4 ㊿	9 ㉚	80	$u_2 = -6$
P_3	13	12	8 ㊺	45	$u_3 = -7$
Demand	90	60	75	225	
Column Number	$v_1 = 8$	$v_2 = 10$	$v_3 = 15$		

After the row and column numbers have been computed, the next step is to evaluate the improvement index by using the relationship

$$c_{ij} - u_i - v_j$$

for each of the unused cells and then identify the cell with the most negative value. If $c_{ij} - u_i - v_j \geq 0$ for each of the cells not used in the solution, then we have reached an optimal solution and no further savings in the delivery cost are possible. The analysis for each of the unused cells is provided in Table 8.16.

Table 8.16

Unused Cell	$c_{ij} - u_i - v_j$	Changes in Cost
(1, 3)	$c_{13} - u_1 - v_3$	$-\$9$
(2, 1)	$c_{21} - u_2 - v_1$	$\$5$
(3, 1)	$c_{31} - u_3 - v_1$	$\$12$
(3, 2)	$c_{32} - u_3 - v_2$	$\$9$

Note that these changes in cost are identical to the ones shown in Table 8.10. We trace a closed path only for the cell that has demonstrated a largest improvement potential. Introducing cell (1, 3), a second solution is obtained that is identical to the corresponding second solution obtained by the stepping-stone method. This solution uses cells

$$(1, 1), (1, 3), (2, 2), (2, 3), (3, 3)$$

To test this solution for further improvement, we recalculate the values of u_i and v_j based on the second solution. Thus, using first the occupied cells, we have the following equations:

$$8 = u_1 + v_1 \qquad 9 = u_2 + v_3$$
$$6 = u_1 + v_3 \qquad 8 = u_3 + v_3$$
$$4 = u_2 + v_2$$

Setting $u_1 = 0$ as before, we have

$$v_1 = 8, v_3 = 6, u_2 = 3, v_2 = 1, u_3 = 2$$

These new row and column numbers along with the second solution are given in Table 8.17.

Table 8.17

From \ To	W_1	W_2	W_3	Supply	Row Number
P_1	8 ⑨⓪	10	6 ⑩	100	$u_1 = 0$
P_2	7	4 ⑥⓪	9 ②⓪	80	$u_2 = 3$
P_3	13	12	8 ④⑤	45	$u_3 = 2$
Demand	90	60	75	225	
Column Number	$v_1 = 8$	$v_2 = 1$	$v_3 = 6$		

Now we use the relationship

$$c_{ij} - u_i - v_j$$

for the unused cells (1, 2), (2, 1), (3, 1), and (3, 2) as before and identify the cell with the most negative value, if any. The analysis is given in Table 8.18.

Table 8.18

Unused Cells	$c_{ij} - u_i - v_j$	Changes in Cost
(1, 2)	$c_{12} - u_1 - v_2$	$9
(2, 1)	$c_{21} - u_2 - v_1$	$-$4
(3, 1)	$c_{31} - u_3 - v_1$	$3
(3, 2)	$c_{32} - u_3 - v_2$	$9

Again, the changes in cost in this table are precisely the same as exhibited in Table 8.12. Introducing cell (2, 1) in the new solution, a third solution is obtained as shown in Table 8.13. That this solution is optimal follows from the analysis of each of the cells (1, 2), (2, 3), (3, 1), and (3, 2) as given in Table 8.14.

8.6 UNEQUAL SUPPLY AND DEMAND CONDITIONS

We have discussed the transportation problem so far under the assumption (8.5) that the demand of the warehouses equals the total production of all the plants. Such a condition would, perhaps, be the exception rather than the rule. In actual practice, a manufacturing company has more orders than it can fill or its available inventory exceeds the demand. In either case, we must add a "dummy" source or destination to establish equality between the total production of the plants and the requirements of the warehouses.

Case 1: Supply Less Than Demand

If the capacity of the plants is not enough to meet the demand of the warehouses, one or more warehouses will not receive the full quantity ordered and this results in lost sales, smaller profits than were possible, and the probable risk of losing customers to competitors. Because the distribution method by the step-by-step procedure is not applicable unless supply equals demand, we must create a dummy source of supply to meet the excess demand. The cost of shipment from the dummy origin to each warehouse is assumed to be zero, because the dummy supplier will schedule no shipment and as such no costs are incurred. As an illustration, let us return to the original problem in Table 8.1 and assume that warehouse W_1 requires an additional 5 units weekly whereas W_2 and W_3 anticipate additional requirements of 10 units each. This means that the total demand is now 250 units, whereas the weekly capacity of the plants remains at 225. These unbalanced conditions necessitate an introduction of an imaginary supplier P_4. The problem can then be solved by using any of three methods we have discussed earlier. Table 8.19 shows an initial basic feasible solution as obtained by the northwest-corner rule.

Table 8.19

From \ To	W_1	W_2	W_3	Supply
P_1	8 (95) →	10 ⑤ ↓	6	100
P_2	7	4 (65) →	9 ⑮ ↓	80
P_3	13	12	8 ㊺ ↓	45
P_4	0	0	0 ㉕	25
Demand	95	70	85	250

The cost of this scheduled shipment is

$$(95)(\$8) + (5)(\$10) + (65)(\$4) + (15)(\$9) + (45)(\$8) + (25)(0) = \$1565$$

We advise the reader to solve the problem through the intervening iterations and verify that the solution in Table 8.20 is optimal with the associated cost of $1430.

Table 8.20

From \ To	W_1	W_2	W_3	Supply
P_1	8 ⑥⓪	10	6 ④⓪	100
P_2	7 ⑩	4 ⑦⓪	9	80
P_3	13	12	8 ④⑤	45
P_4	0 ②⑤	0	0	25
Demand	95	70	85	250

Thus, the optimal solution consists of six cells and

$$x_{11} = 60, \quad x_{12} = 0, \quad x_{13} = 40$$
$$x_{21} = 10, \quad x_{22} = 70, \quad x_{23} = 0$$
$$x_{31} = 0, \quad x_{32} = 0, \quad x_{33} = 45$$
$$x_{41} = 25, \quad x_{42} = 0, \quad x_{43} = 0$$

Note that in this case warehouse W_1 receives a partial shipment of 70 units as against 95 units it has ordered from the company.

Case 2: Supply Greater Than Demand

This unbalanced case represents what usually happens in well-managed inventory situations. The production of the plants exceeds the requirement of the warehouses and the profits are reduced by the loss caused by the unsold quantity. To solve the problem of this nature by the transportation algorithm, it is necessary that we add a dummy warehouse to absorb the excess production of the plants. This addition of warehouse establishes the balanced conditions between the capacities of the plants and the corresponding demand of all warehouses. Because no shipment is involved in the real sense, the transportation costs from the plants to this warehouse are zero. Suppose that in our problem the capacity of plants P_1, P_2, P_3 are 110, 95, and 50, respectively, so that the total supply is 255 units weekly as against the requirements of 225 units of the warehouses. The problem is balanced by introducing a fictitious warehouse W_4 which is scheduled to absorb the excess of the production. The problem is then solved by using the same procedure we have outlined in the preceding sections.

The initial basic feasible solution using the northwest-corner rule is given in Table 8.21.

Table 8.21

From \ To	W_1	W_2	W_3	W_4	Supply
P_1	8 (90) →	10 (20)	6	0	110
P_2	7	4 (40) →	9 (55)	0	95
P_3	13	12 (20) →	8 (30)	0	50
Demand	90	60	75	30	255

The cost of this assignment is

$$(90)(\$8) + (20)(\$10) + (40)(\$4) + (55)(\$9) + (20)(\$8) + (30)(0) = \$1735$$

We leave it for the reader to verify that the solution given in Table 8.22 is optimal and that the shipping cost is $1415.

Table 8.22

From \ To	W_1	W_2	W_3	W_4	Supply
P_1	8 (55)	10	6 (55)	0	110
P_2	7 (35)	4 (60)	9	0	95
P_3	13	12	8 (20)	0 (30)	50
Demand	90	60	75	30	255

EXERCISE 8.2

1. Consider the following transportation problem.

Warehouses

From \ To	W_1	W_2	W_3	Supply
Plants P_1	$6	$12	$4	100
P_2	$5	$9	$7	110
P_3	$8	$10	$6	35
Demand	90	70	85	245

Determine an initial basic feasible solution using each of the following criteria:

a. The northwest-corner rule

b. The minimum entry method

c. Vogel's approximation method

Starting with the initial solution obtained by each method, apply the modified distribution method to obtain the minimum-cost transportation schedule. Compare the number of iterations for the optimal solution in each case.

2. Consider the following transportation problem.

Warehouses

From \ To	W_1	W_2	W_3	Supply
F_1	$12	$17	$9	110
F_2	$10	$14	$12	60
F_3	$13	$15	$11	75
Demand	100	80	65	245

Factories (row label)

Determine an initial basic feasible solution using each of the following criteria:

a. The northwest-corner rule

b. The minimum entry method

c. Vogel's approximation method

Starting with the initial solution obtained by each method, apply the stepping-stone procedure to obtain the minimum-cost transportation schedule. Compare the number of iterations for the optimal solution in each case.

3. Consider the transportation problem given below.

Warehouses

From \ To	W_1	W_2	W_3	Supply
F_1	$8	$16	$10	40
F_2	$11	$17	$9	22
F_3	$10	$20	$21	8
Demand	30	25	15	70

Factories (row label)

Determine an initial basic feasible solution using each of the following methods:

a. The northwest-corner rule

b. The minimum entry method

c. Vogel's approximation method

Apply the modified distribution method to each of the initial solutions and develop the minimum cost transportation schedule.

4. Consider the following transportation problem.

Warehouses

From \ To	W_1	W_2	W_3	Supply
P_1	\$3	\$17	\$11	4
P_2	\$12	\$18	\$10	12
P_3	\$10	\$25	\$24	8
Demand	10	9	5	24

Plants (label at left of P_1, P_2, P_3)

Determine the minimum cost transportation schedule using an initial solution obtained by using each of the following methods:
a. The northwest-corner rule
b. The minimum entry method
c. Vogel's approximation method

5. ABC Manufacturing Company must ship its products from three factories to three warehouses. The weekly production of the factories is

Factories	Production
F_1	120
F_2	75
F_3	55
Total	250

The weekly requirements of the warehouses are

Warehouse	Requirement
W_1	100
W_2	90
W_3	60
Total	250

The shipping cost from each factory to the warehouse is given below:

From \ To	W_1	W_2	W_3
F_1	\$9	\$13	\$11
F_2	\$4	\$6	\$8
F_3	\$6	\$5	\$10

Determine the minimum-cost transportation schedule using an initial basic feasible solution obtained by each of the following methods:
a. The northwest-corner rule
b. The minimum entry method
c. Vogel's approximation method

6. A construction company moves material between three plants and three projects. The weekly production of the plants is as follows:

Plants	Production (in tons)
A	60
B	90
C	50
Total	200

The weekly requirements of the projects are

Project	Weekly Requirement (in tons)
I	100
II	70
III	30
Total	200

The shipping cost from each plant to the project site is given below:

	Project I	Project II	Project III
Plant A	$5	$6	$8
Plant B	$3	$7	$11
Plant C	$6	$8	$9

Determine the minimum transportation-cost schedule using an initial basic feasible solution obtained by each of the following methods:

a. The northwest-corner rule

b. The minimum entry method

c. Vogel's approximation method

7. Three factories are operated by the Austin Manufacturing Company. Currently its products are shipped to four different warehouses in different parts of the state. The weekly production of each factory is as follows:

Factories	Production
F_1	95
F_2	90
F_3	75
Total	260

The demand of the warehouses is

Warehouse	Requirement
W_1	80
W_2	68
W_3	52
W_4	60
Total	260

The freight rate per unit from each factory to each warehouse is given below:

	W_1	W_2	W_3	W_4
F_1	$6	$8	$3	$9
F_2	$5	$10	$9	$6
F_3	$9	$7	$12	$11

Determine the minimum cost shipping schedule using each of the following methods:

a. The minimum entry method

b. Vogel's approximation method

8. A manufacturing company maintains warehouses in Chicago, Louisville, and Cincinnati. Currently, the products are shipped from the warehouses to the customers in Toledo, Indianapolis, and St. Louis. The storage capacity of each warehouse is as follows:

Warehouses	Capacity (in tons)
Chicago	55
Louisville	70
Cincinnati	85
Total	210

The weekly requirements of the customers are as follows:

Customers in	Weekly Requirements (in tons)
Toledo	60
Indianapolis	75
St. Louis	75
Total	210

The shipping cost per ton from each warehouse to the destination is given below:

Destination / Warehouse	Toledo	Indianapolis	St. Louis
Chicago	$23	$18	$29
Louisville	$30	$11	$26
Cincinnati	$20	$10	$34

Determine the minimum transportation-cost schedule using an initial solution obtained by each of the following methods:

a. Vogel's approximation method

b. The minimum entry method

Compare the number of iterations for the optimal solution in each case.

9. A firm operates three factories that ship its goods to three regional warehouses. The production capacity of the factories and the requirements of the warehouses is given below:

Factories	Capacity	Warehouses	Requirements
F_1	80	W_1	95
F_2	90	W_2	55
F_3	75	W_3	70
Total	245	Total	220

The freight rate per unit from each factory to each warehouse is given below:

From \ To	W_1	W_2	W_3
F_1	$5	$4	$6
F_2	$11	$7	$8
F_3	$2	$6	$10

Determine the minimum transportation cost using an initial basic feasible solution obtained by each of the following methods:
a. The minimum entry method
b. Vogel's approximation method

10. A firm producing a single product has three plants and three customers. The shipping cost, requirements of the customers, and the capacities of the plants are given below:

Plants	Supply Available Per Week	Customers	Requirements Per Week
P_1	170	C_1	150
P_2	150	C_2	160
P_3	120	C_3	160
Total	440	Total	470

Cost information:

From \ To	C_1	C_2	C_3
P_1	$14	$9	$12
P_2	$7	$6	$7
P_3	$4	$7	$8

Determine the minimum transportation cost using the initial basic feasible solution obtained by the minimum entry method.

8.7 DEGENERATE CASE

The distribution method requires that an initial basic feasible solution to a transportation problem consists of $m + n - 1$ variables x_{ij}, $i = 1, 2, \ldots, m$, and $j = 1, 2, \ldots, n$. This implies that if m and n are the number of sources and destinations, respectively, then the number of occupied cells must be $m + n - 1$. If a feasible solution occurs with less than $m + n - 1$ occupied cells, the transportation problem is said to be degenerate. In that event it becomes impossible to assign the row numbers u_i and the column numbers v_j, because it is essential that $m + n - 1$ cells be occupied so as to compute row and column numbers after the arbitrary assignment of a row or a column.

Degeneracy in a transportation problem may develop either in the initial assignment or in the subsequent solutions. To resolve degeneracy in the initial feasible solution, we place an ε (epsilon) in one or more of the empty cells so that the number of occupied cells is $m + n - 1$. We treat ε as though it represents a very small quantity of goods to be shipped through that cell route. The ε, which is assumed to be zero when actually used in the movements of goods from one cell to another, is generally placed in one or more cells in such a manner that all empty cells can be evaluated.

As an illustration of the development of degeneracy during the initial solution, let us consider the transportation problem in Table 8.23.

Table 8.23

From \ To	W_1		W_2		W_3		Supply
		8		10		6	
P_1							100
		7		4		9	
P_2							50
		13		12		8	
P_3							45
Demand	90		60		45		195

Following the northwest-corner rule, we obtain the initial assignment as shown in Table 8.24.

Table 8.24

From \ To	W_1		W_2		W_3		Supply
		8		10		6	
P_1	⑨⓪→		⑩				100
		7		4		9	
P_2			㊄⓪				50
		13		12		10	
P_3					㊅⑤		45
Demand	90		60		45		195

Because the number of occupied cells is four whereas $m + n - 1 = 5$, the solution is degenerate. Note that the degeneracy has been caused by an allocation of 50 units to cell (2, 2), which exhausts the supply at source P_2 and also satisfies simultaneously the requirements of warehouse W_2. However, we can resolve this type of degeneracy by an addition of $\varepsilon = 0$ to cell (3, 2) as shown in Table 8.25. This assignment restores the broken chain typical of the northwest-corner rule and helps evaluate whether or not an inclusion of one of the empty cells will reduce the delivery costs.

Table 8.25

From \ To	W_1	W_2	W_3	Supply
P_1	8 (90)→	10 (10)	6	100
P_2	7	4 (50)	9	50
P_3	13	12 ($\varepsilon=0$)→	10 (45)	45
Demand	90	60	45	195

The cost of the assignment is

$$(90)(\$8) + (10)(\$10) + (50)(\$4) + (45)(\$10) = \$1470$$

The number of occupied cells is five and the solution is no longer degenerate. Hence, we can now assign row and column numbers u_i and v_j so as to apply the modified distribution method and test this solution for further improvement. Using the five occupied cells, we have the following equations:

$$8 = u_1 + v_1 \qquad 12 = u_3 + v_2$$
$$10 = u_1 + v_2 \qquad 10 = u_3 + v_3$$
$$4 = u_2 + v_2$$

Setting $u_1 = 0$, we obtain

$$v_1 = 8, v_2 = 10, u_2 = -6, u_3 = 2, v_3 = 8$$

Now we use the relationship

$$c_{ij} - u_i - v_j$$

for each of the unused cells (1, 3), (2, 1) (2, 3), and (3, 1) and identify the cell with the most negative value, if any. The analysis is shown in Table 8.26.

Table 8.26

Unused Cells	$c_{ij} - u_i - v_j$	Changes in Cost
(1, 3)	$c_{13} - u_1 - v_3$	-2
(2, 1)	$c_{21} - u_2 - v_1$	5
(2, 3)	$c_{23} - u_2 - v_3$	7
(3, 1)	$c_{31} - u_3 - v_1$	3

Because $c_{13} - u_1 - v_3 = -2$, the solution in Table 8.25 is not optimal and can therefore be improved. We now trace a closed loop only for cell (1, 3) as shown in Figure 8.9.

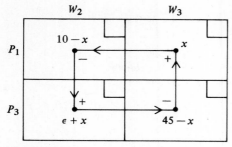

Figure 8.9

Because $10 - x \geq 0$ and $45 - x \geq 0$ and x is to be made as large as possible, we choose $x = 10$. Introducing cell $(1, 3)$, we obtain a second solution as given in Table 8.27.

Table 8.27

From \ To	W_1	W_2	W_3	Supply
P_1	(90) [8]	[10]	(10) [6]	100
P_2	[7]	(50) [4]	[9]	50
P_3	[13]	(10) [12]	(35) [10]	45
Demand	90	60	45	195

The cost associated with this solution is

$$(90)(\$8) + (10)(\$6) + (50)(\$4) + (10)(\$12) + (35)(\$10) = \$1450$$

We urge the reader to go through one more iteration and verify that the solution in Table 8.27 is optimal and that no further savings are possible.

Consider now another transportation problem in Table 8.28 and its initial solution in Table 8.29 as derived by following the northwest-corner rule.

Table 8.28

From \ To	W_1	W_2	W_3	Supply
P_1	[8]	[10]	[6]	105
P_2	[7]	[4]	[8]	70
P_3	[13]	[12]	[10]	50
Demand	60	70	95	225

Table 8.29

From \ To	W_1	W_2	W_3	Supply
P_1	⑧ (60)→	⑩ (45)	⑥	105
P_2	⑦	④ (25)→	⑧ (45)	70
P_3	⑬	⑫	⑩ (50)	50
Demand	60	70	95	225

The cost associated with the initial assignment is

$$(60)(\$8) + (45)(\$10) + (25)(\$4) + (45)(\$8) + (50)(\$10) = \$1770$$

Should we compute the improvement index for each of the unused cells

$$(1, 3), (2, 1), (3, 1), (3, 2)$$

we soon discover that cell $(1, 3)$ is a serious candidate to be considered for the next solution. We trace a closed loop for cell $(1, 3)$ as shown in the next figure, Figure 8.10. Because $45 - x \geq 0$ and x is to be made as large as possible, we choose $x = 45$. This necessitates shifting 45 units each from cells $(2, 3)$ and $(1, 2)$ to cells $(1, 3)$ and $(2, 2)$ as guided by the closed path in Figure 8.10. The solution resulting from this new assignment as given in Table 8.30 is degenerate. Note that the degeneracy has been caused by including an unused cell $(1, 3)$ in the new solution and this has resulted in the simultaneous elimination of two cells $(1, 2)$ and $(1, 3)$ from the solution in Table 8.29. Recall that in a nondegenerate case, addition of an unused cell normally results in the elimination of only one cell.

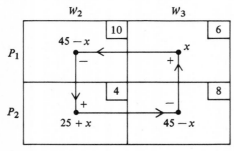

Figure 8.10

Table 8.30

From \ To	W_1	W_2	W_3	Supply
P_1	⑧ (60)	⑩	⑥ (45)	105
P_2	⑦	④ (70)	⑧	70
P_3	⑬	⑫	⑩ (50)	50
Demand	60	70	95	225

Because the degeneracy has developed during the subsequent solution stage, we may resolve it by adding ε to that recently eliminated cell along the closed path in Figure 8.10 that has the lowest shipping cost. If there is a tie and the vacated cells are associated with the same cost, then ε may be added to any one of the cells recently eliminated. Because cell (2, 3) has the lowest shipping cost, we add ε to this cell as shown in Table 8.31.

Table 8.31

From \ To	W_1	W_2	W_3	Supply
P_1	8 (60)	10	6 (45)	105
P_2	7	4 (70)	8 ($\varepsilon=0$)	70
P_3	13	12	10 (50)	50
Demand	60	70	95	225

We can now assign a set of row and column numbers as before, compute the improvement index for each of the unused cells by using the relation $c_{ij} - u_i - v_j$, identify the cell with the most negative value for inclusion in the subsequent solution, and then test it for optimality by using the standard procedure discussed before.

EXERCISE 8.3

Determine the minimum cost solution to each of the following problems using the northwest-corner rule.

1.   Warehouses

Plants	From \ To	W_1	W_2	W_3	Supply
	P_1	$12	$10	$13	150
	P_2	$8	$12	$6	100
	P_3	$9	$10	$10	125
	Demand	130	120	125	375

2.   Warehouses

Plants	From \ To	W_1	W_2	W_3	Supply
	P_1	$7	$6	$2	80
	P_2	$4	$5	$7	120
	P_3	$6	$4	$5	50
	Demand	80	100	70	250

3.

Warehouses

From \ To	W_1	W_2	W_3	Supply
P_1	$9	$10	$10	85
P_2	$10	$14	$8	90
P_3	$12	$10	$9	30
Demand	60	90	55	205

(Plants)

4.

Warehouses

From \ To	W_1	W_2	W_3	Supply
P_1	$8	$10	$5	70
P_2	$7	$4	$18	30
P_3	$13	$12	$10	40
Demand	40	60	40	140

(Plants)

5.

Warehouses

From \ To	W_1	W_2	W_3	Supply
P_1	$8	$12	$18	60
P_2	$12	$8	$12	40
P_3	$15	$8	$15	20
Demand	30	40	50	120

(Plants)

6.

Warehouses

From \ To	W_1	W_2	W_3	Supply
P_1	$7	$6	$8	80
P_2	$10	$9	$11	90
P_3	$5	$10	$12	15
Demand	50	90	45	185

(Plants)

8.8 THE ASSIGNMENT MODEL

The assignment model is a special type of transportation model where the "resources" are allocated to the "destinations" on a one-to-one basis so as to minimize the total cost. Problems of this kind appears in many contexts such as the assignment of the available sales force to different regions, the location of development engineers to several construction sites, the placement of players to different positions on the field, and so on. Management makes assignment on a one-to-one basis in such a manner that the group maximizes the revenue from the sales, the development engineer produces the best product, or the players win the maximum number of games. The approach used in making assignments is based on the assumption that some performance measure such as utility or cost is known for each assignment. With information about the number of assignees i, $i = 1, 2, 3, \ldots, n$, performing the same number of jobs j, $j = 1, 2, \ldots, n$, and the payoff measure c_{ij} available for each assignment, the objective is to determine the strategy that minimizes the total cost or maximizes the total utility.

Suppose, for instance, that the ABC Corporation has established four personnel training centers C_1, C_2, C_3, and C_4 in different parts of the country. Each center is set up to provide the necessary training for a period of three months for a group of employees who have been with the company for the last six months and have been nominated in batches of six by a regional office of the corporation. The teams thus nominated are accepted on the first-come, first-served basis and are assigned to the training centers by the personnel department at the home office. We assume that the corporation offices O_1, O_2, O_3, and O_4 have nominated their employees for training; the estimated daily cost of each trainee based essentially on the traveling distance between the regional office and the training center, boarding, lodging, and other incidental expenses is given in Table 8.32.

Table 8.32

Regional Offices	Training Centers			
	C_1	C_2	C_3	C_4
O_1	$27	$28	$25	$29
O_2	$29	$27	$32	$26
O_3	$23	$25	$26	$28
O_4	$27	$28	$24	$22

There are various methods for making assignments. First, we can use the transportation model for solving this assignment problem. Second, we can enumerate all possible assignments and then identify the one with the minimum cost. For instance, one of the assignments may require the matching of the staff from regional offices O_1, O_2, O_3, and O_4 with the training centers C_3, C_4, C_1, and C_2, respectively. The cost associated with this assignment is

$$\$25 + \$26 + \$23 + \$28 = \$102$$

Third, we may use a much more efficient method for solving such problems. This method, known as Flood's technique or the Hungarian method of assignment, which henceforth will be referred to as the assignment model, consists of three basic steps.

The first step requires that we compute the total opportunity cost from the payoff matrix. This is done by first subtracting the minimum value in each row from the value of every other element in that row and then subtracting the minimum value in each column from the value of every other element in that column. Because the minimum number in the first row is $25, we subtract this value from every element in the first row and derive the regional opportunity cost of O_1 as shown below:

$$O_1 C_1 = \$27 - \$25 = \$2$$
$$O_1 C_2 = \$28 - \$25 = \$3$$
$$O_1 C_3 = \$25 - \$25 = 0$$
$$O_1 C_4 = \$29 - \$25 = \$4$$

Repeating the same procedure for the elements in the remaining rows, we have the regional office opportunity cost as shown in Table 8.33.

Table 8.33

Regional Offices	Training Centers			
	C_1	C_2	C_3	C_4
O_1	$2	$3	$0	$4
O_2	$3	$1	$6	$0
O_3	$0	$2	$3	$5
O_4	$5	$6	$2	$0

Note that "0" in each row is associated with the training center nearest the regional office corresponding to that row. Thus, center C_3 is nearest corporation office O_1, C_1 is nearest O_3, and center C_4 is nearest to two regional offices O_2 and O_4. Next, we compute the opportunity cost of the training centers by subtracting the value of the minimum element in each column from all elements in that column. Thus, we have the total opportunity cost as shown in Table 8.34.

Table 8.34

Regional Offices	Training Centers			
	C_1	C_2	C_3	C_4
O_1	$2	$2	$0	$4
O_2	$3	$0	$6	$0
O_3	$0	$1	$3	$5
O_4	$5	$5	$2	$0

The second step is to determine whether or not an optimal assignment can be made on the basis of the information we have derived in the total opportunity cost matrix. An optimal assignment can always be made if there exists one "0" in each row and in each column. If there are two or more "0's" in the same row (or column), we can determine whether or not an optimal assignment can be made by drawing straight lines (horizontally and vertically) through the total opportunity cost matrix in such a manner that the number of lines necessary to cover all zeros is minimum. If the matrix is $n \times n$ (in this case 4×4) and all "0" in Table 8.34 can be covered by no less than n lines, then an optimal assignment can be made and the problem is solved. On the other hand, if the minimum number of lines necessary to cover all "0" is less than n, then an optimal assignment cannot be made and the total opportunity cost table must be revised. Applying this procedure, we discover that the optimal assignment can be made, because Table 8.35 shows that we require exactly four lines to cover five "0's."

Table 8.35

	C_1	C_2	C_3	C_4
O_1	2	2	0	4
O_2	3	0	6	0
O_3	0	1	3	5
O_4	5	5	2	0

To determine this assignment, we choose a row (or column) with a single "0" in it and box it. If there are other "0's" in the column (or row) containing the boxed "0," circle them. Continue this process until rows and columns with a single "0" are exhausted. If there remains rows and columns having two or more "0's", we continue boxing "0" in each row (or column) and circling other "0's" in its column (or rows) until all "0's" are either boxed or circled. Then the boxed "0's" yield an optimal assignment.

Using the above guidelines, we proceed as follows. Because there is a "0" in cell (1, 3), we box it. There is a single "0" each in the third and fourth rows; we box each of them. There is another "0" in the corresponding column four; we circle it. This leaves a "0" in cell (2, 2) and we box it. This results in Table 8.36.

Table 8.36

	C_1	C_2	C_3	C_4
O_1	2	2	[0]	4
O_2	3	[0]	6	⓪
O_3	[0]	1	3	5
O_4	5	5	2	[0]

Because there is only one boxed "0" in each row and in each column, an optimal assignment is readily apparent. This means that staff from office O_1 goes to training center C_3, the O_2 staff goes to C_2, the O_3 staff goes to C_1, and the O_4 team is assigned to training center C_4. Note that the boxed "0's" in Table 8.36 correspond to the boxed entries in the original Table 8.32 reproduced below:

	C_1	C_2	C_3	C_4
O_1	$27	$28	[$25]	$29
O_2	$29	[$27]	$32	$26
O_3	[$23]	$25	$26	$28
O_4	$27	$28	$24	[$22]

The daily cost of this assignment is

$$\$25 + \$27 + \$23 + \$22 = \$97$$

As soon as this assignment was decided upon, the personnel department at the home office was informed that the group from regional office O_3 would not be able to participate in the training program due to some unavoidable circumstances. Regional office O_5 was next on the list; the new cost matrix is given in Table 8.37.

Table 8.37

	C_1	C_2	C_3	C_4
O_1	$27	$28	$25	$29
O_2	$29	$27	$32	$26
O_5	$35	$33	$31	$28
O_4	$27	$28	$24	$22

Repeating the first step, we have the total opportunity cost shown in Table 8.38(a).

Table 8.38(a)

	C_1	C_2	C_3	C_4
O_1	$0	$2	$0	$4
O_2	$1	$0	$6	$0
O_5	$5	$4	$3	$0
O_4	$3	$5	$2	$0

Following the second step, we find that an optimal assignment cannot be made because two horizontal lines through O_1 and O_2 and one vertical line through column C_4 are enough to cover all "0's" as shown in Table 8.38(b). Because the 4×4 matrix is covered by using less than four lines, we must revise the total opportunity cost table by using the following procedure.

1. Select the lowest entry in the uncovered cells in Table 8.38(b).
2. Subtract this number from all uncovered elements; then add this number to each element covered twice by the horizontal and vertical lines; leave the remaining elements unchanged.

Table 8.38(b)

	C_1	C_2	C_3	C_4
O_1	$0	$2	$0	$4
O_2	$1	$0	$6	$0
O_5	$5	$4	$3	$0
O_4	$3	$5	$2	$0

This results in another total opportunity cost shown in Table 8.39(a). Because all "0's" in this table can be covered by exactly four lines as shown in Table 8.39(b), no further adjustment is necessary.

Table 8.39(a)

	C_1	C_2	C_3	C_4
O_1	0	2	0	6
O_2	1	0	6	2
O_5	3	2	1	0
O_4	1	3	0	0

Table 8.39(b)

	C_1	C_2	C_3	C_4
O_1	0	2	0	6
O_2	1	0	6	2
O_5	3	2	1	0
O_4	1	3	0	0

Let us now determine this assignment. There is a single "0" in the O_2 row; box it. There is no other "0" in the C_2 column. The O_5 row has a single "0"; box it. Note that there is another "0" in the corresponding C_4 column; circle it. This leaves only one "0" in the O_4 row, which we box, and circle the "0" that appears in cell (1, 3). This necessitates boxing a "0" in cell (1, 1) as shown in Table 8.39(c). Note that now there is only one boxed "0" in each row and in each column. Thus, an optimal assignment is that the staff from regional office O_1 goes to training C_1, the staff from O_2 goes to C_2, the O_5 staff is assigned to center C_4 and the O_4 staff goes to center C_3. The boxed "0" in Table 8.39(c) corresponds to the boxed entries in the original Table 8.37 we reproduce below.

Table 8.39(c)

	C_1	C_2	C_3	C_4
O_1	[0]	2	(0)	6
O_2	1	[0]	6	2
O_5	3	2	1	[0]
O_4	1	3	[0]	(0)

	C_1	C_2	C_3	C_4
O_1	[$27]	$28	$25	$29
O_2	$29	[$27]	$32	$26
O_5	$35	$33	$31	[$28]
O_4	$27	$28	[$24]	$22

The daily cost of this assignment is

$$\$27 + \$27 + \$28 + \$24 = \$106$$

EXERCISE 8.4

1. Three workers can be used on three different jobs on a one-to-one basis. Each worker has a different cost for each job, which appears in the following table.

Jobs \ Workers	W_1	W_2	W_3
J_1	$23	$29	$32
J_2	$15	$20	$13
J_3	$18	$22	$25

Determine the best allocation of workers to various jobs so as to minimize costs.

2. The Alexander Products Company has three jobs that can be completed on three machines. Each job can be assigned to one and only one machine. The cost of each job on each machine is given in the following table.

Job	M_1	M_2	M_3
J_1	$23	$29	$21
J_2	$10	$14	$13
J_3	$17	$16	$14

Determine the best assignment of the machines to the jobs in order to minimize costs.

3. The Bishop Manufacturing Company has three types of products that can be produced on three machines. The cost of each product on each machine is given in the following table.

Products	M_1	M_2	M_3
P_1	$12	$16	$19
P_2	$10	$18	$20
P_3	$15	$14	$12

What is the best allocation of the products to the various machines that will reduce costs?

4. The Nielson Construction Company has three development engineers to be assigned to three construction sites on a one-to-one basis. The hourly cost for each personnel on each job is given in the following table.

Projects	E_1	E_2	E_3
P_1	$9	$17	$13
P_2	$8	$12	$15
P_3	$13	$11	$8

Determine the best assignment of the personnel available to various construction projects in order to minimize costs.

5. A Publishing Company has four salespeople available for assignment to four territories in the State of California. The daily cost of each salesperson in each region is given in the following table.

Regions	Salespeople			
	Jim	John	Steve	Bob
R_1	$19	$22	$29	$18
R_2	$23	$21	$22	$16
R_3	$20	$18	$19	$17
R_4	$30	$22	$17	$21

What is the best assignment the management can make to minimize the costs?

6. Suppose that the daily cost of each salesperson in some territories in Exercise 5 has changed during the last six months as shown in the table below.

Regions	Salespeople			
	Jim	John	Steve	Bob
R_1	$21	$24	$31	$20
R_2	$25	$23	$20	$18
R_3	$24	$23	$21	$19
R_4	$32	$21	$19	$23

Examine whether or not any relocation of the salespeople is necessary. If so, determine the new assignment so as to minimize the daily cost incurred by the management.

7. Five workers at an engineering workshop are to be assigned, one each, to five machines. The cost of each worker on each machine is given in the following table.

Workers	Machines				
	M_1	M_2	M_3	M_4	M_5
Dave	$13	$11	$12	$6	$7
Steve	$18	$10	$7	$11	$6
Peter	$20	$12	$7	$11	$8
Bill	$10	$8	$10	$7	$5
Vince	$9	$13	$19	$8	$12

Determine the job schedule so as to minimize cost. Is there more than one optimal assignment?

8. Five salespeople have recently been hired for assignment to five distribution centers on a one-to-one basis. The cost of each salesperson in each distribution center is given in the following table.

Salespeople	Distribution Centers				
	D_1	D_2	D_3	D_4	D_5
Bob	$10	$11	$5	$4	$9
Jim	$5	$10	$8	$12	$9
Kirby	$12	$11	$6	$7	$11
Kerry	$13	$18	$12	$10	$18
Ray	$11	$19	$14	$13	$10

Determine the best assignment of salespeople to the distribution centers so as to minimize costs.

9

Permutations and Combinations

9.1 COUNTING AND THE MULTIPLICATION RULE

Despite the complexity of many procedures available in modern technology, the simple process of counting continues to play a dominant role in our everyday life. One still has to count the number of students in a college, size of a response to a mail order questionnaire, the number of automobiles registered in the State of Nebraska, the number of persons killed in highway accidents, the number of telephone calls received at an office, and so on. Not all counting processes are so simple, however. For example, to compute the number of ways in which n persons can be lined up in a row is a problem that has been of interest for generations. In how many ways can six guests be seated at a round table so that two particular guests do not sit next to each other? In how many ways can three positions be filled if there are ten applicants? What is the number of signals that can be given with six flags of different colors? Although these questions are fascinating in their own right, answers to these questions will be needed in the study of probability which we shall encounter in later chapters.

In the study of "how many" or "what is possible," there are essentially two kinds of problems: First, there arises the problem of a complete listing of all possibilities in a given experiment and, second, there is the problem of determining in how many different ways a specific thing can take place. The latter problem needs more attention, because there are many problems in which we can avoid a complete listing and save ourselves both the time and the effort involved in otherwise exacting work.

It may appear to a casual observer that the first kind of problem is simple and straightforward; this is not always the case. The "simple" methods of counting have practical limitations, and these methods are often inadequate. Suppose, for instance, that four members A, B, C, and D are eligible for nomination for the offices of president and secretary of a mathematics club and we need to determine in how many ways these two positions can be filled. Can you list all the arrangements? How many possibilities are there? To handle problems like this, it helps to have a tree diagram like that of Figure 9.1. Note that the tree diagram takes order into

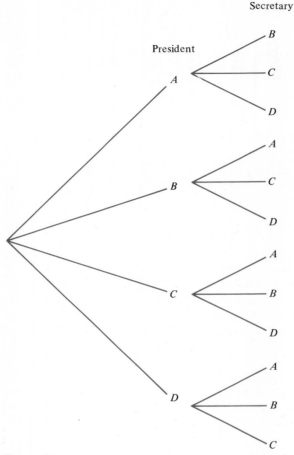

Figure 9.1

account. Thus, AB and BA count as two distinct arrangements; the first one refers to the possibility that A is the president and B is the secretary, whereas the second takes into account that B is the president and A is the secretary. Order is the essence of such arrangements, and any change in order yields a completely different arrangement.

The diagram shows that there are four branches corresponding to the nomination of A, B, C, and D as the president, and after this nomination there are three candidates left and any one of them can be chosen as the secretary. For instance, if A is elected as the president, the club members are free to nominate one of the remaining candidates B, C, or D as the secretary. Because there are three possibilities for secretary corresponding to each of the four possible nominations for president, there are in all $4 \times 3 = 12$ different ways the two positions can be filled. Looking at the tree we see that it has 12 different paths along the branches corresponding to the 12 different ways in which the president and secretary can be nominated.

As another illustration, suppose that a commuter train to New York has five coaches and we need to determine the number of ways in which Mr. White and Mr. Nelson can be assigned to a coach so that no two of them ride in the same coach. Apparently, Mr. White can be assigned to any one of the five coaches, and after he is seated, Mr. Nelson can go in any one of the remaining four coaches. Thus, there are in all $5 \times 4 = 20$ different possibilities. These examples illustrate the following multiplication principle:

> If an operation consists of two separate steps, of which the first can be performed in n different ways and corresponding to each of these n ways there are p ways of performing the second step, then the entire operation can be completed in $n \cdot p$ different ways.

Thus, if a bus line offers 10 routes between New York and Chicago, there are $10 \times 9 = 90$ different ways in which a visitor from New York can go to Chicago and return by a different route; if a menu provides the choice of eight different kinds of pancakes and five kinds of beverages, there are in all $8 \times 5 = 40$ different ways in which one can order pancakes and a beverage. Also, if someone wants to buy one of five available gifts in a catalog and have it sent by parcel post or by first-class mail, then there are in all $5 \times 2 = 10$ different ways in which the whole transaction can take place.

Example 9.1

How many two-digit numerals can be formed from the five digits 1, 2, 3, 4, 5 so that no digits are repeated?

SOLUTION

To form numerals of two digits, we have to fill two places, the tens and the units. Apparently, there are five ways of filling the tens place because any one of the digits 1, 2, 3, 4, 5 can be placed in this position. Because no digit can be repeated, the units place can be filled with any one of the remaining four digits. From the multiplication rule, it follows that two places can be filled in $5 \times 4 = 20$ ways, as follows:

12	13	14	15
21	23	24	25
31	32	34	35
41	42	43	45
51	52	53	54

We now generalize the above rule so that it will apply to operations involving more than two steps:

> If an operation consists of m separate steps, of which the first can be performed in n_1 ways, the second can be completed in n_2 ways, the third can be performed in n_3 ways, and so on, for the m separate steps, then the entire operation can be performed together in

$$n_1 \times n_2 \times n_3 \times \cdots \times n_m \text{ ways.}$$

Thus, if a restaurant menu offers a choice of three soups, five meat dishes, four desserts, and a choice of coffee, tea, or milk, then there are in all $3 \times 5 \times 4 \times 3 = 180$ different ways in which one can order a meal consisting of a soup, a meat dish, a dessert, and a beverage.

Example 9.2

In how many ways can five people be assigned as managers to the five branches of a supermarket chain store?

SOLUTION

The problem requires the filling of five places. Any one of the five people may be assigned to the first branch; four people are left and there are four ways of assigning the second person to the next store, no matter which of the five people was assigned to fill the first spot. The first two places can, therefore, be filled in $5 \times 4 = 20$ ways. Now, there are three people yet to be assigned, and any one of them can be assigned to the third store. Thus, the first three people can be placed in $5 \times 4 \times 3 = 60$ different ways. Following this reasoning, it follows that all five people can be assigned in

$$5 \times 4 \times 3 \times 2 \times 1 = 120$$

ways. ■

EXERCISE 9.1

1. A salesman has five shirts and six ties. How many different combinations of a shirt and tie can he wear?

2. There are five different routes connecting city A to city B. How many ways can a round trip be made from A to B and back?

3. A businessman is planning to go from New York to Cleveland with one stopover at Pittsburgh. He has a choice of a plane, a train, or a bus from New York and a choice of train or bus from Pittsburgh. Draw a tree diagram indicating the different choices for making a complete trip to Chicago.

4. A manufacturer offers a basic kitchen cabinet with three styles of hinges, four styles of doorpulls, and five wood finishes. How many different styles of kitchen cabinets are available?

5. A car manufacturer offers 20 color choices, six choices of body style, and four choices of fabric. How many cars are required for a complete display?

6. A seminar has five speakers. In how many orders can they speak?

7. In how many ways can five executives be seated in a conference room with eight chairs?

8. How many numerals can be formed by using all the digits 2, 4, 5, 7, 8, no digit being repeated? How many of these numbers are multiples of 5? How many of these are even?

9. Given five flags of different colors, how many different signals can be made by hoisting them on a vertical staff if
a. three flags are used for each signal
b. at least two flags must be used for each signal

9.2 PERMUTATIONS

In this section we shall show that the multiplication rule provides a general method for finding the number of distinct arrangements of n different things taken r at a time. For many types of problems, this approach can be shortened by means of convenient symbols and formulas we now introduce.

Definition 9.2.1: The product of the first n positive integers is called n factorial and is denoted by $n!$. If $n = 0$, then we define $0! = 1$. Thus,

$$n! = n \times (n - 1) \times (n - 2) \times \cdots 3 \times 2 \times 1$$

In particular,

$$1! = 1$$
$$2! = 2 \times 1 = 2$$
$$3! = 3 \times 2 \times 1 = 6$$
$$4! = 4 \times 3 \times 2 \times 1 = 24$$
$$5! = 5 \times 4 \times 3 \times 2 \times 1 = 120$$

The factorial notation is very useful for representing large numbers. Note that

$$5! = 5 \times (4!), 6! = 6 \times (5!), \ldots, 100! = 100 \times (99!)$$

In general,

$$n! = n \times (n - 1)!$$

Definition 9.2.2: Any arrangement of r objects taken from a set of n distinct objects is called a permutation of n objects taken r at a time. For the sake of brevity, the number of possible arrangements is denoted by ^nP_r, $r \leq n$.

Proposition 9.2.1: The number of permutations of n different objects taken r of them at a time, when none of the objects is to be repeated in any arrangement, is

$$^nP_r = n(n - 1)(n - 2) \cdots (n - r + 1) = \frac{n!}{(n - r)!}$$

PROOF

The proof follows directly from the multiplication rule. Apparently, r objects are to be chosen from a set of n objects, one at a time. The first object is selected from the set of n distinct objects, the second from the set of $(n - 1)$ remaining objects, and the third from the set of $(n - 2)$ remaining objects, and so on, until finally the rth object is chosen from the set of $[n - (r - 1)]$ remaining objects. From the multiplication principle, it follows that r objects can be selected in

$$^nP_r = n(n - 1)(n - 2) \cdots (n - r + 1)$$

ways. Now we multiply the numerator and denominator of the fraction

$$\frac{n(n - 1)(n - 2) \cdots (n - r + 1)}{1}$$

by $(n - r)(n - r - 1)(n - r - 2) \cdots 2 \cdot 1$. Hence,

$$^nP_r = \frac{n(n - 1)(n - 2)(n - 3) \cdots (n - r + 1)(n - r)(n - r - 1) \cdots 2 \times 1}{(n - r)(n - r - 1) \cdots 2 \times 1}$$

The numerator is the product of the integers from n down to 1, whereas the denominator is the product of the first $(n - r)$ integers, so that

$$^nP_r = \frac{n!}{(n - r)!}$$ ∎

Example 9.3

$$^9P_3 = \frac{9!}{6!} = 9 \times 8 \times 7 = 504$$ ∎

Example 9.4

How many nonsense words of three letters can be formed from the letters a, b, c, d, e using each letter only once?

SOLUTION

Because these letters in different orders constitute different nonsense words, the result is the number of permutations of five objects taken three at a time:

$$^5P_3 = \frac{5!}{2!} = 5 \times 4 \times 3 = 60 \text{ words}$$ ∎

Example 9.5

What is the possible number of ways in which five students can be seated in a classroom with 15 desks?

SOLUTION

There are five seats to fill and 15 desks from which to choose. The result is the number of permutations of 15 distinct objects taken five at a time:

$$^{15}P_5 = \frac{15!}{10!} = 15 \times 14 \times 13 \times 12 \times 11 = 360{,}360$$ ∎

Example 9.6

A passenger train has eight coaches. In how many ways can four students travel if they must ride in different coaches?

SOLUTION

Of eight coaches available in the passenger train, four students need to occupy four coaches. This corresponds to a selection of four objects from a set of eight distinct objects, which can be accomplished in

$$^8P_4 = \frac{8!}{4!} = 8 \times 7 \times 6 \times 5 = 1680$$ ∎

Example 9.7

In how many ways can six students stand in a line to pay their fees at the business office counter?

SOLUTION

This corresponds to the case $r = n$ in Proposition 9.2.1. Because $(n - r) = 0$ and $0! = 1$, it follows that the number of permutations of a set of six different objects, taken all together, is $6! = 720$. In general,

$$^nP_n = n!$$
■

Example 9.8

In how many ways can the letters of the word SOCIAL be arranged so that O and C may always be together?

SOLUTION

Because O and C are to appear together, we may count these as one letter. Then the number of permutations of five different letters

S, (OC), I, A, L

taken all together, is $5! = 120$. But every such arrangement gives $2! = 2$ separate arrangements when O and C are arranged between themselves as OC and CO. Thus, the required number of permutations is

$$5!2! = 120 \times 2 = 240$$
■

EXERCISE 9.2

1. Evaluate
   a. $5!$ **b.** $^8P_4$ **c.** $^9P_3$ **d.** $^7P_7$
2. How many words can be formed from the letters of the words
   a. SOUND   **b.** MATRIX   **c.** COMPUTE
3. How many words can be formed from the letters of the word SPECTRUM taken
   a. three at a time
   b. four at a time
   c. eight at a time
4. How many license plates bearing four letters can be made from the letters of the alphabet if repetition of a letter is not permitted?
5. In how many ways can the letters of the word PAYMENT be arranged? How many of these arrangements begin with P? How many will begin with P and end in T? How many of these have Y and M together?
6. In a Holiday Inn, six rooms in a row are to be assigned at random to six guests, two of whom are from Illinois. What is the number of possible arrangements so that the guests from Illinois are assigned rooms side by side?

7. There are eight invited guests to be seated in eight seats arranged in a row. How many different seating arrangements are possible if
   a. the invitation is accepted by six guests
   b. the invitation is accepted by eight guests and two particular guests ask to be seated next to each other
   c. the invitation is accepted by eight guests but two particular guests wish not to be seated side by side
8. How many six-digit numerals can be formed from the six digits 4, 5, 6, 7, 8, and 9, no digit being repeated? How many of these are even? How many of these are multiples of 5?
9. How many five-digit numerals can be formed from the digits 0, 1, 2, 3, 4, and 5, no digits being repeated?
10. A state report on crime consists of nine volumes numbered 1 to 9. In how many ways can these volumes be placed on a shelf?
11. In how many ways can eight persons stand in a row at a box office?
12. Six students are to take an examination, two in marketing and four in other subjects. In how many ways can they be seated in one row so that the two students taking the examination in marketing do not sit next to each other?
13. Five married couples have bought 10 seats in a row for a certain show. In how many different ways can they be seated? What is the number of seating arrangements if all the men are to sit together and all the women are to sit together?

Proposition 9.2.2: The number of permutations of n different objects taken r at a time, when each object can be repeated any number of times in an arrangement, is n^r.

Once again, we have an application of the multiplication rule. Suppose that we have r children in an elementary school and n different kinds of ice cream are available. The first child can be served with any one of the n flavors; that is, in n ways. When this has been done, there are again n ways of serving the second child corresponding to each of the n flavors that were offered to the first child. Thus, there are $n \times n = n^2$ ways of serving the first two children. The third child can also be given one of the n varieties for each of the n^2 possibilities of treating the first two children. Thus, the first three children can be served in $n^2 \times n = n^3$ ways. We observe that the exponent of n is the same as the number of children enjoying ice cream. It follows, therefore, that the number of ways of serving r children is n^r. ∎

Example 9.9

A multiple-choice test has 20 questions with four possible answers for each question. How many different sets of 20 answers are possible?

SOLUTION
Here, $n = 4$, $r = 20$. Thus, the required permutations are 4^{20}. ∎

Example 9.10

In how many ways can five prizes be given away to four boys when (a) each boy is eligible for all the prizes, and (b) when any boy may win all but one of the prizes?

SOLUTION

a. There are four ways of giving away the first prize because it can be given to any one of the four students; there are again four ways of disposing of the second prize, and so on. The required number of permutations are $4^5 = 1024$.

b. There are only four students and as such there are only four possibilities in which a student may have all the prizes, hence, the number of permutations in this case is four less than for case (a); that is, $4^5 - 4 = 1020$. ∎

Example 9.11

A combination lock consists of five rings each marked with the five digits 1, 2, 3, 4, and 5. What is the largest possible number of unsuccessful attempts in opening the lock if one tries to guess the combination?

SOLUTION

Each of the five rings can be set in a position in five ways. Here, $n = 5$, $r = 5$, so that the number of all positions in which rings can be set is $5^5 = 3125$. Because one of these is the correct combination to open the lock, the total number of unsuccessful attempts is $5^5 - 1 = 3124$. ∎

EXERCISE 9.3

1. For the five objects a, b, c, d, and f, list all permutations of these objects taken two at a time when none of these objects can be repeated in any permutation.
2. Grades of A, B, C, D, and F are assigned to a class of five students in psychology. In how many ways can these students be graded if no two students receive the same grade? How many ways can grades be assigned if only A, B, or C is assigned?
3. How many different ways can a 10-question multiple-choice test be answered if each question has three possibilities?
4. Cliff's Pizza Palace offers pepper, onion, mushroom, sausage, meatball, and anchovy as toppings for the cheese base of the pizza. How many different pizzas can be ordered?
5. An automobile license plate contains two letters followed by four numerals. Assuming that all 26 letters of the alphabet and all numerals, 0 through 9, are used, how many license plates can be made?
6. Consider an urn containing four balls, numbered 1 to 4. What is the possible number of drawing three balls
   a. if a ball is replaced before drawing the next one
   b. if a ball is not replaced before drawing the next one
7. Consider an urn containing six balls, numbered 1 to 6. What is the possible number of drawing four balls
   a. if a ball is replaced before drawing the next ball
   b. if a ball is not replaced before drawing the next one
8. How many four-letter nonsense words can be made from a set of 26 letters of an alphabet if
   a. any letter may be repeated any number of times
   b. a letter may not be repeated

9. How many three-digit numerals can be formed from the digits 2, 3, 4, 5, and 6 if
   a. a digit may be repeated any number of times
   b. a digit may not be repeated
10. How many five-digit numerals can be formed from the digits 0, 1, 2, 3, and 4, when a digit may be repeated any number of times and 0 is not allowed as a first digit?

Proposition 9.2.3: The number of permutations of n objects taken all together, when p of the n objects are alike and of one kind, q others are alike and of another kind, and so on, up to t others alike and of still another kind, is given by

$$\frac{n!}{p!q!\cdots t!}$$

PROOF

Suppose that x is the total number of permutations. In any of these arrangements, replace the p like objects by unlike objects, say, $a_1, a_2, \ldots, a_p$. These p new objects can be arranged among themselves in $p!$ new permutations, and if the corresponding changes are made in each of the x permutations, the total number of arrangements thus formed is $x \times p!$. Similarly, if q like objects were also replaced by distinct and distinguishable objects, say, $b_1, b_2, \ldots, b_q$, the total number of permutations would be $x \times p! \times q!$. Proceeding along these lines, the total number of arrangements would be given by

$$x \times p! \times q! \times \cdots \times t!$$

Note that the objects are now different and n in number and these may be arranged in $n!$ permutations. Thus,

$$x \times p! \times q! \times \cdots \times t! = n!$$

or

$$x = \frac{n!}{p!q!\cdots t!} \qquad\blacksquare$$

Example 9.12

How many different arrangements can be formed from the letters of the word ARRANGEMENT?

SOLUTION

There are eleven letters in all; however, the a's, r's, e's, and n's each appear twice. Thus,

$$n = 11, p = 2, q = 2, r = 2, \text{ and } s = 2$$

and number of distinguishable permutations is

$$\frac{11!}{2!2!2!2!} = 2{,}494{,}800 \qquad\blacksquare$$

Example 9.13

In how many ways can 12 flags be hoisted on a vertical staff if three of them are white, four are red, and five are green?

SOLUTION

Here, $n = 12$, $p = 3$, $q = 4$, and $r = 5$. The number of distinct arrangements is

$$\frac{12!}{3!4!5!} = 27,720$$ ∎

Circular Arrangements

From the previous discussion, we know that six persons invited for dinner may seat themselves in a row in any of 6! or 720 different ways. The answer would be different if the guests were to be seated around a circular table. Denoting the guests by the letters A, B, C, D, E, and F, we assume that one of the possible ways in which the guests can be seated around the circular table is as shown in Figure 9.2.

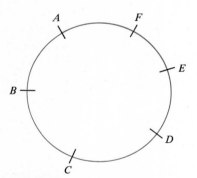

Figure 9.2

Starting with the different letters and reading them in a counterclockwise direction, the various possible seating arrangements may be expressed as

$$ABCDEF, \ BCDEFA, \ CDEFAB, \ DEFABC, \ EFABCD, \ FABCDE$$

Although these are different linear permutations, they are the same when regarded as a circular arrangement. Thus, a single circular arrangement of the six letters results from six different linear permutations. If the required number of circular arrangements of the six letters is x, then the total number of linear arrangements of these persons is $6x$. We have established earlier that six persons can be seated in a linear arrangement in 6! different ways; hence,

$$6x = 6! \quad \text{so that} \quad x = \frac{6!}{6} = 5!$$

Thus, the number of ways in which six persons can be seated around a circular table is 5!. Similarly, the number of distinct circular arrangements of n persons taken n at a time is given by $(n - 1)!$. This seems natural, for the seats are not numbered, there is no first or last seat at a round table, and the only essential feature to be considered is the position of one person relative to the others sitting at the same table. If one person is fixed in one position, then the remaining $(n - 1)$ persons can be arranged among themselves in $(n - 1)!$ different ways.

We wish to emphasize that the above example is applicable if n persons are to be seated around a circular table. The situation is different if we wish to count the number of arrangements in which n persons are to be seated around a circular table in such a way that all persons do not have the same neighbors in any two arrangements.

We have established that the total number of ways in which six guests can be seated at a round table is $5! = 120$ ways. Two of these 120 arrangements are shown in Figure 9.3. All six guests have same neighbors in both the arrangements, with the essential difference that the left-hand neighbor in one becomes the right-hand neighbor in the other. If all persons are not to have the same neighbors in any two permutations, we should accept only one of these arrangements. Thus, the total number of arrangements is $\frac{1}{2}(5!)$ or 60 different ways.

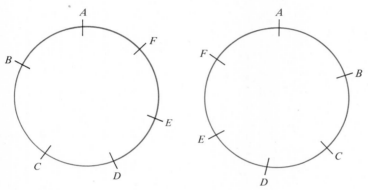

Figure 9.3

In considering similar circular permutations, for example, arrangements of keys on a chain, beads on a necklace, and so on, two permutations are considered the same if one can be obtained from the other by turning the chain or necklace over. Thus, in the case of n objects, there are $\frac{1}{2}(n - 1)!$ distinct arrangements. This formula has meaning if $n \geq 3$.

Example 9.14

In how many ways can eight children sit in a merry-go-round relative to one another? In how many of these arrangements will some children have different children in front of them, the merry-go-round being revolved in either direction?

SOLUTION

We have eight children, hence the number of ways is $7! = 5040$. In half of these arrangements, that is, 2520, some children will have different children in front of them because the merry-go-round can be revolved in two different directions. ■

Example 9.15

In how many ways can six gentlemen and six ladies be seated for a round-table conference so that no ladies sit together?

SOLUTION

The number of ways in which six gentlemen can be seated at a round table occupying alternate seats is given by 5!. Then the ladies have a choice of six remaining seats and this arrangement can be completed in 6! different ways. Now, using the fundamental rule of multiplication, we conclude that the required number is 5! × 6! = 86,400. ∎

EXERCISE 9.4

1. How many different arrangements can be formed from the letters of the following words?
   a. PARALLEL
   b. BLOSSOM
   c. CALCUTTA
   d. DIVIDEND
   e. CONFERENCE
   f. CONNECTICUT
   g. MASSACHUSETTS
   h. MISSISSIPPI

2. A man has six red flags, five green flags, and four black flags. If he uses all flags in a row to form a signal, how many signals are possible?

3. Anita has four quarters, three dimes, and five nickels all minted in the same year with the same mint mark. In how many ways can she arrange them in a line with tails up?

4. In how many ways can nine accounts be assigned to three different accountants so that each one gets three accounts?

5. In how many ways can nine parcels be placed in three bags, each bag containing three parcels, if there are two heavy parcels that cannot be placed in the same bag?

6. In how many different ways can seven ladies be seated at a round table?

7. In how many ways can eight keys be placed on a key ring? Ten keys? Twelve keys?

8. In how many ways can four guests be seated at a round table so that all guests do not have the same neighbors in any two arrangements?

9. A woman is about to string a charm bracelet with 10 different charms. In how many ways can she string the charms?

10. In how many ways can eight beads of different colors be arranged
    a. in a necklace
    b. in a row

11. In how many ways can 12 children at a birthday party be seated
    a. around a circular table
    b. on the same side of a rectangular table

12. In how many ways can 10 children at a birthday party be seated at a round table if two of the children ask to be seated next to each other?

13. In how many ways can five men and five women be seated at a circular table if the men and the women occupy alternate seats?

14. In how many ways can 12 persons be seated around a circular table if three of them must be adjacent?

15. In how many ways can nine different television sets be arranged in a row so that no two particular sets are together? If there are four black-and-white and five color sets, in how many ways can they be arranged in a circle so that no two color sets are together?

9.3 COMBINATIONS

In previous sections, we obtained formulas that enabled us to count the number of ways in which r objects can be arranged in a row or a circle from a set of n different objects. There are many problems that require us to make a selection of r objects from a set of n objects without any regard to "order." For example, a hand of cards consisting of jack, queen, king, ace, and ten of clubs is the same as one that is dealt in the order queen, jack, ace, king, and ten of clubs. Again, choosing an executive committee of three members, "Berman, Michael, and Smith," is the same committee as "Michael, Smith, and Berman." The order in which the members of the committee have been selected plays no role whatsoever. Thus, the fundamental difference between a permutation and a combination lies in the fact that the order in the arrangement is not relevant in a combination, whereas in a permutation problem the order is essential. To illustrate this point further, let us consider the digits 1, 2, 3, and 4 taken three at a time. An application of the multiplication rule results in 24 different arrangements; those involving only 1, 2, and 3 are

$$(1, 2, 3), (1, 3, 2), (2, 1, 3), (2, 3, 1), (3, 1, 2), (3, 2, 1)$$

These permutations constitute the same combination. Similarly, we can take a subset consisting of the three digits 1, 2, and 4 and permute its elements in six ways, yielding the permutations

$$(1, 2, 4), (1, 4, 2), (2, 1, 4), (2, 4, 1), (4, 1, 2), (4, 2, 1)$$

As another illustration, suppose that a club of six persons decide to form an executive council consisting of any three members and we are interested in finding the number of executive councils that can be formed. In the language of sets, we are seeking the number of subsets of three elements that can be obtained from a set of six distinct elements. If the six elements of the set are identified by the letters A, B, C, D, E, and F, then there are 20 possible subsets—each consisting of three elements:

$$ABC, ABD, ABE, ABF, ACD, ACE, ACF, ADE, ADF, AEF$$

$$BCD, BCE, BCF, BDE, BDF, BEF, CDE, CDF, CEF, DEF$$

If we had wished to consider the order in which three members have been selected to form an executive council, the answer would be

$${}^6P_3 = 6 \times 5 \times 4 = 120$$

but each set of three elements would then be counted six times and thus constitute six different permutations. Because this argument is valid for any three members constituting any executive council, the total number of ways in which three members can be selected is given by

$$\frac{{}^6P_3}{6} = \frac{120}{6} = 20$$

These examples underscore the important distinction between a permutation and a combination: In a permutation, order is taken into consideration, whereas in combination problems, the order is of no significance.

It is usually neither desirable nor feasible to list all the possible combinations and then count them in the usual manner. The list may simply get too long in some problems. Thus, in the above example, if there had been 20 members in a club, with six to be selected, the list would have had 38,760 different possible combinations.

Ordinarily, we must decide from the nature of the problem whether it involves permutation formulas or combination techniques. The decision depends mainly on the answer to the question: Is order important in the problem? For example, if we are to arrange four books on a shelf, it is natural to regard *ABCD* and *ADCB* as two different arrangements, and we must take order into the consideration. But if we are selecting four books to take along with us on vacation, order hardly matters and combinations are involved. Likewise, three people, *A*, *B*, and *C*, can stand in a row in six different ways but if they are to constitute a committee, it is evident that there is only one committee.

Definition 9.3.1: Any subset of *r* objects selected with complete disregard to their order from a set of *n* different objects is called a combination of the *n* objects taken *r* at a time. Symbolically, the total number of such possible combinations is denoted by

$$^{n}C_{r} \quad \text{or} \quad \binom{n}{r}, \qquad \text{where } r \leq n$$

Proposition 9.3.1: The number of combinations of *n* different objects taken *r* at a time is given by

$$\binom{n}{r} = {^{n}C_{r}} = \frac{n!}{r!(n-r)!}$$

PROOF

Each of the $\binom{n}{r}$ combinations of *r* objects can be arranged in *r*! different ways. Therefore, $r!\binom{n}{r}$ yields the total number of permutations of *n* objects taken *r* at a time. Hence,

$$r!\binom{n}{r} = {^{n}P_{r}}$$

Using Proposition 9.2.1,

$$\binom{n}{r} = \frac{{^{n}P_{r}}}{r!} = \frac{n!}{r!(n-r)!} \qquad ■$$

Example 9.16

In how many ways can a Congressional subcommittee of five be chosen from a committee of 10 members?

SOLUTION

The number of possibilities of selecting five members from a group of 10 members is given by the formula

$$\binom{10}{5} = \frac{10!}{5!5!} = \frac{10 \times 9 \times 8 \times 7 \times 6}{5 \times 4 \times 3 \times 2 \times 1} = 252 \qquad ■$$

Example 9.17

In how many ways can a poker hand of five cards be dealt from a standard deck of 52 cards?

SOLUTION

The selection of five cards can be made in

$$\binom{52}{5} = \frac{^{52}P_5}{5!}$$

$$= \frac{52 \times 51 \times 50 \times 49 \times 48}{5 \times 4 \times 3 \times 2 \times 1}$$

$$= 2{,}598{,}960 \qquad \blacksquare$$

Example 9.18

A committee of three Republicans and four Democrats is to be selected from among six Republicans and eight Democrats. In how many ways can the committee be formed?

SOLUTION

The Republicans can be chosen in $\binom{6}{3} = 20$ ways, whereas the Democrats can be selected in $\binom{8}{4} = 70$ ways. An application of the multiplication rule yields

$$20 \times 70 = 1400 \text{ ways} \qquad \blacksquare$$

Example 9.19

In how many ways can an employer select 10 new employees from a group of 12 applicants if a particular applicant must be (a) selected, (b) rejected?

SOLUTION

The number of combinations of 12 applicants taken 10 at a time is given by

$$\binom{12}{10} = \frac{12!}{10!2!} = 66$$

a. If one particular applicant must be selected, we need to select nine more of the remaining 11. This can be accomplished in

$$\binom{11}{9} = \frac{11!}{9!2!} = 55 \text{ ways}$$

b. If one applicant is not to be selected, the employer needs to choose 10 applicants from the remaining group of 11. This can be done in

$$\binom{11}{10} = \frac{11!}{10!1!} = 11 \text{ ways} \qquad \blacksquare$$

Example 9.20

In how many ways can $p + q$ detectives be assigned to two zones containing p and q detectives, respectively?

SOLUTION

Each selection of p detectives for the first zone leaves the remaining q detectives to be assigned to the second zone. Hence, the required number of combinations is given by

$$\binom{p + q}{p} = \frac{(p + q)!}{p!q!}$$

Example 9.21

In how many ways can $m + n + p$ salespeople be assigned to three regions containing m, n, and p salespeople, respectively?

SOLUTION

For the first region of p salespeople, there are $m + n + p$ persons available, so that there are $\binom{m+n+p}{p}$ ways in which the p salespeople can be assigned to the first region. This leaves $m + n$ persons available from which one can select the n persons to go in the second region; consequently, the n salespeople for the second zone can be selected in $\binom{m+n}{n}$ ways. This leaves us with m persons to go in the third region. By multiplying these expressions, we obtain the number of ways in which $m + n + p$ salespeople can be assigned to three distinct regions. Thus,

$$\binom{m + n + p}{p} \times \binom{m + n}{n} = \frac{(m + n + p)!}{p!(m + n)!} \cdot \frac{(m + n)!}{n!m!} = \frac{(m + n + p)!}{m!n!p!}$$

Example 9.22

Mr. Kaplan invites a party of $(m + n)$ friends to dinner and places m at one circular table and the remaining n at another circular table. In how many ways can he complete their seating arrangement?

SOLUTION

Evidently, there are $\binom{m+n}{m}$ ways of selecting m friends for the first table. These m people can be seated at the first round table in $(m - 1)!$ ways. This leaves n persons for which the seating arrangement at the second circular table can be completed in $(n - 1)!$ ways. Hence, the total number of arrangements for the $m + n$ friends to be seated at two circular tables is given by

$$\binom{m + n}{m}(m - 1)!(n - 1)! = \frac{(m + n)!(m - 1)!(n - 1)!}{m!n!}$$

$$= \frac{(m + n)!}{mn}$$

EXERCISE 9.5

1. Evaluate:

a. $\binom{8}{3}$ **b.** $\binom{12}{10}$ **c.** $\binom{100}{99}$

2. How many committees of five representatives can be formed from a group of 12 persons?

3. An electronic circuit may fail at eight stages. If it fails at exactly four stages, in how many ways can this happen?

4. In how many ways can a 12-question true-false exam be answered if you make the same number of answers true as you do false?

5. The Boston Red Sox have 40 players on the team. Assume that each player can play any position; in how many ways can the manager choose nine players to play in a game?

6. A contractor needs five bricklayers and 14 apply for the job. In how many ways can five bricklayers be selected?

7. From a company of 15 soldiers, a squad of four is chosen each night. For how many nights could a squad go on duty without two of the squads being identical? In how many of these squads would a particular soldier serve?

8. A salesman's wife plans to accompany him on a sales trip to Chicago. She has four coats and six dresses in her wardrobe; how many ways can she choose three dresses and three coats for the trip?

9. A certain class has eight men and four women.
   a. In how many ways can the teacher select a committee of four students?
   b. How many of the committees would have at least one woman?

10. In how many ways can a congressional committee of three be chosen from four Republicans and four Democrats if
   a. all are equally eligible
   b. the committee must consist of two Democrats and one Republican
   c. members of the same party only serve on the same committee
   d. there must be at least one member from each party

11. Twelve managers apply for promotion to district sales representatives of which four are to be chosen. In how many ways can these promotions be decided? How many of these choices will include a particular candidate?

12. A group of 10 workers decide to send a delegation of three to the management to discuss their grievances.
   a. How many delegations are possible?
   b. If one particular employee must be included in the delegation, how many different delegations are possible?
   c. If one particular employee is not to be included in the delegation, how many delegations are possible?

13. A poker hand is a set of five cards selected from a standard deck of 52 cards. What is the number of poker hands that contain
   a. exactly one ace
   b. three cards of the same denomination
   c. three cards of the same denomination and a pair

14. A bag contains five white and seven black marbles. If five marbles are drawn together, how many different drawings are possible if
   a. the marbles may be of any color
   b. there must be exactly three white marbles
   c. the marbles must be of the same color

15. From a regular deck of 52 cards, five are to be selected. How many different selections are possible if the cards
   a. may be of any suit and any denomination
   b. must include two aces and two kings
   c. must include exactly three spades
   d. must be of the same suit
   e. must include at least three spades
   f. must include exactly two aces or two kings

16. In how many ways can four red balls be drawn from an urn if
   a. the urn contains only four red balls
   b. the urn contains six red balls
   c. the urn contains four red, three white, and two black balls

17. How many different management teams of president, vice-president, secretary, and treasurer can be formed from 12 recent college graduates if
   a. any graduate is eligible for any job
   b. three persons are qualified to be only the president, four are qualified to be only the treasurer, and the remaining are qualified for the remaining jobs

18. A grievance committee of six is to be selected from six labor and six management personnel.
   a. How many different selections are possible?
   b. How many committees have equal representation of labor and management?
   c. How many committees favoring labor are possible?
   d. How many committees favoring management are possible?

19. A committee to consider labor-management problems is composed of six outside arbitrators, seven employees, and two employers. The committee is to be selected from 12 arbitrators, 50 employees, and five employers. How many committees are possible?

20. Ten persons are going on a field trip for a history course in three cars that will hold two, three, and five persons, respectively. In how many ways could they go on the trip?

21. There are three offices available for a staff of 12. The first office can accommodate three persons, the second and third offices can take four and five persons, respectively. How many different assignments of the staff are possible?

22. In how many ways can 12 accounts be assigned to three different salespeople so that each one gets four accounts? What is the number of possibilities if the same salesperson cannot be assigned to one particular pair of accounts?

23. A gentleman has invited a party of 13 guests to a dinner and places eight of them at one round table and the remaining five at another. Find the number of ways in which he can arrange the guests.

24. A businessman has invited 21 of his customers for dinner on a Friday evening. He has decided to place six guests at one round table, eight at another round table, and the remaining seven are to be seated at a third circular table. In how many ways can he complete the seating arrangement?

9.4 THE BINOMIAL THEOREM

The quantities $\binom{n}{r}$ are called binomial coefficients because of the fundamental role these quantities play in the formulation of the binomial theorem. Expansions of integral powers of $(a + b)^n$, that is, for $n = 0, 1, 2, \ldots$, are of frequent occurrence in algebra and are beginning to appear in all phases of mathematics. Moreover, expansions of this nature are important because of their close relationship with the binomial distribution, which we shall study in later chapters. We shall, therefore, undertake here a systematic development of a formula that produces such expansions.

Of course, the following identities could be established by direct multiplication. For example,

$$(a + b)^0 = 1$$
$$(a + b)^1 = a + b$$
$$(a + b)^2 = a^2 + 2ab + b^2$$
$$(a + b)^3 = a^3 + 3a^2b + 3ab^2 + b^3$$
$$(a + b)^4 = a^4 + 4a^3b + 6a^2b^2 + 4ab^3 + b^4$$
$$(a + b)^5 = a^5 + 5a^4b + 10a^3b^2 + 10a^2b^3 + 5ab^4 + b^5$$

As we progress, this process of direct multiplication soon becomes cumbersome, tedious, and somewhat painful, and we begin to wonder if there is a better method to arrive at the same results. Note that as we continue expanding larger and larger powers of $(a + b)$, several patterns emerge leading to a part of the solution. Can you observe any? The following patterns may be evident from the above process of multiplication:

1. The coefficients of the first and last terms are both 1.
2. There are $n + 1$ terms in the expansion of $(a + b)^n$.
3. The exponent of a starts with n and then decreases by 1 until the exponent of a has decreased to 0 in the last term, and the exponent of b is 0 in the first term and then increases by 1 until the exponent of b is n in the last term.
4. The sum of the exponents of a and b in a given term is always n.
5. There is a symmetry about the middle term (for n even) or middle pair (for n odd).

Proceeding along these lines, we see that the $(n + 1)$ terms in the expansion of $(a + b)^n$, without their coefficients, are

$$a^n, a^{n-1}b, a^{n-2}b^2, a^{n-3}b^3, \ldots, a^{n-r}b^r, \ldots, b^n$$

Now there remains the question of determining the coefficients of these terms. Why, in the expansion of $(a + b)^3$, do the terms $3a^2b$ and $3ab^2$ exist? To handle these questions, let us examine the actual multiplication of $(a + b)^3$. We have

$$(a + b)^3 = (a + b)(a + b)(a + b)$$
$$= a \cdot a \cdot a + a \cdot a \cdot b + a \cdot b \cdot a + a \cdot b \cdot b + b \cdot a \cdot a + b \cdot a \cdot b$$
$$+ b \cdot b \cdot a + b \cdot b \cdot b \qquad (8 \text{ terms})$$
$$= a^3 + 3a^2b + 3ab^2 + b^3$$

In the eight terms involved in the expansion of $(a + b)^3$, there are three terms a^2b corresponding to the different ways of selecting two a's and one b, one from each of the factors $(a + b)$. The coefficient of a^3 is 1 because there is only one way in which three a's can be selected, one from each factor $(a + b)$. The coefficient of ab^2 is 3, because there are three ways of selecting one a and two b's, one from each factor $(a + b)$, and the coefficient of b^3 is 1 because there is only one way of selecting three b's, one from each factor $(a + b)$. Let us now try to obtain the expansion of $(a + b)^4$. The terms in the expansion must be of the form

$$a^4, a^3b, a^2b^2, ab^3, b^4$$

and we need to determine how many there are of each type. Each term is obtained by selecting exactly one letter from each factor $(a + b)$. So far as a^4 is concerned, we select no b and four a's, one from each factor $(a + b)$. Because this can be done in only $\binom{4}{0}$ or one way, a^4 occurs exactly once in the expansion and its coefficient is 1. To get the second term in the expansion, we select three a's and one b. This can be accomplished in $\binom{4}{1}$, or four, ways; hence, the coefficient of a^3b is 4. Similarly, the coefficient of a^2b^2 is the number of ways we can select two a's and two b's; namely, $\binom{4}{2}$ or six ways. The term ab^3 can be obtained in $\binom{4}{3}$ or four ways, and the last term b^4 can be obtained in only one way. Proceeding along these lines, we obtain the result

$$(a + b)^4 = \binom{4}{0} a^4 + \binom{4}{1} a^3b + \binom{4}{2} a^2b^2 + \binom{4}{3} ab^3 + \binom{4}{4} b^4$$

If we apply the same reasoning to the expansion of $(a + b)^n$, where n is a positive integer, we obtain the following result.

Binomial Theorem 9.4.1: If n is a positive integer, then

$$(a + b)^n = \binom{n}{0} a^n + \binom{n}{1} a^{n-1}b + \binom{n}{2} a^{n-2}b^2 + \cdots + \binom{n}{r} a^{n-r}b^r + \cdots + \binom{n}{n} b^n$$

Note that the $(n + 1)$ terms in the expansion of $(a + b)^n$, without their coefficients, are

$$a^n, a^{n-1}b, a^{n-2}b^2, a^{n-3}b^3, \ldots, a^{n-r}b^r, \ldots, a^2b^{n-2}, ab^{n-1}, b^n$$

In other words, each term in the expansion is of the form

$$a^{n-r}b^r \qquad r = 0, 1, 2, \ldots, n$$

The coefficient of this general term is $\binom{n}{r}$, because this corresponds to the number of ways in which r b's and $(n - r)$ a's can be selected, and the complete general term is

$$\binom{n}{r} a^{n-r}b^r$$

A summation of this general term for $r = 0, 1, 2, \ldots, n$ yields the above assertion. ∎

Corollary 1: From Proposition 9.4.1, with $a = 1$, it follows that

$$(1 + b)^n = \binom{n}{0} + \binom{n}{1} b + \binom{n}{2} b^2 + \binom{n}{3} b^3 + \cdots + \binom{n}{r} b^r + \cdots + b^n$$

Corollary 2: With $a = b = 1$ in Proposition 9.4.1, it follows that

$$\binom{n}{0} + \binom{n}{1} + \binom{n}{2} + \binom{n}{3} + \cdots + \binom{n}{r} + \cdots + \binom{n}{n} = 2^n$$

Example 9.23

Expand $(x + y)^6$.

SOLUTION

$$(x + y)^6 = \binom{6}{0} x^6 + \binom{6}{1} x^5 y + \binom{6}{2} x^4 y^2 + \binom{6}{3} x^3 y^3 + \binom{6}{4} x^2 y^4$$
$$+ \binom{6}{5} xy^5 + \binom{6}{6} y^6$$
$$= x^6 + 6x^5 y + 15x^4 y^2 + 20x^3 y^3 + 15x^2 y^4 + 6xy^5 + y^6 \qquad ∎$$

The calculation of the coefficients is simplified by making use of the fact that

$$\binom{n}{r} = \binom{n}{n - r}$$

In the preceding example we needed only to compute up to $\binom{6}{3}$ and then recognize that

$$\binom{6}{4} = \binom{6}{2}, \binom{6}{5} = \binom{6}{1}, \text{ and } \binom{6}{6} = \binom{6}{0} = 1 \qquad ∎$$

Example 9.24

Expand $(x + 2y)^7$.

SOLUTION

$$(x + 2y)^7 = \binom{7}{0} x^7 + \binom{7}{1} x^6(2y) + \binom{7}{2} x^5(2y)^2 + \binom{7}{3} x^4(2y)^3 + \binom{7}{4} x^3(2y)^4$$
$$+ \binom{7}{5} x^2(2y)^5 + \binom{7}{6} x(2y)^6 + \binom{7}{7} (2y)^7$$
$$= x^7 + 14x^6 y + 84x^5 y^2 + 280x^4 y^3 + 560x^3 y^4 + 672x^2 y^5$$
$$+ 448xy^6 + 128y^7 \qquad ∎$$

Example 9.25

Expand $(1 + 2x)^6$.

SOLUTION

Letting $n = 6$ and $b = 2x$ in Corollary 1, we have

$$(1 + 2x)^6 = 1 + \binom{6}{1}(2x) + \binom{6}{2}(2x)^2 + \binom{6}{3}(2x)^3 + \binom{6}{4}(2x)^4 + \binom{6}{5}(2x)^5$$

$$+ \binom{6}{6}(2x)^6$$

$$= 1 + 12x + 60x^2 + 160x^3 + 240x^4 + 192x^5 + 64x^6$$

Example 9.26

Expand $(1 - 3x)^4$.

SOLUTION

With $n = 4$ and $b = -3x$ in Corollary 1, we have

$$(1 - 3x)^4 = [1 + (-3x)]^4$$

$$= 1 + \binom{4}{1}(-3x) + \binom{4}{2}(-3x)^2 + \binom{4}{3}(-3x)^3 + \binom{4}{4}(-3x)^4$$

$$= 1 - 12x + 54x^2 - 108x^3 + 81x^4$$

Example 9.27

Expand $(2x - 3y)^5$.

SOLUTION

Because $a - b = a + (-b)$, the expansion of $(2x - 3y)^5$ can be expressed as $[2x + (-3y)]^5$. Then,

$$[2x + (-3y)]^5 = \binom{5}{0}(2x)^5 + \binom{5}{1}(2x)^4(-3y) + \binom{5}{2}(2x)^3(-3y)^2$$

$$+ \binom{5}{3}(2x)^2(-3y)^3 + \binom{5}{4}(2x)(-3y)^4 + \binom{5}{5}(-3y)^5$$

$$= 32x^5 - 240x^4y + 720x^3y^2 - 1080x^2y^3$$

$$+ 810xy^4 - 243y^5$$

Example 9.28

Using the binomial theorem, find the numerical value of $(1.06)^5$.

SOLUTION

Let $n = 5$ and $b = 0.06$ in Corollary 1. It follows that

$$(1 + 0.06)^5 = 1 + \binom{5}{1}(0.06) + \binom{5}{2}(0.06)^2 + \binom{5}{3}(0.06)^3 + \binom{5}{4}(0.06)^4 + (0.06)^5$$

$$= 1 + 5(0.06) + 10(0.06)^2 + 10(0.06)^3 + 5(0.06)^4 + (0.06)^5$$

$$= 1 + 0.30 + 0.036 + 0.00216 + \cdots$$

$$\approx 1.3382$$

This example may serve as a practical illustration of the binomial theorem. Consider, for instance, an investment of $1 in a savings bank that pays 6 percent interest compounded annually and we are interested in knowing how much this investment will be worth five years hence. The answer is generally available in the appropriate tables, but in case such tables are not readily available, we can always obtain an approximate answer by using the first few terms in the binomial expansion. Using the first four terms in the expansion, we can say that our investment of $1 will be worth $1.3382 five years hence.

Example 9.29

Without actual expansion, find the ninth term in the expansion of $(2x + y)^{14}$.

SOLUTION

The general term, the $(r + 1)$st term in the expansion of the binomial theorem, is given by

$$T_{r+1} = \binom{n}{r} a^{n-r} b^r$$

Accordingly, we have

$$T_9 = \binom{14}{8} (2x)^6 y^8$$

$$= \binom{14}{6} (64x^6) y^8 \qquad \left[\binom{14}{8} = \binom{14}{6} \right]$$

$$= 192{,}192 x^6 y^8$$

Example 9.30

Without expanding, find the middle term in the expansion of $[x - (1/x)]^{12}$.

SOLUTION

Because $n = 12$, it follows that there are 13 terms in the expansion of $[x - (1/x)]^{12}$. Accordingly, the seventh term represents the middle term. Thus,

$$T_7 = \binom{12}{6} x^6 \left(-\frac{1}{x} \right)^6 = 924 x^6 (-1)^6 x^{-6} = 924$$

Example 9.31

Find the two middle terms in the expansion of $[2a - (a^2/4)]^9$.

SOLUTION

With $n = 9$, there are 10 terms in this expansion, two middle terms are the fifth and sixth, given by T_5 and T_6.

$$T_5 = \binom{9}{4} (2a)^5 \left(-\frac{a^2}{4} \right)^4 = 126(32a^5) \left(\frac{a^8}{256} \right) = \frac{63}{4} a^{13}$$

$$T_6 = \binom{9}{5} (2a)^4 \left(-\frac{a^2}{4} \right)^5 = 126(16a^4) \left(-\frac{a^{10}}{1024} \right) = -\frac{63}{32} a^{14}$$

Example 9.32

Find the term independent of x in the expansion of $[2x^2 - (1/x)]^{12}$.

SOLUTION

We have

$$T_{r+1} = \binom{12}{r}(2x^2)^{12-r}\left(-\frac{1}{x}\right)^r$$

$$= \binom{12}{r}2^{12-r}x^{24-2r}(-1)^r x^{-r}$$

$$= \binom{12}{r}(-1)^r 2^{12-r}x^{24-3r}$$

It is evident that T_{r+1} will be independent of x if $24 - 3r = 0$; that is, $r = 8$. Thus, T_9 is given by

$$\binom{12}{8}(-1)^8 2^4 = \binom{12}{4}2^4 = 7920$$

■

Example 9.33

Without expanding, find the term of $(2x + 3y)^6$ involving $x^2 y^4$.

SOLUTION

The general term T_{r+1} for this expansion is given by

$$\binom{6}{r}(2x)^{6-r}(3y)^r$$

It is apparent that $r = 4$. Hence, the term involving $x^2 y^4$ is given by

$$\binom{6}{4}(2x)^2(3y)^4 = 15(4x^2)(81y^4) = 4860x^2 y^4$$

■

EXERCISE 9.6

1. Expand the following:
  a. $(3a + 2b)^4$ **b.** $(3ax - 4by)^5$
  c. $(1 - x)^7$ **d.** $(1 + 2x)^8$
  e. $(x - 2y)^6$ **f.** $[x - (1/x)]^{11}$
2. Without actual computations, evaluate the following.

  a. $\binom{4}{0} + \binom{4}{1} + \binom{4}{2} + \binom{4}{3} + \binom{4}{4}$

  b. $\binom{5}{0} + \binom{5}{1} + \binom{5}{2} + \binom{5}{3} + \binom{5}{4} + \binom{5}{5}$

  c. $\binom{6}{0} + \binom{6}{1} + \binom{6}{2} + \binom{6}{3} + \binom{6}{4} + \binom{6}{5} + \binom{6}{6}$

d. $\binom{7}{0} + \binom{7}{1} + \binom{7}{2} + \binom{7}{3} + \binom{7}{4} + \binom{7}{5} + \binom{7}{6} + \binom{7}{7}$

e. $\binom{n}{0} + \binom{n}{1} + \binom{n}{2} + \binom{n}{3} + \binom{n}{4} + \binom{n}{5} + \binom{n}{6} + \binom{n}{7} + \cdots + \binom{n}{n}$

3. Using the binomial formula, find approximations for the following:
   a. $(1.006)^4$ **b.** $(1.05)^5$ **c.** $(0.998)^4$ **d.** $(0.98)^6$

4. Find in a simplified form:
   a. the fourth term in the expansion of $(2x - y)^9$
   b. the sixth term in the expansion of $[(x/3) + (3/x)]^{12}$
   c. the middle term in the expansion of $(2x - 3y)^{14}$
   d. the middle terms in the expansion of $(3x + 4y)^{11}$

5. Find the coefficient of
   a. x^5 in the expansion of $(x + x^{-3})^{17}$
   b. x^n in the expansion of $(1 + x)^{2n}$
   c. x^4 in the expansion of $(x - x^{-2})^{10}$

6. Find the term independent of x in the expansion of $[x^3 - (1/x^2)]^{10}$. What is the sum of all the terms when $x = 1$?

7. Mr. Talbot plans to deposit $1000 in a savings account that pays 5 percent interest compounded annually. How much will he have in his account 10 years hence?

8. A commerical bank A pays 6 percent interest for savings and compounds it monthly, whereas another bank B pays $6\frac{1}{2}$ percent interest on savings but compounds it annually. If a customer wants a maximum yield on his savings, in which bank should he deposit $10,000 he has recently inherited?

9. Three successive coefficients in the expansion of $(1 + x)^n$ are 220, 495, and 792. Determine the value of n.

10. Three successive coefficients in the expansion of $(1 + x)^n$ are 462, 330, and 165. Find n.

11. Prove that

$$\binom{n}{0} - \binom{n}{1} + \binom{n}{2} - \binom{n}{3} + \binom{n}{4} - \cdots + (-1)^n \binom{n}{n} = 0$$

12. Prove that

$$\binom{n}{0} + \binom{n}{2} + \binom{n}{4} + \cdots + \binom{n}{n} = \binom{n}{1} + \binom{n}{3} + \binom{n}{5} + \cdots + \binom{n}{n-1}$$

$$= 2^{n-1}$$

CHAPTER 10
Probability

10.1 INTRODUCTION

Probability is a mathematical discipline dealing with random experiments. Although its original purpose was to describe the exceedingly narrow domain of experience connected with games of chance, it has found an increasing number of applications not only in business, biology, medicine, and the insurance industry, but also in many other scientific fields of human endeavor involving matters as diverse as the study of various characteristics in a Skylab mission, the density of telephone traffic in an election year, the quality of air we breathe, and the motion of particles immersed in a liquid or a gas. The simplest random experiments are provided by tossing a coin, throwing a die, arranging a deck of cards, or drawing a ball of a certain color from an urn containing balls of several colors. All these experiments with their unpredictable results are rather vague descriptions, and we must look for a common characteristic possessed by the various "experiments" we have described. Each of the "experiments" or "random phenomena" is empirical in nature in the sense that its observation under a given set of conditions does not always yield the same results. Physical occurrences frequently considered random phenomena are the arrival of a customer in a jewelry store, the sex of an unborn baby, the number of telephone lines in use at a certain hour, the number of cars registered in the State of Connecticut, the number of students registered in a management course in a college, the number of lottery tickets sold in the State of New York, the number of passengers riding a commuter train between New Jersey and New York, the number of voters eligible for nomination in a mayoral election, and the like. Whether the Democrats will win the next Presidential election and whether a given student will pass a certain course in economics are also random experiments, the outcomes of which can hardly be predicted with certainty.

In this chapter, we introduce the basic ideas of a sample space and an event and then show how quantitative measures of probability can be assigned to certain events in the sample space. Later in the chapter we examine the concept of conditional probability and repeated trials.

10.2 THE FINITE SAMPLE SPACE

One does not talk about probabilities except in relation to a certain idealized experiment and its outcomes. Consider an example of tossing a coin. In actuality, the coin may not necessarily fall heads or tails; it can stand on an edge or it may roll away and get lost. Nevertheless, we agree to regard head and tail as the only possible outcome because at least intuitively either outcome is equally likely and any other outcome is much less likely. If these outcomes are denoted by H and T, respectively, then each outcome of a throw of a coin corresponds to exactly one element of the set $\{H, T\}$.

Definition 10.2.1: A sample space, usually denoted by the letter S, is the set of all possible outcomes of an experiment such that to each element of the set S corresponds an outcome of the experiment and, conversely, to each outcome there is one and only one element in the set S.

We consider it worthwhile pointing out the use of a rather than the in the above definition. Usually many models will describe an experiment; choosing an appropriate sample space is part of the skill that is needed to apply probability concepts to real problems. In general, it is safe to include as much detail as possible when deciding what to consider as an outcome of the experiment. Because we are concerned with the collection of all possible outcomes of an experiment, our set is in a sense a universal set of outcomes. Everything that can occur will be represented in the sample space. Thus, the sample space simply provides a model of an experiment in the sense that every possible outcome of the experiment is completely described by one and only one element in the set S.

Example 10.1

For the experiment of throwing a die, each outcome corresponds to one of the elements of the set $\{1, 2, 3, 4, 5, 6\}$. Six possible outcomes make up the sample space. If the die is not loaded, then these outcomes are equally likely; that is, there is no reason to believe that one of the outcomes of the sample space is likely to occur more frequently than any of the others. If two of the faces are numbered 1, one face is numbered 2, and the remaining three are numbered 3, then the sample space has only three outcomes. Note that these three outcomes are not equally likely. ■

Example 10.2

Consider an experiment of tossing a balanced coin three times. Suppose that our interest lies only in the number of heads obtained. Now, the possible outcomes are 0, 1, 2, or 3 heads, and a sample space can be described as $S = \{0, 1, 2, 3\}$. We may observe that by merely recording the number of heads obtained we lost some valuable information and our classification technique was rather coarse. We can achieve a finer classification by recording whether heads appeared in all three tosses (HHH), heads appeared in the first two tosses followed by tails on the third toss (HHT), the coin fell tails on the three tosses (TTT), and so on. Each possible outcome of the experiment corresponds to one and only one element of the set $S = \{HHH, HHT, HTH, HTT, THH, THT, TTH, TTT\}$ shown in the tree diagram of Figure 10.1. Clearly, the eight points in the set constitute a sample space different from the one in which only the number of heads is recorded.

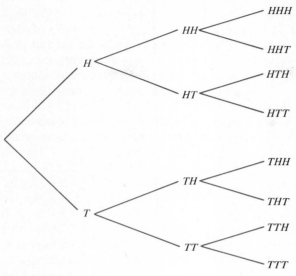

Figure 10.1

Example 10.3

Consider rolling a pair of ordinary dice. The set S consists of three elements 0, 1, 2 if we are interested in recording the number of times "three" has appeared. This set can serve as a sample space because it satisfies the requirement of the definition. Another model can be described if the concern is simply the total number of spots on the uppermost faces when the dice come to rest. The sample space consists of 11 integers 2, 3, 4, 5, 6, 7, 8, 9, 10, 11, and 12. But neither of the two sample spaces is sufficient to answer the question, "Is the number on the first die less than the number appearing on the second die?" If the dice are distinguishable (for instance if one is white and the other green), then we are led to take as sample space the set S consisting of 36 ordered pairs (x, y), where x represents the number of dots on the white die and y indicates the dots on the green die. In terms of this notation, the sample space S is given in Table 10.1.

Table 10.1

{(1, 1),	(1, 2),	(1, 3),	(1, 4),	(1, 5),	(1, 6),
(2, 1),	(2, 2),	(2, 3),	(2, 4),	(2, 5),	(2, 6),
(3, 1),	(3, 2),	(3, 3),	(3, 4),	(3, 5),	(3, 6),
(4, 1),	(4, 2),	(4, 3),	(4, 4),	(4, 5),	(4, 6),
(5, 1),	(5, 2),	(5, 3),	(5, 4),	(5, 5),	(5, 6),
(6, 1),	(6, 2),	(6, 3),	(6, 4),	(6, 5),	(6, 6)}

Example 10.4

A coin is tossed and then a die is rolled. A sample space appropriate for this experiment is as follows:

$$\{(H, 1), (H, 2), (H, 3), (H, 4), (H, 5), (H, 6), (T, 1), (T, 2), (T, 3), (T, 4), (T, 5), (T, 6)\}$$

Each of the 12 ordered pairs, which are equally likely, represents a possible outcome in the experiment.

It should be emphasized that the sample space of an experiment is capable of being described in more than one way. Observers with different conceptions of what could possibly be observed may arrive at different sample spaces. In general, it is desirable to use sample spaces whose points represent equally likely outcomes that cannot be further subdivided; that is, each point in the sample space should not represent two or more possibilities that are further distinguishable. Unless there are special reasons to the contrary, we shall find this rule extremely helpful.

All of the sample spaces we have considered so far are of finite size. However, there is no logical necessity for sample spaces to be finite. We shall briefly mention one example. Suppose that you call your mother in Florida on Mother's Day to wish her many happy returns because Mother's Day also happens to be her birthday. The number of rings before she picks up the telephone is a random experiment. It is conceivable (at least in theory) that you could get an unending sequence of telephone rings if she is not at home at the time and you allow the phone to keep ringing. If she answers, you record the number of telephone rings before she picked up the receiver. The sample space $S = \{1, 2, 3, 4, \ldots\}$ is clearly an infinite set. Although the theory of probability deals with both finite and infinite sample spaces, we shall restrict our attention to finite sample spaces only.

The Events

For each experiment there is a sample space and for each sample space there are events. Having explained what we mean by a sample space, the next logical step is to define the term "events." This is important because probabilities are always associated with the occurrence or nonoccurrence of events.

Definition 10.2.2: An element of a sample space is called a sample point or a simple event.

Definition 10.2.3: An event is a subset of the sample space S.

Definition 10.2.4: A compound event is the union of simple events.

Unless stated otherwise, it is generally assumed that all simple events in the finite sample space are equally likely.

To illustrate the notion of an event, let us return to the experiment of rolling a pair of ordinary dice, one white and the other green. The sample space for this experiment is given by 36 ordered pairs in Table 10.1. Some events that may be of an interest are these:

1. The sum of the numbers on the two dice is five.
2. Each of the two dice shows the same number.
3. At least one of the numbers on the dice is six.

Each of the events we have described is associated with a set whose elements are in the sample space. For instance, the event that the sum of the numbers on the dice is five can be associated with the set

$$\{(1, 4), (2, 3), (3, 2), (4, 1)\}$$

Similarly, the set

$$\{(1, 1), (2, 2), (3, 3), (4, 4), (5, 5), (6, 6)\}$$

represents the event that both the dice show the same number.

The event that at least one of the numbers on the dice is six can be expressed as the set

$$\{(6, 1), (6, 2), (6, 3), (6, 4), (6, 5), (6, 6), (1, 6), (2, 6), (3, 6), (4, 6), (5, 6)\}$$

We note that these sets are subsets of the sample space S.

Example 10.5

A committee of six members, A, B, C, D, E, and F, decides to appoint a subcommittee of three members to study the business management curriculum in a college. List the 20 elements of the appropriate sample space S and find the subset of S containing outcomes in which

   a. A is included
   b. A or B is included
   c. A and B are included
   d. B is not included
   e. Neither A nor B is included

SOLUTION

This is a combination problem. We are interested in the number of possible sub-committees that can be formed from six members taken three at a time. The sample space consisting of 20 elements is

$$\{ABC, ABD, ABE, ABF, ACD, ACE, ACF, ADE, ADF, AEF,$$
$$BCD, BCE, BCF, BDE, BDF, BEF, CDE, CDF, CEF, DEF\}$$

The list below indicates the correspondence between various events and subsets of the sample space S.

Description of Event	Corresponding Subset of S
a. A is included	$\{ABC, ABD, ABE, ABF, ACD, ACE, ACF, ADE, ADF, AEF\}$
b. A or B is included	$\{ABC, ABD, ABE, ABF, ACD, ACE, ACF, ADE, ADF, AEF,$ $BCD, BCE, BCF, BDE, BDF, BEF\}$
c. A and B are included	$\{ABC, ABD, ABE, ABF\}$
d. B is not included	$\{ACD, ACE, ACF, ADE, ADF, AEF, CDE, CDF, CEF, DEF\}$
e. Neither A nor B is included	$\{CDE, CDF, CEF, DEF\}$

EXERCISE 10.1

1. Describe a suitable sample space for the following experiments.
   a. Two coins are tossed.
   b. A die is rolled and then a coin is tossed.
   c. A president and a secretary of a club are to be elected from among five students.
   d. A committee of two is formed from the five members of a club.
   e. Two aces are drawn from a regular bridge deck.
   f. A coin is tossed until either a head appears or three tosses have been made.

2. An ordinary die is rolled. State which of the following sets are suitable sample spaces for this experiment.
   a. $S = \{$odd number, even number$\}$
   b. $S = \{2, 4, 6,$ odd number$\}$
   c. $S = \{$number less than three, number greater than three$\}$
   d. $S = \{1, 2, 3, 4, 5, 6\}$
   e. $S = \{1, 2, 3,$ number greater than 4$\}$

3. A coin is tossed three times. Describe a suitable sample space and list the elements in each of the following events.
   a. The first toss is a tail.
   b. The first and the last toss are the same.
   c. There are more tails than heads.
   d. There are no tails.
   e. There are exactly two heads.
   f. There are at least two heads.

4. For the experiment of tossing a pair of dice (one white and the other green) and with the sample space described in Table 10.1, list each of the following events.
   a. The number on at least one die is 5.
   b. The number on the white die is a multiple of 3.
   c. The number on the green die is odd.
   d. The sum of the numbers on the dice equals 1.

5. The numbers 1, 2, 3, 4, and 5 are written separately on five slips of paper. The slips are then put into a hat and mixed. Two slips are drawn without replacement. Describe a suitable sample space and list the elements in each of the following events.
   a. The sum of the numbers on the slips is less than 9.
   b. Each of the slips shows an even number.
   c. One of the slips has an odd number on it.
   d. Each of the slips shows the same number.
   e. Both the slips show odd numbers.

6. A coin is tossed four times. Describe a suitable sample space and list the elements in each of the following events.
   a. There is exactly one head.
   b. The number of heads and tails is the same.
   c. Heads and tails alternate.
   d. There are exactly three heads.
   e. There are more heads than tails.

10.3 THE CONCEPT OF PROBABILITY

We are now ready to discuss seriously the mathematical meaning of the word "probability." In conducting a survey of families having two children, we generally record the sex of each child in the order of their births. An appropriate sample space in this case is given by the set $\{BB, BG, GB, GG\}$; because each of these simple events is equally probable, we say that the probability of each simple event is $\frac{1}{4}$. The compound event that the children are of the same sex consists of two sample points BB and GG and the probability of the occurrence of this compound event is $\frac{2}{4} = \frac{1}{2}$. Similarly, the probability of drawing an ace from a well-shuffled deck is $\frac{4}{52}$, because the sample space consists of 52 cards each of which is equally likely and there are four aces in the deck. As another example, consider the experiment of drawing a ball from an urn containing eight balls, numbered 1 to 8, of which five balls, numbers 1 to 5, are colored red and the remaining three balls are green. A suitable sample space is given by $S = \{1, 2, 3, 4, 5, 6, 7, 8\}$. The event that the ball drawn is red can be represented by a subset $E = \{1, 2, 3, 4, 5\}$. If all the simple events of S are equally likely (the balls are of the same size and weight), we may arrive at the result that the probability of drawing a red ball is $\frac{5}{8}$.

Definition 10.3.1: If the simple events of a finite sample space S are equally likely, then the probability of an event E is the ratio of the number of simple events in E to the number of all simple events belonging to the sample space.

Thus, the computation of the probability of an event defined in a finite sample space of equally likely outcomes reduces to the simple computation of the size of the subset of "favorable" outcomes and the size of the sample space. Then we assign the probability measure to an event E by

(10.1) $\quad P(E) = \dfrac{n(E)}{n(S)} = \dfrac{\text{number of elements in } E}{\text{number of elements in } S}$

This method of assigning a measure, or a number, to the event E has two immediate consequences: For if there are no sample points corresponding to the event E, then

(10.2) $\quad P(E) = 0 \quad \text{for} \quad n(E) = 0$

and if all points are favorable to the occurrence of the event E, then

(10.3) $\quad P(E) = 1 \quad \text{for} \quad n(E) = n(S)$

It follows that the probability of each event varies between 0 and 1; that is,

(10.4) $\quad 0 \le P(E) \le 1 \quad \text{for} \quad E \subseteq S$

Example 10.6
An ordinary die is thrown. What is the probability of getting a number greater than 2?

SOLUTION
The sample space consists of six points $\{1, 2, 3, 4, 5, 6\}$. If E denotes the event that the number on the uppermost face is greater than 2, then E consists of four sample points $\{3, 4, 5, 6\}$. Hence,

$\qquad P(E) = \frac{4}{6} = \frac{2}{3}$ ∎

Example 10.7
Two coins are tossed. Using the sample space of this experiment as $S = \{HH, HT, TH, TT\}$, find the probability of getting

    a. exactly one head
    b. exactly two heads

SOLUTION

Let A denote the event that there is exactly one head and B denote the event that there are exactly two heads. Then,

$$A = \{HT, TH\} \quad \text{and} \quad B = \{HH\}$$

Clearly,

$$n(A) = 2 \quad \text{and} \quad n(B) = 1$$

Thus,

a. $P(A) = \dfrac{n(A)}{n(S)} = \dfrac{2}{4}$, and

b. $P(B) = \dfrac{n(B)}{n(S)} = \dfrac{1}{4}$ ∎

Example 10.8

Using the sample space of Table 10.1 and assuming that all the sample points are equally probable, determine the probability of

    a. the event that the sum of the numbers on the dice is 7
    b. the number on the white die is greater than the number on the green die by more than 2
    c. the event that the number on the white die is a multiple of 3
    d. the event that the number on at least one die is 6

SOLUTION

Let A, B, C, and D be the subsets of S corresponding to the above events. Then

$$A = \{(1, 6), (2, 5), (3, 4), (4, 3), (5, 2), (6, 1)\}$$
$$B = \{(4, 1), (5, 1), (5, 2), (6, 1), (6, 2), (6, 3)\}$$
$$C = \{(3, 1), (3, 2), (3, 3), (3, 4), (3, 5), (3, 6), (6, 1), (6, 2), (6, 3), (6, 4), (6, 5), (6, 6)\}$$
$$D = \{(6, 1), (6, 2), (6, 3), (6, 4), (6, 5), (6, 6), (1, 6), (2, 6), (3, 6), (4, 6), (5, 6)\}$$

Because all sample points of S are equally likely, we have

a. $P(A) = \dfrac{n(A)}{n(S)} = \dfrac{6}{36} = \dfrac{1}{6}$

b. $P(B) = \dfrac{n(B)}{n(S)} = \dfrac{6}{36} = \dfrac{1}{6}$

c. $P(C) = \dfrac{n(C)}{n(S)} = \dfrac{12}{36} = \dfrac{1}{3}$

d. $P(D) = \dfrac{n(D)}{n(S)} = \dfrac{11}{36}$ ∎

Example 10.9

Assuming that in a three-child family the eight simple points *BBB*, *BBG*, *BGB*, *BGG*, *GBB*, *GBG*, *GGB*, *GGG* are equally likely, determine the probabilities of the following events:

  a. exactly one boy
  b. exactly two boys
  c. all boys
  d. all girls
  e. at most one boy
  f. at least one boy

SOLUTION

The verbal description of the events, the algebraic conditions, the solution sets, and the required probabilities are given in Table 10.2, where x represents the number of boys in the three-child family.

Table 10.2

Verbal Description of the Event	Algebraic Condition	Solution Set (subset of S)	Probability of the Event
a. exactly one boy	$x = 1$	$\{BGG, GBG, GGB\}$	$\frac{3}{8}$
b. exactly two boys	$x = 2$	$\{BBG, BGB, GBB\}$	$\frac{3}{8}$
c. all boys	$x = 3$	$\{BBB\}$	$\frac{1}{8}$
d. all girls	$x = 0$	$\{GGG\}$	$\frac{1}{8}$
e. at most one boy	$x \leq 1$	$\{GGG, BGG, GBG, GGB\}$	$\frac{4}{8} = \frac{1}{2}$
f. at least one boy	$x \geq 1$	$\{BGG, GBG, GGB, BBG, BGB, GBB, BBB\}$	$\frac{7}{8}$

Note that the event that there is at most one boy in the family can be represented by as the union of two disjoint events of exactly one boy (a) and no boys (d). Thus,

$$P(x \leq 1) = P(x = 0) + P(x = 1)$$

Likewise, the probability of the event that there is at least one boy can be obtained by adding the corresponding probabilities of three disjoint events of exactly one boy (a), exactly two boys (b), and all boys (c). In other words,

$$P(x \geq 1) = P(x = 1) + P(x = 2) + P(x = 3)$$

Alternatively, we may take advantage of the fact that because the sample space is the union of four disjoint events of exactly one boy, exactly two boys, exactly three boys, and no boys, we can assert that

$$P(x = 0) + P(x = 1) + P(x = 2) + P(x = 3) = 1$$

which, in turn, implies that

$$P(x \geq 1) = 1 - P(x = 0)$$

Thus, the probability that there is at least one boy can be computed simply by subtracting from one the corresponding probability that there is no male child in the family. ∎

EXERCISE 10.2

1. In a single throw of two dice, what is the probability of getting
   a. a total score of 8
   b. a total score of at most 8
   c. a total score of at least 8

2. In a single throw of three dice, what is the probability of getting
   a. a total score of 5
   b. a total score of at most 5
   c. a total score of at least 19

3. A card is drawn at random from a deck of 52 playing cards. What is the probability of drawing
   a. a red queen
   b. a jack, queen, king, or ace
   c. a diamond or a club
   d. a red card
   e. a 2, 3, 4, 5, 6, or 7
   f. a card that is neither a spade nor a club?

4. An urn contains 20 balls of which 10 are black, 8 are red, and 2 are white. A ball is drawn at random. Find the probability that it is
   a. a red ball
   b. a red or a black ball
   c. a white or a black ball
   d. not a white ball

5. An urn contains 40 balls, of which 12 are red, 10 are white, 15 are blue, and 3 are black. If one ball is drawn at random, find the probability that the ball is
   a. red, white, or blue
   b. white or blue
   c. neither white nor black
   d. neither red nor blue

6. Determine all possible outcomes if a fair coin is tossed four times. What is the probability of getting
   a. exactly four heads
   b. exactly three heads
   c. exactly two heads
   d. at least one head

7. Two boys and two girls are arranged in a row for a panel discussion. What is the probability that the boys and girls alternate in a row?

8. Four mathematicians arrange to meet at a certain hotel in New York. It happens that there are four hotels with the same name in the city. What is the probability that they will choose different hotels?

9. Three couples are attending a charity ball in which the three ladies choose their partners at random among the three men. What is the probability that no gentleman is dancing with his date?

10. Three soliders who sleep in the same barracks arrive home one evening so tired that each soldier chooses at random a bed in which to sleep. What is the probability that no soldier is sleeping in his own bed?

11. Eight gentlemen and their wives have been assigned seats at random at a circular table. What is the probability that no two ladies are sitting together?
12. If 10 guests are seated at a circular table at random, what is the probability that a particular pair of guests are seated next to each other?
13. A magazine prints the photographs of five Presidents and also prints a baby picture of each in scrambled order. What is the probability that a reader by purely random matching of the pictures gets
    a. all of them right
    b. at least one of them wrong

10.4 SOME RULES OF PROBABILITY

Definition 10.4.1: Two events E and F are mutually exclusive if they cannot occur simultaneously.

In the language of sets, two or more events are mutually exclusive if they have no points in common. In other words, the intersection of two or more mutually exclusive events is the empty set.

The discussion in the preceding section leads us to a formal statement that we choose to express in the form of the following axioms.

(10.5)   Axiom 1. $P(E) \geq 0$ for any event $E \subseteq S$

(10.6)   Axiom 2. $P(S) = 1$

(10.7)   Axiom 3. If E and F are mutually exclusive events, then
$$P(E \cup F) = P(E) + P(F).$$

These axioms reinforce the statement that the probability of any event defined on the sample space S is associated with a non-negative number between 0 and 1, the probability of the entire sample space is 1, and the probability of the union of two mutually exclusive events is simply the sum of their separate probabilities.

The result stated in (10.7) can be extended to any finite number of mutually exclusive events. Thus, if $E_1, E_2, E_3, \ldots, E_m$ are all mutually exclusive events such that

$$E_1 \cup E_2 \cup \cdots \cup E_m = S$$

then

$$
\begin{aligned}
P(E_1 \cup E_2 \cup \cdots \cup E_m) &= P(E_1) + P(E_2) + \cdots + P(E_m) \\
&= P(S) \\
&= 1 \quad \text{(Axiom 2)}
\end{aligned}
$$

Example 10.10

Analyzing inflationary trends in the business, three hospital studies were made: The first study claims that the probabilities for the cost of hospitalization to go up, remain unchanged, or go down are respectively 0.74, 0.24, and 0.05; the second study reveals that the respective probabilities are 0.69, 0.25, and 0.06; and the third study shows that the probabilities are 0.72, 0.18, and 0.08, respectively. Are these figures for probabilities acceptable? Why or why not?

SOLUTION

Let A, B, and C be three mutually exclusive events corresponding to the hospital costs going up, remaining steady, or going down, respectively. Note that the probability for an occurrence of each of the events A, B, and C is non-negative and these probabilities add to 1.00 in the second study.

The other studies are not reliable because the sum of the probabilities exceed 1.00 in the first study, whereas in the third study, the sum of probabilities is less than 1.00 and this contradicts axiom 2. ∎

Example 10.11

The probabilities that a graduate student in economics will receive an A, B, C, D, or F in a final examination are 0.26, 0.44, 0.17, 0.08, and 0.05, respectively. What is the probability that he will receive

  a. at least a B
  b. at most a B
  c. neither an A nor an F
  d. a C or D

SOLUTION

Note that the events of receiving an A, B, C, D, or F in an examination are all mutually exclusive. Further, the probability of each of these events is a non-negative number and these probabilities add to 1.00. Thus, the axioms are satisfied and we have

  a. Probability of at least B $= P(A) + P(B) = 0.26 + 0.44 = 0.70$.
  b. Probability of at most a B $= P(B) + P(C) + P(D) + P(F)$
$$= 0.44 + 0.17 + 0.08 + 0.05 = 0.74.$$
  c. Probability of neither an A nor F $= P(B) + P(C) + P(D)$
$$= 0.44 + 0.17 + 0.08 = 0.69.$$
  d. Probability of C or D $= P(C) + P(D) = 0.17 + 0.08 = 0.25$. ∎

Proposition 10.4.1: For any event E in the sample space S,

$$P(E^c) = 1 - P(E)$$

PROOF

The events E and E^c are mutually exclusive: that is, $E \cap E^c = \varnothing$. Hence, by axiom 3 (10.7), we have

$$P(E \cup E^c) = P(E) + P(E^c)$$

But $E \cup E^c = S$ and by axiom 2 (10.6), $P(S) = 1$. Thus,

$$P(E) + P(E^c) = 1$$

from which the assertion follows. ∎

Thus, if the probability that the Democrats will win the next election is 0.73, then the probability that they will lose the election is 0.27. Similarly, if the probability is 0.21 that Miss Douglas will survive a heart attack, then the probability is 0.79 that she will not survive the attack; if the probability is 0.37 that Mr. Buckley will pass the

Civil Service Examination, then the probability is 0.63 that he will not make it; and if the probability is 0.30 that there will be showers tonight, then the probability is 0.70 that there will be no showers.

Example 10.12

A student is worried about his grades in a marketing course. However, he estimates that he will pass the course with a probability of 0.8 and the probability is 0.5 that he will get a grade of C or lower. What is the probability that he will get a grade of C or D?

SOLUTION

Because $P(A \text{ or } B \text{ or } C \text{ or } D) = 0.8$, it follows that $P(F) = 0.2$. Also,

$$P(C \text{ or } D \text{ or } F) = 0.5.$$

Hence,

$$\begin{aligned} P(C \text{ or } D) &= P(C \text{ or } D \text{ or } F) - P(F) \\ &= 0.5 - 0.2 \\ &= 0.3 \end{aligned}$$ ∎

Example 10.13

Two events, E and F, are mutually exclusive and $P(E) = 0.20$, $P(F) = 0.70$. Find the probabilities of

   a. $P(E^c)$
   b. $P(E \cap F)$
   c. $P(E \cup F)$
   d. $P(E^c \cup F^c)$
   e. $P(E^c \cap F^c)$

SOLUTION

   a. $P(E^c) = 1 - P(E) = 1.00 - 0.20 = 0.80$.
   b. $P(E \cap F) = 0$, because E and F are mutually exclusive events.
   c. From axiom 3 (10.7), we have $P(E \cup F) = P(E) + P(F) = 0.20 + 0.70 = 0.90$.

An application of DeMorgan's laws (from Chapter 1) shows that

$$E^c \cup F^c = (E \cap F)^c \quad \text{and} \quad E^c \cap F^c = (E \cup F)^c$$

Hence,

   d. $P(E^c \cup F^c) = P[(E \cap F)^c] = 1 - P(E \cap F) = 1 - 0 = 1$.
   e. $P(E^c \cap F^c) = P(E \cup F)^c = 1 - P(E \cup F) = 1 - 0.90 = 0.10$. ∎

Proposition 10.4.2: For any two events E and F defined on the sample space S,

$$P(E \cap F^c) = P(E) - P(E \cap F)$$

PROOF

The Venn diagram (Figure 10.2) shows that $(E \cap F)$ and $(E \cap F^c)$ are two mutually exclusive events and their union is simply the event E. Then by (10.7),

$$P(E \cap F^c) + P(E \cap F) = P(E)$$

from which the assertion follows.

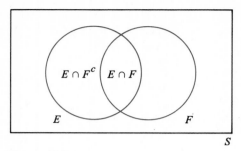

Figure 10.2

Proposition 10.4.3: For any two events E and F defined on the sample space S,

$$P(E \cup F) = P(E) + P(F) - P(E \cap F)$$

PROOF

The union of two events E and F may be represented as the union of two disjoint events F and $E \cap F^c$ (see Figure 10.3); that is,

$$E \cup F = F \cup (E \cap F^c)$$

Then, by (10.7), we have

$$
\begin{aligned}
P(E \cup F) &= P(F) + P(E \cap F^c) \\
&= P(F) + P(E) - P(E \cap F) \qquad \text{(Proposition 10.4.2)}
\end{aligned}
$$

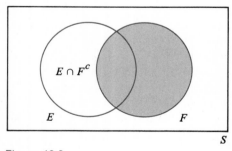

Figure 10.3

The following examples will illustrate these propositions.

Example 10.14

Give that $P(A) = 0.21$, $P(B) = 0.12$, and $P(A \cap B) = 0.05$, compute the following:

    a. $P(A \cup B)$
    b. $P(A \cap B^c)$
    c. $P(A^c \cap B^c)$

SOLUTION

Figure 10.4 is a Venn diagram showing the relation between A, B, and $A \cap B$.

a. From Proposition 10.4.3, $P(A \cup B) = P(A) + P(B) - P(A \cap B)$
$$= 0.21 + 0.12 - 0.05 = 0.28$$

b. From Proposition 10.4.2, we have $P(A \cap B^c) = P(A) - P(A \cap B)$
$$= 0.21 - 0.05 = 0.16$$

c. $P(A^c \cap B^c) = P[(A \cup B)^c]$ (by De Morgan's law)
$$= 1 - P(A \cup B) = 1 - 0.28 = 0.72$$

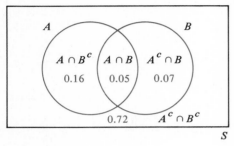

Figure 10.4

To explain further Proposition 10.4.3, let us consider an example. Suppose that a charity group sells raffle tickets numbered 1 to 600. A ticket is drawn at random and we wish to determine the probability that the number on the ticket drawn is divisible by 5 or by 6. We define the sample space, $S = \{1, 2, \ldots, 600\}$ and assume that all sample points in S are equally likely. If E denotes the event that the number selected is divisible by 5 and F the event that the number selected is divisible by 6, then there are 120 members in the event

$$E = \{5, 10, 15, \ldots, 600\}$$

and 100 members in the event

$$F = \{6, 12, 18, \ldots, 600\}$$

$$P(E) = \frac{120}{600}, \qquad P(F) = \frac{100}{600}$$

Among the first 600 numbers there are numbers like 30, 60, 90, 120, ..., 600 that are divisible by both 5 and 6. Hence,

$$P(E \cap F) = \frac{20}{600}$$

By applying Proposition 10.4.3, we have

$$P(E \cup F) = P(E) + P(F) - P(E \cap F)$$
$$= \frac{120}{600} + \frac{100}{600} - \frac{20}{600}$$
$$= \frac{1}{3}$$

As another illustration, suppose that the probability that a truck entering a state park having New York license plates is 0.37, the probability that it is a pick-up truck is 0.42, and the probability that it is a pick-up truck with New York plates is 0.18. We are interested in asking, "What is the probability that such a truck is neither a pick-up truck nor has New York plates?" As before, let E be the event that the truck is a pick-up and F the event the truck has New York plates. Then,

$$P(E) = 0.42 \qquad P(F) = 0.37 \qquad P(E \cap F) = 0.18$$

By applying Proposition 10.4.3, we have

$$P(E \cup F) = 0.42 + 0.37 - 0.18 = 0.61$$
$$P(E^c \cap F^c) = P[(E \cup F)^c] = 1 - P(E \cup F)$$
$$= 1 - 0.61 = 0.39$$

EXERCISE 10.3

1. A coin is tossed. A is the event "getting heads," and B is the event "getting tails." Are events A and B mutually exclusive?
2. Two coins are tossed. A is the event "getting two heads" and B is the event "getting two tails." Are events A and B mutually exclusive?
3. Three coins are tossed. A is the event "getting two heads," B is the event "getting two tails," and C is the event "getting one head." Are the events A and B mutually exclusive? Are B and C mutually exclusive events? Are A and C mutually exclusive? Evaluate $P(B \cup C)$.
4. A die is rolled. A is the event "the die shows an odd number" and B is the event "the die shows 6." Are events A and B mutually exclusive?
5. Explain why the following statements are false.
   a. The probabilities that a student will register for 0, 1, 2, 3, or 4 or more courses next semester are 0.08, 0.29, 0.35, 0.19, and 0.07, respectively.
   b. The probabilities that Mr. Black will receive a grade of A, B, C, D, or F in a course in finite mathematics are, respectively, 0.21, 0.26, 0.32, 0.18, and 0.13.
   c. The probability that Mr. Carlson will register for exactly two courses next fall is 0.67 and the probability that he will register for at least two courses next fall is 0.33.
6. Explain in each case why the following assignments of probability to the five mutually exclusive outcomes A, B, C, D, and E are not permissible:
   a. $P(A) = 0.23$, $P(B) = 0.28$, $P(C) = 0.28$, $P(D) = 0.12$, $P(E) = 0.13$
   b. $P(A) = 0.23$, $P(B) = P(C) = 0.29$, $P(D) = 0.06$, $P(E) = 0.11$
   c. $P(A) = 0.26$, $P(B) = P(C) = P(D) = 0.25$, $P(E) = -0.01$
7. A vice-president of a company visits Chicago often on a business trip. Sometimes he drives his own car, sometimes he drives his company's car, sometimes he takes a bus, sometimes he takes a train, and sometimes he goes by plane. The probabilities for these alternatives are, respectively, 0.24, 0.27, 0.18, 0.19, and 0.12. Find the probability that
   a. he will not catch a plane
   b. he will catch neither a plane nor a train
   c. he will go by car
   d. he will catch a plane or a bus or drive his own car

8. While shopping at a chain store, Mrs. Hawkes uses her credit cards often. Sometimes she uses credit card 1, sometimes she uses credit card 2, sometimes she uses credit card 3, sometimes she pays by her personal check, and, rarely, she pays cash for her merchandise. The probabilities for these alternatives are, respectively, 0.25, 0.29, 0.23, 0.19, and 0.04. What is the probability that she will
   a. not pay cash for her merchandise
   b. not use her credit cards
   c. use her credit card 1 or pay by check or pay cash
   d. pay neither cash nor use her checkbook

9. Of several mutually exclusive possibilities, the probability that Roger will entertain his friends on a Friday evening is 0.28, the probability that he will take Jeannie out for dinner is 0.32, the probability that he will go bowling with Jeannie is 0.12, the probability that he will work around his house is 0.15, and the probability that he will go to bed early is 0.13. What is the probability that Roger will
   a. not go out for bowling
   b. neither fix his house nor take Jeannie out for dinner
   c. not go out
   d. entertain his friends or work around his house

10. Given that A and B are two events defined on the sample space S, such that $P(A) = 0.42$, $P(B) = 0.36$, and $P(A \cap B) = 0.22$, find the probabilities of
    a. $P(A^c)$ b. $P(B^c)$
    c. $P(A^c \cap B)$ d. $P(A \cap B^c)$
    e. $P(A \cup B)$ f. $P(A^c \cup B)$
    g. $P(A^c \cap B^c)$ h. $P(A^c \cup B^c)$

11. Let A and B be two events defined on the sample space S such that $P(A) = 0.63$, $P(B) = 0.27$, $P(A \cap B) = 0.14$. Find the probabilities of
    a. $P(A^c)$ b. $P(B^c)$
    c. $P(A \cup B)$ d. $P(A^c \cap B)$
    e. $P(A^c \cup B)$ f. $P(A \cap B^c)$
    g. $P(A^c \cap B^c)$ h. $P(A^c \cup B^c)$

12. Let A and B be two mutually exclusive events such that $P(A) = 0.32$,

    $P(B) = 0.45$

    Find the probabilities of
    a. $P(A^c)$ b. $P(B^c)$
    c. $P(A \cup B)$ d. $P(A^c \cap B)$
    e. $P(A \cap B^c)$ f. $P(A^c \cup B^c)$
    g. $P(A^c \cap B^c)$ h. $P(A^c \cup B)$

13. A group of 1000 New Yorkers contains 525 persons who read *The New York Times* and 280 who read *The Daily News*. Among these, 135 read both the *Times* and the *Daily News*. What is the probability that a person chosen at random from this group reads either the *Times* or the *Daily News*?

14. Of 300 college students, 115 are enrolled in a course in economics, 245 are in mathematics, and 85 are in both economics and mathematics. What is the probability that a student selected at random is enrolled in
    a. at least one of these courses

b. exactly one course

c. neither of these two courses

15. For married couples living in a certain suburb of Denver, the probability that the husband will vote in a mayoral election is 0.27, the probability that his wife will vote is 0.38, and the probability that both will vote is 0.21. What is the probability that
    a. at least one of them will vote
    b. none of them will vote
    c. exactly one of them will vote
    d. the husband will not vote
    e. the wife will not vote

16. The probability that Gary, who is visiting a contractor, will sign a contract for remodeling his kitchen is 0.09, the probability that he will have his bathroom remodeled is 0.22, and the probability that he will have his kitchen as well as his bathroom remodeled is 0.04. What is the probability that he will have
    a. neither the kitchen nor the bathroom remodeled
    b. the kitchen or the bathroom remodeled, but not both
    c. at least one, bathroom or kitchen, remodeled

17. An integer is selected at random from the set of integers 1 to 10,000 inclusive. What is the probability that the integer selected is divisible by 3 or by 4?

18. An integer is selected at random from the set of integers 1 to 1000 inclusive. What is the probability that the integer selected at random is a multiple of 5 or 6?

19. Every employee of a chain store belongs to at least one of three unions. 300 belong to union A, 200 to union B, 50 to union C, 20 to both A and B, 30 to both B and C, 20 to both A and C, and 10 to all three. If an employee is selected at random, what is the probability that the employee belongs to
    a. at least two unions
    b. exactly two unions
    c. exactly one union

20. A market research organization claims that among 1000 homemakers interviewed over a period of time, 600 regularly buy product X, 720 regularly buy product Y, 560 use product Z, 380 use both X and Y, 270 use both X and Z, 350 use both Y and Z, and 80 regularly buy X, Y, and Z. What is the probability that a homemaker selected at random from this group is using at least one product? at least two products? at most two products? exactly two products? exactly one product?

10.5 RANDOM SELECTIONS

The selection of an object from a group is considered "random" if and only if all objects in the group have the same chance of being selected. Drawing a card from a regular deck of cards is a random process as long as the deck is well shuffled and there are no distinguishing marks on the back of any of the cards in the deck. Similarly, drawing a ball from an urn containing w white and b black balls is random as long as the balls are of the same size and weight and there is nothing to influence one in the selection of a particular ball. As another example, in a lottery the tickets are shuffled in a revolving drum to assure that all the participants in the lottery have the same chance of winning a prize.

To illustrate the notion further, let us consider a committee of six members A, B, C, D, E, and F. To begin with, let us determine the number of possible subcommittees of three members each that can be formed from this larger committee. From Chapter 9 we know that there are $\binom{6}{3}$ or 20 possible ways in which three members can be selected to form a subcommittee from a group of six members.

A selection of any one of these 20 subcommittees is random if we are assured that each of the possible subcommittees has a probability of $\frac{1}{20}$ of being chosen. One way in which this might be done is by writing each combination on a slip of paper, mixing these slips thoroughly, and then drawing one without looking. Generally, in selecting k elements from a set of n objects, there are $\binom{n}{k}$ outcomes if we disregard any orderings among the elements selected. A process represented by the model in which the possible outcomes are assigned equal probabilities is referred to as a random selection; one says that k elements are drawn at random from n elements. The phrase "drawn at random" is always interpreted as meaning that the $\binom{n}{k}$ selections are equally likely and each selection is assigned a probability of $1/\binom{n}{k}$.

Example 10.15

Five television sets are selected at random from a lot containing 25 television sets, five of which are defective. What is the probability that of the five television sets chosen, none is defective?

SOLUTION

The number of ways one can select five out of 25 television sets is given by a combination of 25 objects taken five at a time. The phrase "at random" implies that these $\binom{25}{5} = 53,130$ combinations are to be considered equally probable.

Some of the combinations satisfy the statement "none are defective" and there are as many such combinations as there are ways of selecting five television sets from the 20 good ones. If A is the event that a random sample of five contains no defective set, then $n(A) = \binom{20}{5} = 15,504$. The desired probability is simply the ratio

$$P(A) = \frac{n(A)}{n(S)} = \frac{\dbinom{20}{5}}{\dbinom{25}{5}} = \frac{15,504}{53,130} = 0.2918$$

Example 10.16

Five cards are drawn at random from a well-shuffled deck. What is the probability of getting exactly three clubs?

SOLUTION

The sample space consists of $\binom{52}{5}$ combinations of 52 cards taken five at a time. How many favorable cases are there? To make up a hand containing exactly three clubs, we must make two choices. First, we choose three of the 13 clubs, and this can be done in $\binom{13}{3}$ ways; then we must choose two of the 39 that are not club cards, and there are $\binom{39}{2}$ ways to do this. By the multiplication principle, there are $\binom{13}{3}\binom{39}{2}$

favorable cases. Thus, the probability of exactly three clubs is given by the ratio

$$\frac{\binom{13}{3}\binom{39}{2}}{\binom{52}{5}} = \frac{2,717}{33,320} = 0.0815$$ ∎

Now, we are in a position to state a general rule. Suppose that we have $a + b$ distinct objects divided into two disjoint subsets, one subset containing a elements of type A, and the second subset containing b elements of type B. We select a random sample of size n and ask for the probability that the sample contains r elements of type A and $n - r$ elements of type B. In other words, we let

$$a = \text{number of elements of type A}$$
$$b = \text{number of elements of type B}$$
$$a + b = \text{total number of elements}$$
$$n = \text{number of elements drawn}$$
$$r = \text{number of type A elements drawn}$$

The probability of getting exactly r type A elements and $n - r$ type B elements is

$$\frac{\binom{a}{r}\binom{b}{n-r}}{\binom{a+b}{n}}$$

These quantities are referred to as hypergeometric probabilities. In the preceding example, we have 13 type A elements and 39 type B elements, so $a = 13$, $b = 39$ and $a + b = 52$, $n = 5$, $r = 3$, and $n - r = 2$.

The above formula is applicable in situations where the object once drawn is not replaced before drawing the next one; in other words, sampling is carried out without replacement. Whether a sample is drawn from voters split into Republicans and Democrats, or cards are drawn from a deck divided into diamonds and other suits, or balls are drawn from an urn containing white and black balls, or eggs are drawn from a box containing good and rotten eggs, the technique remains the same.

EXERCISE 10.4

1. Three light bulbs are randomly selected from 10 bulbs, four of which are defective. What is the probability that among the three bulbs chosen
   a. none are defective
   b. one is defective
2. A box contains 20 light bulbs, five of which are known to be defective and the remainder nondefective. What is the probability that of the five bulbs chosen,
   a. none are defective
   b. two are defective

3. One needs four eggs to make omelets for a breakfast. There are 12 eggs in the refrigerator, four of which are rotten. Show that the probability of selecting four good eggs at random is approximately $\frac{1}{7}$.

4. Four razor blades are selected from a box containing 12 blades, five of which are known to be used. What is the probability that those selected are unused?

5. A game warden inspects a fisherman's catch by examining two fish that he selects at random. What is the probability that the fisherman will not be arrested if he has a catch of 10 that includes three undersized fish?

6. Among 25 income tax returns, 10 contain errors favoring the taxpayer. What is the probability that among five returns selected, two contain such an error?

7. A chain store receives a shipment of 25 television sets among which five are considered defective. If a customer selects four television sets at random, what is the probability that he will have no defective sets?

8. Mr. Berman has six matching gray socks and four matching green socks in a drawer. If his little daughter selects at random two socks, what is the probability that the socks will both be gray?

9. Certain television parts are shipped to a chain store in lots of 20. Five parts are examined from each lot and the lot is rejected if any of the parts is found defective. What is the probability that a lot will be accepted if it contains
   a. five defective parts
   b. 10 defective parts

10. A certain class has 10 men and 5 women. If a teacher has to select a committee of five, what is the probability that there is
    a. no woman on the committee
    b. at least one woman on the committee
    c. three men and two women on the committee

11. From the 52 cards of a regular deck, four cards are drawn without replacement. What is the probability of drawing
    a. all diamonds
    b. all cards of the same denomination
    c. all cards of the same suit
    d. two kings and two queens
    e. three aces
    f. no club cards

12. In a fraternity of 25 seniors, 15 juniors, 10 sophomores, and 5 freshmen, a committee of 10 is selected at random. What is the probability that the committee consists of four seniors, three juniors, two sophomores, and one freshman?

13. Five balls are drawn without replacement from an urn containing 18 balls of which five are white, six are red, and seven are blue. What is the probability that the balls drawn are
    a. all white
    b. all of the same color
    c. either red or blue

14. A grievance committee of four members is to be selected from four labor and four management representatives. What is the probability that the committee

so formed will have

a. equal representation of labor and management

b. more management personnel on the committee

15. A Congressional committee of five is to be chosen from among ten Democrats and eight Republicans. What is the probability that there are

a. four Republicans on the committee

b. four Democrats on the committee

c. more Democrats than Republicans on the committee

d. more Republicans than Democrats on the committee

e. all Democrats or all Republicans on the committee

10.6 CONDITIONAL PROBABILITY

We shall now examine how the occurrence or nonoccurrence of one event affects the probability of subsequent events and how the probability of the intersection of two events is related to their separate probabilities. Frequently, we wish to find the probability of an event B but have additional information for an event A that may alter the sample space. Some illustrative examples will be helpful in the formulation of a precise definition of conditional probability, which plays an important part in probability theory.

Example 10.17

Suppose that two cards are drawn without replacement from a well-shuffled deck of playing cards. What is the probability that the first card drawn is an ace? Clearly, the answer is $\frac{4}{52}$. What is the probability that the second card drawn is an ace? The answer to this question depends on whether the first card drawn was actually an ace or not. If the first card was an ace, then the probability for a subsequent card to be an ace is $\frac{3}{51}$, because there are only three aces left among the remaining 51 cards. If the first card was not an ace, we still have four aces in the deck of 51 cards and the desired probability is $\frac{4}{51}$. ∎

Example 10.18

A pair of dice is rolled. What is the probability that the sum of the upturned faces is greater than 10, given that one of the dice has a 6?

SOLUTION

Let B be the event that the sum of the upturned faces is greater than 10 and A the event that one of the dice has a 6 on it. Using the sample space S in Table 10.1, we have

$$A = \{(6, 1), (6, 2), (6, 3), (6, 4), (6, 5), (6, 6), (1, 6), (2, 6), (3, 6), (4, 6), (5, 6)\}$$
$$B = \{(6, 5), (6, 6), (5, 6)\}$$

Relative to the restriction placed on event B by the occurrence of A, $P(B) = \frac{3}{11}$, but relative to the original sample space of 36 sample points, $P(B) = \frac{3}{36}$. This is because we are considering A as a reduced sample space and B as an event of A. ∎

Example 10.19

A recent survey of 400 employees in a large company produced the following information on the employees:

Employment Level	With M.B.A. Degree	Without M.B.A. Degree
Managerial	65	30
Nonmanagerial	80	225

What is the probability that an employee chosen at random

    a. has an M.B.A. degree
    b. is working in a managerial position
    c. has an M.B.A. degree and is employed in a managerial position
    d. is working in a managerial position, given that he has an M.B.A. degree

SOLUTION

Let A represent the event that an employee has an M.B.A. degree and B denote the event that a person is employed as a manager. Clearly, $n(S) = 400$. Then we have

$$\text{a. } P(A) = \frac{n(A)}{n(S)} = \frac{65 + 80}{400} = \frac{145}{400} = \frac{29}{80}$$

$$\text{b. } P(B) = \frac{n(B)}{n(S)} = \frac{65 + 30}{400} = \frac{95}{400} = \frac{19}{80}$$

$$\text{c. } P(A \cap B) = \frac{n(A \cap B)}{n(S)} = \frac{65}{400} = \frac{13}{80}$$

    d. We are now interested in the probability that an employee chosen at random is working as a manager assuming that he has an M.B.A. degree. Because we know the number of employees who have M.B.A. degrees, we need to confine our attention to just such employees. Thus, the reduced sample space that concerns us has 145 possible outcomes, and the required probability is given by the ratio

$$\frac{n(A \cap B)}{n(A)} = \frac{65}{145} = \frac{13}{29}$$

This is called the conditional probability of an event B given that the event A has already occurred and is denoted by $P(B|A)$. In the example above, the conditional probability can also be expressed as

$$P(B|A) = \frac{65/400}{145/400} \quad \text{or} \quad P(B|A) = \frac{P(A \cap B)}{P(A)} \qquad \blacksquare$$

Definition 10.6.1: Let A and B be two events defined on the sample space S. The conditional probability of the event B, given the event A, is defined by

$$P(B|A) = \frac{P(A \cap B)}{P(A)} \qquad P(A) > 0$$

and if $P(A) = 0$, then $P(B|A)$ has no meaning.

Venn diagrams can also be used to illustrate the conditional probability problems. From Figure 10.5, one can determine $P(B|A)$ by reducing the sample space to the set A and then recognizing the fact that $P(B|A)$ is simply the ratio of the probability of that part of B which is also in A to the total probability of the set A.

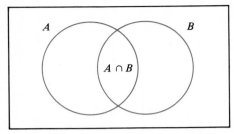

Figure 10.5

Example 10.20

The probability that a customer visiting a department store will buy a color television set is 0.23, the probability that he will buy a stereo complex is 0.26, and the probability that he will buy both is 0.14. What is the probability that a customer in a store will buy

 a. a color television given that he has already purchased a stereo
 b. a stereo complex given that he has already purchased a color television
 c. a color television and a stereo given that he will buy at least one of the two

SOLUTION

Let T denote the event that a customer will buy a color television and S represent the event that he will buy a stereo complex (see Figure 10.6).

$$\text{a. } P(T|S) = \frac{P(T \cap S)}{P(S)} = \frac{0.14}{0.26} = \frac{7}{13}$$

$$\text{b. } P(S|T) = \frac{P(S \cap T)}{P(T)} = \frac{0.14}{0.23} = \frac{14}{23}$$

c. Note that because

$$P(T \cup S) = P(T) + P(S) - P(T \cap S)$$
$$= 0.23 + 0.26 - 0.14 = 0.35$$

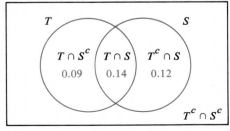

Figure 10.6

we have

$$P(T \cap S | T \cup S) = \frac{P(T \cap S)}{P(T \cup S)} = \frac{0.14}{0.35} = \frac{2}{5}$$

As an immediate consequence of the Definition 10.6.1 of conditional probability, we have the following proposition.

Proposition 10.6.1: For any events A and B,

$$P(A \cap B) = P(A) \cdot P(B|A)$$

Example 10.21
Two cards are drawn without replacement from a well-shuffled deck of playing cards. What is the probability that both cards drawn are aces?

SOLUTION
Let A be the event that first card drawn is an ace. Then $P(A) = \frac{4}{52}$. Next, let B denote the event that second card drawn is an ace. Then $P(B|A) = \frac{3}{51}$. Now, by using the above Proposition 10.6.1, we have

$$P(A \cap B) = \frac{4}{52} \cdot \frac{3}{51} = \frac{1}{221}$$

This rule of multiplication can easily be extended to more than two events. Thus, the probability of several subsequent events is obtained by multiplying the probabilities of the individual events, assuming that these events have occurred.

Example 10.22
A grievance committee of three members is to be selected at random from among 12 labor and 8 management personnel. What is the probability that the committee so formed does not have any management representation on it?

SOLUTION
Let A, B, and C denote, respectively, the events that the first, second, and third member drawn from the available personnel belong to the labor group. Then

$$P(A) = \tfrac{12}{20} \qquad P(B|A) = \tfrac{11}{19} \qquad P(C|A, B) = \tfrac{10}{18}$$

Using the extended rule of multiplication, we have

$$P(A \cap B \cap C) = \tfrac{12}{20} \cdot \tfrac{11}{19} \cdot \tfrac{10}{18}$$
$$= \tfrac{11}{57}$$

Independent Events
When A and B are two events, each with positive probability, we have observed that in general the conditional probability of the event B given the occurrence of the event A differs from the unconditional probability of the event B. However, the case when we have the equality

(10.8) $P(B|A) = P(B)$

is of special significance, for (10.8) expresses the fact that the event B is independent of A in the sense that the occurrence or nonoccurrence of event A does not in any way affect the probability of event B. This leads us to a formal definition.

Definition 10.6.2: Let A and B be two events defined on the probability space S. Event B is said to be independent of event A if and only if

$$P(B|A) = P(B)$$

Notice that

(10.9) $P(B) \cdot P(A|B) = P(A \cap B) = P(A) \cdot P(B|A)$

If B is independent of A, then $P(B|A) = P(B)$ and (10.9) implies that $P(A|B) = P(A)$, which in turn means that A is independent of B. Thus, if B is independent of A, it follows that A is independent of B. It also follows from (10.9) that if A and B are independent events, then

(10.10) $P(A \cap B) = P(A) \cdot P(B)$

Example 10.23

Toss a pair of dice, one white and the other green. The sample space S consists of 36 ordered pairs and is given in Table 10.1. Let A be the event "the white die shows an even number" and B be the event "the green die shows an odd number." Then

$$A \cap B = \{(2, 1), (2, 3), (2, 5), (4, 1), (4, 3), (4, 5), (6, 1), (6, 3), (6, 5)\}$$

and the probabilities are as follows:

$$P(A \cap B) = \tfrac{9}{36} = \tfrac{1}{4}$$
$$P(A) = \tfrac{18}{36} = \tfrac{1}{2} \qquad P(B) = \tfrac{18}{36} = \tfrac{1}{2}$$

In view of (10.10), events A and B are independent.   ■

Example 10.24

A fair coin is tossed twice. Let A be the event "head on the first toss" and B be the event "exactly one head." The usual sample space is given by $\{HH, HT, TH, TT\}$. Assigning a probability of $\tfrac{1}{4}$ to each simple event, we find that

$$P(A) = \tfrac{2}{4} \qquad P(B) = \tfrac{2}{4} \qquad P(A \cap B) = \tfrac{1}{4}$$

Hence

$$P(A \cap B) = P(A) \cdot P(B)$$

If a coin is tossed three times, then the sample space S is given by

$$S = \{HHH, HHT, HTH, HTT, THH, THT, TTH, TTT\}$$

Describing the events A and B as above, we observe that

$$P(A) = \tfrac{4}{8} \qquad P(B) = \tfrac{3}{8} \qquad P(A \cap B) = \tfrac{1}{8}$$

Condition (10.10) does not hold. Consequently, the events A and B as defined above are independent on the sample space of a coin tossed twice, but are not independent on the sample space of the same coin tossed three times.   ■

EXERCISE 10.5

1. One card is drawn at random from a standard deck of cards. What is the probability that the card drawn is
   a. a diamond
   b. a diamond given that it is a red card
   c. a diamond given that it is not a spade card

2. A man tosses a fair coin three times. What is the probability of getting three heads given that there is at least one head?

3. A family has three children. Assume that each child is as likely to be a boy as it is to be a girl. What is the probability that all three children are boys, given that
   a. at least one of the children is a boy
   b. at least two children are boys

4. Two dice, one green and the other red, are rolled. What is the probability that the sum of faces that turn up is greater than nine, given that
   a. at least one of the dice has yielded a 5
   b. the red die has turned up a 4

5. Let a deck of cards consist of the kings and aces selected from a regular deck of 52 cards and let two cards be drawn from the new deck. What is the probability that the cards are both aces, given that
   a. at least one of them is an ace
   b. one card is an ace of diamonds
   c. at least one card is a red ace

6. A recent survey claims that 35 percent of Canadians vacationing in the United States visit New York, 28 percent visit Washington, D.C., and 15 percent visit both New York and Washington, D.C. Find the probability that a randomly selected Canadian vacationing in the United States will visit
   a. New York given that he has visited Washington, D.C.
   b. Washington, D.C., given that he has visited New York

7. The probability that a person is visiting his dentist to have his teeth cleaned is 0.38, the probability that he is going to have a cavity filled is 0.31, and the probability that he will have his teeth cleaned as well as a cavity filled is 0.12. What is the probability that a patient visiting his dentist will have
   a. his teeth cleaned, given that he is also getting a cavity filled
   b. a cavity filled, given that he is also having his teeth cleaned
   c. a cavity filled, given that he may have his teeth cleaned or a cavity filled or possibly both

8. In a group of 300 college students, 135 are enrolled in economics, 119 are enrolled in a marketing course, and 73 are not taking either course.
   a. What is the probability that a student selected at random is enrolled in exactly one course, given that he is attending at least one course?
   b. What is the probability that a student selected at random is enrolled in economics, given that he is also taking a course in marketing?

9. A committee is composed of eight Democrats and four Republicans. Five of the Democrats are men and three of the Republicans are men. If a man is chosen as a chairman of the committee, what is the probability that he is Republican?

10. A student survey on the orientation of a college faculty produced the following results:

	With Ph.D. Degree	Without Ph.D. Degree
Previous teaching experience	78	102
No teaching experience	82	238

One of the professors is chosen at random to serve as an Acting Dean of the College. Let A denote the event that the professor has a Ph.D. degree and B be the event that he has previous teaching experience. Find each of the following probabilities.

a. $P(A)$ **b.** $P(B)$ **c.** $P(B|A)$

d. $P(A|B)$ **e.** $P(A^c|B)$ **f.** $P(B^c|A)$

11. Three cards are drawn from a deck of 52 cards. What is the probability that the hand contains three aces given that
    a. the hand contains at least two aces
    b. the hand contains two red aces

12. A salesman dealing with snowmobiles estimates that the probability of heavy snow this winter is 0.85, and the probability that he will make huge profits selling snowmobiles if heavy snow falls is 0.90. What is the probability that there will be a heavy snow and that he will make huge profits?

13. A shipment consists of 10 color television sets and 5 black-and-white sets. If two sets are selected at random, what is the probability that both are
    a. color sets
    b. black-and-white sets

14. In the meat section of a self-service market there are 100 chickens, 70 of which are fresh and 30 of which are one week old. If two chickens are selected at random, what is the probability that they are both fresh?

15. Referring to Exercise 14, what is the probability that three chickens selected at random are fresh?

16. A package contains 12 seeds for red flowers and 8 seeds for white flowers. If two seeds are selected at random, what is the probability that
    a. both seeds germinate in red flowers
    b. both seeds germinate in white flowers
    c. one seed germinates in red flowers and the other in white flowers

17. A box of 12 ballpoint pens contains three that are defective. If two pens are selected at random, what is the probability that
    a. none are defective
    b. at least one is defective
    c. both are defective
    d. exactly one is defective

18. A grievance committee of three members is to be chosen at random from among a group of eight men and four women. What is the probability that the committee so formed has no
    a. male representative
    b. female representative

19. A fair coin is tossed twice. Show that the events "head on the first toss" and "tail on the second toss" are independent.

20. A green and a red die are rolled. Show that the events "3 on green die" and "6 on red die" are independent.

21. A card is drawn at random from a deck of 52 cards. Let A be the event "the card is a club," B be the event "the card is an ace," and C be the event that "the card is an ace or a king." Are A and B independent? Are A and C independent?

22. A business executive has two secretaries. The probability that one will not show up in the office on a cold morning is 0.1 and the probability that the other will not show up is 0.2. On a cold morning, what is the probability that
a. both will show up
b. neither of them will show up
c. at least one will show up
d. exactly one will show up

23. Two persons are shooting at a target. The probabilities that they miss the target are 0.4 and 0.5, respectively. What is the probability that
a. none will hit the target
b. exactly one will hit the target
c. both will hit the target

24. The probabilities that two snowplowing trucks in a maintenance department will not operate on a cold morning are 0.2 and 0.3, respectively. What is the probability that
a. both trucks will operate
b. none will operate
c. exactly one will operate
d. at least one will operate

10.7 BAYES'S THEOREM

There are many experiments in which the final outcome depends on what happens in various intermediate stages. For example, the success of students in college depends on what they learned in high school, the courses in which they are enrolled and the time they spend studying; the success of salespeople depends on their formal training as well as their experience in their chosen field; the success of a skylab mission depends on many preliminary calculations, the performance of all systems, and the experience of the pilots in conducting previous missions; the election of a Congresswoman depends on her financial backing, campaign strategies, speaking engagements as well as the political support of her party; and so on.

Suppose that three candidates are running for the Senate from a particular state. The probability that a Democrat will be elected is 0.25, the probability that a Republican will be elected is 0.45, and the probability that an Independent will make it to the Senate is 0.30. It is also known that the probabilities for the candidates to work effectively for minorities are, respectively, 0.02, 0.05, and 0.08. What is the probability that the Senator from this state will work effectively for minorities?

It is clear from the tree diagram in Figure 10.7 that the probability of the Democrat's working effectively for minorities is (0.25)(0.02), where we multiplied two probabilities, one corresponding to the election of a Democrat and the other to his ability to work effectively for the minorities in case he is elected. Similarly, the probabilities for the other two branches are (0.45)(0.05) = 0.0225 and (0.30)(0.08) = 0.024. Because the probabilities are mutually exclusive, the desired probability is 0.0050 + 0.0225 + 0.0240 = 0.0515. Note that each term in the sum represents a tree diagram branch leading to the event W that the Senator will work effectively for the cause of the minorities in his state. The first branch leads to W via D, the second leads to W via R, and the third leads to W via I.

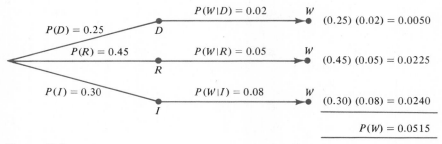

Figure 10.7

An important generalization of this concept is given in the following proposition.

Proposition 10.7.1: If $A_1, A_2, \ldots, A_n$ are n mutually exclusive events, each of positive probability, such that the union of all the sets $A_1, A_2, \ldots, A_n$ is equal to S, then for any event B,

$$P(B) = P(A_1) \cdot P(B|A_1) + P(A_2) \cdot P(B|A_2) + \cdots + P(A_n)P(B|A_n)$$

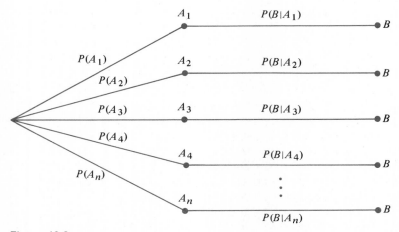

Figure 10.8

PROOF

The tree diagram in Figure 10.8 may facilitate an understanding of what is involved. For any event B,

$$B = B \cap S$$

or

$$B = B \cap (A_1 \cup A_2 \cup A_3 \cup \cdots \cup A_n)$$

so that

$$B = (B \cap A_1) \cup (B \cap A_2) \cup \cdots \cup (B \cap A_n)$$

where we have used the generalized distributive law for union over intersection. Because the sets A_i, $i = 1, 2, \ldots, n$ are mutually exclusive, it follows that the sets $B \cap A_i$, $i = 1, 2, \ldots, n$ are also mutually exclusive. Therefore, by axiom 3 (10.7),

$$P(B) = P(B \cap A_1) + P(B \cap A_2) + \cdots + P(B \cap A_n)$$

Now, applying Proposition 10.6.1 to each term of the summation, we have the desired formula. ∎

Suppose that a commuter in New Jersey who works in New York must either go over the George Washington Bridge, or through the Lincoln Tunnel, or through the Holland Tunnel to get home. He varies his route according to the weather conditions and traffic congestion, choosing the George Washington Bridge with the probability 0.4, the Lincoln Tunnel with the probability 0.35, and the Holland Tunnel with the probability 0.25. If he chooses the George Washington Bridge, he gets home by supper time 55 percent of the time, if he goes through the Lincoln Tunnel, he gets home by supper time 70 percent of the time, and if he goes through the Holland Tunnel he gets home by supper time 80 percent of the time. What is the probability that he will be in time for supper?

Let A_1, A_2, and A_3 be the events that he chooses the George Washington Bridge, the Lincoln Tunnel, or the Holland Tunnel, respectively, and B denote the event that he gets home for supper in time. Then,

$$P(A_1) = 0.40 \qquad P(A_2) = 0.35 \qquad P(A_3) = 0.25$$

and

$$P(B|A_1) = 0.55 \qquad P(B|A_2) = 0.70 \qquad P(B|A_3) = 0.80$$

Thus, the desired probability of event B is

$$(0.40)(0.55) + (0.35)(0.70) + (0.25)(0.80) = 0.665$$

Suppose that we are now interested in another question of entirely different nature: If the commuter gets home by supper time, what is the probability that he used the George Washington Bridge? To answer this question, we need the following theorem, often called Bayes's rule.

Proposition 10.7.2 (Bayes's Theorem): Let $A_1, A_2, \ldots, A_n$ be n mutually exclusive events, each of positive probability. Then for any event B,

$$P(A_i|B) = \frac{P(A_i)P(B|A_i)}{P(A_1)P(B|A_1) + P(A_2)P(B|A_2) + \cdots + P(A_n)P(B|A_n)}$$

PROOF

Using the definition of conditional probability, we have

$$P(B \cap A_i) = P(A_i) \cdot P(B|A_i)$$

and

$$P(B \cap A_i) = P(B) \cdot P(A_i|B)$$

Thus,

$$P(B) \cdot P(A_i|B) = P(A_i) \cdot P(B|A_i)$$

so that

(10.11) $$P(A_i|B) = \frac{P(A_i) \cdot P(B|A_i)}{P(B)}$$

By Proposition 10.7.1, we have

$$P(B) = P(A_1)(B|A_1) + P(A_2)P(B|A_2) + \cdots + P(A_n)P(B|A_n)$$

Substituting this for $P(B)$ in (10.11), we have the desired assertion. ∎

This theorem gives us the probability that an event is reached along a particular path of a tree diagram given that it is reached along one of these paths. In other words, $P(B)$ becomes an important source of reference and the $P(A_i|B)$ is the ratio of the probability of event B through a particular branch A_i to the total probability of event B.

Now we can answer the question, "If the commuter gets home by supper time, what is the probability that he used the George Washington Bridge?"

$$P(A_1|B) = \frac{P(A_1) \cdot P(B|A_1)}{P(A_1)P(B|A) + P(A_2)P(B|A_2) + P(A_3)P(B|A_3)}$$

$$= \frac{(0.40)(0.55)}{(0.40)(0.55) + (0.35)(0.70) + (0.25)(0.80)}$$

$$= \frac{44}{133}$$

The following examples will further illustrate Proposition 10.7.2.

Example 10.25

Forty percent of the members of a singles club are men. Eighty percent of the single men and 90 percent of the single women own automobiles. A car is found double-parked in the club's parking lot and towed away at the owner's expense. What is the probability that the car belongs to a woman?

SOLUTION

Let A and A^c be the events that the member is a male and that the member is a female, respectively, and let B be the event that a member owns the car that is towed away. Then

$$P(A) = 0.4 \qquad P(A^c) = 0.6$$
$$P(B|A) = 0.8 \qquad P(B|A^c) = 0.9$$

Using Proposition 10.7.1, we have

$$P(B) = (0.4)(0.8) + (0.6)(0.9) = 0.86$$

By Proposition 10.7.2, we obtain

$$P(A^c|B) = \frac{P(A^c)P(B|A^c)}{P(A)P(B|A) + P(A^c)P(B|A^c)}$$

$$= \frac{(0.6)(0.9)}{(0.4)(0.8) + (0.6)(0.9)}$$

$$= \frac{27}{43}$$

∎

Example 10.26

Three boxes, identical in appearance, each have two drawers. The first box contains a gold coin in each drawer; the second contains a silver coin in each drawer; but the third contains a gold coin in one drawer and a silver coin in the other. A box is chosen, one of its drawers opened, and a gold coin found. What is the probability that the other drawer contains a silver coin?

SOLUTION

Let A be the event that the box containing a gold coin in each drawer is chosen, B the event that the box with a silver coin in each drawer is selected, and C denote the event that the box with a gold coin in one drawer and a silver coin in the other is chosen at random. Then

$$P(A) = P(B) = P(C) = \tfrac{1}{3}$$

If G represents the event that a drawer contains a gold coin, then

$$P(G|A) = 1 \qquad P(G|B) = 0 \qquad P(G|C) = \tfrac{1}{2}$$

We are interested in the event $P(C|G)$. Using Bayes's theorem, we have

$$P(C|G) = \frac{P(C)P(G|C)}{P(A)P(G|A) + P(B)P(G|B) + P(C)P(G|C)}$$

$$= \frac{\tfrac{1}{3} \cdot \tfrac{1}{2}}{\tfrac{1}{3} \cdot 1 + \tfrac{1}{3} \cdot 0 + \tfrac{1}{3} \cdot \tfrac{1}{2}}$$

$$= \tfrac{1}{3}$$

∎

EXERCISE 10.6

1. A bus driver must rise early and uses an alarm clock that rings properly with a probability of only 0.8. If it rings, the probability is 0.9 that the driver will wake up. If the alarm does not ring, there is probability of 0.4 that he will get up on his own. What is the probability that he will get to the bus depot in time?

2. Of the freshmen in a certain college, it is claimed that 40 percent attended private secondary schools and 60 percent attended public schools. Thirty percent of those who attended private schools and 20 percent of those who attended public schools attain an A average in their freshman year. If a student is selected at random, what is the probability that he is an A student?

3. Jeannie chooses at random one of the integers 1, 2, and 3 and then throws as many dice as are indicated by the number she chose. What is the probability that she will throw a total of 5 points?

4. Consider three urns: Urn 1 contains four white and eight red balls; urn 2 contains three white and five red balls; urn 3 contains one white and three red balls. An urn is selected at random and a ball is drawn from it. What is the probability that ball drawn is white?

5. A student currently enrolled in an economics course has a 60 percent chance of taking another course in economics and a 40 percent chance of switching to a history course next semester. A student currently studying history has an 80 percent chance of taking another course in history and a 20 percent chance of switching to economics. Assuming that he has an equal chance of taking either course in a given semester, what is the probability that he will register for another course in economics next semester?

6. An assembly line has three machines, A, B, and C, producing the same component for color television sets. Machine A produces 60 percent of the output with 95 percent of the parts free of defects, machine B produces 30 percent with 80 percent free of defects, and machine C produces 10 percent with 65 percent free of defects.
   a. If a component is selected at random, what is the probability that it is defective?
   b. If a component selected at random is found defective, what is the probability that it came from machine A? machine B?

7. Three urns contain colored balls as follows: urn 1, three red, four white, and one blue; urn 2, one red, two white, and three blue; urn 3, four red, three white, and two blue. An urn is selected at random and a ball drawn from it. Given that the ball drawn is red, what is the probability that it came from urn 1? urn 2?

8. An instructor in a marketing course estimates that a student who reads the text carefully has a probability of 90 percent of passing the course, whereas a student who does not read the text carefully has only a 20 percent chance of passing the course.
   a. If 25 percent of the students in a large class read their text carefully, what percentage of students are expected to pass?
   b. If a student randomly selected from this class did pass, what is the probability that he read his text carefully?

9. Mrs. Young estimates that the probability of her ex-husband not showing up at the Christmas party is 0.6. In case he does not show up the probability is 0.8

that she will have a good time, but if he shows up, the probability is 0.1 that she will have a good time. If we hear later that Mrs. Young did not have a good time, what is the probability that her ex-husband showed up at the party?

10. Three students are employed to wash dishes in the school cafeteria. Jody, who washes 45 percent of the dishes, breaks 2 percent of the dishes she washes; Tracey, who washes 35 percent of the dishes, breaks 3 percent of the dishes she washes; and Jeannie, who washes the remaining dishes, breaks 5 percent of the dishes she washes each day. Given that a broken dish is found by their supervisor, what is the probability that it was broken by Jeannie?

11. Drivers are classified into three different classes for purposes of automobile insurance. The records indicate that "good risk" drivers constitute 25 percent of the driving force who apply for automobile insurance, "medium risk" drivers cover 45 percent, and "poor risk" drivers constitute the remaining 30 percent of those who apply for insurance. The probabilities that the "good risk," "medium risk," and "poor risk" drivers will have accidents in any two-year period are 0.02, 0.05, and 0.08, respectively. An insurance company sells Mr. Carlson a policy and within a two-year period he has an accident. What is the probability that he is a "good risk" driver? a "poor risk" driver?

12. A commuter who works in New York must either take a train or a bus or drive his own car to work. He chooses a train with probability 0.5, a bus with probability 0.3, and drives his own car with a probability of 0.2. If he goes by train, he gets to work on time with a probability of 0.90, a bus takes him to work on time with a probability of 0.75, and if he drives his own car he gets to his work on time only 70 percent of the time. If he gets to work on time on a given day, what is the probability that he drove his car?

13. An auto dealer is considering an expansion of his sales force. In order to review the educational requirement of new salespeople, he divides his current sales force into four categories: A, high school diploma; B, two years of college; C, a degree in science; D, an M.B.A. degree. He estimates that

$$P(A) = 0.4, P(B) = 0.3, P(C) = 0.2, \text{ and } P(D) = 0.1$$

On the basis of his sales record, he decides that the event $S =$ successful salesperson occurred in the categories as follows:

$$P(S|A) = 0.20, P(S|B) = 0.30, P(S|C) = 0.10, \text{ and } P(S|D) = 0.90$$

If a salesperson randomly selected is found to be successful, what is the probability that he had an M.B.A. degree?

10.8 BERNOULLI TRIALS

The word "trial" in probability theory implies an attempt to produce an event E, the occurrence or nonoccurrence of which cannot be determined with certainty. The outcome of a trial is classified into one of two categories—"success" if the event E occurs, and "failure" if E does not occur. For instance, if E represents the drawing of an ace from a standard deck of playing cards, the "trial" consists of drawing a card at random and we have a "success" or a "failure" depending on whether the card drawn is an ace or not. Such an experiment, which has only two possible outcomes, is called a Bernoulli trial. The probabilities of the "success" and "failure" in a Bernoulli trial are usually denoted by p and q, respectively, where

$$p \geq 0 \qquad q \geq 0 \qquad p + q = 1$$

Suppose, for example, that a balanced die is rolled four times in succession. What is the probability that a 5 will appear exactly two times? Clearly, we have a sequence of Bernoulli trials in which the probability of a "success" that a 5 appears on a given throw is $\frac{1}{6}$ and the probability of a "failure" that a 5 fails to appear on that throw is $\frac{5}{6}$. Had we specified the order in which 5 was to appear, say, on the first two throws and not on the last two throws, then the probability is given by

$$\frac{1}{6} \cdot \frac{1}{6} \cdot \frac{5}{6} \cdot \frac{5}{6} = \frac{25}{1296}$$

In the absence of any such restriction on the order, we can only assume that a 5 is to appear twice in four throws in any order. Because there are $^4C_2 = 6$ ways in which a 5 may appear and the probability for each of these ways is 25/1296, it follows that the required probability is

$$6 \left(\frac{25}{1296} \right) = \frac{25}{216}$$

Proposition 10.8.1: If an experiment consists of n independent Bernoulli trials, each with probability p of success and probability q of failure, then the probability of having exactly k successes and $n - k$ failures is given by

$$P(k) = \binom{n}{k} p^k q^{n-k}$$

PROOF

Because the outcomes for the n trials are independent, the probability of k successes and $n - k$ failures in any specified order is $p^k q^{n-k}$. There is one factor p for each success, one factor q for each failure, and the k factors p and $(n - k)$ factors q are multiplied together because of the assumption of independence. Among the 2^n points in the sample space, there are $\binom{n}{k}$ points with successes, each point having the probability $p^k q^{n-k}$ assigned to it. Therefore, the probability of exactly k successes in n Bernoulli trials with probability p of success and q of failure is

$$P(k) = \binom{n}{k} p^k q^{n-k} \qquad k = 0, 1, 2, \dots, n \qquad \blacksquare$$

Example 10.27

Calculate the probability of getting three heads and seven tails in 10 throws of a fair coin.

SOLUTION

A substitution of $k = 3$, $n = 10$, $p = \frac{1}{2}$, and $q = \frac{1}{2}$ in the above formula gives

$$\binom{10}{3} \left(\frac{1}{2} \right)^3 \left(\frac{1}{2} \right)^7 = \frac{15}{128} \qquad \blacksquare$$

Example 10.28

The probability that Mr. Jones will hit a small target on a single shot is 0.25. If he shoots five times, what is the probability that he will score

    a. exactly two hits
    b. at least one hit
    c. at most one hit

SOLUTION

    a. Substituting $k = 2$, $n = 5$, $p = 0.25$, and $q = 0.75$, we have

$$\binom{5}{2}(0.25)^2(0.75)^3 = 0.2637$$

    b. The event "at least one hit" is the subset $\{1, 2, 3, 4, 5\}$. The required probability is given by

$$P(k \geq 1) = 1 - P(k = 0)$$

$$= 1 - \binom{5}{0}(0.25)^0(0.75)^5 = 0.7627$$

    c. The event "at most one hit" consists of the subset $\{0, 1\}$. The required probability is therefore given by

$$P(k \leq 1) = P(k = 0) + P(k = 1) = (0.75)^5 + \binom{5}{1}(0.25)^1(0.75)^4$$

$$= 0.2373 + 0.3955$$

$$= 0.6328$$

EXERCISE 10.7

1. A coin is tossed four times. What is the probability of exactly two heads?
2. The probability that a single radar set will detect an enemy plane is 0.8. If we have 10 radar sets, what is the probability that exactly eight sets will detect the plane?
3. Suppose that 90 percent of the students taking economics pass the course. What is the probability that five students in a class of 10 will pass the course?
4. Assuming that each sex is equally likely in a birth, what is the probability that a family of four children will have
    a. exactly one boy
    b. exactly one girl
    c. at least one boy
    d. at least one girl
5. An airplane dropping a bomb has a probability of 0.7 of hitting the target. What is the probability that a plane dropping five bombs will score
    a. no hit
    b. exactly one hit
    c. exactly two hits
    d. at least two hits

6. The probability that a given television set from a certain plant is defective is estimated to be 0.20. If a sample of 10 sets is selected at random, what is the probability that the sample contains
   a. no defectives
   b. exactly two defectives

7. It is known that incompatibility is the legal reason for nine out of 10 divorce cases. What is the probability that among eight divorce cases, exactly four are attributed to this ground? at least four? at most four?

8. Ninety percent of all persons passing a job aptitude test over the last several years have been successful performers on that job. What is the probability that six of the eight applicants who have just passed the test will be successful workers?

9. Roger, who is waiting for Jeannie, decides to walk under the following set of rules. He tosses a fair coin. If the coin falls heads, he walks 10 steps north; if the coin falls tails, he walks 10 steps south. What is the probability that after walking 100 steps he is
   a. back at the starting point
   b. 20 steps from the starting point
   c. 40 steps from the starting point

10. In a large population, 10 percent of the members are left-handed. If a sample of 10 persons is selected at random, what is the probability that the sample contains
    a. two left-handed persons
    b. no left-handed person
    c. at least one left-handed person
    d. at most two left-handed persons

11. It is estimated that 25 percent of a certain population have blood group B. If a sample of 12 persons is selected at random, what is the probability that this sample contains
    a. exactly three persons with blood group B
    b. none with blood group B
    c. at least one person with blood group B
    d. at most one person with blood group B

12. A recent survey conducted by a construction company shows that 70 percent of retired persons prefer to live in apartments. If a sample of 5 retired persons is selected at random, what is the probability that the sample contains
    a. no one who prefers to live in apartments
    b. at least one who prefers to live in apartments
    c. exactly 3 persons who prefer to live in apartments
    d. at most one person who prefers to live in apartments

11

Expectation, Variation, and Normal Distribution

11.1 RANDOM VARIABLE

What is the number of heads if a coin is tossed four times? How many students will register for quantitative courses in management next semester? How many new houses will be built next year? How many new cars will be sold by an automobile dealer next week? How many homemakers in Detroit will buy detergent X next month? What is the number of calls that will arrive tomorrow at the switchboard during rush hour? These questions cannot be answered with absolute certainty; an element of chance enters in each case. Further, to state a possible answer to any of these questions can hardly be considered satisfactory, because our primary interest lies in the probability with which a particular value occurs when an experiment is conducted.

Essentially, a random variable is a function whose domain is the finite sample space and whose range is the subset of real numbers. The number of cars in a parking lot, the scores of students on an examination, the number of customers waiting to be served in a restaurant, and the number of long-distance calls handled by an operator are all examples of random variables. For instance, if a coin is thrown four times, the number of heads X is a random variable; the probability that $X = 4$ is $\frac{1}{16}$. The sum X of the numbers on two dice is a random variable; the probability that X assumes a value 8 is $\frac{5}{36}$, and the probability that X assumes a value 7 or 11, $P(X = 7$ or 11), is $\frac{8}{36}$. Because only events are associated with probabilities, it is reasonable that we set up a structure within which $\{X = 8\}$ or $\{X = 7$ or 11$\}$ are events. This can be accomplished by defining a random variable that assigns to each simple event in the sample space a number. This is precisely how the concept of the function was introduced in Chapter 2. The sample space on which this rule operates is called the domain of the function, whereas the set of values that a random variable assumes at each simple event in S is called the range.

Definition 11.1.1: A function whose domain is the finite sample space S and whose range is a subset of real numbers is called a random variable. If X is a random variable defined on the sample space $S = \{a_1, a_2, \ldots, a_n\}$, then $X(a_j)$ denotes the value of the random variable for the simple event $\{a_j\}$.

Example 11.1

You match coins with Smith, winning a dollar if you match, losing a dollar if you do not. The usual sample space consists of four simple events: HH, HT, TH, TT. If Smith's winning is the random variable X defined on this sample space, then at each of the simple events HH and TT it has the value $+1$, and at each of the simple events HT and TH it has the value -1. The range of X is thus the set of values $\{-1, +1\}$. ∎

Example 11.2

Consider a family of three children. The sample space S is given by

$$\{BBB, BBG, BGB, BGG, GBB, GBG, GGB, GGG\}$$

If the random variable X on this sample space is defined to be the number of boys in the family, then

$$X(BBB) = 3, X(BBG) = X(BGB) = X(GBB) = 2,$$
$$X(BGG) = X(GBG) = X(GGB) = 1, X(GGG) = 0$$

and the range of X is $\{0, 1, 2, 3\}$.

Let us define another random variable Y on this sample space S to be $+1$ if there are more boys than girls, -1 if there are more girls than boys, and 0 if there are the same number of boys and girls. In this case,

$$Y(BBB) = Y(BBG) = Y(GBB) = Y(BGB) = +1$$
$$Y(BGG) = Y(GBG) = Y(GGB) = Y(GGG) = -1$$

The range of Y is evidently $\{-1, +1\}$. ∎

Example 11.3

A pair of dice is rolled. The sample space is

$$S = \{(x, y)\,|\,1 \leq x \leq 6, 1 \leq y \leq 6\}$$

Let the random variable X defined on this sample space be the sum of the numbers on the two dice. Then the range of X is the set

$$\{2, 3, 4, 5, 6, 7, 8, 9, 10, 11, 12\}$$ ∎

11.2 EXPECTED VALUE OF A RANDOM VARIABLE

An important concept in probability theory that had its origin in games of chance is the mean, or expected value, of the random variable. In its simplest form, the expected value of a random variable is the sum of the products of a player's possible gains with their associated probabilities. Consider, for instance, the experiment of rolling a die. Mr. Jones receives a number of dollars equal to the number of spots that turn up. What should Mr. Jones pay to make this a fair game? The random variable X, representing the number of dollars Mr. Jones may win, assumes the value 1, 2, 3, 4, 5, or 6, each with a probability of $\frac{1}{6}$. Thus, Mr. Jones expects to win

$$\$1(\tfrac{1}{6}) + \$2(\tfrac{1}{6}) + \$3(\tfrac{1}{6}) + \$4(\tfrac{1}{6}) + \$5(\tfrac{1}{6}) + \$6(\tfrac{1}{6}) = \$3.50$$

This determines the fair price of the game.

Generalizing this example, we have the following definition.

Definition 11.2.1: Let X be a random variable that assumes the set of values x_1, $x_2, \ldots, x_n$ with corresponding probabilities $P(X = x_i)$, where $i = 1, 2, \ldots, n$. Then the mean or expected value of X, denoted by $E(X)$, is the number

$$E(X) = x_1 P(X = x_1) + x_2 P(X = x_2) + \cdots + x_n P(X = x_n)$$

$$= \sum_{i=1}^{n} {}^{*} x_i P(X = x_i)$$

Note that each value of the variable is multiplied by the corresponding probability, and $E(X)$ is simply the sum of the products thus obtained.

Example 11.4

Using the following data, compute $E(X)$.

Values of X; $x =$	10	20	30	40	50	60
$P(X = x)$:	0.05	0.15	0.30	0.30	0.15	0.05

SOLUTION

$$E(X) = 10(0.05) + 20(0.15) + 30(0.30) + 40(0.30) + 50(0.15) + 60(0.05)$$
$$= 35.0$$

Example 11.5

Marilyn holds one of 1000 raffle tickets for which the first prize is an automobile worth $3000, the second prize is a color television worth $500, the third prize is a movie camera worth $300, the fourth prize is $200 cash, and the remaining tickets pay nothing. Determine the fair price of her ticket.

SOLUTION

The following table gives the value of each prize and the associated probabilities.

Prize	Value of the Prize $X = x$	Probability of Winning $P(X = x)$
Automobile	$3000	0.001
Color television	500	0.001
Movie camera	300	0.001
Cash	200	0.001
	0	0.996

* A discussion of summation notation is available in Appendix B.

The last row provides the information that 996 tickets do not pay anything at all. Thus, the fair price of a ticket is

$$E(X) = \$3000(0.001) + \$500(0.001) + \$300(0.001) + \$200(0.001) + \$0(0.996)$$
$$= \$4.00 \quad \blacksquare$$

Example 11.6

The probability that a 23-year-old male will survive the next year is 0.998, and the probability that he will die within the next year is 0.002. An insurance company offers to sell such a man a $1000 one-year term policy for a premium of $10. What is the company's expected gain?

SOLUTION

The random variable X, which represents the profit of the company, assumes a value $+\$10$ with a probability 0.998 and a value $-\$990$ with a probability 0.002 (if the insured dies). Hence,

$$E(X) = 10 \cdot (0.998) + (-990) \cdot (0.002) = \$8.00 \quad \blacksquare$$

Example 11.7

The following table gives the distribution of weekly unit sales and the associated probabilities:

Units Sold	Probability of Selling These Units
80	0.10
90	0.30
100	0.35
110	0.20
120	0.05

Determine the average weekly sales.

SOLUTION

The random variable X, which represents the number of units sold, assumes a value 80, 90, 100, 110, and 120 with probabilities 0.10, 0.30, 0.35, 0.20, and 0.05, respectively. Hence,

$$E(X) = 80(0.10) + 90(0.30) + 100(0.35) + 110(0.20) + 120(0.05) = 98 \quad \blacksquare$$

The concept of the expected value of a random variable is particularly useful for management-making decisions on optimum stocking under conditions of uncertainty. In many situations where the exact demand for a product cannot be determined with any degree of certainty, management can base their decisions on the expected value of a random variable and be more nearly correct in their estimates than they would be if they based their decisions on some form of intuitive notions associated with pure guesses and hunches.

Proposition 11.2.1: If X is a random variable with finite mean and a and b are any arbitrary numbers, then $E(aX + b) = aE(X) + b$. $\quad \blacksquare$

Corollary: If X is a random variable with finite mean and a and b are arbitrary numbers, then (1) $E(X + b) = E(X) + b$ and (2) $E(aX) = aE(X)$. ∎

This corollary implies that adding a constant b to each value of the random variable X adds this constant to the expected value of the random variable, whereas multiplying each value of the random variable by a constant multiplies the expected value of the random variable by that constant. Consider, for instance, the following example.

Example 11.8
The random variable X has the following probability function:

Values of X; $x = $ -2 -1 0 1 2
$P(X = x)$: 0.1 0.2 0.4 0.1 0.2

Compute the expected value of (a) X, (b) $X + 2$, and (c) $3X$.

SOLUTION
a. $E(X) = (-2)(0.1) + (-1)(0.2) + 0(0.4) + 1(0.1) + 2(0.2) = 0.1$.
b. The values of a new random variable $X + 2$ and the associated probabilities are as follows:

Values of $X + 2$: 0 1 2 3 4
$P(X = x)$: 0.1 0.2 0.4 0.1 0.2

Thus,

$$E(X + 2) = 0(0.1) + 1(0.2) + 2(0.4) + 3(0.1) + 4(0.2)$$
$$= 2.1 = E(X) + 2$$

This means that adding 2 to each value of the random variable X increases its expected value by 2.
c. The values of $3X$ and its corresponding probabilities are

Values of $3X$: -6 -3 0 3 6
$P(X = x)$: 0.1 0.2 0.4 0.1 0.2

Thus,

$$E(3X) = (-6)(0.1) + (-3)(0.2) + 0(0.4) + 3(0.1) + 6(0.2)$$
$$= 0.3$$

which is precisely the same as $3E(X)$. ∎

To illustrate how the calculations are simplified using Proposition 11.2.1, let us recompute the mean of the random variable X in Example 11.7.
Let $Y = (X - 80)/10$ be a new random variable whose probability function is as follows.

y_i: 0 1 2 3 4
$P(Y = y_i)$: 0.10 0.30 0.35 0.20 0.05

Then

$$E(Y) = 0(0.10) + 1(0.30) + 2(0.35) + 3(0.20) + 4(0.05) = 1.80$$

Because $Y = (X - 80)/10$, we obtain

$$X = 80 + 10 \cdot Y$$

Substituting $a = 10$ and $b = 80$ in Proposition 11.2.1, we have

$$E(X) = 80 + 10 \cdot E(Y)$$
$$= 80 + 10(1.80) = 98$$

which agrees with the result we established earlier. This shortcut device saves a good deal of time and energy if the random variable X assumes a large number of values.

We now turn our attention to another important application. Suppose that we want to know the expected number of heads in six throws of a balanced coin. Because the outcomes for six trials are independent, we can apply our knowledge of binomial experiments. If X denotes the number of heads obtained, then $P(X = x_i)$ for $x_i = 0, 1, \ldots, 6$ is as follows:

$$
\begin{array}{c|ccccccc}
x_i: & 0 & 1 & 2 & 3 & 4 & 5 & 6 \\
P(X = x_i): & \frac{1}{64} & \frac{6}{64} & \frac{15}{64} & \frac{20}{64} & \frac{15}{64} & \frac{6}{64} & \frac{1}{64}
\end{array}
$$

Hence,

$$E(X) = 0(\tfrac{1}{64}) + 1(\tfrac{6}{64}) + 2(\tfrac{15}{64}) + 3(\tfrac{20}{64}) + 4(\tfrac{15}{64}) + 5(\tfrac{6}{64}) + 6(\tfrac{1}{64})$$
$$= \frac{6 + 30 + 60 + 60 + 30 + 6}{64} = 3$$

Thus, one can expect three heads in six throws of a balanced coin.

Consider now that we want to know the average number of drivers among 600 randomly selected who use seat belts on a turnpike. Assume that the probability is 0.75 that a driver on a turnpike uses a seat belt. We could compute the 601 probabilities corresponding to 0, 1, 2, ..., 600 drivers using seat belts on the turnpike and then use Definition 11.2.1 to compute the mean. It appears that whenever a random variable assumes a large number of values, the calculation of the expected value of the random variable is time-consuming and laborious. We therefore state (without proof) the following proposition, which proves to be of special significance.

Proposition 11.2.2: If X is the number of successes in n trials of a binomial experiment where the probability of success at each trial is p, then $E(X) = np$. ■

Thus, the mean of a binomial distribution is simply the product of the number of trials and the probability of an occurrence of the event in an individual trial. For the expected number of heads in six throws of a balanced coin, we have

$$n = 6 \qquad p = 0.5$$

Thus, the average number of heads in six throws of a balanced coin is simply

$$6 \cdot (0.5) = 3$$

If 75 percent of the drivers use seat belts on long trips, then among 600 randomly selected drivers on a turnpike, one can "expect" $600(0.75) = 450$ drivers to use seat belts. Again, if it is claimed that 80 percent of the married couples seeking divorce use incompatibility as a legal reason, then it is reasonable to expect that among 700 married couples seeking divorce, $700 \cdot (0.80) = 560$ couples will use incompatibility as a legal ground for the divorce.

EXERCISE 11.1

In Exercises 1 through 3, the probability function of a random variable X is specified. Find the expected value of X.

1.
x_i:	1	2	3	4	5
$P(X = x_i)$:	0.10	0.20	0.40	0.20	0.10

2.
x_i:	0	1	2	3	4	5
$P(X = x_i)$:	$\frac{1}{32}$	$\frac{5}{32}$	$\frac{10}{32}$	$\frac{10}{32}$	$\frac{5}{32}$	$\frac{1}{32}$

3.
x_i:	0	1	2	3	4
$P(X = x_i)$:	0.36	0.40	0.16	0.04	0.04

4. The probabilities that Roger will sell his piece of real estate property at a profit of $10,000, $8000, $5000, $3000, and $2000 are 0.05, 0.10, 0.20, 0.30, and 0.35, respectively. What is his expected profit?

5. Mr. Thompson must sell his house to raise immediate cash to defray some unforeseen expenses. The probability that he will sell it at a profit of $2000 is 0.10, the probability that he will break even is 0.60, and the probability is 0.30 that he will sell it for a loss of $2000. What is his expected profit?

6. Mrs. Keating holds one of 200 raffle tickets for which there are six prizes, one of $500, one of $100, and the remaining four prizes each worth $50. What are her expected winnings?

7. Mr. Smith has two half-dollars, four quarters, and four nickels in his pocket, and he plans to buy a newspaper worth $0.30. A newspaper boy offers to sell him a paper in exchange for a coin selected at random. Is this a fair proposition? If not, to whom is it favorable?

8. The probability that a 30-year-old salesperson will survive next year is 0.996 and the probability that he will die within the next year is 0.004. An insurance company offers to sell such a salesperson a $1000 one-year term policy for $5. What is the company's expected gain?

9. The probability that a coal miner will live to age 65 is 0.90. Assuming that no administrative costs are involved, what would be a fair premium an insurance company must charge for a $15,000 life insurance contract to age 65 if there is one single-payment premium?

10. If the expected value of the random variable X is 15, what is the expected value of
   a. $X + 4$ **b.** $2X$ **c.** $3X + 8$

11. If the expected value of the random variable is 20, determine the expected value of
   a. $4X$ **b.** $2X + 5$ **c.** $5X - 10$

12. The following table gives the distribution of number of articles sold in one year.

Units Sold	Probability
1000	0.45
2000	0.30
3000	0.10
4000	0.07
5000	0.06
6000	0.02

Use Definition 11.2.1 to determine the average sales.

13. A fair coin is tossed 100 times. Let X denote the number of heads that appear. Find $E(X)$.

14. Let X denote the number of cars with faulty brakes among 500 cars stopped at a road block. If the probability that a car selected at random has defective brakes is 0.10, what is $E(X)$?

15. In a class of 400, let X denote the number of students who always come late. What is $E(X)$ if the probability that a randomly selected student is late for his class is 0.10?

16. Prove Proposition 11.2.1.

11.3 VARIANCE OF A RANDOM VARIABLE

The expected value or mean of a random variable is simply the "weighted average" of the random variable; it provides no information as to how the individual values of the random variable are spread out. Not all probability distributions are similar; essentially, they differ in two respects. First, random variables with different probability functions may have the same weighted average, yet the values of the variables may be differently scattered. Consider, for example, random variables X_1 and X_2 with the following probability functions:

$$
\begin{array}{lccccc}
x: & -2 & -1 & 0 & 1 & 2 \\
P(X_1 = x): & 0.1 & 0.2 & 0.4 & 0.2 & 0.1
\end{array}
$$

$$
\begin{array}{lccccccc}
x: & -3 & -2 & -1 & 0 & 1 & 2 & 3 \\
P(X_2 = x): & 0.05 & 0.10 & 0.20 & 0.30 & 0.20 & 0.10 & 0.05
\end{array}
$$

These probability functions are symmetrical about $x = 0$ [see Figures 11.1(a) and 11.1(b)]; the expected value of X_1 and the expected value of X_2 are both equal to zero. Thus, several random variables may have the same expected value, yet an expected value alone does not reveal that the probability functions are different. In fact, an expected value does not relay any information about the spread of the probability function from which it was computed; it indicates only the central position of the probability function and what lies behind that position is not its task to reveal. Note that $E(X_1) = E(X_2)$, yet X_1 and X_2 differ in many respects. The expected value of X_1 is based on five values, whereas the expected value of X_2 takes seven values in account. Thus, the extent to which the individual values of the random variable spread out along the x axis is larger for X_2 than for X_1; that is, the graph for the random variable X_2 has a larger spread than the corresponding graph for X_1.

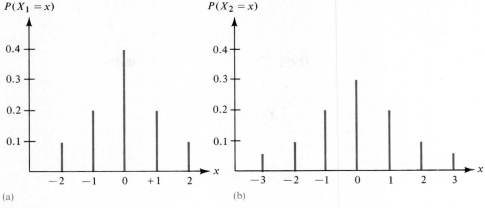

(a)   (b)

Figure 11.1

As another illustration, consider random variables X_3 and X_4 with the following probability functions:

$$
\begin{array}{lccccc}
x: & 1 & 2 & 3 & 4 & 5 \\
P(X_3 = x): & 0.1 & 0.2 & 0.4 & 0.2 & 0.1 \\
x: & -4 & -2 & 0 & 2 & 4 \\
P(X_4 = x): & 0.1 & 0.2 & 0.4 & 0.2 & 0.1
\end{array}
$$

The corresponding graphs are shown in Figures 11.2(a) and 11.2(b).

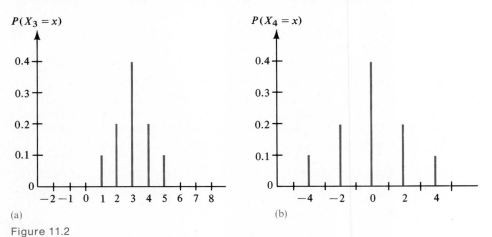

(a)   (b)

Figure 11.2

The reader can verify that $E(X_3) = 3$ and that $X_3 = X_1 + 3$ so that adding 3 to each value of the random variable X_1 increases its expected value by that amount, that the graphs of X_1 and X_3 are identical in shape with the only difference that the mean of the random variable X_3 is pushed three units further along the horizontal axis. Thus, any measure of variability that is proposed should remain the same for both the random variables X_1 and X_3.

Let us now compare the values of the random variables X_1 and X_4. Note that each value of X_4 is twice that of the corresponding value of X_1 and $E(X_4) = 2E(X_1) = 0$, but the graph of X_4 in Figure 11.2(b) has a wider spread on the horizontal axis as compared to the graph of X_1 in Figure 11.1(a). Thus, whatever the measure of dispersion, it should be larger for X_4 than for X_1.

Thus, we recognize the need of more information in addition to what $E(X)$ can provide. The range (difference between the largest and smallest value of the variable) is not a satisfactory measure, because it does not take into account all the values of the variable. A different measure of dispersion arises when we measure the deviation of each value of the variable from $E(X)$ and then form the weighted average, that is,

$$\sum_{i=1}^{n} [x_i - E(X)]P(X = x_i)$$

but this turns out to be zero. (Why?) This difficulty can be resolved if we square the deviation of each of the values of the random variable from its expected value and then calculate the weighted average of the squared deviations. This weighted mean of all squared deviations, each weighted according to the probability, is called the variance and is denoted by $V(X)$.

Definition 11.3.1: Let X be a random variable whose values $x_1, x_2, \ldots, x_n$ occur with probabilities $P(X = x_1), P(X = x_2), \ldots, P(X = x_n)$, respectively. Then the variance of X, denoted by $V(X)$ is

$$V(X) = E[(X - E(X))^2]$$
$$= \sum_{i=1}^{i=n} [x_i - E(X)]^2 P(X = x_i) \qquad \blacksquare$$

Note that the formula for $V(X)$ involves squaring the deviations of each of the values of the random variable X from its expected value. This means that $V(X)$ are in "squares" of units of X; that is, if X is in inches, $V(X)$ would be in square inches and if X is measured in feet, then $V(X)$ would be in square feet. Because it is only logical that the variability of X about its expected value should be in the same unit as the random variable X, we take the positive square root of $V(X)$.

Definition 11.3.2: The positive square root of $V(X)$, denoted by $\sigma(X)$, is called the standard deviation of the random variable X; that is,

$$\sigma(X) = \sqrt{V(X)} \qquad \blacksquare$$

We wish to remark that the standard deviation of a random variable X measures in some sense the dispersion of the probability distribution of X from its expected value. A small standard deviation of X means that X assumes values that are concentrated near its expected value, whereas a large standard deviation of X indicates that probabilities associated with the values of X are scattered widely about its expected value.

Let us now calculate $\sigma(X)$ in the following example.

Example 11.9

Let X be a random variable with the following probability function.

$$x_i:\quad 4\quad 6\quad 8\quad 10\quad 12$$
$$P(X = x): 0.10\quad 0.20\quad 0.40\quad 0.20\quad 0.10$$

Compute (a) $V(X)$ and (b) $\sigma(X)$.

SOLUTION

The mean or expected value of the random variable X is

$$E(X) = 4(0.10) + 6(0.20) + 8(0.40) + 10(0.20) + 12(0.10)$$
$$= 8.0$$

Using Definition 11.3.1, we have

$$V(X) = (4 - 8)^2(0.10) + (6 - 8)^2(0.20) + (8 - 8)^2(0.40) + (10 - 8)^2(0.20)$$
$$+ (12 - 8)^2(0.10)$$
$$= 1.60 + 0.80 + 0.80 + 1.60$$
$$= 4.80$$

The standard deviation is the positive square root of $V(X)$. Hence,

$$\sigma(X) = \sqrt{4.80} = 2.19$$

That the calculations of $V(X)$ and $\sigma(X)$ were straightforward in the above example is largely because the values assumed by the random variable X, its mean value $E(X)$, and also the deviations from the mean were all whole numbers. If the values of X and its mean are not whole numbers, the following proposition can save us considerable time and effort. ■

Proposition 11.3.1: $V(X) = E(X^2) - \mu^2$, where $\mu = E(X)$. ■

A distinct advantage in using Proposition 11.3.1 is that it does not require that we find the deviations from the expected value of the random variable and then calculate the weighted average of the squared deviations; instead we simply compute $E(X)$ and $E(X^2)$ and then use the formula

(11.1) $V(X) = E(X^2) - [E(X)]^2$

Example 11.10

Let X denote the number of points obtained in rolling a fair die. Then

$$x_i:\quad 1\quad 2\quad 3\quad 4\quad 5\quad 6$$
$$P(X = x_i): 1/6\quad 1/6\quad 1/6\quad 1/6\quad 1/6\quad 1/6$$
$$E(X) = 1 \cdot \tfrac{1}{6} + 2 \cdot \tfrac{1}{6} + 3 \cdot \tfrac{1}{6} + 4 \cdot \tfrac{1}{6} + 5 \cdot \tfrac{1}{6} + 6 \cdot \tfrac{1}{6} = \tfrac{7}{2}$$
$$E(X^2) = 1^2 \cdot \tfrac{1}{6} + 2^2 \cdot \tfrac{1}{6} + 3^2 \cdot \tfrac{1}{6} + 4^2 \cdot \tfrac{1}{6} + 5^2 \cdot \tfrac{1}{6} + 6^2 \cdot \tfrac{1}{6} = \tfrac{91}{6}$$
$$V(X) = E(X^2) - [E(X)]^2$$
$$= \tfrac{91}{6} - (\tfrac{7}{2})^2 = \tfrac{35}{12}$$

Hence,

$$\sigma(X) \approx 1.7 \qquad \blacksquare$$

Example 11.11

Compute the variance of the random variables X_1 whose probability function is given in Figure 11.1(a), that is,

$$x: -2 \quad -1 \quad 0 \quad 1 \quad 2$$
$$P(X_1 = x): 0.1 \quad 0.2 \quad 0.4 \quad 0.2 \quad 0.1$$

Recall that $E(X_1) = 0$, whereas

$$E(X_1{}^2) = (-2)^2(0.1) + (-1)^2(0.2) + 1^2(0.2) + 2^2(0.1) = 1.2$$

Using Proposition 11.3.1, we have

$$V(X_1) = E(X_1{}^2) = 1.2 \qquad \blacksquare$$

Let us now examine the variance of X_3 and X_4 in relation to the random variable X_1. The probability function of X_3 [as given in Figure 11.2(a)] is

$$x: 1 \quad 2 \quad 3 \quad 4 \quad 5$$
$$P(X_3 = x): 0.1 \quad 0.2 \quad 0.4 \quad 0.2 \quad 0.1$$

We have observed earlier that

$$X_3 = X_1 + 3$$

and

$$E(X_3) = 3$$

whereas

$$E(X_3{}^2) = 1^2(0.1) + 2^2(0.2) + 3^2(0.4) + 4^2(0.2) + 5^2(0.1) = 10.2$$

Because

$$V(X_3) = E(X_3{}^2) - [E(X_3)]^2$$
$$= 10.2 - 9 = 1.2$$

it follows that

$$V(X_3) = V(X_1)$$

and this agrees with our earlier observation that the X_1 and X_3 have the same variability. This suggests that adding or subtracting an arbitrary constant from each value assumed by the random variable has no effect on its variance. Thus, in general, if $Y = X + c$, where c is a constant, then

(11.2) $\quad V(Y) = V(X + c) = V(X)$

How is the variance affected if we multiply the values of the random variable by a constant c? Consider, for example, the probability function of the random variable X_4.

$$x: -4 \quad -2 \quad 0 \quad 2 \quad 4$$
$$P(X_4 = x): 0.1 \quad 0.2 \quad 0.4 \quad 0.2 \quad 0.1$$

Recall that $E(X_4) = 0$. Because

$$E(X_4^2) = (-4)^2(0.1) + (-2)^2(0.2) + 2^2(0.2) + 4^2(0.1)$$
$$= 4.8$$

and

$$V(X_4) = E(X_4^2) - [E(X_4)]^2 \qquad \text{(Proposition 11.3.1)}$$

it follows that

$$V(X_4) = 4.8 = 4V(X_1)$$

Note carefully that $X_4 = 2X_1$ and

$$V(X_4) = 2^2 V(X_1)$$

In general, if $Z = cX$, where c is a constant, then

(11.3) $\quad V(Z) = c^2 V(X)$

Observe that both (11.2) and (11.3) are special cases of the following proposition, which we state without proof.

Proposition 11.3.2: Let X be a random variable defined on the sample space $S = \{x_1, x_2, \ldots, x_n\}$. If a and b are arbitrary numbers, then

$$V(aX + b) = a^2 V(X) \qquad\qquad ■$$

As another illustration, let us consider the following example.

Example 11.12

Let X be a random variable with the probability function

$$x_i: 50 \quad 55 \quad 60 \quad 65 \quad 70$$
$$P(X = x_i): 0.20 \quad 0.20 \quad 0.30 \quad 0.20 \quad 0.10$$

Let $Y = (X - 60)/5$ be a new random variable whose probability function is

$$y_i: -2 \quad -1 \quad 0 \quad 1 \quad 2$$
$$P(Y = y_i): 0.20 \quad 0.20 \quad 0.30 \quad 0.20 \quad 0.10$$

Then

$$E(Y) = (-2)(0.20) + (-1)(0.20) + 1(0.20) + 2(0.10) = -0.20$$
$$E(Y^2) = (-2)^2(0.20) + (-1)^2(0.20) + 1^2(0.20) + 2^2(0.10) = 1.60$$

Because

$$V(Y) = E(Y^2) - [E(Y)]^2$$

we have

$$V(Y) = 1.60 - (-0.2)^2$$
$$= 1.56$$

Because

$$Y = \frac{X - 60}{5}$$

it follows that we have

$$X = 60 + 5Y$$

Substituting $a = 5$ and $b = 60$ in Proposition 11.3.2, we have

$$V(X) = V(5Y)$$
$$= 25V(Y)$$
$$= 25(1.56)$$
$$= 39$$

∎

To illustrate the calculation of the variance of a binomial random variable, let us return to the example on page 322 regarding the probability function of the number of heads X in six throws of a balanced coin. The probability function is as follows.

x_i:	0	1	2	3	4	5	6
$P(X = x_i)$:	$\frac{1}{64}$	$\frac{6}{64}$	$\frac{15}{64}$	$\frac{20}{64}$	$\frac{15}{64}$	$\frac{6}{64}$	$\frac{1}{64}$

We established earlier that $E(X) = 3$. Now

$$E(X^2) = \sum_{x=0}^{6} x^2 \cdot P(X = x)$$
$$= 0^2(\tfrac{1}{64}) + 1^2(\tfrac{6}{64}) + 2^2(\tfrac{15}{64}) + 3^2(\tfrac{20}{64}) + 4^2(\tfrac{15}{64}) + 5^2(\tfrac{6}{64})$$
$$= 6^2(\tfrac{1}{64})$$
$$= \tfrac{21}{2}$$

Hence, using Proposition 11.3.1, we have

$$V(X) = E(X^2) - [E(X)]^2$$
$$= (\tfrac{21}{2}) - 9$$
$$= \tfrac{3}{2}$$

That these calculations can be further simplified is a consequence of the following proposition.

Proposition 11.3.3: If X is the number of successes in n trials of binomial experiment with p as the probability of success and q as the probability of failure in each trial, then

$$V(X) = npq \qquad \text{where } q = 1 - p \qquad \blacksquare$$

Thus, for the distribution of the number of heads X that we obtain in 100 throws of a balanced coin, we have $n = 100$ and $p = \frac{1}{2}$, and Proposition 11.3.3 yields

$$V(X) = npq = 100(\tfrac{1}{2})(\tfrac{1}{2}) = 25$$

and

$$\sigma(X) = \sqrt{V(X)} = \sqrt{25} = 5$$

Similarly, for the distribution of the number of automobile accidents due to faulty brakes where $n = 400$ and $p = 0.10$, we have

$$V(X) = 400(0.10)(0.90) = 36$$

and

$$\sigma(X) = \sqrt{36} = 6$$

EXERCISE 11.2

In each of the following exercises, the probability function of a random variable X is specified. Find the variance and standard deviation of X.

1.

x_i:	0	1	2	3
$P(X = x_i)$:	$\frac{1}{8}$	$\frac{3}{8}$	$\frac{3}{8}$	$\frac{1}{8}$

2.

x_i:	1	2	6	7	8
$P(X = x_i)$:	$\frac{1}{8}$	$\frac{1}{4}$	$\frac{3}{8}$	$\frac{1}{8}$	$\frac{1}{8}$

3.

x_i:	1	2	3	4
$P(X = x_i)$:	0.1	0.4	0.2	0.3

4.

x_i:	100	105	110	115	120
$P(X = x_i)$:	0.20	0.20	0.30	0.20	0.10

5.

x_i:	950	1000	1050	1100	1150
$P(X = x_i)$:	0.10	0.20	0.40	0.20	0.10

6. If the variance of the random variable X is 2.5, what is the variance of $4X$, $4X + 3$, $2X$, $2X - 5$, $\frac{1}{2}X$? (Hint: Use Proposition 11.3.2.)

7. A fair coin is tossed 400 times. Let X denote the number of heads that appear. Find $E(X)$, $V(X)$, and $\sigma(X)$.

8. Let X denote the number of 3's in 3600 rolls of a balanced die. Find $E(X)$, $V(X)$, and $\sigma(X)$.

9. Let X denote the number of cars with faulty brakes among 144 cars stopped at a road block. If the probability that a car selected at random has faulty brakes is (0.10), what is $\sigma(X)$?

10. A tabulation of recent demand for a product is as follows:

Units Sold	Probability of Selling These Units
150	0.10
160	0.30
170	0.35
180	0.15
200	0.10

If X represents the units sold, compute $E(X)$, $V(X)$, and $\sigma(X)$.

11. A department store provides the following discrete distribution of past sales of a certain product:

Daily Sales	Probability of Selling These Units
200	0.05
210	0.10
220	0.25
230	0.30
240	0.20
250	0.10

If X represents the number of units sold daily, find $V(X)$ and $\sigma(X)$ by using Proposition 11.3.2.

12. Alexander's department store gives the following discrete distributions of past sales of electric fans in summer 1976.

Daily Sales	Number of Days This Quantity Sold
120	2
125	4
130	10
135	12
140	8
145	4

If X denotes daily sales of the electric fans, compute $V(X)$ and $\sigma(X)$ by using Proposition 11.3.2.

11.4 CHEBYSHEV'S INEQUALITY

Recall that the variance and the standard deviation of a random variable X measure in some sense the compactness or the dispersion of the probability distribution of X from its expected value; a large variance or standard deviation means that probabilities associated with the values of the random variable X are at a considerable distance from the mean, whereas a small variance or standard deviation means a high probability that the random variable will assume a value "close" to the mean. This important idea was expressed by a Russian mathematician, P. L. Chebyshev (1821–1894), in a theorem now called Chebyshev's inequality. According to this statement, we are certain that for any kind of distribution, the proportion of the values of X falling within k standard deviations of the expected value is at least $1 - (1/k^2)$. This also implies that the probability that the random variable X assumes a value differing from the mean by more than k standard deviations is at most $1/k^2$.

Proposition 11.4.1: Let X be a random variable with $E(X) = \mu$ and $V(X) = \sigma^2$. Then for any arbitrary positive value of k,

$$(11.4) \qquad P\{\mu - k\sigma \leq X \leq \mu + k\sigma\} \geq 1 - \frac{1}{k^2}$$

$$(11.5) \quad P\{X < \mu - k\sigma \text{ or } X > \mu + k\sigma\} \leq \frac{1}{k^2} \qquad \blacksquare$$

Example 11.13
The probability is $\frac{1}{5}$ that a driver of a car with faulty headlights is stopped by a highway patrol. Let X denote the number of cars with faulty headlights among 625 automobiles. Because X is a binomial random variable with $n = 625$, $p = \frac{1}{5}$, and $q = \frac{4}{5}$, we have

$$\mu = E(X) = 625(\tfrac{1}{5}) = 125$$

and

$$\sigma(X) = \sqrt{npq} = \sqrt{625(\tfrac{1}{5})(\tfrac{4}{5})} = \sqrt{100} = 10$$

We wish to determine $P\{100 \leq X \leq 150\}$, the probability that the number of automobiles with defective headlights stopped by a highway patrol varies anywhere between 100 and 150.

This problem falls in the domain of the first inequality (11.4) of Proposition 11.4.1. Clearly,

$$\mu - k\sigma = 100 \quad \text{and} \quad \mu + k\sigma = 150$$

Because $\mu = 125$ and $\sigma(X) = 10$, it follows that $k = \frac{5}{2}$. Thus, the required probability is at least

$$1 - \frac{1}{k^2} = 1 - \frac{4}{25} = \frac{21}{25} \qquad \blacksquare$$

Example 11.14
An admission office at a state college reports that 75 percent of the students accepted for admission to the freshman class actually show up for the fall semester. What can you assert from Chebyshev's inequality about the probability of more than 1350 students showing up among 1768 students accepted by the college?

SOLUTION
Clearly, the random variable X has a binomial distribution with $n = 1768$ and $p = 0.75$. Thus

$$\mu = E(X) = 1768(0.75) = 1296$$
$$\sigma(X) = \sqrt{npq} = \sqrt{1768(0.75)(0.25)} = 18$$

We wish to compute $P(X > 1350)$. According to Chebyshev's inequality (11.5),

$$P\{X < \mu - k\sigma \text{ or } X > \mu + k\sigma\} \le \frac{1}{k^2}$$

Evidently $\mu + k\sigma = 1350$. Because $\mu = 1296$ and $\sigma = 18$, it follows that $k = 3$. Thus,

$$P\{X > 1350\} \le \tfrac{1}{9}$$

That is, probability is at most $\tfrac{1}{9}$ that more than 1350 students among 1768 will actually register for the fall semester. ∎

EXERCISE 11.3

1. A random variable X has mean $\mu = 2$ and standard deviation $\sigma = 1$. Obtain a lower bound on the $P\{-2 \le X \le 6\}$.
2. A random variable X has mean $\mu = 50$ and standard deviation $\sigma = 10$. Obtain a lower bound on the $P(30 \le X \le 70)$.
3. On the average, three-fifths of the seeds of a certain variety germinate. If 600 seeds are planted, obtain an upper bound for the probability using Chebyshev's inequality that the number germinating will differ from the expected value by more than 24.
4. A fair coin is tossed 900 times. Using Chebyshev's inequality, obtain a lower bound on the probability that the number of heads obtained varies anywhere between 405 and 495.
5. The number of customers served dinners on weekends in a certain restaurant averages $\mu = 150$ with a standard deviation of $\sigma = 5$. What can you assert, from Chebyshev's inequality, about the number of dinners served varying between 125 and 175?
6. The number of building permits issued in a certain county during the month of May averages $\mu = 144$ with a standard deviation of $\sigma = 6$. With what probability can you assert, from Chebyshev's inequality, that the number of building permits issued in May lies between 120 and 168?
7. The number of airplanes taking off from an international airport in any 15-minute period averages $\mu = 60$ with a standard deviation of $\sigma = 5$. Using Chebyshev's inequality, obtain a lower bound for the probability that the number of airplanes taking off in a given 15-minute period varies between 50 and 70.
8. The probability that a passenger on a cruise ship will get seasick is 0.20. Using Chebyshev's inequality, obtain a lower bound on the probability that the number of passengers getting seasick on the cruise ship varies anywhere between 156 and 204 if there are 900 passengers on the ship.

11.5 CONTINUOUS DISTRIBUTIONS

Thus far, we have discussed only those random variables that assume a finite set of values or as many values as there are integers. These variables are called discrete random variables. The number of customers in a department store, the number of passengers in a plane, the number of students in a management course, and the number of new automobiles sold in a month are all examples of discrete random variables. If a coin is thrown until a head appears for the first time, then the number of throws of the coin is also given by a discrete random variable, which can assume as many values as there are positive integers. This also holds true for a random variable having the binomial distribution and the hypergeometric distribution we introduced in Chapter 10.

In order that we discuss the normal distribution, one of the important distributions in probability, we must first understand the concept of continuous random variables and continuous distributions. A continuous random variable assumes values on a continuous scale and is associated with the sample space representing the infinitely large number of sample points contained in an interval. The length of life of a flashlight battery, the height of an individual, the temperature reading of a patient, the consumption of gasoline in a racing car, the amount of alcohol in a wine, the amount of nicotine in a cigarette, and the time needed to reach a college campus are all typical examples of outcomes given by continuous random variables. Although we may round our answers to the nearest whole number or to a few decimal places, there remain a continuum of possibilities in each of these examples.

Recall that a discrete distribution is described by listing probabilities associated with the possible integer values of the discrete random variable. In the continuous case the probabilities associated with the individual points of the continuous sample space are zero. Thus, if X is a continuous random variable, then $P(X = 8.0) = 0$, $P(X = 3.2) = 0$, $P(X = 2.356) = 0$, and so on. This seems paradoxical, because the random variable must assume some values on the real line. We recognize that each point on a line segment has a length zero, whereas the collection of all points in the interval taken together gives a segment of positive length. It is, therefore, reasonable to assume that a probability of a continuous random variable X assuming a particular value is zero but that the variable has a positive probability of taking some value in a given interval. Consequently, the probabilities associated with individual points of the continuous sample space are of no interest to us, but we do seek probabilities associated with intervals or regions. We may ask, for instance, for the probability that a newborn baby will weigh between 6 and 8 pounds, that the height of a randomly selected freshman will vary between 65 and 69 inches, that the gasoline consumption for a new car of certain make varies between 18.3 and 25.8 miles per gallon, that a commuter train will arrive at the railroad station within the next 10 minutes, that a racing car will be traveling between 95 and 120 miles an hour, and so on.

In discrete cases, the probabilities may be represented by constructing histograms to illustrate the distribution. For example, the areas of the rectangles of Figure 11.3 give the probabilities of 0, 1, 2, . . . , 12 successes in 12 independent trials; the probability that a random variable defined on the sample space takes the value 5 is given by the area of the shaded rectangle. This distribution can also be approximated by a continuous curve where a random variable takes any value between 0 and 12 and each number in the original discrete distribution is represented by an interval extending one-half unit in each direction below and above the number. Thus, 5 would be represented by an interval from 4.5 to 5.5, and the area under the curve from 4.5 to 5.5 would be approximately the probability that a random variable assumes the value 5.

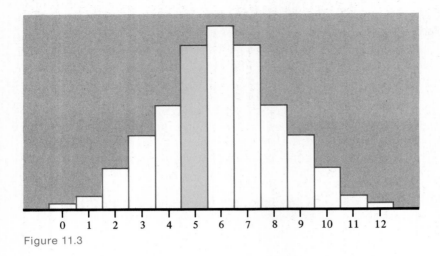

Figure 11.3

Curves like the one in Figure 11.4 represent graphs of the functions that are referred to as continuous distributions. We assume that the total area under the curve is 1.0 and that the probability of a continuous random variable having a value between a and b is given by the area bounded by the curve, the horizontal axis, and the vertical lines $x = a$ and $x = b$. In other words,

$P(a < X < b)$ = cross-hatched area

Note that there is no difference between $P(a < X < b)$, $P(a < X \leq b)$, $P(a \leq X < b)$, and $P(a \leq X \leq b)$, because the probability is zero that a continuous random variable X assumes a particular value a or b.

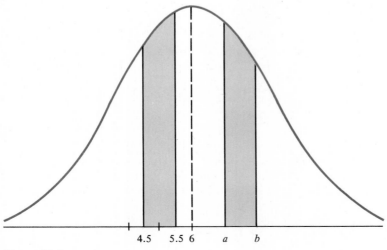

Figure 11.4

The mean and the standard deviation of a continuous distribution that approximates in some sense a distribution of a discrete random variable are approximately equal to those of the discrete distribution with the essential difference that these constants in the continuous case are obtained through the use of integral calculus. Nevertheless, μ and σ still measure, respectively, the approximate center and the "spread" or "dispersion" of the distribution. This fact will be very useful in finding approximations of binomial probabilities such as the probability of getting between 150 and 250 heads in 400 tosses of a balanced coin, the probability that the number of television viewers who watch a particular program ranges from 40 to 60 in a random sample of 250 persons, the probability that fewer than 50 charge accounts in a sample of 300 have an average balance of $125, and so on.

11.6 THE NORMAL DISTRIBUTION

One of the most important and useful distributions in probability is the normal distribution. The graph of the normal distribution is that of a bell-shaped curve that is symmetrical about its mean μ. The curve extends infinitely in both directions, coming closer and closer to the horizontal axis but never quite touching it. (See Figure 11.5.) Notice that as we move along the normal curve away from the point P, we pass through two points A and B located on either side of the vertical line $x = \mu$. These points, where the curve changes its downward course to the concave-up position, are called inflection points for the curve. Observe that the horizontal distance from A (or B) to the line $x = \mu$ is one unit of standard deviation.

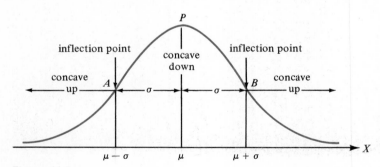

Figure 11.5

In actual practice, it is not necessary to extend the tails of the curve very far, because the area under the curve becomes negligible as we move away more than three standard deviations from the mean μ of the distribution. An important feature of a normal distribution is that it is completely determined by its mean μ and standard deviation σ. The curve has the following additional characteristics:

1. The curve has a single maximum at $x = \mu$.
2. The curve is symmetrical about the vertical line through $x = \mu$. Thus, the height of the curve at some point, say, $x = \mu + \sigma$, is the same as the height of the curve at $x = \mu - \sigma$.

3. The curve is concave downward between $x = \mu - \sigma$ and $x = \mu + \sigma$, and concave upward for values of x outside that interval.
4. Because the curve is symmetrical about $x = \mu$ and the total area under the curve is 1.0, it follows that the area on either side of the vertical line $x = \mu$ is 0.5.
5. As x moves away on either side of the mean μ, the height of the curve decreases but remains non-negative for all real values of x.

The distribution in Figure 11.5 having the above characteristics is called the normal distribution. Note that if X is a normal random variable with parameters μ and σ, then

(11.6) $E(X) = \mu$ and $V(X) = \sigma^2$

Conversely, there is one and only one normal distribution that has a given mean μ and given standard deviation.

Figure 11.6 shows two normal distributions that have the same mean but different standard deviations σ_1 and σ_2, whereas Figure 11.7 illustrates two normal distributions that have the same standard deviation but different means μ_1 and μ_2. Because both the parameters μ and σ can assume any finite value, we can generate an infinite number of normal distributions, one for each pair of μ and σ. Because a separate table of areas for each of these bell-shaped curves is obviously impractical, we convert the unit of measurement of an arbitrary normal distribution into standard units (see Figure 11.8) by using the formula

(11.7) $Z = \dfrac{X - \mu}{\sigma}$

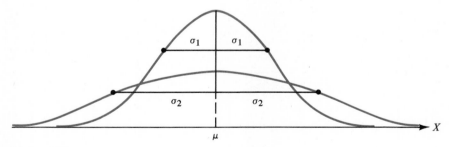

Figure 11.6

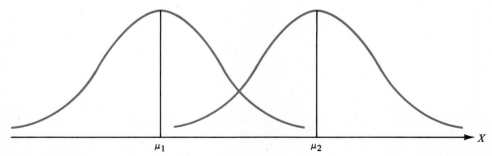

Figure 11.7

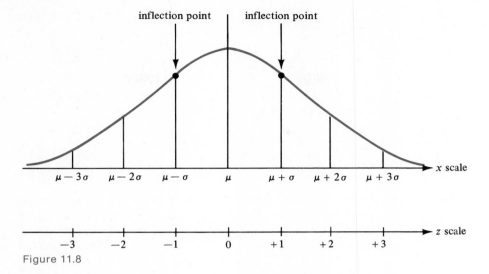

Figure 11.8

so that

$$X = \mu + \sigma Z$$

The normal distribution of Z having the mean 0 and standard deviation 1 is called the standard normal distribution. The probabilities for the standard normal curve are given in Table 1 in the Appendix, where z, correct to the nearest tenth, is recorded in the left-hand column and the second decimal place for z, corresponding to hundredths, is given across the top row in the table. The entries in the table give the area to the left of the number. We introduce the notation

$$\Phi(z) = P(Z < z)$$
$$= \text{area under the normal curve to the left of } z$$

where Z denotes the standard normal random variable. In Figure 11.9 we show the area to the left of $z = 1.48$. To determine the area for $z = 1.48$, we find the entry in the row labeled 1.4 and the column labeled 0.08. Thus,

$$\Phi(1.48) = P(Z < 1.48) = 0.9306$$

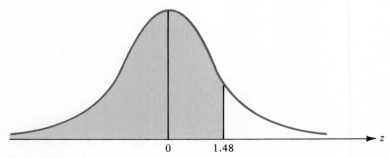

Figure 11.9

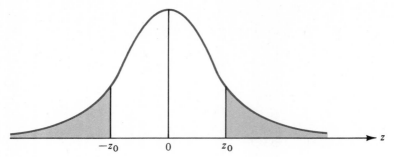

Figure 11.10

To find the area to the left of $z = -z_0$ where $-z_0 < 0$, we note that the area to the right of z_0 is equal to the area to the left of $-z_0$ as shown in Figure 11.10. Thus,

$$\Phi(-z_0) = 1 - \Phi(z_0)$$

For example,

$$\Phi(-1.48) = 1 - \Phi(1.48)$$
$$= 1 - 0.9306 = 0.0694$$

Again, the area between $z = -2.14$ and $z = -0.36$ is the same as the area between $z = 0.36$ and $z = 2.14$. (See Figure 11.11.) Thus,

$$P(-2.14 < Z < -0.36) = P(0.36 < Z < 2.14)$$
$$= \Phi(2.14) - \Phi(0.36)$$
$$= 0.9838 - 0.6406$$
$$= 0.3432$$

In general, for any pair $z_1 < z_2$, we have

$$P(z_1 < Z < z_2) = \Phi(z_2) - \Phi(z_1)$$

To find the area to the right of $z = z_0$, we simply subtract the area to the left of $z = z_0$ from 1; that is,

$$P(Z > z_0) = 1 - P(Z < z_0)$$
$$= 1 - \Phi(z_0)$$

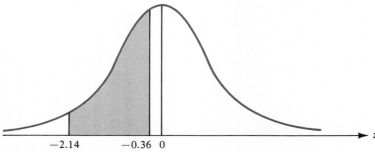

Figure 11.11

Example 11.15

Find the area under the standard normal distribution that lies between

a. $z = 0.23$ and $z = 1.73$
b. $z = -2.0$ and $z = 2.0$
c. $z = -0.62$ and $z = -1.81$
d. to the right of $z = 1.28$
e. to the left of $z = 0.47$

SOLUTION

a.

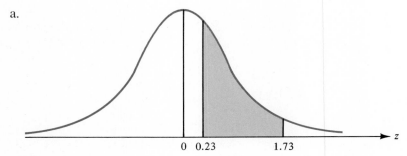

0 0.23   1.73   z

Figure 11.12

$$P(0.23 < z < 1.73) = \Phi(1.73) - \Phi(0.23)$$
$$= 0.9582 - 0.5910$$
$$= 0.3672$$

b.

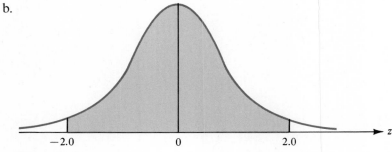

−2.0   0   2.0   z

Figure 11.13

$$P(-2 < Z < 2) = \Phi(2.0) - \Phi(-2.0)$$
$$= \Phi(2.0) - [1 - \Phi(2.0)]$$
$$= 2\Phi(2.0) - 1$$
$$= 2(0.9772) - 1$$
$$= 0.9544$$

c.

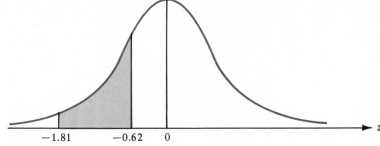

Figure 11.14

$$P(-1.81 < Z < -0.62) = \Phi(-0.62) - \Phi(-1.81)$$
$$= [1 - \Phi(0.62)] - [1 - \Phi(1.81)]$$
$$= \Phi(1.81) - \Phi(0.62)$$
$$= 0.9649 - 0.7324$$
$$= 0.2325$$

d.

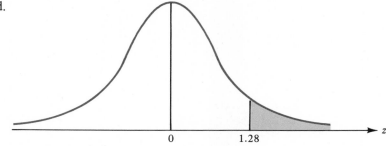

Figure 11.15

$$P(Z > 1.28) = 1 - P(Z < 1.28)$$
$$= 1 - \Phi(1.28)$$
$$= 1 - 0.8997$$
$$= 0.1003$$

e.

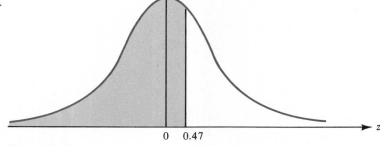

Figure 11.16

$$P(Z < 0.47) = \Phi(0.47)$$
$$= 0.6808$$

Example 11.16

Find the value of z if the area

    a. between 0 and z is 0.4357
    b. to the right of z is 0.8643
    c. to the left of z is 0.1711
    d. between $-z$ and z is 0.6826

SOLUTION

    a.

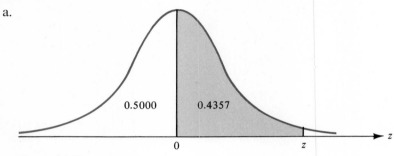

Figure 11.17

The area to the left of z is $0.4357 + 0.5000 = 0.9357$. The problem now reduces to: What is z so that $\Phi(z) = 0.9357$? A reference to Table 1 in the Appendix shows that $z = 1.52$.

    b.

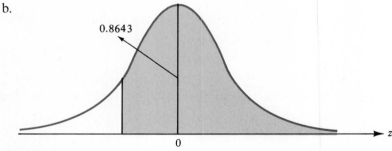

Figure 11.18

Using Table 1, we see that $\Phi(1.1) = 0.8643$. Because z happens to be to the left of $z = 0$, we conclude that $z = -1.10$.

    c.

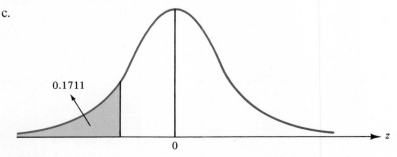

Figure 11.19

The area to the right of z is $1 - 0.1711 = 0.8289$. Using Table 1, we note that $\Phi(0.95) = 0.8289$. Again, z happens to be to the left of $z = 0$, we conclude that $z = -0.95$ is the required value.

d.

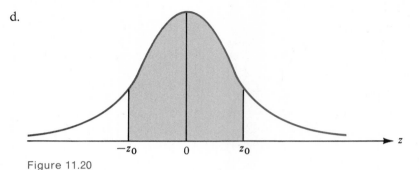

Figure 11.20

Here, we need to determine z_0 such that

$$P(-z_0 < Z < z_0) = 0.6826$$

Note that

$$\begin{aligned} P(-z_0 < Z < z_0) &= \Phi(z_0) - \Phi(-z_0) \\ &= \Phi(z_0) - [1 - \Phi(z_0)] \\ &= 2\Phi(z_0) - 1 \end{aligned}$$

If $2\Phi(z_0) - 1 = 0.6826$, then $\Phi(z_0) = 0.8413$. Using Table 1, we note that $z_0 = 1.00$. ∎

EXERCISE 11.4

1. Calculate each of the following probabilities for the standard normal distribution using Table 1.
  a. $P(Z < 1.38)$ **b.** $P(0 < Z < 1.2)$
  c. $P(Z > 1.41)$ **d.** $P(0.37 < Z < 0.86)$
  e. $P(-1.28 < Z < 1.28)$ **f.** $P(-1.75 < Z < -1.23)$
2. If Z is the standard normal variable, use Table 1 to calculate each of the following probabilities.
  a. $P(Z < 1.14)$ **b.** $P(1.20 < Z < 1.75)$
  c. $P(-1.29 < Z < 1.74)$ **d.** $P(Z < 0.38)$
  e. $P(-1.35 < Z < 1.35)$ **f.** $P(-0.76 < Z < 2.03)$
  g. $P(Z < 1.64)$ **h.** $P(Z > -1.07)$
  i. $P(-1.96 < Z < 1.96)$ **j.** $P(Z > 0.68)$
3. Given that Z is the standard normal variable, use Table 1 to find z_0 in each of the following.
  a. $P(Z > z_0) = 0.90$ **b.** $P(-z_0 < Z < z_0) = 0.9892$
  c. $P(Z < z_0) = 0.8365$ **d.** $P(0 < Z < z_0) = 0.0753$
  e. $P(Z > z_0) = 0.025$ **f.** $P(0 < Z < z_0) = 0.3708$
  g. $P(-1.5 < Z < z_0) = 0.0919$ **h.** $P(-0.62 < Z < z_0) = 0.5809$

4. Find z_0 if the normal curve area

    a. between 0 and z_0 is 0.4826   **b.** to the right of z_0 is 0.0040

    c. to the left of z_0 is 0.05   **d.** to the right of z_0 is 0.95

    e. between $-z_0$ and z_0 is 0.8788   **f.** between $-z_0$ and z_0 is 0.8664

    g. between $-z_0$ and z_0 is 0.9974   **h.** between $-z_0$ and z_0 is 0.9634

Let us now turn to areas under a normal curve whose mean and standard deviation are not 0 and 1, respectively. Recall that in this case, we simply convert the number on the x scale in Figure 11.8 to the number on the z scale and then use Table 1 to determine the area. For instance,

$$P(X < b) = P(\mu + \sigma Z < b)$$
$$= P\left(Z < \frac{b - \mu}{a}\right)$$
$$= \Phi\left(\frac{b - \mu}{a}\right)$$

Similarly,

$$P(a < X < b) = P(a < \sigma Z + \mu < b)$$
$$= P(a - \mu < \sigma Z < b - \mu)$$
$$= P\left(\frac{a - \mu}{\sigma} < Z < \frac{b - \mu}{\sigma}\right)$$
$$= \Phi\left(\frac{b - \mu}{\sigma}\right) - \Phi\left(\frac{a - \mu}{\sigma}\right)$$

As another example,

$$P(X > b) = P(\sigma Z + \mu > b)$$
$$= P\left(Z > \frac{b - \mu}{\sigma}\right)$$
$$= 1 - P\left(Z < \frac{b - \mu}{\sigma}\right)$$
$$= 1 - \Phi\left(\frac{b - \mu}{\sigma}\right)$$

where $\Phi(z)$ represents the area to the left of z under the standard normal curve.

Example 11.17

Let X be a normal random variable with mean 15 and standard deviation 5. Express $P(10 < X < 18)$ in terms of $\Phi(z)$ and then compute the probability.

SOLUTION

Let

$$Z = \frac{X - \mu}{\sigma} = \frac{X - 15}{5}$$

corresponding to $a = 10$ and $b = 12$ in the above equation. Hence,

$$P(10 < X < 18) = P\left(\frac{10 - 15}{5} < Z < \frac{18 - 15}{5}\right)$$

$$= P(-1 < Z < 0.60)$$

$$= \Phi(0.60) - \Phi(-1)$$

$$= \Phi(0.60) - [1 - \Phi(1)]$$

$$= 0.7257 - 0.1587$$

$$= 0.5670$$

■

Example 11.18

Given that X is a normal random variable with $\mu = 520$ and $\sigma = 20$, find

a. $P(X < 540)$
b. $P(504 < X < 544)$
c. $P(X > 480)$
d. $P(498 < X < 516)$

SOLUTION

a. $P(X < 540) = P\left(\dfrac{X - 520}{20} < \dfrac{540 - 520}{20}\right)$

$$= P(Z < 1)$$

$$= \Phi(1)$$

$$= 0.8413$$

b. $P(504 < X < 544) = P\left(\dfrac{504 - 520}{20} < \dfrac{X - 520}{20} < \dfrac{544 - 520}{20}\right)$

$$= P(-0.80 < Z < 1.20)$$

$$= \Phi(1.20) - \Phi(-0.80)$$

$$= 0.8849 - 0.2119$$

$$= 0.6730$$

c. $P(X > 480) = P\left(\dfrac{X - 520}{20} > \dfrac{480 - 520}{20}\right)$

$$= P(Z > -2)$$

$$= 1 - P(Z < -2)$$

$$= 1 - \Phi(-2)$$

$$= 1 - [1 - \Phi(2)]$$

$$= \Phi(2)$$

$$= 0.9772$$

d. $P(498 < X < 516) = P\left(\dfrac{498 - 520}{20} < \dfrac{X - 520}{20} < \dfrac{516 - 520}{20}\right)$

$= P(-1.10 < Z < -0.20)$

$= \Phi(-0.20) - \Phi(-1.10)$

$= [1 - \Phi(0.20)] - [1 - \Phi(1.10)]$ ·

$= \Phi(1.10) - \Phi(0.20)$

$= 0.8643 - 0.5793$

$= 0.2850$ ∎

Example 11.19

The charge account at a certain department store is approximately normally distributed with an average balance of \$80 and a standard deviation of \$30. What is the probability that a charge account randomly selected has a balance

a. over \$125
b. between \$65 and \$95
c. less than \$50

SOLUTION

Let X be the normal random variable with $\mu = 80$ and $\sigma = 30$. Let

$$Z = \frac{X - 80}{30}$$

Then,

a. $P(X > 125) = P\left(\dfrac{X - 80}{30} > \dfrac{125 - 80}{30}\right)$

$= P(Z > 1.50)$

$= 1 - P(Z < 1.50)$

$= 1 - \Phi(1.50)$

$= 1 - 0.9332$

$= 0.0668$

b. $P(65 < X < 95) = P\left(\dfrac{65 - 80}{30} < \dfrac{X - 80}{30} < \dfrac{95 - 80}{30}\right)$

$= P(-0.50 < Z < 0.50)$

$= \Phi(0.50) - \Phi(-0.50)$

$= \Phi(0.50) - [1 - \Phi(0.50)]$

$= 2\Phi(0.50) - 1$

$= 2(0.6915) - 1$

$= 0.3830$

c. $P(X < 50) = P\left(\dfrac{X - 80}{30} < \dfrac{50 - 80}{30}\right)$

$\qquad\qquad = P(Z < -1.0)$

$\qquad\qquad = \Phi(-1.0)$

$\qquad\qquad = 1 - \Phi(0.1)$

$\qquad\qquad = 1 - 0.8413$

$\qquad\qquad = 0.1587$ ∎

EXERCISE 11.5

1. Suppose that X is a normal random variable with mean 100 and standard deviation 15. Compute each of the following.
   a. $P(X > 122.5)$　　　　　　　　b. $P(X < 70)$
   c. $P(X > 92.5)$　　　　　　　　　d. $P(85 < X < 115)$
2. Suppose that X is a random variable with mean 100 and standard deviation 16. Find each of the following.
   a. $P(X < 140)$　　　　　　　　　b. $P(X > 132)$
   c. $P(84 < X < 116)$　　　　　　d. $P(76 < X < 92)$
3. The College Board verbal score for the students at an American university is given by a normal random variable with $\mu = 615$ and $\sigma = 75$. What is the probability that a randomly selected student will have a score below 600?
4. The gasoline consumption for new automobiles of a certain make is approximately normally distributed, with $\mu = 23.3$ miles per gallon and standard deviation $\sigma = 2.5$. If a new car of this make is purchased, what is the probability that it will get
   a. at least 20 miles per gallon
   b. between 25.8 and 28.3 miles per gallon
   c. between 20.8 and 25.8 miles per gallon
5. The length of life in hours of a flashlight battery is approximately normally distributed with a mean of 120 hours and a standard deviation of 36. What is the probability that a flashlight battery of this type will have a life
   a. between 84 and 138 hours
   b. longer than 156 hours
   c. less than 84 hours
6. The height of all freshmen in a certain school is approximately normally distributed, with $\mu = 69.0$ inches and $\sigma = 2.5$ inches. What is the probability that a freshman selected at random will have a height
   a. between 66.5 and 71.5 inches
   b. more than 74 inches
   c. less than 64 inches
7. The annual snowfall in a region is approximately normally distributed with a mean of 45 inches and a standard deviation of 5 inches. What is the probability that the snowfall in a particular year is
   a. more than 53.2 inches

b. between 40 and 50 inches

c. less than 35 inches

8. A company maintains a pool of typists in order to answer its mail correspondence. The number of letters received each week is approximately normally distributed with $\mu = 350$ and $\sigma = 20$. What is the probability that the number of letters received in a particular week is

   a. more than 370

   b. between 320 and 360

   c. less than 310

9. The life of a particular model of electric bulb is normally distributed with a mean of 1000 and a standard deviation of 100 hours. What is the probability that an electric bulb randomly selected will last

   a. between 1000 and 1150 hours

   b. between 900 and 1100 hours

   c. more than 1200 hours

   d. less than 800 hours

10. In a certain high rent district of Chicago, the monthly rent for apartments is approximately normally distributed, with a mean of \$384.22 and a standard deviation of \$126.40. Above what value are the highest 30 percent of the monthly rentals in this district?

11. The grade on an examination taken by a large number of students is approximately normally distributed with $\mu = 80$ and $\sigma = 6$. If the instructor assigns A's to 10 percent of his class, above what numerical grade would he give an A?

12. A certain professor believes that grades of his students are approximately normally distributed. He assigns A's to 3 percent, B's to 13 percent, C's to 68 percent, D's to 13 percent, and F's to 3 percent of his students. If his examination in a course in management has a mean of 60 and a standard deviation of 10, find the range of examination scores for the letter grades A, B, C, D, and F.

13. A new filling station estimates that the weekly demand for gasoline is approximately normally distributed with $\mu = 1000$ and $\sigma = 50$ gallons. Assuming that the station is supplied its gasoline once a week, what must be the capacity of its tank if the probability that its supply will be exhausted in a given week is to be no more than 1 percent?

14. The average length of time required for a civil service examination was found to be approximately normally distributed with $\mu = 70$ minutes and a standard deviation of 12 minutes. When should the examination be terminated if 90 percent of those taking the examination must complete it?

15. The length of life of a type of automatic washer is approximately normally distributed with $\mu = 3.1$ years and $\sigma = 1.2$ years. If this type of washer is guaranteed for one year, what fraction of original sales will require replacement?

16. A student answers 48 questions in a multiple-choice test in which there are four possible answers to each question. Determine the probability that he will get anywhere from 6 to 18 correct answers using

   a. Chebyshev's inequality

   b. normal distribution

17. The sales of a certain company average $\mu = 320$ units per week with a standard deviation of $\sigma = 16$ units. Determine the probability that the sales of the company in a given week varies anywhere from 300 to 340 units using
a. Chebyshev's inequality
b. normal distribution

18. The number of telephone calls arriving at a switchboard during a rush hour is a random variable with $\mu = 64$ and $\sigma = 4$. Find the probability that there will be more than 70 calls using
a. Chebyshev's inequality
b. normal distribution

11.7 NORMAL APPROXIMATION OF THE BINOMIAL DISTRIBUTION

In the preceding chapter, we have considered several applications of a random variable obeying the binomial probability distribution

$$P(X = k) = \binom{n}{k} p^k q^{n-k} \qquad k = 0, 1, 2, \ldots, n$$

These problems, which required the computation of probabilities of k successes in n independent repeated trials with probability p of success in each trial, involved reasonably small values of n. If n is large, the calculations involved in using the above formula become a formidable task. Suppose, for example, that a door-to-door salesman reports that on the average 30 percent of the homemakers he calls upon actually buy his product and we want to determine the probability that at least 10 homemakers among 50 will buy the product he is selling. In other words, we want to compute the probability of getting at least 10 successes in 50 repeated trials, given that the probability of success in any individual trial is 0.30. The binomial distribution requires that we compute the individual probabilities for $k = 10, 11, 12, \ldots, 50$ and then determine the sum. Because this involves exceedingly lengthy calculations, a good simple approximation to the binomial distribution should prove to be a very useful tool. Such an approximation exists in the form of normal distribution and was first encountered in 1733 by De Moivre. It can be shown that for sufficiently large n, the binomial random variable X is approximately normally distributed with np as its mean and $\sqrt{npq}$ as its standard deviation. Because a formal proof needs some advanced mathematics, we shall use only histograms to suggest it and numerical examples to illustrate it. Figure 11.21 shows histograms of the binomial distributions for $p = 0.5$ and $n = 2, 4, 6, 10,$ and 20. The height of each bar in the histogram represents the probability given by the above formula for the corresponding value of k. Notice that as n increases, these distributions approach the symmetrical bell-shaped curve of the normal distributions. In fact, a normal curve with mean $\mu = np = 20(\frac{1}{2}) = 10$ and standard deviation $\sigma = \sqrt{npq} = \sqrt{20(\frac{1}{2})(\frac{1}{2})} = 2.24$ superimposed on the last histogram in Figure 11.21 results in a fairly good fit, despite the fact that $n = 20$ is a small value of n. The fact that this fit can be improved for large values of n is a consequence of the following proposition, which we state without proof.

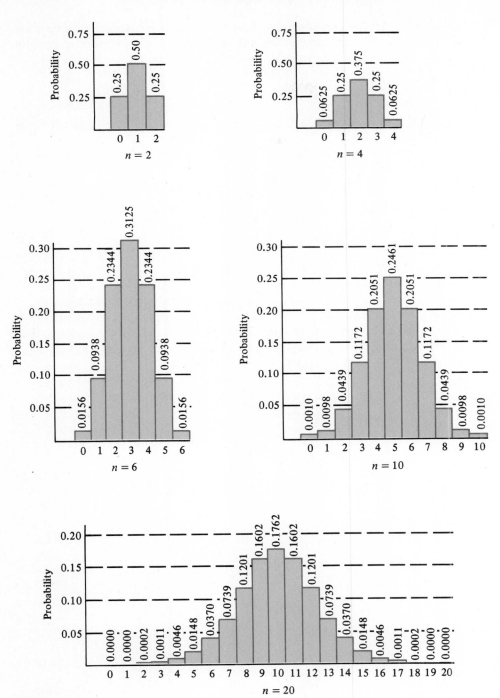

Figure 11.21

Proposition 11.7.1: If X is the number of successes in n independent repeated trials with probability p of success and q of failure in each trial, then for large values of n, the random variable Z, given by

$$Z = \frac{X - np}{\sqrt{npq}} \qquad q = 1 - p$$

is approximately normally distributed with mean 0 and standard deviation 1. ∎

Thus, the probability of at most k successes in n independent trials is given by

$$P(X \le k) = P\left(\frac{X - np}{\sqrt{npq}} \le \frac{k - np}{\sqrt{npq}}\right)$$

$$= P\left(Z \le \frac{k - np}{\sqrt{npq}}\right)$$

$$= \Phi(z_0) \qquad \text{where } z_0 = \frac{k - np}{\sqrt{npq}}$$

and $\Phi(z_0)$ denotes the area to the left of z_0 under the standard normal curve.

Because X is a discrete random variable that assumes a finite set of values, we can improve the approximation by using what is called a continuity correction. This consists of representing each integer k by an interval from $k - \frac{1}{2}$ to $k + \frac{1}{2}$. Thus, the probability of at most k successes is

$$P(X \le k) = P(X < k + \tfrac{1}{2})$$

$$= P\left(\frac{X - np}{\sqrt{npq}} < \frac{k + \frac{1}{2} - np}{\sqrt{npq}}\right)$$

$$= \Phi\left(\frac{k + \frac{1}{2} - np}{\sqrt{npq}}\right)$$

The probability of at least k successes is

$$P(X \ge k) = P(X > k - \tfrac{1}{2})$$

$$= P\left(\frac{X - np}{\sqrt{npq}} > \frac{k - \frac{1}{2} - np}{\sqrt{npq}}\right)$$

$$= 1 - \Phi\left(\frac{k - \frac{1}{2} - np}{\sqrt{npq}}\right)$$

Similarly,

$$P(a \le X \le b) = P(a - \tfrac{1}{2} < X < b + \tfrac{1}{2})$$

$$= P\left(\frac{a - \frac{1}{2} - np}{\sqrt{npq}} < \frac{X - np}{\sqrt{npq}} < \frac{b + \frac{1}{2} - np}{\sqrt{npq}}\right)$$

$$= \Phi\left(\frac{b + \frac{1}{2} - np}{\sqrt{npq}}\right) - \Phi\left(\frac{a - \frac{1}{2} - np}{\sqrt{npq}}\right)$$

As a special case of this, we have

$$P(X = k) = P(k - \tfrac{1}{2} < X < k + \tfrac{1}{2})$$

$$= \Phi\left(\frac{k + \tfrac{1}{2} - np}{\sqrt{npq}}\right) - \Phi\left(\frac{k - \tfrac{1}{2} - np}{\sqrt{npq}}\right)$$

Let us now return to the example of the door-to-door salesman who is calling upon different homemakers to sell his product. If X is the binomial random variable that denotes the number of successful calls, then because $n = 50$, $p = 0.30$, and $q = 0.70$, we obtain

$$E(X) = np = 50(0.30) = 15$$

and

$$\sigma(X) = \sqrt{npq} = \sqrt{50(0.30)(0.70)} = 3.24$$

Thus, the probability of 10 or more effective calls is given by

$$P(X \geq 10) = P(X > 9.5)$$

$$= P\left(\frac{X - 15}{3.24} > \frac{9.5 - 15}{3.24}\right)$$

$$= P(Z > -1.70)$$

$$= 1 - \Phi(-1.70)$$

$$= 1 - [1 - \Phi(1.70)]$$

$$= \Phi(1.70)$$

$$= 0.9554$$

The accuracy of the approximation depends on both the size of n and the value of p. For values of p extremely close to $\tfrac{1}{2}$, the approximation is good even for small values of n (say, $n = 12$). For other values of p, large values of n are necessary to assure a satisfactory approximation by the standard normal curve, and this approximation improves for any p as the number of successes k gets closer to np.

Example 11.20
Find the probability of four heads in 10 tosses of a balanced coin using

a. the binomial distribution
b. the normal curve approximation

SOLUTION
a. Here $n = 10$, $p = \tfrac{1}{2}$, $k = 4$. Thus

$$P(X = 4) = \binom{10}{4}\left(\frac{1}{2}\right)^4 \left(\frac{1}{2}\right)^6 = \frac{210}{1024} = 0.2051$$

b. Because X is a discrete random variable, we represent $k = 4$ by the interval 3.5 to 4.5. The mean $\mu = 10(0.5) = 5$ and the standard deviation $\sigma = \sqrt{npq} = \sqrt{10(0.5)(0.5)} = 1.58$. Thus, we have

$$P(X = 4) = P(3.5 < X < 4.5)$$

$$= P\left(\frac{3.5 - 5}{1.58} < \frac{X - 5}{1.58} < \frac{4.5 - 5}{1.58}\right)$$

$$= P(-0.95 < Z < -0.31)$$

$$= \Phi(-0.31) - \Phi(-0.95)$$

$$= \Phi(0.95) - \Phi(0.31) = 0.8289 - 0.6217 = 0.2072$$

The difference between this value and the one obtained by the binomial distribution gets smaller as the number of heads gets closer to $np = 10(\frac{1}{2}) = 5$. ∎

Example 11.21

An advertising agency claims that 20 percent of all television viewers watch a particular program. If these claims were correct, what is the probability that in a random sample of 225 persons interviewed

a. at least 55 persons watch the program
b. at most 37 persons watch the program

SOLUTION

Let X be the number of television viewers who watch the particular program. Then

$$E(X) = 225(0.20) = 45$$

$$\sigma(X) = \sqrt{225(0.20)(0.80)} = 6$$

Thus,

a. $P(X \geq 55) = P(X > 54\cdot5)$

$$= P\left(\frac{X - 45}{6} > \frac{54.5 - 45}{6}\right)$$

$$= P(Z > 1.58)$$

$$= 1 - \Phi(1.58)$$

$$= 1 - 0.9429$$

$$= 0.0571$$

b. $P(X \leq 37) = P(X < 37.5)$

$$= P\left(\frac{X - 45}{6} < \frac{37.5 - 45}{6}\right)$$

$$= P(Z < -1.25)$$

$$= \Phi(-1.25)$$

$$= 1 - \Phi(1.25)$$

$$= 1 - 0.8944$$

$$= 0.1056$$

∎

Example 11.22

A certain insurance company has 100 executives. Assume that the probability is 0.20 that an executive will need the services of a secretary at the beginning of a business day. If the probability is to be at least 0.90 that a secretary will be available, how many secretaries should be hired to constitute a pool of secretaries for a group of 100 executives?

SOLUTION

Let X be the binomial random variable that denotes the number of secretaries available for the executives. Because $n = 100$, $p = 0.20$, and $q = 0.80$, we have

$$\mu = E(X) = np = 100(0.20) = 20$$
$$\sigma(X) = \sqrt{npq} = \sqrt{100(0.20)(0.80)} = 4$$

What is k so that $P(X \geq k) = 0.95$?

$$P(X \geq k) = P(X > k - 0.5)$$
$$= P\left(\frac{X - np}{\sqrt{npq}} > \frac{k - 0.5 - 20}{4}\right)$$
$$= 1 - \Phi\left(\frac{k - 20.5}{4}\right)$$

Because

$$1 - \Phi\left(\frac{k - 20.5}{4}\right) \geq 0.90$$

it follows that

$$\frac{k - 20.5}{4} = -1.28$$

so that $k = 15$ is a reasonable result. ∎

EXERCISE 11.6

1. Find the probability of getting four heads in 12 tosses of a balanced coin using
   a. the binomial distribution
   b. the normal curve approximation
2. Find the probability that a student will get at least 60 correct answers in a true-false test if he answers each of the 100 questions by flipping a balanced coin.
3. A manufacturer knows from his past experience that on the average 5 percent of his products are defective. Using the normal curve approximation, what is the probability that a lot of 400 pieces will contain exactly 25 defectives?
4. A manufacturer knows from his past experience that on the average 20 percent of his products are defective. Using the normal curve approximation, what is the probability that a lot of 400 pieces will contain
   a. at least 90 defectives
   b. exactly 90 defectives

5. In a large orchard 10 percent of the apples are wormy. What is the probability that among 100 apples selected at random, the number of wormy apples is
    a. at least 15
    b. between 8 and 12
    c. less than 7

6. A firm estimates that 3 percent of its accounts receivable cannot be collected. What is the probability that out of 200 current accounts receivable, eight or more will be uncollectable?

7. If 30 percent of homemakers use credit cards for shopping in a department store, what is the probability that among 625 homemakers, fewer than 200 will use their credit cards?

8. A manufacturer estimates that 80 percent of his consumers prefer his product. Using the normal curve approximation, determine the probability of obtaining fewer than 76 customers who prefer his product in a random sample of 100?

9. Assume that the IQ's of elementary school children as measured by a certain test have a mean of 100 and a standard deviation 12. What is the probability that a student selected at random will have an IQ of 120 or higher?

10. The time spent for breakfast by patrons in a restaurant is approximately normally distributed with $\mu = 25$ minutes and $\sigma = 10$ minutes. If 450 people are having breakfast on a particular morning, how many customers are expected to stay at the table for more than 40 minutes?

11. The waiting time before a customer in a restaurant is served lunch is approximately normally distributed with $\mu = 15$ minutes and $\sigma = 5$ minutes. If 50 customers have their reservations for lunch, how many of them will wait for at most 5 minutes?

12. On a final examination in economics, the average grade was 70.0 and the standard deviation 10.0. What is the probability that a student selected at random will have a score from 61 to 79 inclusive?

13. A teachers' union claims that 10 percent of the teachers are opposed to a strike in the school system. If these claims are correct, what is the probability of obtaining more than 52 opponents in a sample of 400 teachers?

14. An instructor assigns 10 percent A's, 20 percent B's, 40 percent C's, 20 percent D's, and 10 percent F's. He gives an examination in psychology on which the average score is 56 and the standard deviation is 20. Find
    a. the highest score a student can get and yet fail the test
    b. the lowest score a student can get to get an A in the test
    c. the highest score to be assigned a grade of C
    d. the lowest score to be asigned a grade of D

12
Decisions Under Uncertainty – A Stocking Problem

12.1 INTRODUCTION

A managerial decision is usually made to attain or further the objectives of the business. Many of these decisions are associated with some degree of uncertainty arising from an ill-defined feeling for the current trends in the business market and a possible accumulation of past experiences. Retailers may decide to increase their stock because they expect prices to be higher in the future, or they may decide to reduce their inventory because they feel that the boom has run its course. Unquestionably a large proportion of managerial decisions are based on some form of intuitive judgment associated with pure guesses or hunches. Nevertheless, the management of a firm must buy and stock products that may lose all or part of their utility if not sold during a certain time span. The problem becomes complex because management is unable to predict the exact demand for its products nor can it expect to determine the costs, profits, or even possible losses based on fluctuating demand. Because management needs to decide in advance on some definite quantity, it cannot avoid seeking a rational development of "best" forecasts of sales, costs, and profits including a built-in "safety valve" that would minimize losses, if any. The concept of probability, which has found an increasing application in the business world, serves as a powerful tool in the area of potential demand of consumer products. A rational approach examines the demand for the products in the past several years and assigns different probabilities to possible future sales of the products in question. This procedure is based on the fundamental assumption that future sales are closely related to those in the past and assigns very little weight to a possible change in tastes or purchasing habits of the consumers.

In this chapter we shall consider briefly several ways to determine an optimum number of products that the dealer may stock. Expected monetary profit and loss tables will be developed under conditions of uncertainty. The concept of marginal analysis will be examined to determine the quantity a dealer must stock in order to eliminate the possibility of heavy losses. Later in the chapter we shall attempt to show how the normal distribution helps us to handle decisions of optimum stock under uncertainty.

12.2 DISCRETE PROBABILITY DISTRIBUTION

Consider a grocery store that buys fresh milk every Saturday from a local dairy for $0.99 a gallon and sells it for $1.32 a gallon. We assume that the milk preserves its freshness in refrigerators for at most one week and that any quantity of milk not sold by next Friday is a net loss to the store. The demand for the milk is a random variable that takes integer values. The store manager's problem is to determine the optimum quantity of milk to order so as to maximize expected profits. On weeks when the store stocks more than it sells, profits are reduced by the loss caused by the unsold quantity, and if the store happens to have less in stock than customers demand, the result is lost sales, smaller profits than were possible, and the probable risk of losing the customers who may transfer all their grocery needs to a competitor.

Suppose that the manager of the store has kept a record of past sales for the last 50 weeks as shown in Table 12.1.

Table 12.1 Distribution of Past Sales

Weekly Sales in Gallons x	Number of Weeks	Probability $P(X = x)$
53	5	0.10
54	5	0.10
55	10	0.20
56	10	0.20
57	10	0.20
58	5	0.10
59	5	0.10
	50	1.00

The various possible levels of demand expressed into the table are of purely random character and appear in no predictable sequence. This means that the manager has no way of knowing accurately what quantity of milk to order on a given Saturday for the next week's consumption. Nevertheless, we can calculate the expected sales per week, based on the above data, as follows:

$$\mu = E(X) = \sum xP(X = x)$$
$$= 53(0.10) + 54(0.10) + 55(0.20) + 56(0.20)$$
$$+ 57(0.20) + 58(0.10) + 59(0.10)$$
$$= 56 \text{ gallons}$$

The variance of past sales is given by

$$V(X) = \sum(x - \mu)^2 P(X = x)$$
$$= (53 - 56)^2(0.10) + (54 - 56)^2(0.10) + (55 - 56)^2(0.20)$$
$$+ (56 - 56)^2(0.20) + (57 - 56)^2(0.20) + (58 - 56)^2(0.10)$$
$$+ (59 - 56)^2(0.10)$$
$$= 3 \text{ gallons}$$

The expected sales of 56 gallons in no way implies that the next week's consumption of the milk in the store will be 56 gallons. It is only an indication that the average sales over a long period of time turns out to be around 56 gallons. The variance is simply an indication of how widely dispersed this data has been. Both these concepts are useful in making decisions under uncertainty. Quite frequently, management makes decisions on expected sales and these are generally more nearly correct in their estimates than they would be if they made their decisions on some form of intuitive judgment. Their stock may fall short of actual demand during some weeks, but over long periods of time their decisions will be more nearly optimal than if they guessed their requirements every week.

12.3 CONDITIONAL AND EXPECTED PROFITS

Most business decisions made under conditions of uncertainty are associated with financial considerations. Some firms and department stores buy and stock products that may lose all or part of their utility if not sold within a certain time after receipt. Overstocking may result in unexpected losses to the store, whereas selling out all stock early will reduce the profits that the store would have made had it been able to meet the demands of all its customers.

The term conditional profits refers to the profits the firm can anticipate by considering all possible combinations of customers' demand and the firm's ability to supply. In the above illustration, the only values of purchases and sales that are of significance to the store are 53, 54, 55, 56, 57, 58, and 59 gallons of milk. There is hardly any reason for the store manager to order a quantity less than 53 or more than 59 gallons of milk. Table 12.2 shows the profits resulting from several possible combinations of demand and supply. The stocking of 53 gallons of milk each week assures the store of a net profit of $17.49. If the demand for milk goes as high as 59 gallons, the manager can sell only the quantity in stock. This results in lost sales—an action hardly conducive to the growth of successful business. If the sales are less than what the store has in stock, then its profits are reduced because the milk not sold during the week is of no value to the store. Thus, a stock of 54 gallons increases the profits to $17.82 during weeks that customers request at least 54 gallons of milk, and the probability that this situation occurs is 0.90. The probability is only 0.10 that the store has 54 gallons in stock and customers request only 53 gallons. The risk is therefore very small that the profits of the store will drop to $16.50. Similarly, a stock of 55 gallons increases the weekly profits of the store to $18.15 when there is a

Table 12.2 Conditional Profits

Possible Demand in Gallons	Possible Stock (in Gallons)							Probability
	53	54	55	56	57	58	59	
53	$17.49	$16.50	$15.51	$14.52	$13.53	$12.54	$11.55	0.10
54	17.49	17.82	16.83	15.84	14.85	13.86	12.87	0.10
55	17.49	17.82	18.15	17.16	16.17	15.18	14.19	0.20
56	17.49	17.82	18.15	18.48	17.49	16.50	15.51	0.20
57	17.49	17.82	18.15	18.48	18.81	17.82	16.83	0.20
58	17.49	17.82	18.15	18.48	18.81	19.14	18.15	0.10
59	17.49	17.82	18.15	18.48	18.81	19.14	19.47	0.10

market for at least 55 gallons of milk, but if the store cannot sell its entire stock, the profits are reduced. For example, with a stock of 55 gallons at hand and sales of only 53 gallons, the profit is $15.51—the profit of $17.49 on 53 gallons is reduced by the cost of 2 gallons of unsold milk. If the store sells 54 gallons, the profits of $17.82 on this quantity sold drop to $16.83.

A conditional profit table does not, however, tell management how many gallons of milk to stock every week to maximize profits. It only provides information as to what profits or economic losses will be if a certain quantity is stocked and a certain quantity sold. Under conditions of uncertainty that prevail in all business situations, management must decide in advance the optimum quantity it should stock consistently every week to serve most of the customers and thus maximize profits.

Having determined the conditional profits arising from all relevant combinations of consumer demand and retailer's ability to supply, we now examine the expected monetary profit of each possible stock action. This brings in the probabilities associated with several stocking actions, and we assume that these probabilities remain the same for specific inventories over a long period of time. The expected monetary profits for seven different stock actions are shown in Table 12.3.

Table 12.3 Expected Monetary Profits

Stock	Conditional Profits	Probability of Conditional Profit	Expected Profit	Total Expected Profit
53	$17.49	1.00	$17.49	$17.49
54	16.50	0.10	16.50(0.10) = 1.65	
	17.82	0.90	17.82(0.90) = 16.04	17.69
55	15.51	0.10	15.51(0.10) = 1.55	
	16.83	0.10	16.83(0.10) = 1.68	
	18.15	0.80	18.15(0.80) = 14.52	17.75
56	14.52	0.10	14.52(0.10) = 1.45	
	15.84	0.10	15.84(0.10) = 1.58	
	17.16	0.20	17.16(0.20) = 3.43	
	18.48	0.60	18.48(0.60) = 11.09	17.55
57	13.53	0.10	13.53(0.10) = 1.35	
	14.85	0.10	14.85(0.10) = 1.49	
	16.17	0.20	16.17(0.20) = 3.23	
	17.49	0.20	17.49(0.20) = 3.50	
	18.81	0.40	18.81(0.40) = 7.52	17.09
58	12.54	0.10	12.54(0.10) = 1.25	
	13.86	0.10	13.86(0.10) = 1.39	
	15.18	0.20	15.18(0.20) = 3.04	
	16.50	0.20	16.50(0.20) = 3.30	
	17.82	0.20	17.82(0.20) = 3.56	
	19.14	0.20	19.14(0.20) = 3.83	16.37
59	11.55	0.10	11.55(0.10) = 1.16	
	12.87	0.10	12.87(0.10) = 1.29	
	14.19	0.20	14.19(0.20) = 2.84	
	15.51	0.20	15.51(0.20) = 3.10	
	16.83	0.20	16.83(0.20) = 3.37	
	18.15	0.10	18.15(0.10) = 1.82	
	19.47	0.10	19.47(0.10) = 1.95	15.53

The optimum stock level is the one that yields the highest expected monetary profit. This action will result in the highest weekly profits and maximum profits over a period of time if the given probability distribution persists. We wish to remind the reader that we have in no way attempted to remove the element of uncertainty facing the store; rather, we have used past experience to determine the best course of action. Management still does not know exactly how much quantity to order in any specific week. However, if it stocks 55 gallons of milk every week, it will average a profit of $17.75 per week, and this is the best course of action open to the store because any other option will result in smaller profits over a long period of time. We shall, however, underscore the fact that although stocking 55 gallons of milk every week yields an average profit of $17.75, it meets the needs of only 40 percent of the customers' demands. The management of the store is aware from past experience that there is a probability of 10 percent that consumption will be 56 gallons, 10 percent that consumers will demand 57 gallons, and 5 percent each that demand will go as high as 58 or 59 gallons in some weeks. Despite the risk involved in losing customers to its competitors, it is in the economic interest of the store to stock 55 gallons of milk each week if the past experience of the store is any indication.

12.4 CONDITIONAL LOSSES

We shall now consider an alternative approach to solving the problem of optimum stocking. Instead of maximizing the expected weekly profits, we can calculate the amounts by which the maximum profits are reduced by several stocking actions of the retailer. Then we choose the particular stocking action as most appropriate that minimizes these reductions.

In any stocking problem, management is confronted with two types of losses: obsolescence losses and opportunity losses. Obsolescence losses are those that are caused by overstocking products, whereas opportunity losses result from demands that cannot be met. An opportunity loss is not a loss in any real sense; it is only an indication of the profits that the management of the store would have made had they been able to fulfill the actual level of the consumers' demand for the given time period.

Table 12.4 provides conditional losses for the store manager. The figures on the main diagonal indicate that there is no profit or loss because these figures are representative of the minimum possible conditional loss to the retailer.

Table 12.4 Conditional Losses

Possible Demand in Gallons	Possible Stock (in Gallons)							Probability
	53	54	55	56	57	58	59	
53	$0.00	$0.99	$1.98	$2.97	$3.96	$4.95	$5.94	0.10
54	0.33	0.00	0.99	1.98	2.97	3.96	4.95	0.10
55	0.66	0.33	0.00	0.99	1.98	2.97	3.96	0.20
56	0.99	0.66	0.33	0.00	0.99	1.98	2.97	0.20
57	1.32	0.99	0.66	0.33	0.00	0.99	1.98	0.20
58	1.65	1.32	0.99	0.66	0.33	0.00	0.99	0.10
59	1.98	1.65	1.32	0.99	0.66	0.33	0.00	0.10

If the stock in a week is the same as the demand for the product, there is no loss; on the contrary, this stocking action gives the highest monetary profit and the element of uncertainty is missing. The figures to the left and below the main diagonal represent opportunity losses or those sales that are lost by being out of stock and consumer demand not being met. The figures to the right and above the diagonal represent losses actually sustained by the store, because these losses arise from inventory when the quantity in stock exceeds the number of items sold. For example, if 55 gallons of milk are stocked in a week and only 53 gallons are sold, there is a net loss of $1.98 resulting from the cost of 2 gallons of unsold milk. The loss is reduced to $0.99 if 54 gallons are sold and 55 gallons are stocked.

The last column assigns probabilities to various demands given in the first column. Applying these probabilities to the conditional losses, the expected losses can be calculated. We recall that the term loss is used in the sense of reduction from the maximum profits possible for each stocking action. Table 12.5 shows the expected losses resulting from decisions to stock 53, 54, 55, 56, 57, 58, and 59 gallons of milk per week. The stocking of 55 gallons of milk produces the lowest expected loss just as it yields the highest expected profits. Thus, both the earlier approach of maximizing conditional profits and this approach of minimizing conditional losses call for the stocking of 55 gallons of milk each week.

Table 12.5 Expected Loss Table

Possible Stock (in Gallons)	Expected Losses
53	$0.33(0.10) + 0.66(0.20) + 0.99(0.20) + 1.32(0.20) + 1.65(0.10) + 1.98(0.10) = \$0.99$
54	$0.99(0.10) + 0.33(0.20) + 0.66(0.20) + 0.99(0.20) + 1.32(0.10) + 1.65(0.10) = \$0.79$
55	$1.98(0.10) + 0.99(0.10) + 0.33(0.20) + 0.66(0.20) + 0.99(0.10) + 1.32(0.10) = \$0.73$
56	$2.97(0.10) + 1.98(0.10) + 0.99(0.20) + 0.33(0.20) + 0.66(0.10) + 0.99(0.10) = \$0.92$
57	$3.96(0.10) + 2.97(0.10) + 1.98(0.20) + 0.99(0.20) + 0.33(0.10) + 0.66(0.10) = \$1.39$
58	$4.95(0.10) + 3.96(0.10) + 2.97(0.20) + 1.98(0.20) + 0.99(0.20) + 0.33(0.10) = \$2.11$
59	$5.94(0.10) + 4.95(0.10) + 3.96(0.20) + 2.97(0.20) + 1.98(0.20) + 0.99(0.10) = \$2.97$

12.5 EXPECTED PROFITS WITH PERFECT INFORMATION

Suppose that the management of the store somehow has developed forecasts for exact sales and costs and knows in advance what the exact demand for its products will be. This information, if accurate, removes all uncertainty from the problem. The level of demand may vary from one week to the next, yet the retail store manager knows in advance how many gallons of milk are needed by customers in a particular week. Generally, retail stores enter into an agreement with the milk suppliers so that any quantity of milk left unsold after a week will be removed by the supplier without any expense to the store. This means that a store pays only for the quantity actually consumed by its customers. Under these ideal conditions, the conditional profits on the main diagonal in Table 12.2 are multiplied by the respective probabilities to obtain the highest expected monetary profits. Thus, the maximum expected profit is

$$17.49(0.10) + 17.82(0.10) + 18.15(0.20) + 18.48(0.20)$$
$$+ 18.81(0.20) + 19.14(0.10) + 19.47(0.10) = \$18.48$$

If the conditional loss table is used, then the zeros on the main diagonal in Table 12.4 are multiplied by the respective probabilities, assuring the retailer that he will never find himself in a losing proposition if he can anticipate correctly future demand of the product or knows in advance that any products not sold can be returned to the supplier without any cost to the retail store.

12.6 MARGINAL ANALYSIS APPROACH

We have considered decision making in the previous sections through conditional profit and conditional loss tables that determine the highest expected monetary profits for a discrete distribution. In the illustrative problem, we considered seven possible stocking actions and seven possible sales levels resulting in $7 \times 7 = 49$ calculations each for the conditional profit and conditional loss tables. If we had considered 50 possible stock actions, say, 51 to 100 gallons of milk, and an equal number of sales levels, we would have been confronted with $50 \times 50 = 2500$ calculations in determing conditional and expected profit from each possible combination. In addition, the wide range of demand for several hundreds or thousands of other products in the store would require similar calculations for each product. The marginal analysis approach avoids these computations.

We recall from our discussion in Chapter 10 that if the probability of rain on a New Year's Eve is 0.35, then the probability is 0.65 that it will not rain on that day. Similarly, if the probability that a seed will germinate is 0.76, then the probability that it will not germinate is 0.24; if the probability that Mr. Talbot will win a certain poker hand is 0.85, then the probability is 0.15 that he will not win the poker hand. When an additional gallon of milk is stocked, two events are possible: Either the additional gallon of milk is sold or it remains unsold, and the sum of the probabilities of these two mutually exclusive events must be 1. If p denotes the probability that the additional stock is sold, then $q = 1 - p$ is the probability that the additional stock remains unsold. The sale of an additional unit results in an increase in the conditional profits, which in turn is associated with the corresponding increase in the expected profits. This last increase is referred to in economics as marginal profit (MP). In the illustrative problem, the marginal profit from the sale of an additional gallon of milk is $0.33 (selling price minus cost price). The concept of marginal profit was in effect in the Table 12.2. If 53 gallons of milk are stocked and consumers demand at least that quantity, the net conditional profit is $17.49. If an additional gallon of milk is stocked and sold, the conditional profit is increased to $17.82, and this occurs 90 percent of the time.

The stocking of an additional unit and not selling it reduces the conditional profits. This amount of reduction is called marginal loss (ML). In the problem, the marginal loss is the cost of the unsold gallon of milk less the salvage value, if any.

Suppose that the store stocks 55 gallons of milk but sells only 53 gallons; then the net profit of $17.49 earned on the sale of 53 gallons is reduced by $1.98, the cost of 2 gallons of unsold milk and thus the conditional profit drops to $15.51. If 55 gallons are stocked but only 54 gallons are sold, the conditional profit drops only to $16.83.

The basic rule is to stock the additional units as long as the expected marginal profit from stocking each unit is greater than the expected marginal loss from stocking that unit. The expected marginal profit from stocking and selling the additional unit is the marginal profit of that unit multiplied by the probability of selling that unit. Similarly, the expected marginal loss from stocking an additional unit and not selling it is the marginal loss multiplied by the probability of not selling that unit. Thus

$$\text{Expected marginal profit} = p \, MP$$
$$\text{Expected marginal loss} = (1 - p) \, ML$$

The additional unit should be stocked as long as

$$p \, MP \geq (1 - p) \, ML$$

That is,

$$p(ML + MP) \geq ML$$

This, in turn, implies that

$$p \geq p_0 \qquad \text{where } p_0 = \frac{ML}{ML + MP}$$

Hence, the general rule is that additional units should be stocked as long as the probability of selling the additional unit is greater than p_0. The condition of equality in the above equation is an exception to the rule and is an indication of an even exchange of dollars for the last unit; it does not maximize the store's return on its total assets. This is applicable in department stores that are trying to maximize profits as well as the customer's satisfaction (i.e., the probability that customers will find the item in the store when they need it). Several department stores who desire not to run the risk of losing their customers to their competitors prefer to use "greater than or equal to" in the above equations, because their management is aware that turning customers away will have a direct effect on the return on total assets of the firm.

The letter p_0 in the above equations represents the minimum probability of selling an additional unit in order to justify the stocking of that unit. Thus, the size of an order should be increased to the point where the probability p of selling an additional unit is at least equal to the calculated value of p_0. In the above illustration, we have

$$MP = \$0.33 \qquad ML = \$0.99$$

$$p_0 = \frac{0.99}{0.99 + 0.33} = 0.75$$

This means that to justify stocking an additional gallon of milk, we must have a probability of at least 0.75 of selling that additional gallon of milk. Such a probability is called a cumulative probability. The cumulative probabilities that represent the probabilities that sales will reach or exceed each of the seven sales levels of the example are given in Table 12.6. In our problem, the cumulative probability for stocking 54 gallons of milk is 0.90, which is certainly greater than 0.75. This comparison justifies the stocking of 54 gallons. We can now go to the next higher level of sales, 55 gallons. The cumulative probability of stocking and selling 55 gallons is 0.80, which also satisfies our rule. The stocking of 56 gallons of milk is not advisable, because the cumulative probability of stocking and selling this quantity no longer exceeds the value $p_0 = 0.75$. Thus, we would stock 55 and not 56 gallons of milk every week. Notice that the marginal approach leads us to the same conclusion that we reached with the use of conditional profit or loss analysis. Both approaches result in a decision to stock 55 gallons of milk.

Table 12.6 Cumulative Probability of Sales

Weekly Sales in Gallons (x)	Probability $P(X = x)$	Cumulative Probability $P(X \geq x)$
53	0.10	1.00
54	0.10	0.90
55	0.20	0.80
56	0.20	0.60
57	0.20	0.40
58	0.10	0.20
59	0.10	0.10

EXERCISE 12.1

1. A company buys a certain product for $6 and sells it for $10. A tabulation of recent demand for the product is as follows.

Quantity Sold	Number of Days
30	10
31	35
32	50
33	5

a. What is the expected demand for this product?
b. Prepare tables of conditional profits and conditional losses.
c. Compute tables of expected profits and expected losses under uncertainty.
2. The following table gives a discrete distribution of the past daily sales of a product.

Quantity Sold	Probability of Selling These Units
60	0.10
61	0.30
62	0.45
63	0.15

The selling price of each unit is $12, whereas the cost price is $10.

a. What is the expected profit per day if the number of units stocked are (i) 60, (ii) 61, (iii) 62, and (iv) 63?

b. What quantity should be stocked so as to maximize daily profits under uncertainty?

c. What is the expected value of the perfect information?

3. The Jones Company produces certain items for the Christmas season. The distribution of the demand of the product is as follows.

Units Sold	Probability
1000	0.10
2000	0.20
3000	0.40
4000	0.20
5000	0.10

a. What are the expected sales over a long period?

b. How many items should be stocked if each unit costing $0.60 is sold for $1?

c. What is the expected value of the perfect information?

4. The Pearson Company specializes in a frozen food that it sells to many retail outlets in the area. The frozen food, supplied in units of 12, is sold for $3 per dozen and costs $2 per dozen. Any unsold quantity of frozen food left at the end of the week is redeemed at $0.50 per dozen (for purposes other than human consumption). The demand for the frozen food during the winter months is relatively constant but varies from one week to another. The following data was compiled from the company records.

Weekly Demand	Probability of Selling
70	0.01
120	0.10
170	0.37
220	0.36
270	0.13
320	0.02
370	0.01

a. What is the expected weekly demand over a long period?

b. Determine the optimal quantity of frozen food the company should stock every week.

c. What is the maximum expected profit under uncertainty based on the given schedule for demand?

d. What is the expected value of the perfect information?

5. A car rental company at an international airport leases automobiles from a large leasing firm in the city for $8 per day and rents them to customers for $12 per day. The cars leased from the firm and not used by the company cost the company $4 per day. The leasing firms pays the maintenance cost and the customer pays for the gasoline and oil. The rental company must specify the number of cars it intends to use on a given day at least one week in advance. The following data were compiled from the records of the rental company covering a 150-day period.

Number of Cars Leased (x)	Number of Days the Cars Were Rented
23	15
24	15
25	30
26	30
27	30
28	15
29	15

a. What is the expected daily demand over a long period?

b. Determine the optimum number of cars the company should lease daily.

c. What is the maximum expected profits under uncertainty based on the given data?

d. What is the expected value of the perfect information?

6. The Alexander Company buys a certain item for $10 that it then sells for $15. The distribution of the daily demand of the product is as follows.

Units Sold	Probability
100	0.05
101	0.05
102	0.10
103	0.15
104	0.20
105	0.25
106	0.15
107	0.05

a. What is the expected daily demand for the product?

b. Should 106 units be stocked? If not, what level of inventory should be carried daily?

12.7 CONTINUOUS PROBABILITY DISTRIBUTION

In the illustrative problem discussed in the previous sections, we developed the basic framework for combining probabilities, past sales of the product and some financial considerations to determine optimal stocking. The demand for the product was a discrete random variable that assumed only a few integer values. However, in many inventory problems, sales take on any value within a wide range depending on changes in tastes, availability of substitutes, and possible seasonal fluctuations in the market. We shall assume that the distribution of the sales can be approximated by a normal curve with mean μ and standard deviation σ because the normal distribution is in many cases a reasonable approximation of many groups of historical data such as past daily sales of a product—there are very few days when sales are exceedingly small and very few days when sales hit a level beyond our reasonable expectations.

Consider, for example, a newspaper dealer who has kept a record of her sales during a 100-day period that she considers to be representative. The data are given in Table 12.7. We shall use this data to provide a concrete illustration of a frequency distribution and then calculate the mean and standard deviation of the distribution. Performing the actual tally and counting the number of values that correspond to the daily sales of newspapers, we get Table 12.8. The probability, $P(X = x)$, in column 3 is obtained by dividing the number of days in column 2 by the total number of days: 100. Then, using Definition 11.2.1, the average daily sales are given by

$$\mu = \sum x \cdot P(X = x) = 50.20$$

The calculation of the standard deviation of a random variable X can be simple and straightforward if the arithmetic average, $E(X)$, is a whole number. Otherwise, calculation of the standard deviation using Definition 11.3.1 is a fairly tedious and time-consuming process. In such cases, the shortcut approach of computing the standard deviation provided by Proposition 11.3.1 is usefully employed in place of Definition 11.3.1.

Table 12.7 Sales of Newspapers

49	51	50	53	45	49	50	56	46	54
48	51	60	46	52	46	52	50	57	51
50	52	49	51	40	54	50	55	47	53
49	50	51	54	53	50	52	51	48	44
52	51	47	49	61	52	39	52	57	45
47	48	46	46	50	47	50	51	47	53
50	51	50	48	52	61	49	45	54	60
56	44	45	50	46	47	55	47	53	49
50	41	54	53	50	52	51	45	51	50
49	51	53	46	49	48	46	51	50	49

Table 12.8 Distribution of Past Sales of Newspapers

Daily Sales of Newspapers (x)	Number of days (f)	$P(X = x)$	$x \cdot P(X = x)$	$x^2 \cdot P(X = x)$
39	1	0.01	0.39	15.21
40	1	0.01	0.40	16.00
44	2	0.02	0.88	38.72
45	5	0.05	2.25	101.25
46	8	0.08	3.68	169.28
47	7	0.07	3.29	154.63
48	5	0.05	2.40	115.20
49	10	0.10	4.90	240.10
50	16	0.16	8.00	400.00
51	14	0.14	7.14	364.14
52	9	0.09	4.68	243.36
53	7	0.07	3.71	196.63
54	5	0.05	2.70	145.80
55	2	0.02	1.10	60.50
56	2	0.02	1.12	62.72
57	2	0.02	1.14	64.98
60	2	0.02	1.20	72.00
61	2	0.02	1.22	74.42
Total	100	1.00	50.20	2534.94

Using Proposition 11.3.1, we have

$$V(X) = \sum[x^2 P(X = x)] - \mu^2$$
$$= 2534.94 - (50.2)^2 = 14.90$$

Thus,

$$\sigma(X) = \sqrt{14.90} = 3.86$$

A further simplification in the calculation of $E(X)$ and $V(X)$ consists of adding or subtracting an arbitrary constant from each value assumed by the random variable X. Proposition 11.3.2 guarantees that this would have no effect on the variation of X. To illustrate this useful technique, let us define a new random variable

$$Y = X - 50$$

Subtracting 50 from each value of x and assuming the same probability distribution, we have Table 12.9. Because $X = Y + 50$, we have

$$E(X) = E(Y) + 50 \qquad \text{(Proposition 11.2.1)}$$
$$= [\sum y \cdot P(Y = y)] + 50$$
$$= 0.20 + 50 = 50.20$$

Also,

$$V(X) = V(Y + 50) = V(Y) \qquad \text{(Proposition 11.3.2)}$$
$$= E(Y^2) - [E(Y)]^2$$
$$= 14.94 - 0.04 = 14.90$$

which agrees with our earlier assertion.

Table 12.9

y	$P(Y = y)$	$y \cdot P(Y = y)$	$y^2 \cdot P(Y = y)$
-11	0.01	-0.11	1.21
-10	0.01	-0.10	1.00
-6	0.02	-0.12	0.72
-5	0.05	-0.25	1.25
-4	0.08	-0.32	1.28
-3	0.07	-0.21	0.63
-2	0.05	-0.10	0.20
-1	0.10	-0.10	0.10
0	0.16	0.00	0.00
1	0.14	0.14	0.14
2	0.09	0.18	0.36
3	0.07	0.21	0.63
4	0.05	0.20	0.80
5	0.02	0.10	0.50
6	0.02	0.12	0.72
7	0.02	0.14	0.98
10	0.02	0.20	2.00
11	0.02	0.22	2.42
Total	1.00	0.20	14.94

Because the distribution of sales can be approximated closely by a normal curve with mean μ and standard deviation σ, it can be established that

68.26 percent of sales fall in the interval $\mu \pm \sigma$
95.45 percent of sales fall in the interval $\mu \pm 2\sigma$
99.97 percent of sales fall in the interval $\mu \pm 3\sigma$

Applying these facts to the problem where $\mu = 50.2$ and $\sigma = 3.86$, we can conclude that approximately 68 percent of future demand will lie between 46.34 and 54.06 if the curve is perfectly normal. Similarly, 95 percent of sales are expected to fall between 42.48 and 57.92 and approximately 99.97 percent of future sales will lie between 38.62 and 61.78, that is, between 39 and 62 newspapers.

Suppose now that a newspaper costs the dealer $0.12 and she sells it to the customer for $0.15, thus making a profit of $0.03 on each newspaper she sells. Let us further assume that the papers not sold by the evening can be salvaged for $0.10 each. Clearly, marginal profit for each paper sold is $0.03 and marginal loss for each paper unsold is $0.02 (cost of the newspaper minus the salvage value). Thus,

$$p_0 = \frac{ML}{MP + ML} = \frac{2}{3 + 2} = 0.40$$

We recall that 0.40 is the minimum probability of selling an additional newspaper in order to justify stocking that paper, and the size of the order is to be increased only to the point where the probability of selling an additional paper is at least equal to 0.40. Now the problem is reduced to the determination of an integer k such that

$$P(X \leq k) \geq 0.40$$

where X is a random variable having a normal distribution with mean 50.2 and a standard deviation $\sigma = 3.86$ (see Figure 12.1). Here

$$Z = \frac{X - 50.2}{3.86}$$

Thus,

$$P(X \leq k) = P\left(\frac{X - 50.2}{3.86} \leq \frac{k - 50.2}{3.86}\right)$$

$$= P\left(Z \leq \frac{k - 50.2}{3.86}\right)$$

$$= \Phi\left(\frac{k - 50.2}{3.86}\right)$$

What is the value of k so that

$$\Phi\left(\frac{k - 50.2}{3.86}\right) \geq 0.40$$

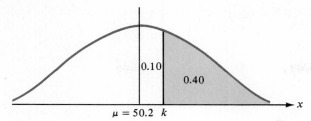

Figure 12.1

Clearly,

$$\Phi\left(\frac{k - 50.2}{3.86}\right) \le 0.60$$

Using Table 1 in the Appendix, we get

$$\frac{k - 50.2}{3.86} \le 0.25$$

$$k \le 51.165$$

This means that the newspaper dealer should not order more than 51 papers on any day. As we move to the right of the vertical line $\mu = 50.2$, the probability that a certain quantity of newspaper can be sold decreases. Thus, the dealer is advised to stock an additional quantity until she reaches the first integer value less than or equal to k.

Example 12.1

A razor company has found that sales of its products are normally distributed with an average of 250 units per day and a standard deviation of 20 units. Each unit is sold for $24 and costs $22. If the unit is unsold, it has a salvage value of $16. What is the optimum level of stock the company should carry?

SOLUTION
Here, $ML = \$6$, $MP = \$2$, and

$$p_0 = \frac{ML}{ML + MP} = \frac{6}{6 + 2} = 0.75$$

We need to determine the value of k such that $P(X \le k) \ge 0.75$.

$$P(X \le k) = P\left(\frac{X - 250}{20} \le \frac{k - 250}{20}\right)$$

$$= P\left(Z \le \frac{k - 250}{20}\right)$$

$$= \Phi\left(\frac{k - 250}{20}\right)$$

Because $\Phi[(k - 250)/20] \leq 0.25$, it follows from Table 1 that

$$\frac{k - 250}{20} \leq -0.67$$

Thus,

$$k \leq 236.6$$

EXERCISE 12.2

1. A salesman for Richmond and Naylor, Inc., has gathered the following daily sales data for his principal product.

28	25	18	23	28	34	31	16	24	26
26	21	23	27	21	22	23	22	25	18
29	27	27	28	23	27	26	27	28	16
18	20	24	25	27	20	29	23	25	28
20	21	16	18	26	29	21	27	18	26

a. Group this data into a frequency distribution.
b. Calculate the mean and standard deviation using a shortcut method.

2. The management of a restaurant recorded the following number of steak dinners it served during the last 50 consecutive Fridays.

48	35	38	41	46	45	34	39	36	32
45	42	48	42	40	48	45	42	41	40
48	40	41	38	48	35	41	38	39	34
39	43	44	34	44	38	40	40	34	44
34	39	45	41	42	43	47	38	35	39

a. Group this data into a frequency distribution.
b. Calculate the mean and standard deviation of the number of steaks served. Use a direct as well as a shortcut approach and compare the results.

3. An industrial organization gives to all applicants for employment an aptitude test. The results for 150 persons who have recently taken the test are as follows.

Score (x)	Frequency (f)
9	5
8	10
7	25
6	20
5	38
4	22
3	17
2	8
1	5

For these data, calculate
a. the mean
b. the standard deviation

4. Find (a) the mean, (b) the variance, (c) the standard deviation for the following frequency distribution.

Score (x)	Frequency (f)
5	5
8	12
11	14
14	35
17	33
20	12
23	6
26	4

5. Calculate (a) the mean, (b) the variance, (c) the standard deviation for the following frequency distribution.

Score (x)	Frequency (f)
15	6
20	13
25	22
30	35
35	15
40	9

6. The Sloan Baking Company sells fresh bread for $0.44 a loaf. A loaf costs $0.26 plus $0.06 for fixed and variable costs of the company. If the bread is not sold in one day, it is salvaged for only $0.24. Analysis of past sales data indicates that daily sales are approximately normally distributed, with $\mu = 1140$ and $\sigma = 40$. What level of optimum stock should the company carry?

7. Suppose that Richmond and Naylor, Inc., is considering the use of scientifically developed quantitative techniques to determine the optimum stock of their principal product and approach you with the data given in Exercise 1. The product costs $14 from the wholesaler plus $8 for fixed and variable costs of the company and is sold for $30. The products unsold by the end of the season can be sold back for $10. If the sales are normally distributed, what optimum level of stock would you recommend to the company?

8. The average daily sales of Jones Bros. are approximately normally distributed with $\mu = 100$ and $\sigma = 10$ units. Each unit sells for $20 and costs $14. If the unit is not sold, it can be returned to the company for $12. What is the optimum stock the firm should carry?

9. A grocery store buys its doughnuts from the Alexander Baking Company for $0.60 a dozen delivered to the store and sells them for $0.90 a dozen. Doughnuts left at the end of the evening are sold next day at $0.42 a dozen. Analysis of past

data shows that sales are approximately normally distributed, with $\mu = 50.4$ and $\sigma = 28.8$. What is the optimum stock the grocery store should carry?

10. The weekly demand for a certain product of the company is approximately normally distributed with $\mu = 40$ and $\sigma = 12$ units. Each unit that sells for $5.00 costs $2.00. The products unsold by the end of the week have no salvage value. What is the optimum stock the company should carry?

CHAPTER 13

Theory of Games and Finite Markov Chains

13.1 INTRODUCTION

The theory of games, a relatively new branch of mathematics, is intended mainly as a theory of rational behavior in practical situations that involve conflicting interests and in which the outcome is determined by the "best" strategies chosen by intelligent opponents. This dynamic theory, which is not limited to parlor games (bridge, poker, chess, checkers, tic-tac-toe) or sports, has recently found increasing applications in problems related to economic, political, social, and military operations. The players may be commercial rivals engaged in competition, union leaders and management in an industry trying to reach a labor contract, campaign managers of candidates trying to get elected to political office, generals in an army trying to win a war, attorneys in a lawsuit trying for the best settlement for their clients, and so on. The theory of games finds applications in all situations in which parties involved have opposing goals, use their best strategy, and yet cannot completely dominate the final outcome. We shall, however, limit our discussion here to two-person games, that is, situations of conflict where there are only two participants. Later in this chapter we shall discuss finite Markov chains—another application of matrix theory to some questions involving probabilities.

13.2 TWO-PERSON, ZERO-SUM MATRIX GAMES

The term two-person means that two players, R and C, with conflicting interests, are making use of their ingenuity to outwit each other, and zero-sum means that any loss to one player is the gain of the other. It is assumed that player R has a choice of m moves, which may be identified as $R_1, R_2, \ldots, R_m$. After he has selected his move, player C, without being informed of the choice of his opponent R, makes his move among several alternatives $C_1, C_2, \ldots, C_n$. The moves of two players are then compared and the winner declared according to the rules of the game. The payoffs, which are assigned a numerical value, are generally represented in the form of an $m \times n$ matrix such as the one given here:

$$
\text{Player } R \quad
\begin{array}{c}
\text{Player } C \\[4pt]
\begin{bmatrix}
a_{11} & a_{12} & \cdots & a_{1n} \\
a_{21} & a_{22} & \cdots & a_{2n} \\
\vdots & & & \\
a_{m1} & a_{m2} & \cdots & a_{mn}
\end{bmatrix}
\end{array}
$$

Each row of the matrix corresponds to one of the m possible moves of player R, whereas each column corresponds to C's n possible choices. The element a_{ij} represents the payoff to R when he selects move R_i and C selects move C_j. Positive amounts correspond to payments C makes to R, whereas negative amounts represent amounts player R pays to player C.

Example 13.1

Casey writes one of the numbers 1 or 2 on a slip of paper. Simultaneously, Rick writes one of the numbers 1 or 2 on another slip of paper. The numbers are then compared and the payoff depends on whether the numbers match. Explain the following payoff matrix.

$$
\text{Rick} \quad
\begin{array}{c}
\text{Casey} \\[4pt]
\begin{array}{cc}
\;\;1 & \;\;2
\end{array} \\[2pt]
\begin{array}{c} 1 \\ 2 \end{array}
\begin{bmatrix}
\$0.04 & -\$0.05 \\
-\$0.05 & \$0.08
\end{bmatrix}
\end{array}
$$

SOLUTION

If both players, Casey and Rick, write the number 1 on their slips, then Casey pays $0.04 to Rick; if number 2 appears on both slips, Casey loses $0.08 to Rick. If the numbers do not match, Casey wins $0.05 and this is the amount Rick loses. ∎

Example 13.2

Explain the following payoff matrix:

$$
\text{Player } R \quad
\begin{array}{c}
\text{Player } C \\[4pt]
\begin{bmatrix}
1 & 2 & 4 \\
-3 & -1 & 2
\end{bmatrix}
\end{array}
$$

SOLUTION

Player C has three distinct choices, whereas player R has only two, and all but two of the payoffs go from player C to player R. If C chooses column 1 and R selects row 2, R loses $0.03, let us say. In case R chooses row 1, he wins $0.01, $0.02, or $0.04 depending on whether C chooses columns 1, 2, or 3, respectively, but if R chooses row 2 and C selects column 3, then R gains only $0.02. ∎

EXERCISE 13.1

For each of the following two-person, zero-sum games, write the game matrix.

1. Roger and Clark agree to announce simultaneously a number. If the sum of the numbers is even, Roger wins $0.50, and if it is odd, he loses $0.50.

2. Richard and Chipper agree to write a number 1, 2, or 3 simultaneously. If the sum of the numbers is even, Richard gets that many dollars, and if it is odd, Richard pays Chipper that many dollars.

3. Roosevelt and Cox agree to play a game involving a nickel, a dime, and a quarter. Each of them is supposed to show a coin simultaneously. If the value of the two coins is even, Roosevelt wins the money; otherwise Cox wins it.

4. Robinson has a $1, $5, or $10 bill in his wallet. His wife Cathy guesses a number 1, 5, or 10 and wins the amount if she guesses correctly; otherwise she pays her husband an amount she guesses incorrectly.

5. Roger and Jeanie are supposed to meet for lunch at a restaurant. If both come early, they spend more time together, which gives them a joy value of 50 points. If Roger gets there on time and she is late, the joy value is 10 points. If she gets there on time and Roger is late, she gets very grouchy and difficult and thus reduces the joy value to −10. If both are late, they spend very little time together and their joy value is 25 points.

13.3 STRICTLY DETERMINED GAMES

The important question that arises in the theory of games is to determine whether there is a best move for players who wish to maximize their gains (or at least minimize their losses), that is, whether one player should prefer one move over another to maximize his gains. To illustrate, let us consider the following example, in which we propose to determine the best move for each player.

Example 13.3

Two players, Ricci and Caldwall, agree to play a game. Ricci chooses a number from the set {1, 2, 3}. Then, Caldwall, without knowing the choice of his opponent, chooses a number from the set {1, 2, 3, 4}. The numbers are then compared by the referee, who determines the winner and announces the reward or penalty according to the following payoff matrix:

$$
\begin{array}{c}
\quad\quad\quad\quad \text{Caldwall} \\
\quad\quad\quad 1 \quad 2 \quad 3 \quad 4 \\
\text{Ricci} \quad
\begin{array}{c} 1 \\ 2 \\ 3 \end{array}
\left[
\begin{array}{cccc}
4 & 2 & 3 & 9 \\
5 & 6 & 5 & 7 \\
6 & 8 & 4 & 3
\end{array}
\right]
\end{array}
$$

Assuming that both players wish to maximize their profits, determine the best move for each player and the corresponding payoff.

SOLUTION

First, consider the game from Ricci's point of view. If he chooses row 1, he may win $4, $2, $3, or $9 depending on what his opponent intends to do. In any case, he is sure to win at least the minimum of the amounts in the first row, that is, $2. In the event that Ricci selects row 2, he is guaranteed at least $5 regardless of what Caldwall has in his mind, and if Ricci chooses row 3, he can gain at least $3 no matter what countermove Caldwall intends to make. If he knew in advance what Caldwall is going to do, his decision would be easy and he would hardly need any professional assistance to determine his best move. If Caldwall selects column 1 or column 2, Ricci would have no difficulty in selecting row 3 so as to maximize his winnings; if Caldwall chooses column 3, Ricci would select row 2, and if Caldwall selects column 4, Ricci would opt for row 1. Note that in each of these situations, Ricci is anxious to maximize his winnings. Similarly, Caldwall would play smart if he knew his opponent's choices. If Ricci chooses row 1, Caldwall would select column 2; if he chooses row 2, Caldwall would opt for either column 1 or column 3; and if Ricci selects row 3, Caldwall would go for column 4. In each of these cases, Caldwall is making every possible effort to minimize his losses.

Unfortunately, opponents in any game do not disclose their strategy, and each player must consider how his opponent would respond if he knew exactly what move the other player is going to make. Nevertheless, the minimum in each row and the maximum in each column seem to play an important role in the determination of best moves. The least amount that Ricci can win in each row is as follows:

Row 1   min(4, 2, 3, 9) = 2
Row 2   min(5, 6, 5, 7) = 5
Row 3   min(6, 8, 4, 3) = 3

Clearly, Ricci can win at least $5 by selecting row 2.

Let us now examine the game further from Caldwall's point of view. We recognize that Ricci has made the first move and Caldwall is totally unaware of the choice his opponent has made. The most he can lose by selecting the numbers 1 through 4 is as follows:

Column 1   max(4, 5, 6) = 6
Column 2   max(2, 6, 8) = 8
Column 3   max(3, 5, 4) = 5
Column 4   max(9, 7, 3) = 9

Because he is interested in minimizing his losses, he must select column 3 as his best possible move.

Ricci is interested in a sure win of as much as possible, whereas his opponent is considering every possible move so as not to lose more than he has to. Thus, Ricci would play row 2 whereas Caldwall would play column 3. These choices, which guarantee Ricci to win $5, (the amount Caldwall loses in this game) is called the value of the game. ∎

This leads us to the following definition.

Definition 13.3.1: An $m \times n$ game matrix A is said to be strictly determined if the matrix has an element that is the minimum in its row and the maximum in its column. This entry is called the saddle point, and the numerical value v associated with it is the value of the game.

The game is fair if $v = 0$. In a strictly determined game, the row containing v is the best strategy for player R and the column containing v is the best possible strategy for player C. It is likely that an $m \times n$ matrix may have one or more saddle points; in that event, each player may have more than one optimal strategy. The value of the game, however, remains unchanged.

Example 13.4

Consider a game with the following payoff matrix:

$$\text{Player } R \begin{array}{c} \text{Player } C \\ \begin{bmatrix} 5 & 0 & -3 \\ 3 & 1 & 2 \\ -4 & -2 & 6 \end{bmatrix} \end{array}$$

Determine the saddle point, the best strategies for each player, and the value of the game. Is it a fair game?

SOLUTION

Player R, anxious to win \$6, must carefully weigh the possible countermoves of his opponent, C, who may select column 1 and win \$4 or play column 2 and win \$2 instead of losing \$6 to player C. It is expected that player R plans his strategy with utmost care and determines the least possible amount he can win in each row if his opponent C makes the worst possible countermove unfavorable to R. The least amount that R can win in each row is as follows:

Row 1 $\min(5, 0, -3) = -3$

Row 2 $\min(3, 1, 2) = 1$

Row 3 $\min(-4, -2, 6) = -4$

Thus,

$\max(-3, 1, -4) = 1$

Player C, on the other hand, chooses the maximum in each column as follows:

Column 1 $\max(5, 3, -4) = 5$

Column 2 $\max(0, 1, -2) = 1$

Column 3 $\max(-3, -2, 6) = 6$

and

$\min(5, 1, 6) = 1$

Thus, the maximum of the minimum in each row is exactly the same as the minimum of the maximum in each column of the payoff matrix. The value of the game is \$1. Accordingly, the game is not fair.

The saddle point exists in the second row and second column, because the best strategy for player R is to choose row 2 and the best strategy for player C is to select column 2. ∎

Example 13.5

A pair of coins is thrown. Two players, Bob and Steve, agree to guess the possible number of heads from the set $\{0, 1, 2\}$. First, Steve makes his choice and then Bob, without having been informed what choice Steve has made, also chooses a number from the same set. The payoff matrix associated with this game is given below:

$$
\begin{array}{c c}
 & \text{Bob} \\
 & \begin{array}{c c c}
 0 & \ 1 & 2
 \end{array} \\
\text{Steve}\ \begin{array}{c} 0 \\ 1 \\ 2 \end{array} &
\left[\begin{array}{c c c}
0 & 2 & 4 \\
-2 & 0 & 2 \\
-4 & -2 & 0
\end{array}\right]
\end{array}
$$

Determine the best possible strategies for Bob and Steve. Is this a fair game?

SOLUTION

Both Steve and Bob have a choice of three numbers from the set $\{0, 1, 2\}$. Each row of the matrix corresponds to the choices of Steve, whereas each column represents Bob's possible choices from the same set. For instance, if Steve chooses row 2 and Bob selects column 3, then Bob pays Steve \$2; if Steve chooses row 3 and Bob selects column 1, then Steve pays Bob \$4. As before, positive amounts correspond to what Bob pays Steve and negative amounts represent what Steve pays Bob.

Note that each element of the first row is greater than the corresponding element of the second row and is also greater than the corresponding element of the third row. Thus, no matter what number Bob chooses, Steve must select row 1 as his optimal strategy. Again, because each element in the first column is less than the corresponding element of the second column, which in turn is less than the corresponding element of the third column, Bob's optimal strategy is to choose column 1 regardless of his opponent's choice. The saddle point appears in the first row and first column. The value of the game is zero and hence it is a fair game. ∎

Note that in each of the above examples, player R determines the minimum of the ith row; that is

$$
\begin{aligned}
r_i &= \min(a_{i1}, a_{i2}, \ldots, a_{ij}, \ldots, a_{in}) \\
&= \min_j(a_{ij})
\end{aligned}
$$

and then choose the row as his optimal strategy that corresponds to

$$
r = \max(r_1, r_2, \ldots, r_m)
$$

the largest value of the minima. Player C, whose interests are directly in conflict with those of his opponent, first determines the maximum of the jth column; that is,

$$
\begin{aligned}
c_j &= \max(a_{1j}, a_{2j}, \ldots, a_{ij}, \ldots, a_{mj}) \\
&= \max_i(a_{ij})
\end{aligned}
$$

and then selects the column as his optimal strategy that corresponds to

$$c = \min(c_1, c_2, \ldots, c_n)$$

the smallest value of these maxima. If $r = c$, then we have a saddle point in a strictly determined game.

To solve strictly determined games, player R simply determines the minimum value in each row of the payoff matrix and then encircles the largest value(s). Player C, on the other hand, finds the maximum value in each column and circles the smallest of these maximum(s). Consider, for example, the following payoff matrix:

		Player C			Row minimum
	6	4	5	11	4
Player R	7	8	7	9	⑦
	8	10	6	5	5
Column maximum	8	10	⑦	11	

The encircled elements agree and 7 units is the value of the game. The best strategies for the players R and C are to play row 2 and column 3, respectively.

EXERCISE 13.2

In each of the following matrices, determine the saddle point, the value of each game, and the best strategies of the players.

1. Player R $\begin{bmatrix} -3 & -5 \\ 1 & 2 \end{bmatrix}$ Player C

2. Player R $\begin{bmatrix} 5 & 3 \\ 4 & 2 \end{bmatrix}$ Player C

3. Player R $\begin{bmatrix} 5 & 8 \\ 3 & 10 \end{bmatrix}$ Player C

4. Player R $\begin{bmatrix} 10 & 6 \\ 14 & 8 \end{bmatrix}$ Player C

5. Player R $\begin{bmatrix} 1 & -3 \\ 5 & 6 \end{bmatrix}$ Player C

6. Player R $\begin{bmatrix} 4 & 3 & 10 \\ 7 & 4 & 12 \end{bmatrix}$ Player C

7. Tracey $\begin{bmatrix} -4 & -5 & 2 \\ -1 & -4 & 3 \end{bmatrix}$ Jodey

8. Dick $\begin{bmatrix} 6 & 5 & 12 \\ 9 & 6 & 14 \end{bmatrix}$ Kathy

9. Player R $\begin{bmatrix} 1 & 2 & 4 \\ -3 & 0 & 2 \\ -3 & -4 & 5 \end{bmatrix}$ Player C

10. Susan $\begin{bmatrix} 7 & 9 & 10 \\ 4 & 2 & 8 \\ 5 & 1 & 7 \end{bmatrix}$ Janice

11. Tracey $\begin{bmatrix} 1 & 4 & 6 \\ 8 & 6 & 7 \\ 3 & 2 & 9 \end{bmatrix}$ Anita

12. Mary $\begin{bmatrix} 1 & 3 & 5 \\ 9 & 7 & 8 \\ 2 & 5 & 3 \end{bmatrix}$ Kerry

Maryann

13. Karen $\begin{bmatrix} -4 & 3 & -5 \\ 3 & 6 & 7 \\ -5 & -8 & 9 \end{bmatrix}$

Elaine

14. Kerry $\begin{bmatrix} 8 & 10 & 11 \\ 5 & 3 & 9 \\ 6 & 2 & 8 \end{bmatrix}$

Helen

15. Gail $\begin{bmatrix} 1 & 3 & 6 \\ 7 & 4 & 8 \\ 5 & 2 & 7 \end{bmatrix}$

Dorothy

16. Julius $\begin{bmatrix} 5 & 10 & 12 & 18 \\ 15 & 16 & 14 & 17 \\ 12 & 8 & 10 & 5 \end{bmatrix}$

Jeanie

17. Jodey $\begin{bmatrix} -1 & -3 & -2 & 4 \\ 0 & 1 & 0 & 2 \\ 1 & 3 & -1 & -2 \end{bmatrix}$

Sunil

18. Peter $\begin{bmatrix} 0 & 5 & 10 & 15 \\ -5 & 0 & 5 & 10 \\ -10 & -5 & 0 & 20 \\ -15 & -10 & -20 & 0 \end{bmatrix}$

13.4 MIXED STRATEGIES IN 2 × 2 MATRIX GAMES

We have shown that strictly determined games always have a value, because each player can determine his opponent's best possible strategy and make his move accordingly. Unfortunately, most payoff matrices do not have saddle points.

Consider, for example, a matrix game

Player C

Player R $\begin{bmatrix} -1 & 7 \\ 6 & -2 \end{bmatrix}$

that has no saddle point. If players choose to play this game only once, we have no professional advice for them at this stage and they will have to use their own rational thinking as to what strategy is best for them.

Matrix games are generally played more than once. A reasonable approach for player R in the above game is to choose row 1, because he has a chance of winning $7 or may at worst lose $1 in some cases. If he uses this strategy too often and plays it most of the time, his opponent can foil him by choosing column 1 and thus receive $1 from him instead of losing $7 to him. It is also reasonable that R may sometimes play row 2 so as to win $6 at best or lose $2. Thus, C would be well advised to choose column 1 if his opponent R selects row 1 and selects column 2 if R chooses row 2. This would work very nicely for C if he knew in advance precisely what R plans to do.

Suppose that player C makes the first move and selects column 1. In that event, R would choose row 2 to assure himself of $6. If C selects column 2, player R would be smart to select row 1 and win $7. An important aspect in game theory is that players do not disclose their strategies—at least not to their opponents. The rules of the game may simply require each player to write the number 1 or 2 on a slip of paper and hand it over to a referee who may declare the winner and the associated payoff. Because each player is trying to outsmart his opponent, both are equally anxious to mix their strategies so as not to establish any pattern at all. These types of strategies keep R from winning too much and protect C from losing too much in the long run.

Consider a 2 × 2 game matrix

$$A = \begin{bmatrix} a_{11} & a_{12} \\ a_{21} & a_{22} \end{bmatrix}$$

in which $P = (p_1, p_2), p_1 \geq 0, p_2 \geq 0, p_1 + p_2 = 1$, and $Q = \begin{pmatrix} q_1 \\ q_2 \end{pmatrix}, q_1 \geq 0, q_2 \geq 0,$ $q_1 + q_2 = 1$ are the strategies of players R and C, respectively. The probability that R wins the amount a_{ij} is $p_i q_j$ because if p_i is the probability that R selects row i and q_j is the probability that C chooses column j, the product $p_i q_j$ is the probability that R chooses row i and C selects column j. Thus, the probabilities that R wins the amounts a_{11}, a_{12}, a_{21}, and a_{22} are given by $p_1 q_1, p_1 q_2, p_2 q_1$, and $p_2 q_2$, respectively. The expected value of the game is

$$p_1 q_1 a_{11} + p_1 q_2 a_{12} + p_2 q_1 a_{21} + p_2 q_2 a_{22}$$

which is precisely the matrix product

$$PAQ = [p_1 p_2] \begin{bmatrix} a_{11} & a_{12} \\ a_{21} & a_{22} \end{bmatrix} \begin{bmatrix} q_1 \\ q_2 \end{bmatrix}$$

This leads us to the following definition.

Definition 13.4.1: If $P = (p_1, p_2, \ldots, p_m)$ and

$$Q = \begin{bmatrix} q_1 \\ q_2 \\ \vdots \\ q_n \end{bmatrix}$$

are strategies of the players R and C in a payoff matrix

$$A = \begin{bmatrix} a_{11} & a_{12} & \cdots & a_{1n} \\ a_{21} & a_{22} & \cdots & a_{2n} \\ \vdots & & & \\ a_{m1} & a_{m2} & \cdots & a_{mn} \end{bmatrix}$$

then expected value of the game is defined by

$$E(P, Q) = PAQ$$

Definition 13.4.2: If the expected value of the game is zero, then it is a fair game.

Example 13.6

Suppose that R uses the strategy $P = (0, 1, 0)$ and Q decides to use the strategy

$$Q = \begin{bmatrix} 1 \\ 0 \\ 0 \end{bmatrix}$$

If the payoff matrix is

$$\begin{bmatrix} 5 & 3 & 9 \\ 8 & 10 & 11 \\ 6 & 2 & 8 \end{bmatrix}$$

then

$$E(P, Q) = PAQ = (0, 1, 0) \begin{bmatrix} 5 & 3 & 9 \\ 8 & 10 & 11 \\ 6 & 2 & 8 \end{bmatrix} \begin{bmatrix} 1 \\ 0 \\ 0 \end{bmatrix} = \begin{bmatrix} 8 & 10 & 11 \end{bmatrix} \begin{bmatrix} 1 \\ 0 \\ 0 \end{bmatrix} = 8$$

This implies that if player R always selects the second row and player C always chooses the first column, R will be guaranteed winnings of $8 and C will lose that amount. These strategies, where player R always selects the same row and player C always chooses the particular column, are called pure strategies. ∎

EXERCISE 13.3

Determine $E(P, Q)$ for each of the following payoff matrices with strategies P and Q of players.

1. $A = \begin{bmatrix} 6 & 2 \\ 5 & 1 \end{bmatrix}$, $P = (1, 0)$, $Q = \begin{bmatrix} 0 \\ 1 \end{bmatrix}$

2. $A = \begin{bmatrix} 5 & 3 & 2 \\ 4 & 0 & 1 \end{bmatrix}$, $P = (1, 0)$, $Q = \begin{bmatrix} 0 \\ 0 \\ 1 \end{bmatrix}$

3. $A = \begin{bmatrix} 4 & 6 & 1 \\ 6 & 7 & 8 \\ 2 & 9 & 3 \end{bmatrix}$, $P = (0, 1, 0)$, $Q = \begin{bmatrix} 1 \\ 0 \\ 0 \end{bmatrix}$

4. $A = \begin{bmatrix} 1 & 3 & 5 \\ 9 & 7 & 8 \\ 6 & 5 & 4 \end{bmatrix}$, $P = (0, 1, 0)$, $Q = \begin{bmatrix} 0 \\ 1 \\ 0 \end{bmatrix}$

We have observed that if P and Q are strategies of players R and C, respectively, then the expected value of the game is given by $E(P, Q) = PAQ$, where A is the payoff matrix. The next step is to determine the "best" strategy for each player. An optimal strategy for player R consists of choosing a course of action that would maximize his winnings regardless of what his opponent intends to do. The aim of player C in the game is to choose a strategy that would minimize his losses, no matter what strategy R plans to use.

Consider an abstract 2×2 game matrix

$$\begin{bmatrix} a & b \\ c & d \end{bmatrix}$$

in which a, b, c, and d are numbers. The following proposition will help the reader in determining whether or not we have a strictly determined game.

Proposition 13.4.1: Any 2 × 2 matrix game

$$A = \begin{bmatrix} a & b \\ c & d \end{bmatrix}$$

is nonstrictly determined if and only if

   (a) both a and d are greater than b and c, or
   (b) both b and c are greater than a and d.   ■

Proposition 13.4.2: In any nonstrictly determined 2 × 2 matrix game

$$A = \begin{bmatrix} a & b \\ c & d \end{bmatrix}$$

the optimal strategies

$$P = (p_1, p_2) \quad \text{and} \quad Q = \begin{bmatrix} q_1 \\ q_2 \end{bmatrix}$$

of the players R and C are given by

$$p_1 = \frac{d - c}{a + d - b - c} \qquad p_2 = \frac{a - b}{a + d - b - c}$$

$$q_1 = \frac{d - b}{a + d - b - c} \qquad q_2 = \frac{a - c}{a + d - b - c}$$

The value of the game is given by

$$v = \frac{ad - bc}{a + d - b - c}$$ ■

Corollary: If every entry in a payoff matrix

$$\begin{bmatrix} a & b \\ c & d \end{bmatrix}$$

is increased by k, then the value of the game is also increased by k but the strategies of the players are not affected.

Example 13.7
Determine the optimal strategies of the players and the value of the game

$$A = \begin{bmatrix} 3 & -2 \\ -4 & 7 \end{bmatrix}$$

Is it a fair game?

SOLUTION

Here, $a = 3$, $b = -2$, $c = -4$, and $d = 7$. Thus,

$$a + d - b - c = 16$$

Using the above proposition, we have $p_1 = \frac{11}{16}$, $p_2 = \frac{5}{16}$, $q_1 = \frac{9}{16}$, and $q_2 = \frac{7}{16}$. Thus, player R's optimal strategy is to select row 1 with probability $\frac{11}{16}$ and row 2 with probability $\frac{5}{16}$. Similarly, player C must choose 1 with probability $\frac{9}{16}$ and column 2 with probability $\frac{7}{16}$.

The value of the game is

$$v = \frac{ad - bc}{a + d - b - c}$$

$$= \tfrac{13}{16}$$

and thus it is not a fair game. ∎

Example 13.8

Determine the optimal strategies of players R and C and the value of the game with the following payoff matrix:

$$\begin{bmatrix} 3 & -9 \\ -2 & 6 \end{bmatrix}$$

Is it a fair game?

SOLUTION

Because $a = 3$, $b = -9$, $c = -2$, and $d = 6$, it follows that

$$p_1 = \tfrac{2}{5}, p_2 = \tfrac{3}{5}, q_1 = \tfrac{3}{4}, \text{ and } q_2 = \tfrac{1}{4}$$

Thus, the optimal strategy for player R is to choose the first row with probability 0.40 and the second row with probability 0.60. Player C must choose column 1 with probability 0.75 and column 2 with probability 0.25. Because

$$ad - bc = (3) \cdot (6) - (-9) \cdot (-2) = 0$$

we conclude that it is a fair game. ∎

EXERCISE 13.4

Determine the optimal strategies of the players and the value in each of the nonstrictly determined games in Exercises 1 through 8.

1. $\begin{bmatrix} 1 & -1 \\ -1 & 1 \end{bmatrix}$

2. $\begin{bmatrix} 3 & 2 \\ 1 & 4 \end{bmatrix}$

3. $\begin{bmatrix} 4 & -2 \\ -5 & 3 \end{bmatrix}$

4. $\begin{bmatrix} 6 & 1 \\ 4 & 5 \end{bmatrix}$

5. $\begin{bmatrix} 4 & -3 \\ -3 & 4 \end{bmatrix}$

6. $\begin{bmatrix} 2 & -1 \\ -1 & 2 \end{bmatrix}$

7. $\begin{bmatrix} 3 & -2 \\ -3 & 7 \end{bmatrix}$

8. $\begin{bmatrix} 5 & 1 \\ 3 & 4 \end{bmatrix}$

13.5 RELATIONS OF DOMINANCE

Sometimes it is possible to reduce many seemingly complex matrix games by a careful elimination of certain rows and certain columns. Consider, for example, a simple game characterized by the payoff matrix

Player C

Player R $\begin{bmatrix} -4 & -1 & 3 \\ 3 & 2 & 5 \end{bmatrix}$

Notice that every element of the second row is greater than the corresponding elements of the first row. It would be unwise for player R to choose row 1 as his optimal strategy when row 2 yields more than row 1 regardless of the choice of his opponent. Row 1, with smaller elements, is dominated by row 2, with larger corresponding elements, and is therefore eliminated from further consideration without affecting the optimal strategies of the players or the value of the game. This reduces the problem to the matrix game

$$[3 \quad 2 \quad 5]$$

which is the only strategy left for player R. Clearly, player C's optimal strategy is to choose column 2 if he wants to minimize his losses. The value of the game is 2 units.

Consider another example of a strictly determined, zero-sum, two-person game shown in the following payoff matrix:

Player C

Player R $\begin{bmatrix} 4 & 2 & 7 \\ 5 & 4 & 9 \\ 8 & -2 & 4 \end{bmatrix}$

Clearly, no optimal strategy for player R would assign a positive probability to row 1, because every element in row 2 is greater than the corresponding element in row 1. Thus, one would solve the game whose matrix is

$$\begin{bmatrix} 5 & 4 & 9 \\ 8 & -2 & 11 \end{bmatrix}$$

The value of the game remains the same and the players have the same strategies in both matrix games.

Note that in this new 2×3 matrix, every element of the first column is smaller than the corresponding element of the third column. The first column is dominated by the third column. Because player C wants to minimize his payoff to R, it is only reasonable that he drop the third column, thus obtaining the 2×2 matrix

$$\begin{bmatrix} 5 & 4 \\ 8 & -2 \end{bmatrix}$$

Using the techniques already developed for strictly determined games, the reader can verify that the optimal strategy for player R is to select row 1, whereas the best strategy for player C is to choose column 2. The value of the game is 4 units.

To consider another example, suppose that the matrix game is given by

$$\text{Player } R \begin{array}{c} \text{Player } C \\ \begin{bmatrix} 4 & -5 & 2 \\ -1 & 2 & -3 \\ 7 & -4 & 6 \end{bmatrix} \end{array}$$

There is no saddle point. However, player R would realize that row 3 dominates row 1 and that he needs to solve the reduced 2×3 matrix

$$\begin{bmatrix} -1 & 2 & -3 \\ 7 & -4 & 6 \end{bmatrix}$$

Player C, in his attempt to minimize the payoff, would immediately notice that column 3 is dominated by column 1, because elements in the third column are smaller than the corresponding elements of the first column. Thus, he needs to analyze the matrix

$$\begin{bmatrix} 2 & -3 \\ -4 & 6 \end{bmatrix}$$

Because the game matrix is not strictly determined, players must use mixed strategies. Applying Proposition 13.5.2, we have

$$a = 2, \quad b = -3, \quad c = -4, \quad d = 6$$
$$a + d - b - c = 15$$

Thus,

$$p_2 = \frac{6 - (-4)}{15} = \frac{10}{15} = \frac{2}{3} \qquad p_3 = 1 - p_2 = \frac{1}{3}$$

and

$$q_2 = \frac{6 - (-3)}{15} = \frac{9}{15} = \frac{3}{5} \qquad q_3 = 1 - q_2 = \frac{2}{5}$$

Thus, player R must choose row 1 with probability 0, row 2 with probability $\frac{2}{3}$ and row 3 with probability $\frac{1}{3}$. Similarly, player C selects column 1 with probability 0, column 2 with probability $\frac{3}{5}$ and column 3 with probability $\frac{2}{5}$.

Thus,

$$P = (0, \tfrac{2}{3}, \tfrac{1}{3}) \quad \text{and} \quad Q = \begin{bmatrix} 0 \\ \tfrac{3}{5} \\ \tfrac{2}{5} \end{bmatrix}$$

The value of the game is

$$6 \cdot 2 - (-3)(-4) = 0$$

EXERCISE 13.5

In each of the payoff matrices in Exercises 1 through 6, determine the saddle point and the value of the game by making use of "dominance."

1. $\begin{bmatrix} 6 & 2 & 4 \\ 7 & -3 & 6 \\ 8 & 4 & 7 \end{bmatrix}$

2. $\begin{bmatrix} 6 & 2 & 4 \\ 7 & 3 & 6 \\ 8 & 1 & 7 \end{bmatrix}$

3. $\begin{bmatrix} 2 & 1 & 3 \\ 4 & -1 & 5 \\ 1 & -2 & 2 \end{bmatrix}$

4. $\begin{bmatrix} 1 & 2 & 1 \\ 3 & 2 & 4 \\ -1 & 1 & 0 \end{bmatrix}$

5. $\begin{bmatrix} -1 & 0 & 1 & -2 & 3 \\ 1 & 2 & 3 & 1 & 4 \\ 2 & -1 & 4 & -3 & 5 \end{bmatrix}$

6. $\begin{bmatrix} 6 & 4 & 5 \\ 4 & -1 & 1 \\ 3 & -2 & 2 \end{bmatrix}$

Determine the optimal strategies and the value of the game in Exercises 7 through 12 by making use of "dominance."

7. $\begin{bmatrix} 1 & 2 & 3 & 1 \\ 4 & 1 & 2 & 3 \end{bmatrix}$

8. $\begin{bmatrix} 1 & 7 & 6 & 8 \\ 8 & 1 & -3 & 4 \end{bmatrix}$

9. $\begin{bmatrix} 1 & 4 & 3 \\ 1 & 7 & 6 \\ 8 & 1 & -3 \end{bmatrix}$

10. $\begin{bmatrix} 2 & 9 & 8 \\ 2 & 4 & -1 \\ 8 & 2 & -3 \end{bmatrix}$

11. $\begin{bmatrix} 7 & 8 & 2 \\ 4 & 5 & 1 \\ 5 & 6 & 6 \\ 3 & 4 & 0 \end{bmatrix}$

12. $\begin{bmatrix} -6 & 4 & 5 \\ 4 & -1 & 1 \\ 3 & -2 & 0 \end{bmatrix}$

13.6 OPTIMAL STRATEGIES AND SIMPLEX METHOD

Consider an $m \times n$ nonstrictly determined matrix game that cannot be reduced to an equivalent 2×2 matrix by eliminating dominating rows and dominated columns.

As a first step, we set up a game matrix A,

$$A = \begin{bmatrix} a_{11} & a_{12} & a_{13} & \cdots & a_{1n} \\ a_{21} & a_{22} & a_{23} & \cdots & a_{2n} \\ a_{31} & a_{32} & a_{33} & \cdots & a_{3n} \\ \vdots & & & & \\ a_{m1} & a_{m2} & a_{m3} & \cdots & a_{mn} \end{bmatrix}$$

and assume that all entries of this matrix are positive. If some of the entries are negative, a suitable constant k is added to every entry of the matrix so that all new entries are positive. This procedure increases the value of the game by the constant k but has no effect on the strategies of the players.

Suppose that players R and C have mixed strategies P and Q, where

$$P = (p_1, p_2, \ldots, p_m) \quad \text{and} \quad Q = \begin{bmatrix} q_1 \\ q_2 \\ \vdots \\ q_n \end{bmatrix}$$

and that v is the value of the game. Because player R chooses his optimal strategy so as to maximize v, it follows that the product of the row vector P with any column vector of A must be greater or equal to v. Thus,

$$p_1 a_{11} + p_2 a_{21} + \cdots + p_m a_{m1} \geq v$$
$$p_1 a_{12} + p_2 a_{22} + \cdots + p_m a_{m2} \geq v$$
$$\vdots$$
$$p_1 a_{1n} + p_2 p_{2n} + \cdots + p_m a_{mn} \geq v$$

Because v is positive, dividing each inequality by v, we get

$$\begin{aligned} a_{11} y_1 + a_{21} y_2 + \cdots + a_{m1} y_m &\geq 1 \\ a_{12} y_1 + a_{22} y_2 + \cdots + a_{m2} y_m &\geq 1 \\ \vdots \\ a_{1n} y_1 + a_{2n} y_2 + \cdots + a_{mn} y_m &\geq 1 \end{aligned}$$

(13.1)

where $y_i = p_i/v$ for $i = 1, 2, 3, \ldots, m$. The problem now reduces to minimization of the objective function

$$M = y_1 + y_2 + \cdots + y_m = \frac{1}{v}$$

subject to the linear constraints (13.1) above. Player R needs to determine a minimum value of $1/v$, which implies finding a maximum value of v.

Let us now analyze the situation from player C's point of view. He is interested in choosing an optimal strategy that will minimize his expected payoff to his opponent. This implies that the product of any row vector of the matrix A with the column vector Q must not exceed v. In other words,

$$a_{11}q_1 + a_{12}q_2 + \cdots + a_{1n}q_n \leq v$$
$$a_{12}q_1 + a_{22}q_2 + \cdots + a_{2n}q_n \leq v$$
$$\vdots$$
$$a_{m1}q_1 + a_{m2}q_2 + \cdots + a_{mn}q_n \leq v$$

or

(13.2)
$$a_{11}x_1 + a_{12}x_2 + \cdots + a_{1n}x_n \leq 1$$
$$a_{12}x_1 + a_{22}x_2 + \cdots + a_{2n}x_n \leq 1$$
$$\vdots$$
$$a_{m1}x_1 + a_{m2}x_2 + \cdots + a_{mn}x_n \leq 1$$

where $x_j = q_j/v$ for $j = 1, 2, 3, \ldots, n$.

Thus, the problem of finding an optimal strategy Q for player C reduces to the maximization of the objective function

$$N = x_1 + x_2 + \cdots + x_n = \frac{1}{v}$$

subject to linear constraints (13.2). But this is precisely the type of basic linear programming problem that can be solved by the simplex method we have explained in Chapter 7. It is, perhaps, worthwhile reminding the reader that the problem of minimizing $M = y_1 + y_2 + \cdots + y_n$ subject to (13.1) is directly related to the problem of maximizing $N = x_1 + x_2 + \cdots + x_n$ subject to (13.2) through the concept of a dual problem discussed also in Chapter 7. The maximum of N and minimum of M have the same value. The values of x_i in the last column of the terminal tableau correspond to the solution of the maximum linear programming problem, whereas the values y_j under the slack variable columns in the last row correspond to the solution of the minimum linear programming problem.

Example 13.9

Using the simplex method, determine the optimal strategies of the players R and C in the following 2×2 matrix game:

$$\text{Player } R \begin{array}{c} \text{Player } C \\ \begin{bmatrix} 2 & -2 \\ -4 & -1 \end{bmatrix} \end{array}$$

SOLUTION
Because some of the entries in the above matrix are negative, we must add a suitable constant k to each term so that all new terms are positive. If we let $k = 5$, we obtain the new matrix

$$A = \begin{bmatrix} 7 & 3 \\ 1 & 4 \end{bmatrix}$$

Suppose that player C has an optimal strategy

$$Q = \begin{bmatrix} q_1 \\ q_2 \end{bmatrix}$$

so that

$$\begin{bmatrix} 7 & 3 \\ 1 & 4 \end{bmatrix} \begin{bmatrix} q_1 \\ q_2 \end{bmatrix} \leq \begin{bmatrix} v \\ v \end{bmatrix}$$

It follows that

$$7q_1 + 3q_2 \leq v$$
$$q_1 + 4q_2 \leq v$$

or

$$7x_1 + 3x_2 \leq 1$$
$$x_1 + 4x_2 \leq 1$$

where $x_i = q_i/v$, $i = 1, 2$. The problem now reduces to:

Maximize	$N = x_1 + x_2$
subject to	$7x_1 + 3x_2 \leq 1$
	$x_1 + 4x_2 \leq 1$
	$x_1 \geq 0 \qquad x_2 \geq 0$

The initial simplex tableau is

$$\begin{array}{c} \\ \text{Pivotal row} \rightarrow \\ \\ \\ \end{array} \quad \begin{array}{ccccc} x_1 & x_2 & x_3 & x_4 & N \\ \boxed{7} & 3 & 1 & 0 & 0 & 1 \\ 1 & 4 & 0 & 1 & 0 & 1 \\ -1 & -1 & 0 & 0 & 1 & 0 \end{array}$$

$$\uparrow$$
$$\text{Pivotal}$$
$$\text{column}$$

Selecting the first column as the pivotal column, we have 7 as the pivot element. Dividing the elements in the first row by 7, we obtain

$$\begin{array}{ccccc} x_1 & x_2 & x_3 & x_4 & N \\ 1 & \frac{3}{7} & \frac{1}{7} & 0 & 0 & \frac{1}{7} \\ 1 & 4 & 0 & 1 & 0 & 1 \\ -1 & -1 & 0 & 0 & 1 & 0 \end{array}$$

The row operations

$$R_2{}' = R_2 + (-1)R_1$$
$$R_3{}' = R_3 + R_1$$

transform the above tableau into

$$
\begin{array}{ccccc}
x_1 & x_2 & x_3 & x_4 & N \\
\end{array}
$$

$$
\left[
\begin{array}{ccc|ccc|c}
1 & \frac{3}{7} & \frac{1}{7} & 0 & 0 & \frac{1}{7} \\
0 & \boxed{\frac{25}{7}} & -\frac{1}{7} & 1 & 0 & \frac{6}{7} \\
0 & -\frac{4}{7} & \frac{1}{7} & 0 & 1 & \frac{1}{7}
\end{array}
\right]
$$

Because there is a negative element in the last row, we must select a new pivot. Dividing elements in the second row by this new pivot, we have

$$
\begin{array}{ccccc}
x_1 & x_2 & x_3 & x_4 & N \\
\end{array}
$$

$$
\left[
\begin{array}{ccc|ccc|c}
1 & \frac{3}{7} & \frac{1}{7} & 0 & 0 & \frac{1}{7} \\
0 & 1 & -\frac{1}{25} & \frac{7}{25} & 0 & \frac{6}{25} \\
0 & -\frac{4}{7} & \frac{1}{7} & 0 & 1 & \frac{1}{7}
\end{array}
\right]
$$

Adding suitable multiples of the second row to the remaining rows, we obtain the terminal tableau

$$
\begin{array}{ccccc}
x_1 & x_2 & x_3 & x_4 & N \\
\end{array}
$$

$$
\left[
\begin{array}{cc|ccc|c}
\boxed{1} & 0 & \frac{4}{25} & -\frac{3}{25} & 0 & \boxed{\frac{1}{25}} \\
0 & \boxed{1} & -\frac{1}{25} & \frac{7}{25} & 0 & \boxed{\frac{6}{25}} \\
0 & 0 & \frac{3}{25} & \frac{4}{25} & 1 & \frac{7}{25}
\end{array}
\right]
$$

The maximum value of $N = x_1 + x_2 = 1/v$ is $\frac{7}{25}$. Thus,

$$
v = \frac{25}{7} \qquad x_1 = \frac{1}{25} \qquad x_2 = \frac{6}{25}
$$

Because

$$
x_1 = \frac{q_1}{v} \quad \text{and} \quad x_2 = \frac{q_2}{v}
$$

it follows that

$$
q_1 = x_1 v = \frac{1}{25} \cdot \frac{25}{7} = \frac{1}{7}
$$
$$
q_2 = x_2 v = \frac{6}{25} \cdot \frac{25}{7} = \frac{6}{7}
$$

Thus

$$
Q = \begin{bmatrix} \frac{1}{7} \\ \frac{6}{7} \end{bmatrix}
$$

is an optimal strategy for player C.

Note that the values

$$
y_1 = \frac{3}{25} \quad \text{and} \quad y_2 = \frac{4}{25}
$$

under the slack variable columns in the last row correspond to the solution of the minimum linear programming problem. Because

$$
y_1 = \frac{p_1}{v} \quad \text{and} \quad y_2 = \frac{p_2}{v}
$$

it follows that

$$p_1 = y_1 v = \tfrac{3}{25} \cdot \tfrac{25}{7} = \tfrac{3}{7}$$
$$p_2 = y_2 v = \tfrac{4}{25} \cdot \tfrac{25}{7} = \tfrac{4}{7}$$

or that

$$P = [\tfrac{3}{7} \quad \tfrac{4}{7}]$$

is an optimal strategy for player R. The value of the original matrix is

$$\tfrac{25}{7} - k = \tfrac{25}{7} - 5 = -\tfrac{10}{7} \qquad \blacksquare$$

Example 13.10

Using the simplex method, determine the optimal strategies of the players and the value of the matrix game

$$\begin{bmatrix} 3 & 4 & 5 \\ 4 & 3 & 1 \end{bmatrix}$$

SOLUTION
Suppose that player C has an optimum strategy given by

$$Q = \begin{bmatrix} q_1 \\ q_2 \\ q_3 \end{bmatrix}$$

$$3q_1 + 4q_2 + 5q_3 \leq v$$
$$4q_1 + 3q_2 + q_3 \leq v$$

or

$$3x_1 + 4x_2 + 5x_3 \leq 1$$
$$4x_1 + 3x_2 + x_3 \leq 1$$

where $x_i = q_i/v$, $i = 1, 2, 3$. We want to maximize

$$N = x_1 + x_2 + x_3 = \frac{1}{v}$$

subject to the above linear constraints. The initial simplex tableau including slack variables is

	x_1	x_2	x_3	x_4	x_5	N	
	3	4	5	1	0	0	1
Pivotal row →	④	3	1	0	1	0	1
	−1	−1	−1	0	0	1	0

↑
Pivotal
column

Selecting the first column as the pivotal column, we determine that the element 4 in the second row is the pivot. The operations

$$R_2' = \tfrac{1}{4}R_2$$
$$R_1' = R_1 + (-3)R_2'$$
$$R_3' = R_3 + R_2'$$

transform the above tableau into

$$
\text{Pivotal row} \rightarrow
\begin{array}{c}
x_1 \quad x_2 \quad x_3 \quad\quad x_4 \quad\quad x_5 \quad\ N
\end{array}
$$

	x_1	x_2	x_3	x_4	x_5	N	
Pivotal row →	0	$\frac{7}{4}$	$\boxed{\frac{17}{4}}$	1	$-\frac{3}{4}$	0	$\frac{1}{4}$
	1	$\frac{3}{4}$	$\frac{1}{4}$	0	$\frac{1}{4}$	0	$\frac{1}{4}$
	0	$-\frac{1}{4}$	$-\frac{3}{4}$	0	$\frac{1}{4}$	1	$\frac{1}{4}$

$$\uparrow$$
Pivotal
column

We now select the most negative element in the last row. The elementary row operations

$$R_1'' = \tfrac{7}{4} \cdot R_1'$$
$$R_2'' = R_2' + (-\tfrac{1}{4})R_1''$$
$$R_3'' = R_3' + (\tfrac{3}{4})R_1''$$

yield the following terminal tableau:

	x_1	x_2	x_3	x_4	x_5	N	
	0	$\frac{7}{17}$	$\boxed{1}$	$\frac{4}{17}$	$-\frac{3}{17}$	0	$\boxed{\frac{1}{17}}$
	$\boxed{1}$	$\frac{11}{17}$	0	$-\frac{1}{17}$	$\frac{5}{17}$	0	$\boxed{\frac{4}{17}}$
	0	$\frac{1}{17}$	0	$\frac{3}{17}$	$\frac{2}{17}$	1	$\frac{5}{17}$

Thus,

$$x_1 = \tfrac{4}{17}, \; x_2 = 0, \; x_3 = \tfrac{1}{17} \qquad y_1 = \tfrac{3}{17}, \; y_2 = \tfrac{2}{17}$$

with

$$\frac{1}{v} = \frac{5}{17} \quad \text{or} \quad v = \frac{17}{5}$$

Because

$$x_j = \frac{q_j}{v} \text{ for } j = 1, 2, 3 \quad \text{and} \quad y_i = \frac{p_i}{v} \text{ for } i = 1, 2$$

we obtain

$$q_1 = \frac{4}{5} \qquad q_2 = 0 \qquad q_3 = \frac{1}{5}$$

and

$$p_1 = \frac{3}{5} \qquad p_2 = \frac{2}{5}$$

Thus,

$$P = (\tfrac{3}{5}, \tfrac{2}{5}) \text{ and } Q = \begin{bmatrix} \frac{4}{5} \\ 0 \\ \frac{1}{5} \end{bmatrix}$$

are the optimal strategies of players R and C, respectively. The value of the game is $\frac{17}{5}$. ∎

Example 13.11

Determine the optimal strategies and the value of the following 3×3 matrix game:

$$\begin{bmatrix} 7 & 2 & 3 \\ 2 & 3 & 4 \\ 4 & 6 & 2 \end{bmatrix}$$

SOLUTION

The matrix does not have a saddle point. Further, no row or column dominance is evident. The initial simplex tableau is

	x_1	x_2	x_3	x_4	x_5	x_6	N	
Pivotal row →	⑦	2	3	1	0	0	0	1
	2	3	4	0	1	0	0	1
	4	6	2	0	0	1	0	1
	−1	−1	−1	0	0	0	1	0
	↑							
	Pivotal							
	column							

The elementary row operations performed in the specified order,

$$R_1' = \tfrac{1}{7}R_1$$
$$R_2' = R_2 + (-2)R_1'$$
$$R_3' = R_3 + (-4)R_1'$$
$$R_4' = R_4 + R_1'$$

transform the above tableau into

	x_1	x_2	x_3	x_4	x_5	x_6	N		
	1	$\frac{2}{7}$	$\frac{3}{7}$	$\frac{1}{7}$	0	0	0	$\frac{1}{7}$	$\frac{1}{7} \div \frac{2}{7} = \frac{1}{2}$
	0	$\frac{17}{7}$	$\frac{22}{7}$	$-\frac{2}{7}$	1	0	0	$\frac{5}{7}$	$\frac{5}{7} \div \frac{17}{7} = \frac{5}{17}$
Pivotal row →	0	㉞⁄₇	$\frac{2}{7}$	$-\frac{4}{7}$	0	1	0	$\frac{3}{7}$	$\frac{3}{7} \div \frac{34}{7} = \frac{3}{34}$
	0	$-\frac{5}{7}$	$-\frac{4}{7}$	$\frac{1}{7}$	0	0	1	$\frac{1}{7}$	
		↑							
		Pivotal							
		column							

We now perform the following row operations:

$$R_3'' = \tfrac{7}{34}R_3'$$
$$R_1'' = R_1' + (-\tfrac{2}{7})R_3''$$
$$R_2'' = R_2' + (-\tfrac{17}{7})R_3''$$
$$R_4'' = R_4' + \tfrac{5}{7}R_3''$$

The above tableau is transformed into

	x_1	x_2	x_3	x_4	x_5	x_6	N		
	1	0	$\frac{7}{17}$	$\frac{3}{17}$	0	$-\frac{1}{17}$	0	$\frac{2}{17}$	$\frac{2}{17} \div \frac{7}{17} = \frac{2}{7}$
Pivotal row →	0	0	③	0	1	$-\frac{1}{2}$	0	$\frac{1}{2}$	$\frac{1}{2} \div 3 = \frac{1}{6}$
	0	1	$\frac{1}{17}$	$-\frac{2}{17}$	0	$\frac{7}{34}$	0	$\frac{3}{34}$	$\frac{3}{34} \div \frac{1}{17} = \frac{3}{2}$
	0	0	$-\frac{9}{17}$	$\frac{1}{17}$	0	$\frac{5}{34}$	1	$\frac{7}{34}$	

$$\uparrow$$
$$\text{Pivotal}$$
$$\text{column}$$

Because there still remains a negative element in the last row, we must repeat the process. The new pivotal element is 3. Performing the following operations,

$$R_2''' = \tfrac{1}{3}R_2''$$
$$R_1''' = R_1'' + (-\tfrac{7}{17})R_2'''$$
$$R_3''' = R_3'' + (-\tfrac{1}{17})R_2'''$$
$$R_4''' = R_4'' + \tfrac{9}{17}R_2'''$$

we obtain the terminal tableau:

	x_1	x_2	x_3	x_4	x_5	x_6	N	
	①	0	0	$\frac{3}{17}$	$-\frac{7}{51}$	$\frac{1}{102}$	0	$\frac{5}{102}$
	0	0	①	0	$\frac{1}{3}$	$-\frac{1}{6}$	0	$\frac{1}{6}$
	0	①	0	$-\frac{2}{17}$	$-\frac{1}{51}$	$\frac{11}{51}$	0	$\frac{4}{51}$
	0	0	0	$\frac{1}{17}$	$\frac{3}{17}$	$\frac{1}{17}$	1	$\frac{5}{17}$

Thus,

$$x_1 = \tfrac{5}{102}, \; x_2 = \tfrac{4}{51}, \; x_3 = \tfrac{1}{6}$$
$$y_1 = \tfrac{1}{17}, \; y_2 = \tfrac{3}{17}, \; y_3 = \tfrac{1}{17}$$

with

$$\frac{1}{v} = \frac{5}{17} \quad \text{or} \quad v = \frac{17}{5}$$

Because $x_j = q_j/v, j = 1, 2, 3$, and $y_i = p_i/v, i = 1, 2, 3$, it follows that

$$q_1 = x_1 v = \tfrac{5}{102} \cdot \tfrac{17}{5} = \tfrac{1}{6}$$
$$q_2 = x_2 v = \tfrac{4}{51} \cdot \tfrac{17}{5} = \tfrac{4}{15}$$
$$q_3 = x_3 v = \tfrac{1}{6} \cdot \tfrac{17}{5} = \tfrac{17}{30}$$

and

$$p_1 = y_1v = \tfrac{1}{17} \cdot \tfrac{17}{5} = \tfrac{1}{5}$$
$$p_2 = y_2v = \tfrac{3}{17} \cdot \tfrac{17}{5} = \tfrac{3}{5}$$
$$p_3 = y_3v = \tfrac{1}{17} \cdot \tfrac{17}{5} = \tfrac{1}{5}$$

Thus,

$$P = (\tfrac{1}{5}, \tfrac{3}{5}, \tfrac{1}{5}) \quad \text{and} \quad Q = \begin{bmatrix} \tfrac{1}{6} \\ \tfrac{4}{15} \\ \tfrac{17}{30} \end{bmatrix}$$

are optimal strategies for players R and C, respectively, and the value of the game is $\tfrac{17}{5}$. ∎

EXERCISE 13.6

Using the simplex method, determine the optimal strategies of the players and the value of the game in Exercises 1 through 14.

1. $\begin{bmatrix} 3 & -1 \\ -3 & 0 \end{bmatrix}$

2. $\begin{bmatrix} 4 & -1 \\ -3 & 8 \end{bmatrix}$

3. $\begin{bmatrix} 5 & -2 \\ -2 & 5 \end{bmatrix}$

4. $\begin{bmatrix} 5 & 2 \\ 2 & 5 \end{bmatrix}$

5. $\begin{bmatrix} 4 & 2 & 5 \\ 3 & 4 & 3 \end{bmatrix}$

6. $\begin{bmatrix} -2 & -3 & 2 \\ -3 & 2 & 0 \end{bmatrix}$

7. $\begin{bmatrix} 0 & 1 & 2 \\ 1 & -2 & -1 \end{bmatrix}$

8. $\begin{bmatrix} 4 & 3 & 0 \\ -2 & -1 & 1 \end{bmatrix}$

9. $\begin{bmatrix} 0 & 1 & 9 \\ 5 & 3 & 0 \end{bmatrix}$

10. $\begin{bmatrix} 5 & 2 & 8 \\ 4 & 7 & -1 \end{bmatrix}$

11. $\begin{bmatrix} 6 & 3 & 5 \\ 4 & 7 & 5 \\ 1 & 3 & 6 \end{bmatrix}$

12. $\begin{bmatrix} 4 & 2 & 3 \\ 3 & 6 & 3 \\ 3 & 3 & 6 \end{bmatrix}$

13. $\begin{bmatrix} 1 & 2 & 3 \\ 6 & 1 & 2 \\ 3 & 5 & 1 \end{bmatrix}$

14. $\begin{bmatrix} 2 & 6 & 0 \\ 5 & 3 & 6 \\ 5 & 4 & 3 \end{bmatrix}$

13.7 FINITE MARKOV CHAINS

In several applications of probability theory in Chapter 10, we assumed that the random events or random variables under consideration are independent. However, there are many problems in probability where the assumption of independence does not hold. It was during the investigation of dependent events that A. A. Markov (1856–1922) distinguished a series of experiments in which the outcome of any particular experiment depends only on the results of the immediately preceding experiment and not on any other experiment conducted in the past.

Consider, for example, that Kathy is being wooed by Roger, who tries not to be late for their dates too often. If he is late on one date, the probability is 90 percent that he will be on time for his subsequent date, and if he is on time on one date, the probability is 30 percent that he will be late next time. How often is he late in the long run? Consider as another example a group of n children in an elementary school. One of the students, say A, starts a rumor by telling another student, say B, that there will be no school on Monday. Then B repeats the news to C, who in turn relays it to D, and he passes it on to another student, and so on. However, with probability $p > 0$, a student reverses the sense of the rumor before passing it on to the next student in the school. What is the probability that the nth student in the school will be told that there will be no school next Monday? The theory of Markov chains, which deals in general with questions of this nature, is a powerful tool in business and is widely used to analyze the current status of a product in an effort to predict its future. This useful technique in marketing examines and forecasts the behavior of customers from the standpoint of their loyalty to one department store and their habits of switching to other stores.

Imagine that we have a series of experiments and as a result of each experiment there is one and only one outcome from a finite number of r possible outcomes $a_1, a_2, \ldots, a_r$. Instead of speaking of n trials of an experiment each with r possible outcomes, we observe at time n the state of a random variable that has r possible states. These states are all distinct and can be ordered by an index k, where $k = 1, 2, \ldots, r$. At the start of a certain interval, the system may or may not change from its present state to any one of the remaining $r - 1$ states. We assume that the conditional probability of an event a_j on any given trial k depends only on the outcome of the immediately preceding trial $k - 1$ and is in no way related to the earlier $k - 2$ trials conducted in the past. Next, we denote by p_{ij} the conditional probability that at kth trial the system passes into state a_j, assuming that after $k - 1$ trials it was in state a_i.

Definition 13.7.1: A sequence of experiments constitutes a Markov chain with r states if each experiment has r possible outcomes $a_1, a_2, \ldots, a_r$, and the probability p_{ij} of a particular outcome on any trial depends only on the outcome of the immediately preceding trial.

Definition 13.7.2: The probability p_{ij} is called the transition probability from the state a_i to the state a_j in one trial.

Definition 13.7.3: The matrix with transition probabilities p_{ij} as elements is called the transition matrix T, where

(13.3) $\quad T = \begin{bmatrix} p_{11} & p_{12} & p_{13} & \cdots & p_{1r} \\ p_{21} & p_{22} & p_{23} & \cdots & p_{2r} \\ \vdots & & & & \\ p_{r1} & p_{r2} & p_{r3} & \cdots & p_{rr} \end{bmatrix}$

We observe that p_{11} represents the probability that a system remains in state a_1 after one trial, p_{23} is the probability that a system moves from state a_2 to state a_3 in one step, p_{35} is the probability that a system moves from state a_3 to state a_5 after one trial, and so on. Suppose that the system is in state a_i and as a result of one experiment, the system remains either in state a_i or moves to any other position $a_j, j \neq i$. Because the events $a_1, a_2, \ldots, a_r$ are all mutually exclusive and p_{ij} are the associated probabilities, it follows that

$$(13.4) \quad \sum_{i=1}^{i=r} p_{ij} = 1 \quad \text{for } j = 1, 2, 3, \ldots, r$$

This implies that the sum of the terms in each row of the transition matrix equals 1.

Example 13.12

Jeannie has scheduled a series of dental appointments over a period of six months. She tries not to be late for her appointments too often. If she is late once, the probability is 0.95 that she will be on time for her subsequent appointment. If she is on time, then there is a 70 percent chance of her being late for her next appointment. Again, we have two states, a_1 (late), and a_2 (on time), and

$$p_{11} = 0.05 \qquad p_{12} = 0.95$$
$$p_{21} = 0.70 \qquad p_{22} = 0.30$$

The transition matrix is

$$T = \begin{bmatrix} 0.05 & 0.95 \\ 0.70 & 0.30 \end{bmatrix}$$

■

Example 13.13

A group of three children play a game consisting of throwing a ball to one another. At each stage, the child with the ball is equally likely to throw it to any of the two other children. We have three states in this problem and the associated probabilities are

$$p_{ij} = 0 \qquad i = j \qquad i, j = 1, 2, 3$$
$$p_{ij} = 0.5 \qquad i \neq j \qquad i, j = 1, 2, 3$$

The transition matrix T is given by

$$T = \begin{bmatrix} 0 & 0.5 & 0.5 \\ 0.5 & 0 & 0.5 \\ 0.5 & 0.5 & 0 \end{bmatrix}$$

■

Example 13.14

Consider a problem in which the states are the four grocery stores a_1, a_2, a_3, and a_4 in a small town and the transition probabilities correspond to consumers moving from one grocery store to its competitors. Consumers usually switch from one store to another due to advertisements, promotional sales, price and quality of the products, time spent in waiting for services to be rendered, dissatisfaction with store employees, and the like. We assume that a sample of 500 customers selected at random is representative of the entire group whose switching patterns we have undertaken to investigate. Table 13.1 gives the number of customers in January 1976 who buy regularly from the stores of their choice.

Table 13.1

Stores	Number of Customers in January 1976	Customers		Number of Customers in July 1976
		Lost	Gained	
a_1	100	16	36	120
a_2	120	48	32	104
a_3	160	56	24	128
a_4	120	24	52	148
Total	500	144	144	500

The inflationary trends in the domestic economy during the six-month period forced some customers to switch their purchases to other stores. Clearly, most of the customers remained loyal to their respective stores, although some stores managed to increase the number of customers at the expense of their competitors. A more detailed analysis of the above information is provided in matrix A:

$$A = \begin{array}{c} \\ a_1 \\ a_2 \\ a_3 \\ a_4 \\ \\ \end{array} \begin{array}{cccc} a_1 & a_2 & a_3 & a_4 \\ \left[\begin{array}{cccc} 84 & 8 & 8 & 0 \\ 12 & 72 & 0 & 36 \\ 16 & 24 & 104 & 16 \\ 8 & 0 & 16 & 96 \end{array}\right] & & & \\ 120 & 104 & 128 & 148 \end{array} \begin{array}{c} = 100 \\ = 120 \\ = 160 \\ = 120 \end{array}$$

The rows in matrix A show the retention of customers and the loss of customers to other stores, whereas the columns indicate the customers retained and the customers gained from competitors during the period of six months. Dividing the numbers in each row of the matrix by the respective row total, we have the following transition probability matrix T:

$$T = \begin{array}{c} \\ a_1 \\ a_2 \\ a_3 \\ a_4 \end{array} \begin{array}{cccc} a_1 & a_2 & a_3 & a_4 \\ \left[\begin{array}{cccc} 0.84 & 0.08 & 0.08 & 0 \\ 0.10 & 0.60 & 0 & 0.30 \\ 0.10 & 0.15 & 0.65 & 0.10 \\ 0.07 & 0 & 0.13 & 0.80 \end{array}\right] \end{array}$$

The elements along the main diagonal reflect the percentage of customers retained by the stores, whereas the elements above (or below) the main diagonal provide information concerning the gain (or loss) in the number of customers during the period under study. Thus, the element a_{11} in row 1 shows that the store a_1 retained 84 percent of its customers, a_{12} and a_{13} indicate that store a_1 lost 8 percent of its customers each to stores a_2 and a_3, respectively; the elements a_{21}, a_{31}, and a_{41} in the first column show that store a_1 gained 10 percent each of the customers from stores a_2 and a_3 and 7 percent of the customers who regularly shop at store a_4. Similarly, the elements in the second row show that store a_2 retained 60 percent of its customers, losing 10 percent to store a_1 and 30 percent to store a_4. The elements in the second column account for the fact that store a_2 picked up 8 percent of customers of a_2 and 15 percent of the customers of a_3. ∎

The transition matrix T assists management in analyzing its promotional efforts in terms of what effect it has on the gain or loss of its market share. This matrix can forecast the rate at which a store will gain or lose its share of the market and also indicate the probability of some market equilibrium in the future.

Let us return to Example 13.12 and assume that the matrix T of transition probabilities remains stable. If the probability is 80 percent that Jeannie is on time for her kth appointment, what is the probability that she will also be on time for her subsequent appointment? The transition matrix T is

$$\begin{bmatrix} 0.05 & 0.95 \\ 0.70 & 0.30 \end{bmatrix}$$

The fact that the probability is 80 percent for her to be on time and 20 percent for her to be late at the kth appointment can be represented in the form of a vector

$$\mathbf{p}^{(k)} = (0.8, 0.2)$$

The tree diagram in Figure 13.1 suggests that the probability for the process to be in state a_1 at the $(k + 1)$th step is

(13.5) $\quad p_1^{(k+1)} = p_1^{(k)}p_{11} + p_2^{(k)}p_{21}$

Similarly, the probability for the process to be in state a_2 at the $(k + 1)$th step is

(13.6) $\quad p_2^{(k+1)} = p_1^{(k)}p_{12} + p_2^{(k)}p_{22}$

These equations can be represented in matrix form as follows:

(13.7) $\quad (p_1^{(k+1)}, p_2^{(k+1)}) = (p_1^{(k)}, p_2^{(k)}) \begin{bmatrix} p_{11} & p_{12} \\ p_{21} & p_{22} \end{bmatrix}$

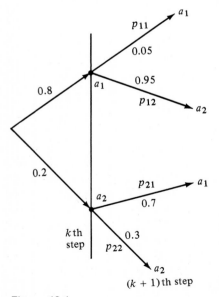

Figure 13.1

Thus,

(13.8) $\mathbf{p}^{(k+1)} = \mathbf{p}^{(k)}T$ where $\mathbf{p}^{(j)} = (p_1^{(j)}, p_2^{(j)})$

The desired probability vector

$$\mathbf{p}^{(k+1)} = (0.8, 0.2)\begin{bmatrix} 0.05 & 0.95 \\ 0.70 & 0.30 \end{bmatrix} = (0.18, 0.82)$$

Thus, the probability is 0.82 that she will be on time for her subsequent appointment.

Definition 13.7.4: Suppose that the system is in state a_i with probability $p_i^{(0)}$, $i = 1, 2, 3, \ldots, r$. Then

$$\mathbf{p}^{(0)} = (p_1^{(0)}, p_2^{(0)}, p_3^{(0)}, \ldots, p_r^{(0)})$$

represents the initial probability vector. The vector $\mathbf{p}^{(n)}$ of the probabilities $p_j^{(n)}$ that the system is in state a_j after n trials is denoted by

$$\mathbf{p}^{(n)} = (p_1^{(n)}, p_2^{(n)}, \ldots, p_r^{(n)})$$

Consider, for example, that the market shares for brands A, B, and C are 35, 40, and 25 percent, respectively, in the month of June. Management would benefit greatly if they could find out what customer choices of brands will be at some future point of time. The probable market shares in the month of July can be computed as before by simply premultiplying the probability transition matrix T by the initial probability vector $\mathbf{p}^{(0)}$. If the transition matrix T is

$$T = \begin{bmatrix} 0.75 & 0.15 & 0.10 \\ 0.10 & 0.70 & 0.20 \\ 0.15 & 0.05 & 0.80 \end{bmatrix}$$

and

$$\mathbf{p}^{(0)} = (0.35, 0.40, 0.25)$$

then

$$\mathbf{p}^{(1)} = \mathbf{p}^{(0)} \cdot T = (0.35 \quad 0.40 \quad 0.25) \cdot \begin{bmatrix} 0.75 & 0.15 & 0.10 \\ 0.10 & 0.70 & 0.20 \\ 0.15 & 0.05 & 0.80 \end{bmatrix}$$

$$= (0.2645 + 0.04 + 0.0375, 0.0525 + 0.28 + 0.0125,$$
$$0.035 + 0.08 + 0.0125)$$

$$= (0.34 \quad 0.345 \quad 0.315)$$

Similarly, the market shares for these brands in August are given by

$$\mathbf{p}^{(2)} = \mathbf{p}^{(1)} \cdot T = (0.34 \quad 0.345 \quad 0.315) \cdot \begin{bmatrix} 0.75 & 0.15 & 0.10 \\ 0.10 & 0.70 & 0.20 \\ 0.15 & 0.05 & 0.80 \end{bmatrix}$$

$$= (0.33675 \quad 0.30825 \quad 0.355)$$

Many marketing research studies have shown that management is interested in the changes that occur in consumer choices from one period to another. Thus, the market shares for brands A, B, and C in September may be computed as

$$\mathbf{p}^{(3)} = \mathbf{p}^{(2)} \cdot T = (\mathbf{p}^{(1)} \cdot T) \cdot T = \mathbf{p}^{(1)} \cdot T^2 = (\mathbf{p}^{(0)}T) \cdot T^2 = \mathbf{p}^{(0)} \cdot T^3$$

However, if the interest lies in the study of the market for a specified period in the future, then we raise the matrix T to the power that represents the number of time units in the period. The probable market shares for the month of December, for example, is given by

$$\mathbf{p}^{(6)} = \mathbf{p}^{(0)} \cdot T^6$$

In general, we have

$$\mathbf{p}^{(n)} = \mathbf{p}^{(0)} \cdot T^n$$

Thus, if the vector $\mathbf{p}^{(0)}$ of initial probabilities is multiplied by the nth power of the transition matrix T, we get the vector $\mathbf{p}^{(n)}$, the components of which gives the probabilities of the market shares for brands A, B, and C after n months.

Example 13.15

In a T maze, a rat is given food if it turns left and an electric shock if it turns right. On the first trial there is an equal chance that a rat will turn either way. If a rat turned left on a given trial, the probability is 0.6 that it will turn left again on the next trial; if it turned right on a given trial, the probability that it will turn right on the next trial is 0.3. What is the probability that a rat will turn left on the

    a. second trial
    b. third trial
    c. fourth trial

SOLUTION

Clearly, the initial probability vector $\mathbf{p}^{(0)} = (0.5, 0.5)$ and the transition probability matrix T is given by

$$\begin{array}{c} \\ L \\ R \end{array} \begin{array}{cc} L & R \\ \begin{bmatrix} 0.6 & 0.4 \\ 0.7 & 0.3 \end{bmatrix} \end{array}$$

a. $\mathbf{p}^{(1)} = \mathbf{p}^{(0)} \cdot T = (0.5 \quad 0.5) \begin{bmatrix} 0.6 & 0.4 \\ 0.7 & 0.3 \end{bmatrix} = (0.65, 0.35)$

The required probability is 0.65 that a rat will turn left on the second trial.

b. $\mathbf{p}^{(2)} = \mathbf{p}^{(1)} \cdot T = (0.65 \quad 0.35) \begin{bmatrix} 0.6 & 0.4 \\ 0.7 & 0.3 \end{bmatrix} = (0.635 \quad 0.365)$

The probability that a rat will turn left on the third trial is 0.635.

c. Similarly,

$$\mathbf{p}^{(3)} = \mathbf{p}^{(2)} \cdot T = (0.635 \quad 0.365) \begin{bmatrix} 0.6 & 0.4 \\ 0.7 & 0.3 \end{bmatrix} = (0.6365 \quad 0.3635)$$

The required probability is 0.6365. ∎

EXERCISE 13.7

Describe the transition probability matrix in Exercises 1 through 6.

1. Elaine, who loves to sleep, often gets up late for her first morning class. If she is late once, she is 80 percent sure to attend her next class. If she is on time one day, then there is a 60 percent chance that she will oversleep for her next class.

2. A communication system transmits the digits 0 and 1. Each digit must pass through several stages before reaching its final destination. However, the probability is 0.75 that a digit entering a certain stage will be unchanged when it leaves.

3. Four points are marked on a circle. A particle has probability of 0.50 of moving to the point on its right, 0.25 of moving to its left, and 0.25 of staying in the same position.

4. Mrs. Hawkes does her grocery shopping on Fridays in one of the stores A, B, C, and D. If she bought from one store, the probability is 0.7 that she goes back to the same store the following week and the probability is 0.1 each that she will visit one of the remaining three stores.

5. Consider a suburb in which there are three grocery stores A, B, and C. Each week, store A retains 80 percent of its customers, losing 10 percent each to other stores. Store B retains 70 percent of its customers and loses 20 percent of them to store A and 10 percent to store C. Store C retains 75 percent of its customers, losing 12 percent to store A and 13 percent to store B.

6. The weather in England can be described as sunny, rainy, or foggy. The record shows that following a sunny day, the probabilities of a sunny, rainy, or foggy day are 0.4, 0.3, and 0.3, respectively. Following a rainy day, the probabilities for a sunny, rainy, or foggy day are 0.2, 0.3, and 0.5, respectively. Following a foggy day, the probabilities of a rainy or sunny day is 0.3 each and of a foggy day is 0.4.

7. Assume that of the sons of skilled workers, 70 percent remain skilled and the rest choose jobs requiring no skill; of the sons of unskilled workers, 60 percent remain unskilled whereas 40 percent prefer skilled jobs. What is the probability that a grandson of a skilled worker is also a skilled worker?

8. A certain blond is being wooed by a certain young man. The young man tries not to be late for their dates too often. If he is late on one date, he is 90 percent sure to be on time on the next date and if he is on time once, then there is a 60 percent chance that he will be late on his subsequent date. If the probability is 0.30 that he is late for the first date, what is the probability that he will be on time for the
   a. second date
   b. third date
   c. fourth date

9. A commuter who works in New York City must take a subway or a bus or drive his own car to work. If he uses the subway one day, the probabilities that he will use a subway or bus or his own car the next day are 0.4, 0.3, and 0.3, respectively. If he uses the bus one day, the corresponding probabilities for using a bus, a subway, or his own car the following day are 0.2, 0.5, and 0.3, respectively, and if he drives his own car to work one day, the corresponding probabilities that he will use his own car, a bus, or a subway the following day are 0.2, 0.3, and 0.5, respectively. What is the probability that the commuter will use the subway on Wednesday if he had gone to work on Monday by subway?

10. The probability is 60 percent that the rain or fog on any arbitrary day is the same as on the previous day. If the probability of fog is 0.40 on the first day of the month, what is the probability of fog on the

    a. second day

    b. third day

    c. fourth day

11. On August 1, 1977, each of three bakeries had one-third of the local market. Over the past year, bakery A retained 88 percent of its customers while losing 6 percent to bakery B and 6 percent to bakery C. Bakery B retained 86 percent of its customers while losing 10 percent to A and 4 percent to C. Bakery C retained 80 percent of its customers while losing 13 percent to A and 7 percent to B. What will be each bakery's share on August 1, 1978?

12. Mrs. Johnson does her weekly grocery shopping in one of the stores A, B, and C. If she bought from one store, the probability is 0.5 that she will go back to the same store the following week and the probability is 0.25 each that she will visit one of the other two stores. Assuming that in the first week the probability is 40 percent that she visits store A, 35 percent that she visits store B, and 25 percent that she visits store C, what is the probability that next week she will do her shopping at store B?

13.8 REGULAR MARKOV CHAINS

Definition 13.8.1: A transition probability matrix T is regular if for some positive integer m, all entries of T^m are positive.

Example 13.16

The transition probability matrix T of the Markov chain

$$T = \begin{bmatrix} 0 & 1 \\ \frac{1}{2} & \frac{1}{2} \end{bmatrix}$$

is regular because a two-step transition probability matrix T^2 is

$$T^2 = \begin{bmatrix} 0 & 1 \\ \frac{1}{2} & \frac{1}{2} \end{bmatrix} \cdot \begin{bmatrix} 0 & 1 \\ \frac{1}{2} & \frac{1}{2} \end{bmatrix} = \begin{bmatrix} \frac{1}{2} & \frac{1}{2} \\ \frac{1}{4} & \frac{3}{4} \end{bmatrix}$$

and all entries of this matrix are positive. ∎

Example 13.17

The transition probability matrix T of the Markov chain

$$T = \begin{bmatrix} 1 & 0 \\ \frac{1}{2} & \frac{1}{2} \end{bmatrix}$$

is not regular, because

$$T^2 = \begin{bmatrix} 1 & 0 \\ \frac{1}{2} & \frac{1}{2} \end{bmatrix} \cdot \begin{bmatrix} 1 & 0 \\ \frac{1}{2} & \frac{1}{2} \end{bmatrix} = \begin{bmatrix} 1 & 0 \\ \frac{3}{4} & \frac{1}{4} \end{bmatrix}, T^3 = \begin{bmatrix} 1 & 0 \\ \frac{7}{8} & \frac{1}{8} \end{bmatrix},$$

$$T^4 = \begin{bmatrix} 1 & 0 \\ \frac{15}{16} & \frac{1}{16} \end{bmatrix}, T^5 = \begin{bmatrix} 1 & 0 \\ \frac{31}{32} & \frac{1}{32} \end{bmatrix}$$

In general,

$$T^m = \begin{bmatrix} 1 & 0 \\ 1 - (\frac{1}{2})^m & (\frac{1}{2})^m \end{bmatrix} \qquad \text{for } m = 1, 2, 3, \ldots$$

and every power of T has the same first row vector and there is no way that we can have a positive element in the a_{12} position. ■

Equilibrium Conditions

Several transition probability matrices can be used to illustrate equilibrium conditions reached over a long period of time. Consider, for example, the matrix

$$T = \begin{bmatrix} 0.80 & 0.10 & 0.10 \\ 0 & 0.80 & 0.20 \\ 0 & 0.40 & 0.60 \end{bmatrix}$$

representing the exchange of passengers during one month in terms of retentions, gains or losses by three airlines A, B, and C. It is reasonable to assume that a state of equilibrium is reached in the long run, because airlines B and C will eventually take away all the passengers of airline A in view of the fact that airline A loses 10 percent of its customers each to airlines B and C while gaining none from its competitors. It is not difficult to predict that unless airline A makes drastic changes in its schedules, improves its services considerably, and launches an extensive advertising program to attract passengers, it will force itself out of business in the not too distant future. Commonly, where no one or two businesses capture the entire market, some conditions of equilibrium eventually develop, and powers of the transition matrix are essentially equal from that point on.

Example 13.18

An executive vice-president of a manufacturing company flies to Boston almost every Friday on a business trip. He has a choice of two airlines, A and B. If he goes on airline A one week, he is 90 percent sure that he will use airline B on his return trip. If he flies on airline B one Friday, there is a 30 percent chance that he will switch to airline A for his return. How often does he use airline A?

SOLUTION

We have two states A and B in this problem, and the associated probabilities are

$$p_{11} = 0.10 \qquad p_{12} = 0.90$$
$$p_{21} = 0.30 \qquad p_{22} = 0.70$$

The transition probability matrix T is given by

$$T = \begin{bmatrix} 0.10 & 0.90 \\ 0.30 & 0.70 \end{bmatrix}$$

Let us now compute some of the powers of the matrix T.

$$T^2 = T \cdot T = \begin{bmatrix} 0.10 & 0.90 \\ 0.30 & 0.70 \end{bmatrix} \begin{bmatrix} 0.10 & 0.90 \\ 0.30 & 0.70 \end{bmatrix} = \begin{bmatrix} 0.28 & 0.72 \\ 0.24 & 0.76 \end{bmatrix}$$

$$T^3 = T^2 \cdot T = \begin{bmatrix} 0.28 & 0.72 \\ 0.24 & 0.76 \end{bmatrix} \begin{bmatrix} 0.10 & 0.90 \\ 0.30 & 0.70 \end{bmatrix} = \begin{bmatrix} 0.244 & 0.756 \\ 0.252 & 0.748 \end{bmatrix}$$

$$T^4 = T^3 \cdot T = \begin{bmatrix} 0.244 & 0.756 \\ 0.252 & 0.748 \end{bmatrix} \begin{bmatrix} 0.10 & 0.90 \\ 0.30 & 0.70 \end{bmatrix} = \begin{bmatrix} 0.2512 & 0.7488 \\ 0.2496 & 0.7504 \end{bmatrix}$$

$$T^5 = T^4 \cdot T = \begin{bmatrix} 0.2512 & 0.7488 \\ 0.2496 & 0.7504 \end{bmatrix} \begin{bmatrix} 0.10 & 0.90 \\ 0.30 & 0.70 \end{bmatrix} = \begin{bmatrix} 0.24976 & 0.75024 \\ 0.25008 & 0.74992 \end{bmatrix}$$

It appears that for large value of m, the matrix T^m approaches the matrix P, where

$$P = \begin{bmatrix} 0.25 & 0.75 \\ 0.25 & 0.75 \end{bmatrix}$$

Thus, a state of equilibrium is reached with a fixed vector $\mathbf{p} = (0.25\ 0.75)$. It is, therefore, reasonable to conclude that this passenger will, in the long-run, use airline A 25 percent of the time. ∎

The method of raising the matrix T to powers of m, $m = 2, 3, 4, \ldots$, involves laborious and exacting calculations, particularly if the transition matrix T is based on Markov chains with more than two states. The following discussion provides an alternative approach to determine whether or not the process attains an equilibrium.

Definition 13.8.2: A vector $\mathbf{p}$ is called the equilibrium probability vector of the transition matrix T if

$$\mathbf{p} \cdot T = \mathbf{p}$$

One can easily verify that $(0.25\ 0.75)$ is the equilibrium vector in the above example, because

$$(0.25 \quad 0.75) \begin{bmatrix} 0.10 & 0.90 \\ 0.30 & 0.70 \end{bmatrix} = (0.25 \quad 0.75)$$

Proposition 13.8.1: Let T be a regular transition probability matrix. Then,

    a. As the positive integer m approaches infinity, matrix T^m approaches a matrix P, each row of which has the some probability vector $\mathbf{p}$, all of whose elements are positive; and

    b. $\mathbf{p} \cdot T = \mathbf{p}$ ■

This proposition has a significant interpretation. If a transition matrix T is regular, then after a large number of trials the Markov chain attains a state of equilibrium in the sense that the probability that the process is in state a_j after n trials is approximately p_j and is independent of the initial conditions given by the initial probability vector $\mathbf{p}^{(0)}$.

Example 13.19

Three airlines operate transatlantic flights from Boston. Based on a recent study by a marketing research firm, the following data was compiled. Airline A retains 80 percent of its customers while losing 10 percent each to airlines B and C. Airline B retains 70 percent of passengers and loses 10 percent to airline A and 20 percent to airline C. Airline C also retains 70 percent of its customers and loses 20 percent to airline A and 10 percent to airline B. What proportion of passengers does each airline retain over a long period of time?

SOLUTION

The transition probability matrix T is

$$\begin{bmatrix} 0.80 & 0.10 & 0.10 \\ 0.10 & 0.70 & 0.20 \\ 0.20 & 0.10 & 0.70 \end{bmatrix}$$

We need to find the fixed probability vector $\mathbf{p} = (x, y, z)$, where $x + y + z = 1$, such that $\mathbf{p} \cdot T = \mathbf{p}$. In other words,

$$(x, y, z) \begin{bmatrix} 0.80 & 0.10 & 0.10 \\ 0.10 & 0.70 & 0.20 \\ 0.20 & 0.10 & 0.70 \end{bmatrix} = (x, y, z)$$

which in turn leads to the following system of linear equations:

$$0.8x + 0.1y + 0.2z = x$$
$$0.1x + 0.7y + 0.1z = y$$
$$0.1x + 0.2y + 0.7z = z$$
$$x + y + z = 1$$

Solving the above equations, we have the unique solution given by

$$x = \tfrac{7}{16} \qquad y = \tfrac{1}{4} \qquad z = \tfrac{5}{16}$$

Thus, 43.75 percent of the passengers stay with airline A, 25 percent stay with airline B, and 31.25 percent of the customers continue their loyalty to airline C over a reasonably long period of time. ■

Definition 13.8.3: A transition probability matrix T is called a stable matrix if

$$\sum_{i=1}^{r} p_{ij} = 1 \qquad \text{for } j = 1, 2, 3, \dots, r$$

and

$$\sum_{j=1}^{r} p_{ij} = 1 \qquad \text{for } i = 1, 2, 3, \dots, r$$

This means that the sum of the entries in any row and any column is equal to 1.

Proposition 13.8.2: Let T be a regular and stable transition probability matrix with k states. Then as the positive integer m approaches infinity, the matrix T^m approaches a matrix P, all of whose elements are equal to $1/k$. In other words,

$$p_{ij} = \frac{1}{k} \qquad \text{for all } i \text{ and } j \qquad\qquad ■$$

Example 13.20

Consider the probability transition matrix T

$$\begin{bmatrix} 0.50 & 0.25 & 0.25 \\ 0.25 & 0.50 & 0.25 \\ 0.25 & 0.25 & 0.50 \end{bmatrix}$$

Clearly, matrix T is stable. We wish to find the equilibrium probability vector $\mathbf{p} = (x, y, z)$, $x + y + z = 1$, such that $\mathbf{p} \cdot T = \mathbf{p}$. This gives the following system of linear equations:

$$0.50x + 0.25y + 0.25z = x$$
$$0.25x + 0.50y + 0.25z = y$$
$$0.25x + 0.25y + 0.50z = z$$

Also,

$$x + y + z = 1$$

These equations provide the unique solution

$$x = y = z = \tfrac{1}{3} \qquad\qquad ■$$

EXERCISE 13.8

1. Determine whether each of the following matrices is regular.

a. $\begin{bmatrix} 0 & 1 \\ 1 & 0 \end{bmatrix}$

b. $\begin{bmatrix} 0 & 1 \\ \frac{1}{3} & \frac{2}{3} \end{bmatrix}$

c. $\begin{bmatrix} 1 & 0 \\ \frac{1}{3} & \frac{2}{3} \end{bmatrix}$

d. $\begin{bmatrix} 1 & 0 \\ 0 & 1 \end{bmatrix}$

e. $\begin{bmatrix} 1 & 0 & 0 \\ 0 & 1 & 0 \\ \frac{1}{4} & \frac{1}{2} & \frac{1}{2} \end{bmatrix}$

f. $\begin{bmatrix} \frac{1}{2} & \frac{1}{2} & 0 \\ 0 & \frac{1}{2} & \frac{1}{2} \\ \frac{1}{2} & \frac{1}{2} & 0 \end{bmatrix}$

g. $\begin{bmatrix} \frac{1}{2} & \frac{1}{2} & 0 \\ \frac{1}{2} & \frac{1}{2} & 0 \\ 0 & \frac{1}{2} & \frac{1}{2} \end{bmatrix}$

h. $\begin{bmatrix} \frac{1}{2} & \frac{1}{4} & \frac{1}{4} \\ \frac{1}{4} & \frac{1}{2} & \frac{1}{4} \\ 0 & 0 & 1 \end{bmatrix}$

i. $\begin{bmatrix} \frac{1}{4} & \frac{1}{4} & \frac{1}{2} \\ 0 & \frac{2}{3} & \frac{1}{3} \\ \frac{3}{4} & \frac{1}{4} & 0 \end{bmatrix}$

j. $\begin{bmatrix} 0 & 1 & 0 \\ 0 & 0 & 1 \\ \frac{1}{4} & \frac{1}{2} & \frac{1}{2} \end{bmatrix}$

k. $\begin{bmatrix} 0 & 0 & 1 \\ \frac{1}{2} & 0 & \frac{1}{2} \\ \frac{1}{2} & \frac{1}{2} & 0 \end{bmatrix}$

l. $\begin{bmatrix} 0 & \frac{1}{3} & \frac{2}{3} \\ \frac{2}{3} & 0 & \frac{1}{3} \\ \frac{1}{3} & \frac{2}{3} & 0 \end{bmatrix}$

m. $\begin{bmatrix} 1 & 0 & 0 \\ \frac{1}{4} & \frac{3}{8} & \frac{3}{8} \\ \frac{5}{8} & \frac{3}{16} & \frac{3}{16} \end{bmatrix}$

n. $\begin{bmatrix} 1 & 0 & 0 \\ 0 & \frac{1}{2} & \frac{1}{2} \\ \frac{1}{2} & \frac{1}{4} & \frac{1}{4} \end{bmatrix}$

2. Compute the first five powers of the transition probability matrix

$$T = \begin{bmatrix} 0.20 & 0.80 \\ 0.40 & 0.60 \end{bmatrix}$$

Can you guess the equilibrium vector **p** from T^5?

3. Compute the first six powers of the transition probability matrix

$$T = \begin{bmatrix} 0.75 & 0.25 \\ 0.50 & 0.50 \end{bmatrix}$$

What is the equilibrium probability vector?

4. Find the equilibrium probability vector for each of the following regular matrices.

a. $\begin{bmatrix} 0 & 1 \\ \frac{1}{3} & \frac{2}{3} \end{bmatrix}$

b. $\begin{bmatrix} 0.70 & 0.30 \\ 0.20 & 0.80 \end{bmatrix}$

c. $\begin{bmatrix} 0.70 & 0.30 \\ 0.30 & 0.70 \end{bmatrix}$

d. $\begin{bmatrix} 0.20 & 0.80 \\ 0.40 & 0.60 \end{bmatrix}$

e. $\begin{bmatrix} 0.20 & 0.80 \\ 0.80 & 0.20 \end{bmatrix}$

f. $\begin{bmatrix} \frac{2}{3} & \frac{1}{3} \\ \frac{1}{3} & \frac{2}{3} \end{bmatrix}$

5. For each of the following regular matrices, compute the equilibrium probability vector.

a. $\begin{bmatrix} 0.4 & 0.3 & 0.3 \\ 0.2 & 0.5 & 0.3 \\ 0.2 & 0.3 & 0.5 \end{bmatrix}$

b. $\begin{bmatrix} 0.5 & 0.2 & 0.3 \\ 0.5 & 0.3 & 0.2 \\ 0.4 & 0.3 & 0.3 \end{bmatrix}$

c. $\begin{bmatrix} 0.75 & 0.15 & 0.10 \\ 0.10 & 0.70 & 0.20 \\ 0.15 & 0.05 & 0.80 \end{bmatrix}$

d. $\begin{bmatrix} 0.4 & 0.3 & 0.3 \\ 0.3 & 0.4 & 0.3 \\ 0.3 & 0.3 & 0.4 \end{bmatrix}$

e. $\begin{bmatrix} 0.5 & 0.2 & 0.3 \\ 0.2 & 0.5 & 0.3 \\ 0.3 & 0.3 & 0.4 \end{bmatrix}$

f. $\begin{bmatrix} 0.5 & 0.3 & 0.2 \\ 0.2 & 0.5 & 0.3 \\ 0.3 & 0.2 & 0.5 \end{bmatrix}$

6. Five points are marked on a circle. A particle has a probability of 0.50 of moving to the point on its right, 0.25 of moving to the left, and 0.25 of staying in the same position.

a. Set up the transition probability matrix.

b. Is the transition matrix stable? If so, what is the equilibrium probability vector?

7. Assuming that the transition matrix for an inheritance trait for a genetics problem is given by

$$
\begin{array}{c}
\qquad\qquad\text{Offspring} \\
\begin{array}{cc}
 & \begin{array}{ccc} R & \quad H & \quad D \end{array} \\
\text{Parent} \quad \begin{array}{c} R \\ H \\ D \end{array} & \left[\begin{array}{ccc} 0.25 & 0.75 & 0 \\ 0.25 & 0.50 & 0.25 \\ 0 & 0.75 & 0.25 \end{array} \right]
\end{array}
\end{array}
$$

Find the equilibrium probability vector and interpret your results.

8. Consider a group of n students in Chico State College. One of the students, say A, starts a rumor by telling another student, B, that the President of their college was involved in the Watergate scandal. Then B repeats the news to C, who in turn passes it on to D, who relays it to another student, and so on. However, with probability $a > 0$, a student changes the news from "was involved" to "was not involved" before passing it on to the next student and the probability is $b > 0$ that a student will change the sense of the rumor from "was not involved" to "was involved." What is the probability that the nth student in the college will be told that their President was involved in the Watergate scandal?

14
Exponential and Logarithmic Functions

14.1 INTRODUCTION

Although the linear functions are important in setting up mathematical models in real-life situations, exponential functions and the closely related logarithmic functions have widespread applications related to learning theory, charges on an electrical condensor, money invested at compound interest, grams of decaying radioactive substances, and the like. These special functions are particularly useful in describing various processes of growth and decay in biology, the social sciences, marketing, and management fields. Of all these various applications, we shall study in this chapter how exponential functions provide important models for the description of growth of an industry with time, or increase in crimes in large cities, or the sharp drop in construction of new houses in the presence of rising material and labor costs. We shall review some elementary algebra in the first section and then investigate exponential and logarithmic functions in this chapter.

14.2 INTEGRAL AND RATIONAL EXPONENTS

The reader is probably familiar with symbols of the form x^m, where x is any real number and m is a non-negative integer.

Definition 14.2.1: If x is any real number and m is a positive integer, then

$$x^m = \underbrace{x \cdot x \cdot \cdots \cdot x}_{m \text{ factors}}$$

In the symbol x^m, the m is called an exponent, and the x is called the base. The use of exponents is governed by several rules, which we shall derive and also illustrate.

Proposition 14.2.1: For any real number x and any positive integers m and n,

$$x^m x^n = x^{m+n}$$

PROOF

To prove this proposition, we need to observe that

$$x^m \cdot x^n = \underbrace{(x \cdot x \cdot x \cdots \cdot x)}_{m \text{ factors}} \underbrace{(x \cdot x \cdots \cdot x)}_{n \text{ factors}}$$

$$= \underbrace{(x \cdot x \cdots \cdot x)}_{(m+n) \text{ factors}}$$

$$= x^{m+n} \qquad \blacksquare$$

This proposition suggests that to multiply two powers of the same base, we add the exponents.

Example 14.1

   a. $3^4 \cdot 3^2 = 3^{4+2} = 3^6 = 729$.

   b. $b^3 \cdot b^5 = b^{3+5} = b^8$.

   c. $a^{3r} \cdot a^{2t} = a^{3r+2t}$, where r and t are positive integers. $\qquad \blacksquare$

Proposition 14.2.2: For any real number $x \neq 0$ and any positive integers m and n,

$$\frac{x^m}{x^n} = \begin{cases} x^{m-n} & \text{if } m > n \\[2mm] \dfrac{1}{x^{n-m}} & \text{if } m < n \\[2mm] 1 & \text{if } m = n \end{cases}$$

PROOF

For $m > n$, we have

$$\frac{x^m}{x^n} = \frac{x \cdot x \cdot x \cdots \cdot x_{(m \text{ factors})}}{x \cdot x \cdot x \cdots \cdot x_{(n \text{ factors})}}$$

$$= \frac{(x \cdot x \cdots \cdot x_{(n \text{ factors})})(x \cdot x \cdots \cdot x_{(m-n \text{ factors})})}{x \cdot x \cdot x \cdots \cdot x_{(n \text{ factors})}}$$

$$= (x \cdot x \cdots \cdot x_{(m-n \text{ factors})})$$

$$= x^{m-n}$$

If $m < n$, then

$$\frac{x^m}{x^n} = \frac{x \cdot x \cdots \cdot x_{(m \text{ factors})}}{x \cdot x \cdots \cdot x_{(n \text{ factors})}}$$

$$= \frac{x \cdot x \cdots \cdot x_{(m \text{ factors})}}{(x \cdot x \cdots \cdot x_{(m \text{ factors})})(x \cdot x \cdots \cdot x_{(n-m \text{ factors})})}$$

$$= \frac{1}{x \cdot x \cdots \cdot x_{(n-m \text{ factors})}}$$

$$= \frac{1}{x^{n-m}}$$

If $m = n$, then

$$\frac{x^m}{x^m} = \frac{x \cdot x \cdots\cdots x_{(m \text{ factors})}}{x \cdot x \cdots\cdots x_{(m \text{ factors})}}$$

Cancelling each x in the numerator with the corresponding x in the denominator, we have

$$\frac{\cancel{x} \cdot \cancel{x} \cdots\cdots \cancel{x}_{(m \text{ factors})}}{\cancel{x} \cdot \cancel{x} \cdots\cdots \cancel{x}_{(m \text{ factors})}} = 1$$

Example 14.2

a. $\dfrac{2^7}{2^4} = 2^{7-4} = 2^3$

b. $\dfrac{a^8}{a^6} = a^{8-6} = a^2 \quad (a \neq 0)$

c. $\dfrac{b^4 \cdot b^7}{b^9} = \dfrac{b^{4+7}}{b^9} = \dfrac{b^{11}}{b^9} = b^{11-9} = b^2 \quad (b \neq 0)$

d. $\dfrac{c^3}{c^3} = 1 \quad (c \neq 0)$

Example 14.3

a. $\dfrac{3^5}{3^7} = \dfrac{1}{3^{7-5}} = \dfrac{1}{3^2} = \dfrac{1}{9}$

b. $\dfrac{a^{12}}{a^{18}} = \dfrac{1}{a^{18-12}} = \dfrac{1}{a^6} \quad (a \neq 0)$

c. $\dfrac{b^2 \cdot b^3}{b^8} = \dfrac{b^{2+3}}{b^8} = \dfrac{b^5}{b^8} = \dfrac{1}{b^{8-5}} = \dfrac{1}{b^3} \quad (b \neq 0)$

Proposition 14.2.3: If m and n are positive integers, then for any real number x,

$$(x^m)^n = x^{mn}$$

PROOF
To prove this assertion, note that

$$(x^m)^n = \underbrace{x^m \cdot x^m \cdots\cdots x^m}_{n \text{ factors}}$$

$$= x^{m+m+\cdots+m \ (n \text{ addends})}$$

$$= x^{mn}$$

Example 14.4

a. $(a^2)^5 = a^{2 \cdot 5} = a^{10}$

b. $(3^4)^2 = 3^{4 \cdot 2} = 3^8 = 6561$

Proposition 14.2.4: If x and y are real numbers, then for any positive integer m,

$$(xy)^m = x^m \cdot y^m$$

PROOF

$$(xy)^m = (xy)(xy)(xy) \cdots (xy)_{(m \text{ factors})}$$
$$= (x \cdot x \cdots \cdots x_{(m \text{ factors})})(y \quad y \cdots \cdots y_{(m \text{ factors})})$$
$$= x^m \cdot y^m \qquad \blacksquare$$

Example 14.5

a. $(ab)^6 = a^6 \cdot b^6$
b. $(a^2 b^4)^5 = (a^{2 \cdot 5})(b^{4 \cdot 5}) = a^{10} \cdot b^{20}$ $\qquad \blacksquare$

Proposition 14.2.5: Let x and y be any real numbers with $y \neq 0$. Then for any positive integer m,

$$\left(\frac{x}{y}\right)^m = \frac{x^m}{y^m}$$

We leave the proof as an exercise for the reader. $\qquad \blacksquare$

Example 14.6

a. $\left(\dfrac{2}{3}\right)^8 = \dfrac{2^8}{3^8}$

b. $\left(\dfrac{a^2 b}{c}\right)^5 = \dfrac{a^{10} \cdot b^5}{c^5} \qquad (c \neq 0)$ $\qquad \blacksquare$

Thus far, we have discussed only positive integers as exponents. We now extend the concept of an exponent to the set of all integers so that expressions of the form x^0 and x^{-3} carry useful meanings. The underlying principle in the formulation of definitions for these new types of exponents is that they must conform to the various laws of exponents we have established above.

First, we consider the meaning of x^0, where x is any real number different from zero. If Proposition 14.2.1 is to hold for $n = 0$, then we must have

$$x^m \cdot x^0 = x^{m+0}$$

but because

$$m + 0 = m$$

it follows that

$$x^{m+0} = x^m$$

Hence,

$$x^m \cdot x^0 = x^m$$

and we must have $x^0 = 1$.

We now discuss the meaning of x^{-m}, where $x \neq 0$ and m is a positive integer. Assuming Proposition 14.2.1 for $n = -m$ and $x \neq 0$, we have

$$x^m \cdot x^{-m} = x^{m+(-m)}$$

But

$$m + (-m) = (-m) + m = 0$$

for all integers, because

$$x^{m+(-m)} = x^{(-m)+m} = x^0 = 1$$

We conclude that $x^m \cdot x^{-m} = 1$ and thus

$$x^{-m} = \frac{1}{x^m} \qquad \text{if } x \neq 0$$

Example 14.7

a. $5^0 = 1$
b. $8 \cdot x^0 = 8 \qquad (x \neq 0)$
c. $2(xy)^0 z = 2z \qquad (xy \neq 0)$

Example 14.8

a. $5^{-2} = \dfrac{1}{5^2} = \dfrac{1}{25}$

b. $x^{-3} = \dfrac{1}{x^3} \qquad (x \neq 0)$

c. $x^2 y^{-3} = \dfrac{x^2}{y^3} \qquad (y \neq 0)$

Next, we consider expressions of the form $(16)^{1/2}$, $(81)^{3/4}$, or $x^{2/3}$, where the exponents are of the type m/n, where m and n are integers and $n \neq 0$. First, we shall assign meanings to expressions of the form $x^{1/n}$ so as to be consistent with the laws of exponents we have established. For example,

$$(16)^{1/2} \cdot (16)^{1/2} = [(16)^{1/2}]^2 = (16)^1 = 16$$

and

$$x^{1/3} \cdot x^{1/3} \cdot x^{1/3} = (x^{1/3})^3 = x^{1/3 \cdot 3} = x$$

Thus, if some number exists whose third power is x, we denote that number by $x^{1/3}$ or $\sqrt[3]{x}$ and call it a cube root of x. In general, if n is a positive integer, then

$$\underbrace{x^{1/n} \cdot x^{1/n} \cdot x^{1/n} \cdots \cdots x^{1/n}}_{n \text{ factors}} = (x^{1/n})^n = x^{(1/n) \cdot n} = x$$

where $x^{1/n}$ is called an nth root of x. Further, if x is positive, then there is exactly one positive number y such that

$$y^n = x$$

This positive number y, which is denoted by $x^{1/n}$, is called the principal nth root of x. Thus, 3 is the principal square root of 9; 2 is the principal cube root of 8, and so on. If x is negative, then there does not exist any positive nth root of x, but there is one negative nth root of x if n is odd. This negative number is the principal nth root of x. Thus, (-2) is the principal cube root of (-8); (-5) is the principal cube root of (-125), and so on.

Example 14.9

a. $(64)^{1/3} = (4 \cdot 4 \cdot 4)^{1/3} = (4^3)^{1/3} = 4^{3 \cdot (1/3)} = 4$
b. $(-32)^{1/5} = [(-2)^5]^{1/5} = (-2)^{5 \cdot (1/5)} = -2$
c. $(729)^{1/6} = (3^6)^{1/6} = 3^{6 \cdot (1/6)} = 3$
d. $(625)^{1/4} = (5^4)^{1/4} = 5^{4 \cdot (1/4)} = 5$

What about $\sqrt{-36}$? Certainly, there is no real number whose square is -36. Thus, $\sqrt{-36}$ is not a real number. In general, if x is a negative number and n is an even integer, then $x^{1/n}$ is not a real number. But for any real number x and n an odd integer, $x^{1/n}$ represents exactly one real number.

Example 14.10

a. $\sqrt{25} = (5^2)^{1/2} = 5^{2 \cdot (1/2)} = 5$

b. $\left(\dfrac{1}{343}\right)^{1/3} = \left[\left(\dfrac{1}{7}\right)^3\right]^{1/3} = \left(\dfrac{1}{7}\right)^{3 \cdot (1/3)} = \dfrac{1}{7}$

c. $\sqrt[3]{-125} = [(-5)^3]^{1/3} = -5$

d. $\sqrt{-25}$ is not a real number. ∎

Now that we know what $x^{1/n}$ means, we must extend the concept of an exponent so that it has a meaning for expressions of the form $x^{m/n}$, where x is a real number and m and n are integers with $n \neq 0$. Notice that we can write $x^{3/4} = (x^{1/4})^3$, because $\frac{3}{4} = \frac{1}{4} \cdot 3$ and call $x^{3/4}$ the third power of $x^{1/4}$. In general,

$$x^{m/n} = \underbrace{x^{1/n} \cdot x^{1/n} \cdot \cdots \cdot x^{1/n}}_{m \text{ factors}} = (x^{1/n})^m$$

or equivalently

$$x^{m/n} = (x^m)^{1/n}$$

Thus,

$$(32)^{4/5} = [(32)^{1/5}]^4 = [(2^5)^{1/5}]^4 = [2^{5 \cdot (1/5)}]^4 = 2^4 = 16$$

Alternatively, we could also evaluate $(32)^{4/5}$ as follows:

$$(32)^{4/5} = [(32)^4]^{1/5} = (1{,}048{,}576)^{1/5} = [(16)^5]^{1/5} = 16$$

Clearly, the second method is time-consuming and laborious.

Example 14.11

a. $(-125)^{2/3} = [(-5)^3]^{2/3} = (-5)^{3 \cdot (2/3)} = (-5)^2 = 25$
b. $(64)^{5/6} = (2^6)^{5/6} = 2^{6 \cdot (5/6)} = 2^5 = 32$
c. $(81)^{5/4} = (3^4)^{5/4} = 3^{4 \cdot (5/4)} = 3^5 = 243$

■

Notice that because

$$x^{-m} = \frac{1}{x^m} \qquad (x \neq 0)$$

we can express

$$x^{-m/n} = x^{1/(m/n)} \qquad (x \neq 0)$$

where m and n are integers and $n \neq 0$. Thus,

$$(16)^{-5/4} = \frac{1}{(16)^{5/4}} = \frac{1}{(2^4)^{5/4}} = \frac{1}{2^{[4 \cdot (5/4)]}} = \frac{1}{2^5} = \frac{1}{32}$$

$$(216)^{-2/3} = \frac{1}{(216)^{2/3}} = \frac{1}{(6^3)^{2/3}} = \frac{1}{6^{[3 \cdot (2/3)]}} = \frac{1}{6^2} = \frac{1}{36}$$

$$(-128)^{-3/7} = \frac{1}{(-128)^{3/7}} = \frac{1}{[(-2)^7]^{3/7}} = \frac{1}{(-2)^{[7 \cdot (3/7)]}} = \frac{1}{(-2)^3} = -\frac{1}{8}$$

EXERCISE 14.1

1. Evaluate the following.

  a. $2^3 \cdot 2^2$ **b.** $3^2 \cdot 3$
  c. $(2^2)^4$ **d.** $(3^3)^2$
  e. $(2^3 \cdot 3^2)^4$ **f.** $(5^2 \cdot 3^3)^3$
  g. $\left(\frac{2}{3}\right)^3 \left(\frac{3}{4}\right)^4$ **h.** $\left(\frac{4}{5}\right)^2 \left(\frac{5}{4}\right)^3$

2. Evaluate each of the following.

  a. $\dfrac{2^5}{2^2}$ **b.** $\dfrac{4^3}{2^4}$

  c. $\dfrac{3^8 \cdot 3^4}{3^9}$ **d.** $\dfrac{(3^4)^2 \cdot 2^4}{(2^3)^2(3^2)^3}$

  e. $\left(\frac{2}{3}\right)^4 \left(\frac{3}{2}\right)^2$ **f.** $\dfrac{3^5 \cdot 3^{11}}{(3^2)^4}$

3. Simplify each of the following expressions.

  a. $(a^2 b)^4$ **b.** $(a^2 b^3 c^4)^3$

  c. $\dfrac{(ab^2)^4}{a^2 b^3}$ **d.** $\dfrac{(abc^2)^3}{(a^3 b^2 c^6)^2}$

e. $\dfrac{(c^2 d^3)^4 a^{-2}}{a^4 (c^3 d^2)^3}$

f. $\left(\dfrac{a}{b}\right)^4 \left(\dfrac{b^2}{c^3}\right)^2 \left(\dfrac{c^4}{a}\right)^3$

g. $\left(\dfrac{2a}{b}\right)^3 \left(\dfrac{b}{3a}\right)^4$

h. $\dfrac{(3a)^2 (2b)^3}{(a^2)^4 (b^3)^3}$

4. Evaluate each of the following expressions.

a. $\dfrac{3^{-2} 4^{-3}}{3^4 2^{-4}}$

b. $\dfrac{4^{-3} \cdot 5^{-2}}{4^{-7} 2^3}$

c. $\dfrac{2^{-3} 4^{-2}}{5^{-2} 4^{-5}}$

d. $\dfrac{3^4 \cdot 4^{-3}}{2^{-5} \cdot 3^5}$

5. Find the value of each of the following numbers.
a. $(8)^{1/3}$

b. $(16)^{1/2}$

c. $(-243)^{1/5}$

d. $(125)^{2/3}$

e. $(729)^{2/3}$

f. $\left(\frac{16}{81}\right)^{1/4}$

g. $\left(\frac{32}{243}\right)^{2/5}$

h. $\left(\frac{64}{343}\right)^{1/3}$

6. Find the value of each of the following numbers.

a. $\dfrac{(-343)^{1/3}(243)^{2/5}}{(64)^{1/6}(-32)^{1/5}}$

b. $\left(\dfrac{27}{8}\right)^{1/3} \dfrac{(64)^{1/6}}{(243)^{2/5}}$

c. $\dfrac{(625)^{-3/4}(16)^{-5/4}}{(216)^{2/3}(-128)^{2/7}}$

d. $\dfrac{(81)^{5/4}(-125)^{1/3}}{(512)^{2/9}(729)^{5/6}}$

14.3 EXPONENTIAL FUNCTIONS

In the preceding section, we have discussed expressions of the type x^p, where the base x is a variable and the exponent p is any integer or rational number. We consider it worth our while to remark that irrational numbers also satisfy the exponent rules, but a rigorous proof of this statement and the propositions we have stated earlier is beyond our present scope.

Now, we turn our attention to situations where the base is constant and the exponent is an independent variable. Consider, for example, an equation of the form $y = b^x$, where b is any positive number but not equal to 1, and the variable x appears as an exponent. This equation is referred to as an exponential function because after the base b is selected, the value of y depends only on x.

Definition 14.3.1: A function $f(x) = b^x$, where $b > 0$ and $b \neq 1$ and the exponent x is any real number, is called an exponential function.

We wish to emphasize that the base b must be a positive real number, for if it were negative, b^x would not be a real number for $x = \frac{1}{2}, \frac{1}{4}$, or any other fraction with an even denominator. If $b = 1$, the function b^x equals 1 for all values of x. The domain of

$f(x) = b^x$ is the set of all real numbers, and the range is the set of all positive real numbers if $b \neq 1$ and $b > 0$.

The following examples illustrate several properties of exponential functions.

Example 14.12

Plot the graph of the function

$$f(x) = 2^x$$

SOLUTION

The following table below shows the value of $f(x)$ corresponding to some values of x.

x	-4	-3	-2	-1	0	1	2	3	4
$f(x)$	$\frac{1}{16}$	$\frac{1}{8}$	$\frac{1}{4}$	$\frac{1}{2}$	1	2	4	8	16

Plotting the ordered pairs $(x, f(x))$ in the table, and connecting these points in the plane, we have the graph of $f(x) = 2^x$ in Figure 14.1.

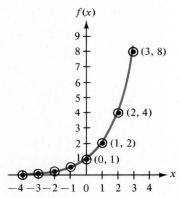

Figure 14.1

Example 14.13

Plot the graph of the function

$$f(x) = 3^x$$

SOLUTION

Plotting the ordered pairs $(x, f(x))$ as given in the following table and connecting them with a smooth curve, we have the graph of the function in Figure 14.2.

x	-2	-1	0	1	2
$f(x)$	$\frac{1}{9}$	$\frac{1}{3}$	1	3	9

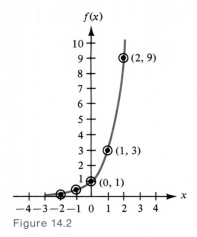

Figure 14.2

Of all the exponential functions an important one is the function $f(x) = e^x$, where e is an irrational number approximately equal to 2.7182. Because of its importance and frequent use, Table 2 for e^x and e^{-x} is given at the end of the book.

Example 14.14

Assuming that $e = 2.7182$, plot the graph of $f(x) = e^x$.

SOLUTION

The following table below shows the value of $f(x)$ corresponding to some values of x.

x	-4	-3	-2	-1	0	1	1.5	2	2.5	3
$f(x)$	0.02	0.05	0.14	0.37	1.00	2.71	4.48	7.39	12.18	20.01

Plotting the ordered pairs $(x, f(x))$, we have the graph of $f(x)$ in Figure 14.3.

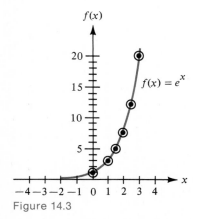

Figure 14.3

The above examples suggest the following observations concerning the graph of b^x when $b > 1$.

1. $b^0 = 1$, so the graph of b^x passes through the point $(0,1)$.
2. $b^x > 0$ for all values of x; hence, the graph lies above the x axis.
3. As x increases, the value of b^x increases.
4. As x decreases along the negative x axis, the value of b^x decreases and approaches the x axis very closely for points sufficiently far to the left.
5. $f(x) = b^x$ represents a one-to-one function.

Next, we examine the graph of b^x for $0 < b < 1$, which has a different appearance. The following example provides an illustration.

Example 14.15
Plot the graph of

$$g(x) = (\tfrac{1}{2})^x$$

SOLUTION
The following table below shows the value of $g(x)$ corresponding to some values of x.

x	-4	-3	-2	-1	0	1	2	3	4
$g(x)$	16	8	4	2	1	$\frac{1}{2}$	$\frac{1}{4}$	$\frac{1}{8}$	$\frac{1}{16}$

Plotting the ordered pairs $(x, g(x))$ in the table, we have the graph of $g(x) = (\tfrac{1}{2})^x$ in Figure 14.4.

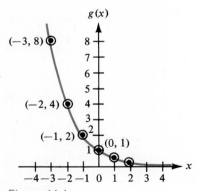

Figure 14.4

The following properties of exponential functions hold within the framework we have so far established.

Properties of the Exponential Functions $f(x) = b^x$, $b > 0$, $b = 1$

1. $b^x = 1$ for $x = 0$.
2. $b^x > 0$ for all values of x.
3. As x increases, the value of b^x increases for $b > 1$ and decreases for $0 < b < 1$.
4. $b^{-x} = (1/b)^x$.

Exponential Equations

An equation that uses a variable as an exponent is referred to as an exponential equation. These equations are solved by using the following fundamental property:

If $b^x = b^y$, then $x = y$.

The following examples illustrate a simple method of solving exponential equations.

Example 14.16

Solve $2^x = 32$ for x.

SOLUTION

In order that both sides of the equation have the same base, we express 32 as a power of base 2. Thus, we have

$$2^x = 2^5$$

from which it follows that $x = 5$. ∎

Example 14.17

Solve $9^x = 243$ for x.

SOLUTION

We must first rewrite both sides of the equation so they have the same base. Because $9 = 3^2$ and $243 = 3^5$, we have

$$(3^2)^x = 3^5$$
$$3^{2x} = 3^5$$

which implies that $2x = 5$ and $x = \frac{5}{2}$. ∎

EXERCISE 14.2

Plot the graph of each of the following functions.

1. $f(x) = 2^{x+1}$
2. $f(x) = 3^{x+1}$
3. $f(x) = 2^{x-1}$
4. $f(x) = 3^{x-2}$
5. $f(x) = 4^x$
6. $f(x) = 4^{-x}$
7. $f(x) = 2^x + 1$
8. $f(x) = 2^x - 1$
9. $f(x) = 2(3^x)$
10. $f(x) = 3(2^x)$
11. $f(x) = 3(\frac{1}{2})^x$
12. $f(x) = (\frac{1}{3})^x$
13. $f(x) = 2(\frac{1}{3})^x$
14. $f(x) = (\frac{1}{3})^{x+1}$

15. Assuming that $e = 2.7183$, plot the graph of

    a. $f(x) = e^{2x}$ **b.** $f(x) = 2e^{-x}$

Solve each of the following equations for x.

16. $2^x = 1$ **17.** $2^x = 4$

18. $3^x = 27$ **19.** $5^x = 125$

20. $(25)^x = 125$ **21.** $(16)^x = 128$

22. $(\frac{1}{3})^x = 81$ **23.** $5^x = 0.008$

24. $(10)^x = 0.0001$ **25.** $7^x = \frac{1}{343}$

26. $4^{-2x} = \frac{1}{256}$ **27.** $(\frac{2}{3})^x = \frac{16}{81}$

28. $(\frac{4}{5})^{-x} = \frac{125}{64}$ **29.** $(\frac{3}{4})^{-x} = \frac{1024}{243}$

14.4 APPLICATIONS OF EXPONENTIAL FUNCTIONS

Many practical situations involving growth and decay can be described by means of an exponential function of the form

$$f(t) = Ae^{kt}$$

where A reflects the amount of a substance present at time $t = 0$, k is a constant, and $f(t)$ denotes the amount present at time t. At time $t = 0$,

$$f(0) = A \cdot e^{k \cdot 0} = Ae^0 = A$$

Thus,

$$f(t) = f(0) \cdot e^{kt}$$

When $k > 0$, the function $f(t)$ increases and we speak of exponential growth. On the other hand, if $k < 0$, the function $f(t)$ decreases and we speak of exponential decay. As mentioned earlier, these functions have important applications in learning theory, growth of a sum of money earning compound interest, the growth of a culture of bacteria, the increase in sales of a new product, the decay of radioactive substances, the sharp drop in the construction of new houses in the presence of higher material and labor costs, and so on.

Example 14.18

A company's gross income is given by the formula

$$P(t) = \$10,000 \cdot e^{(0.5)(t - 1)}$$

t being measured in years. Calculate the gross income of the company for $t = 1, 2,$ 3, 4, 5, and 6 years. Graph $P(t)$.

SOLUTION

The earnings at time $t = 1$ is given by

$$P(1) = \$10,000 \cdot e^0$$
$$= \$10,000$$

Using Table 2, we have

$$P(2) = \$10,000e^{0.5}$$
$$= \$10,000(1.6487) = \$16,487$$
$$P(3) = \$10,000e^{(0.5)(2)}$$
$$= \$10,000e^1$$
$$= \$10,000(2.7183) = \$27,183$$
$$P(4) = \$10,000e^{(0.5)(3)}$$
$$= \$10,000e^{1.5}$$
$$= \$10,000(4.4817) = \$44,817$$
$$P(5) = \$10,000e^{(0.5)(4)}$$
$$= \$10,000e^2$$
$$= \$10,000(7.3891) = \$73,891$$
$$P(6) = \$10,000e^{(0.5)(5)}$$
$$= \$10,000e^{2.5}$$
$$= \$10,000(12.182) = \$121,820$$

Plotting $(t, P(t))$ for $t = 1, 2, 3, 4, 5,$ and 6 and connecting them with a smooth curve, we have the graph in Figure 14.5.

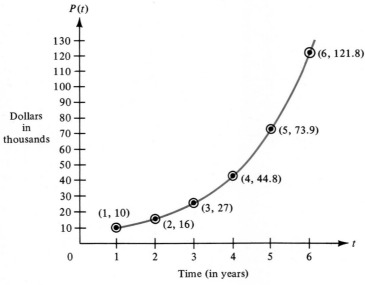

Figure 14.5

Example 14.19

The annual profit of a publisher from the sales of a certain book is given by

$$P(t) = \$5000 + \$10,000e^{-0.4(t-1)}$$

where t is the number of years that the text is on the market. Determine the annual profit at the end of 1, 2, 3, 4, 5, and 10 years. Graph $P(t)$.

SOLUTION

The following table below shows the value of $P(t)$ for different values of t.

t in Years	$P(t)$ in Dollars
1	$5000 + 10,000e^0 = 15,000$
2	$5000 + 10,000e^{-0.4} = 5000 + 10,000(0.67032)$ $= 11,703$
3	$5000 + 10,000(e^{-0.8}) = 5000 + 10,000(0.44933)$ $= 9493$
4	$5000 + 10,000(e^{-1.2}) = 5000 + 10,000(0.30119)$ $= 8012$
5	$5000 + 10,000(e^{-1.6}) = 5000 + 10,000(0.20190)$ $= 7019$
6	$5000 + 10,000(e^{-2.0}) = 5000 + 10,000(0.13534)$ $= 6353$
10	$5000 + 10,000(e^{-3.6}) = 5000 + 10,000(0.02732)$ $= 5273$

Plotting the ordered pairs $(t, P(t))$, we obtain the graph as shown in Figure 14.6. This shows that profit tends to level off with time and gradually approaches a level of $5000.

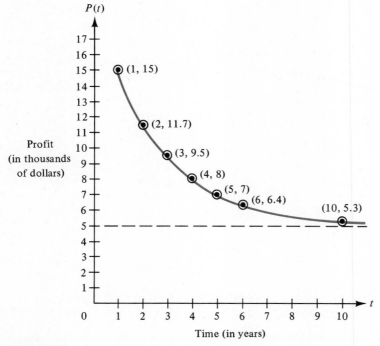

Figure 14.6

Example 14.20

The market research organization of a frozen food company estimates that monthly demand for chickens is given by the equation

$$D(t) = 1000(8 - 7e^{-0.8(t-1)})$$

where t is measured in months. Find the estimated sales after $t = 1, 2, 3, 4, 5, 6, 8, 10,$ and 12 months. Graph $D(t)$.

SOLUTION

The demand function $D(t)$ for different values of t is given in the following table.

t (in Months)	Demand (in Thousands)
1	$8 - 7e^0 = 8 - 7 = 1$
2	$8 - 7e^{-0.8} = 8 - 7(0.44933) = 8 - 3.14531$
	$= 4.85469$
3	$8 - 7e^{-1.6} = 8 - 7(0.2019) = 8 - 1.4133$
	$= 6.5867$
4	$8 - 7e^{-2.4} = 8 - 7(0.09072) = 8 - 0.63504$
	$= 7.36496$
5	$8 - 7e^{-3.2} = 8 - 7(0.04076) = 8 - 0.28532$
	$= 7.71468$
6	$8 - 7e^{-4} = 8 - 7(0.01832) = 8 - 0.12824$
	$= 7.87176$
8	$8 - 7e^{-5.6} = 8 - 7(0.00369) = 8 - 0.02583$
	$= 7.97417$
10	$8 - 7e^{-7.2} = 8 - 7(0.00074) = 8 - 0.00518$
	$= 7.99482$
12	$8 - 7e^{-8.8} = 8 - 7(0.00015) = 8 - 0.00105$
	$= 7.99895$

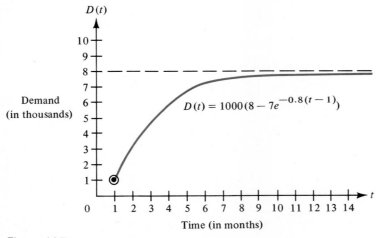

Figure 14.7

Plotting the ordered pairs $(t, D(t))$ and connecting these points with a smooth curve, we have the graph as in Figure 14.7. Note that the demand increases due, perhaps, to some promotional and advertising campaign, and finally levels off as time passes. ■

EXERCISE 14.3

1. The number of bacteria, $N(t)$, present in a certain culture at time t is given by $N(t) = 500e^{(0.3)t}$, where t is measured in hours. Find the number of bacteria present at time
   a. $t = 0$ **b.** $t = 2$ **c.** $t = 5$

2. Assume that the number of bacteria, $N(t)$, in a certain culture is given by $N(t) = 1000e^{(0.2)t}$, where t is measured in hours. Find the number of bacteria present when
   a. $t = 0$ **b.** $t = 10$ **c.** $t = 20$

3. The size of a population of a certain city at time t is given by $P(t) = 10^5 e^{(0.05)t}$, where t is measured in years. Determine the size of the population when
   a. $t = 2$ **b.** $t = 5$ **c.** $t = 10$ **d.** $t = 20$

4. The quantity of radium, $Q(t)$, measured in milligrams, at time t is given by $Q(t) = 1000e^{(-0.04)t}$, where t is measured in centuries. Determine the quantity present when
   a. $t = 5$ **b.** $t = 10$ **c.** $t = 15$ **d.** $t = 20$

5. The annual profit of a manufacturer from the sales of a certain product is given by

   $$P(t) = \$10{,}000(1 + e^{-0.3t})$$

   where t is the number of years the product is on the market.
   a. Determine $P(t)$ at $t = 1, 2, 3, 4, 5, 6, 8,$ and 10.
   b. Graph $P(t)$.

6. The annual raise in the salaries of the faculty in a university are determined by the formula

   $$S(t) = \$15{,}000e^{-1.2t}$$

   after t years of service.
   a. Determine the raise in salaries after $t = 1, 2, 3, 4,$ and 5 years.
   b. Plot the graph of $S(t)$.

7. The sales of a new product of the ABC Company in Chicago are approximated by the equation

   $$S(t) = 10{,}000 + 8000e^{-0.5t}$$

   where t is the number of months the product is advertised.
   a. Calculate the sales for $t = 1, 2, 3, 4, 5, 6, 7, 8,$ and 12.
   b. Plot the graph of $S(t)$.

8. The annual sales of a new edition of a textbook are approximated by the equation

   $$S(t) = 50{,}000(1 - e^{-0.4t})$$

   where t is the number of years the textbook remains on the market. Calculate $S(t)$ for $t = 1, 2, 3, 4,$ and 5 and plot the graph of $S(t)$.

9. The monthly sales of a new model of an automobile in the state of Connecticut are approximated by

$$S(t) = 4000e^{-0.3t}$$

where t is the number of months this model remains in production. Calculate $S(t)$ for $t = 1, 2, \ldots, 12$ and plot the graph of $S(t)$.

10. The decline in sales of a product is approximated by the equation

$$S(t) = 22{,}000e^{-0.2t}$$

where t is the number of months the product was not advertised due to rising material and labor costs. Calculate $S(t)$ for $t = 1, 2, 3, \ldots, 12$ and plot the graph of $S(t)$.

14.5 LOGARITHMIC FUNCTIONS

Thus far, we have discussed exponential functions represented by the equation $y = b^x$, where $b > 0$, $b \neq 1$, and x is any real number. Although the exponential equation $y = b^x$ is not usually easy to solve for x when y and b are known, one can visualize that the equation does have a solution. Further, the graphs of $y = b^x$ for $b > 1$ in Figure 14.1 and for $0 < b < 1$ in Figure 14.3 represent a one-to-one correspondence between the set of all real numbers x and the set of all positive real values of y. This means that the exponential function $y = b^x$ has an inverse that is also a function. We call this inverse the logarithmic function, that is, if $y = b^x$, then we say that $x = \log_b y$. The number x is called the logarithm of y to the base b.

Definition 14.5.1: For $b > 0$, $b \neq 1$, and $y > 0$,

$$x = \log_b y \qquad \text{if and only if } y = b^x$$

In words, the logarithm of a positive number to a given base is the exponent to which the base must be raised to yield that number. Thus, if we write $3^4 = 81$, then the logarithm of 81 to the base 3 is 4; that is, $\log_3 81 = 4$. Again, if we write $10^3 = 1000$, then $\log_{10} 1000 = 3$. For further illustrations, consider the following examples.

Example 14.21
Determine $\log_2 64$.

SOLUTION
Let $x = \log_2 64$. Using the definition of logarithmic function, we obtain the exponential equation

$$2^x = 64$$

Because $64 = 2^6$, we see that $x = 6$ and so

$$\log_2 64 = 6$$

■

Example 14.22
Determine $\log_3(\frac{1}{27})$.

SOLUTION

Let $x = \log_3(\frac{1}{27})$. Then

$$3^x = \tfrac{1}{27}$$

Expressing $\frac{1}{27}$ as a power of base 3, we have

$$(\tfrac{1}{3})^3 = 3^{-3}$$

Thus,

$$3^x = 3^{-3}$$

which implies that $x = -3$.

Example 14.23

Find $\log_8 16$.

SOLUTION

If $x = \log_8 16$, then $8^x = 16$. Because $8 = 2^3$ and $16 = 2^4$, we have

$$2^{3x} = 2^4$$

which implies that $3x = 4$ or $x = \frac{4}{3}$ and hence $\log_8 16 = \frac{4}{3}$.

We consider it worthwhile to reinforce the fact that a logarithm is an exponent and that the functions $y = \log_b x$ and $y = b^x$ are inverses of each other. Thus, if we want to plot the graph of $y = \log_b x$ for $b > 1$, we plot the graph of its inverse function $y = b^x$ and then reflect it in the line $y = x$.

The graph of $y = \log_b x$ is given in Figure 14.8.

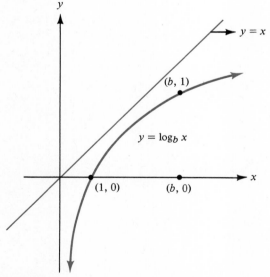

Figure 14.8

From the graph, we observe that

1. $\log_b x$ is defined only for $x > 0$.
2. $\log_b x < 0$ for $0 < x < 1$.
3. $\log_b x = 0$ for $x = 1$.
4. $\log_b x > 0$ for $x > 1$.
5. $\log_b x = 1$ if $x = b$.
6. $\log_b x$ is an increasing function and it has an inverse.

14.6 FUNDAMENTAL PROPERTIES OF LOGARITHMIC FUNCTIONS

Because a logarithm is an exponent, there is a close relationship between exponential and logarithmic functions, and it is only natural that we develop a comprehensive list of properties of logarithmic functions from the properties of exponents we studied in Section 14.2.

Proposition 14.6.1: If m and n are positive numbers and b is any base (that is, $b > 0$ and $b \neq 1$), then

a. $\log_b(mn) = \log_b m + \log_b n$
b. $\log_b(m/n) = \log_b m - \log_b n$

PROOF

Let $\log_b m = p$ and $\log_b n = q$. Using Definition 14.5.1, we have

$$m = b^p \quad \text{and} \quad n = b^q$$

Then

$$mn = b^p \cdot b^q = b^{p+q}$$

and

$$\frac{m}{n} = \frac{b^p}{b^q} = b^{p-q}$$

Hence

$$\log_b(mn) = p + q = \log_b m + \log_b n$$

and

$$\log_b\left(\frac{m}{n}\right) = p - q = \log_b m - \log_b n$$

which proves our assertion. ∎

For an application of this proposition, consider the following example.

Example 14.24

Given that $\log_b 2 = 0.69$, $\log_b 3 = 1.10$, $\log_b 5 = 1.61$, find the following.
   a. $\log_b 6$ b. $\log_b 15$ c. $\log_b(\frac{3}{2})$ d. $\log_b(\frac{10}{3})$

SOLUTION

a. $\log_b 6 = \log_b(2 \times 3) = \log_b 2 + \log_b 3 = 0.69 + 1.10 = 1.79$

b. $\log_b 15 = \log_b(3 \times 5) = \log_b 3 + \log_b 5 = 1.10 + 1.61 = 2.71$

c. $\log_b(\frac{3}{2}) = \log_b 3 - \log_b 2 = 1.10 - 0.69 = 0.41$

d. $\log_b(\frac{10}{3}) = \log_b(\frac{5 \times 2}{3}) = \log_b 5 + \log_b 2 - \log_b 3 = 1.61 + 0.69 - 1.10$
$$= 1.20$$

Proposition 14.6.2: Let m be any positive real number and r any real number. Then

$$\log_b(m^r) = r \log_b m$$

PROOF

Let $\log_b m = p$. Then $m = b^p$ and $m^r = b^{pr}$. Hence,

$$\log_b(m^r) = rp = r \cdot \log_b(m)$$

Example 14.25

Given that $\log_b 2 = 0.69$ and $\log_b 3 = 1.10$, determine

a. $\log_b \sqrt{2}$ b. $\log_b 72$

SOLUTION

a. $\log_b \sqrt{2} = \log_b(2)^{1/2} = \frac{1}{2} \log_b 2 = \frac{1}{2}(0.69) = 0.345$

b. $\log_b 72 = \log_b(2^3 \cdot 3^2) = \log_b(2^3) + \log_b(3^2)$ (Proposition 14.6.1)
$$= 3 \log_b 2 + 2 \log_b 3$$
$$= 3(0.69) + 2(1.10) \quad \text{(Proposition 14.6.2)}$$
$$= 4.27$$

Proposition 14.6.3: Let a and b be two bases and m any positive number. Then

$$\log_a m = \frac{\log_b m}{\log_b a}$$

PROOF

Let $\log_a m = p$, which implies that $m = a^p$. Similarly, if $\log_b a = n$, then $a = b^n$. Thus,

$$m = a^p = (b^n)^p = b^{np}$$

This statement implies that

$$\log_b m = np = (\log_b a) \cdot (\log_a m)$$

which proves our assertion.

Example 14.26

If $\log_b 2 = 0.69$, $\log_b 3 = 1.10$, and $\log_b 5 = 1.61$, determine

a. $\log_3 5$ b. $\log_2 3$

SOLUTION

a. $\log_3 5 = \dfrac{\log_b 5}{\log_b 3} = \dfrac{1.61}{1.10} = 1.463$

b. $\log_2 3 = \dfrac{\log_b 3}{\log_b 2} = \dfrac{1.10}{0.69} = 1.45$

∎

EXERCISE 14.4

1. Express each of the following equations in logarithmic form.
   a. $2^3 = 8$ **b.** $3^2 = 9$
   c. $5^4 = 625$ **d.** $(16)^{1/2} = 4$
   e. $(32)^{3/5} = 8$ **f.** $(216)^{2/3} = 36$

2. Express each of the following equations in exponential form.
   a. $\log_3 27 = 3$ **b.** $\log_2 64 = 6$
   c. $\log_4 256 = 4$ **d.** $\log_8 4 = \frac{2}{3}$
   e. $\log_{32} 2 = \frac{1}{5}$ **f.** $\log_6 1 = 0$

3. Solve the following equations.
   a. $\log_3 x = 4$ **b.** $\log_2 x = 7$
   c. $\log_8 512 = x$ **d.** $\log_2(\frac{1}{8}) = x$
   e. $\log_5 x = -2$ **f.** $\log_5 125 = x$
   g. $\log_x 16 = 4$ **h.** $\log_9 3 = x$
   i. $\log_x 25 = -2$ **j.** $\log_x 343 = 3$

4. Solve the following equations.
   a. $\log_2(2^4) = x$ **b.** $\log_3(x^5) = 5$
   c. $\log_x(3^5) = 5$ **d.** $\log_5(3x) = 2$

5. Given that

   $$\log_b 2 = 0.69, \ \log_b 3 = 1.10, \ \log_b 5 = 1.61, \ \log_b 7 = 1.95,$$

   determine the following.
   a. $\log_b(\frac{2}{7})$ **b.** $\log_b(21)$
   c. $\log_b(35)$ **d.** $\log_b(25)$
   e. $\log_b(128)$ **f.** $\log_b(343)$

6. If $\log_{10} 2 = 0.3010$, $\log_{10} 3 = 0.4771$, $\log_{10} 7 = 0.8451$, determine the following.
   a. $\log_{10}\sqrt{2}$ **b.** $\log_{10}(\frac{21}{2})$
   c. $\log_{10}(\frac{14}{3})$ **d.** $\log_3 7$
   e. $\log_2 3$ **f.** $\log_{10} 42$
   g. $\log_3 2$ **h.** $\log_{10}(21)^{1/3}$
   i. $\log_{10}(\frac{9}{4})$ **j.** $\log_{10}(12)^{1/3}$
   k. $\log_{10}(3\sqrt{8})$ **l.** $\log_{10}\sqrt{63}$

7. Given that $\log_{10} 2 = 0.3010$ and $\log_{10} 3 = 0.4771$, find the logarithms of 4, 6, 8, 9, 12, and 16.

8. Prove that

   $$(\log_a b)(\log_b a) = 1$$

9. Prove that if m, n, and p are positive numbers and b is any base, then

$$\log_b(mnp) = \log_b m + \log_b n + \log_b p$$

10. Prove that

$$b^{\log_b x} = x$$

for $x > 0$.

14.7 COMMON LOGARITHMS

Logarithms have been used in mathematics as an effective tool for simplifying numerical work. Because the number system is in base 10, logarithms to base 10 are most convenient for numerical calculations. Such logarithms are called common logarithms. In other words, the common logarithm of a number is the exponent to which base 10 must be raised to yield that number. Because

$$10^1 = 10;\ 10^2 = 100;\ 10^3 = 1000;\ 10^4 = 10,000;\ 10^5 = 100,000$$

it follows that the common logarithm of 10 is 1; the common logarithm of 100 is 2; the common logarithm of 1000 is 3; and so on. Thus, the following statements are equivalent.

$$10^1 = 10 \quad \text{and} \quad \log_{10} 10 = 1$$
$$10^2 = 100 \quad \text{and} \quad \log_{10} 100 = 2$$
$$10^3 = 1000 \quad \text{and} \quad \log_{10} 1000 = 3$$
$$10^4 = 10,000 \quad \text{and} \quad \log_{10} 10,000 = 4$$

For the sake of brevity, we shall interpret $\log x$ to mean logarithm of x to the base 10. Further, because

$$10^{-1} = 0.1 \quad \text{then} \quad \log 0.1 = -1$$
$$10^{-2} = 0.01 \quad \text{then} \quad \log 0.01 = -2$$
$$10^{-3} = 0.001 \quad \text{then} \quad \log 0.001 = -3$$

Thus, the logarithms of the integral powers of 10 are precisely those integers. Evidently, if

$$10^x = 75$$

then x must be a number between 1 and 2. That is, x is an integer plus a decimal fraction. Thus, a logarithm may be expressed as a sum of an integer and a decimal fraction.

Definition 14.7.1: The integral part of the common logarithm is called the characteristic. The decimal part of the common logarithm is called the mantissa.

Because any positive number x can be expressed in the form

$$x = n \times 10^c$$

where c is an integer (which may be positive, zero, or negative) and n satisfies the inequality $1 \leq n < 10$, it follows that

$$\log x = \log n + \log 10^c \qquad \text{(Proposition 14.6.1)}$$
$$= (\log n) + c$$

where c is the characteristic and $\log n$ is the mantissa.

The mantissa, $\log n$, is obtained from Table 3 at the end of the book, which lists the logarithms of the numbers from 1.00 to 9.99 in steps of 0.01. Consider, for example, $\log 2.35$. Referring to Table 3, we locate the row for 2.3, and then move across this row until we are under the column headed 5 and find the entry 0.3711. Again, we may use this table to determine that

$$\log 7.82 = 0.8932 \qquad \log 5.47 = 0.7380 \qquad \log 3.59 = 0.5551$$

and so on.

Example 14.27
Find $\log 4350$.

SOLUTION
Because $4350 = 4.350 \times 10^3$, it follows that $c = 3$ and $n = 4.350$. Using Table 3, we find that $\log 4.350 = 0.6385$. Thus,

$$\log 4350 = 0.6385 + 3$$
$$= 3.6385 \qquad\blacksquare$$

Example 14.28
Find $\log 0.0728$.

SOLUTION
Because

$$0.0728 = 7.28 \times 10^{-2}$$

we have the characteristic $c = -2$ and $n = 7.28$. Thus,

$$\log 0.0728 = (\log 7.28) + (-2)$$
$$= 0.8621 - 2$$
$$= -1.1379 \qquad\blacksquare$$

We have explained above how to find $\log_{10} x$ for a given positive number x. If $\log_{10} x$ is given, how do we determine x? First, we write $\log x$ in the form

$$\log x = (\log n) + c$$

where c is the characteristic and $\log n$ is the mantissa. Because this statement is equivalent to

$$x = n \times 10^c$$

we determine x by finding n and then multiplying it by 10^c. Note that $\log n$ is a number between 0 and 1 and is listed in the body of Table 3.

Example 14.29

Find x if $\log x = 1.8021$.

SOLUTION

Because

$$\log x = 0.8021 + 1$$

it follows that $c = 1$ and $\log n = 0.8021$. From Table 3, we find that mantissa 0.8021 corresponds to the number $n = 6.34$. Thus,

$$x = n \times 10^1$$
$$= 6.34 \times 10$$
$$= 63.4$$

Example 14.30

Find x if $\log x = -1.1232$.

SOLUTION

We must express $\log x$ in the form $(\log n) + c$, where $\log n$ is a positive decimal fraction. Thus, adding and subtracting 2, we have

$$\log x = -1.1232 + 2 - 2$$
$$= 0.8768 + (-2)$$

which implies that $c = -2$ and $\log n = 0.8768$. Table 3 tells us that $n = 7.53$. Thus,

$$x = n \times 10^c$$
$$= (7.53) \times 10^{-2}$$
$$= 0.0753$$

Example 14.31

Find $x = (1.19)^{20}$.

SOLUTION

$$\log x = \log(1.19)^{20}$$
$$= 20 \log 1.19 \qquad \text{(Proposition 14.6.2)}$$
$$= 20(0.0755)$$
$$= 1.51$$

To determine x, note that $c = 1$ and $\log n = 0.51$. Referring to Table 3, we have $n = 3.24$ and

$$x = n \times 10^c$$
$$= 3.24 \times 10^1$$
$$= 32.40$$

Example 14.32

Find the value of

$$(215)^{1/3} \cdot (80)^{1/5} \cdot (0.0025)^{1/4}$$

SOLUTION

Let $x = (215)^{1/3}(80)^{1/5}(0.0025)^{1/4}$. Using Proposition 14.6.1, we have

$$
\begin{aligned}
\log x &= \log(215)^{1/3} + \log(80)^{1/5} + \log(0.0025)^{1/4} \\
&= \tfrac{1}{3}\log 215 + \tfrac{1}{5}\log 80 + \tfrac{1}{4}\log(0.0025) \qquad \text{(Proposition 14.6.2)}
\end{aligned}
$$

From Table 3, we have

$$
\begin{aligned}
\log 215 &= 2.3324 \\
\log 80 &= 1.9031
\end{aligned}
$$

and

$$
\begin{aligned}
\log 0.0025 &= \log(2.5 \times 10^{-3}) \\
&= (\log 2.5) - 3 \\
&= 0.3979 - 3 = -2.6021
\end{aligned}
$$

Thus,

$$
\begin{aligned}
\log x &= \tfrac{1}{3}(2.3324) + \tfrac{1}{5}(1.9031) + \tfrac{1}{4}(-2.6021) \\
&= 0.7775 + 0.3806 - 0.6505 \\
&= 0.5076
\end{aligned}
$$

To determine x, note that $c = 0$ and $\log n = 0.5076$. From Table 3, we find that $n = 3.22$. Thus,

$$
\begin{aligned}
x &= n \times 10^c \\
&= 3.22
\end{aligned}
$$

Example 14.33

Find the value of

$$\frac{(32.5)(40.8)^{1/3}}{(4.72)}$$

SOLUTION

Let

$$x = \frac{(32.5)(40.8)^{1/3}}{(4.72)}$$

Applying Proposition 14.6.1, we have

$$\log x = \log 32.5 + \log(40.8)^{1/3} - \log 4.72$$
$$= \log 32.5 + \tfrac{1}{3}\log 40.8 - \log 4.72 \qquad \text{(Proposition 14.6.2)}$$

From Table 3, we find that

$$\log 32.5 = 1.5119$$
$$\log 40.8 = 1.6107$$

and

$$\log 4.72 = 0.6739$$

Thus,

$$\log x = 1.5119 + \tfrac{1}{3}(1.6107) - 0.6739$$
$$= 1.3749$$

To determine x, note that $c = 1$ and $\log n = 0.3749$. Referring to Table 3, we have $n = 2.37$ and

$$x = n \times 10^c$$
$$= (2.37) \times 10^1$$
$$= 23.70 \qquad \blacksquare$$

14.8 INTERPOLATION

We can determine from Table 3 the logarithm of 3.45 and also the number whose logarithm is 0.4014. But how do we find log 3.456 or the number whose logarithm is 0.4695? It may be necessary to interpolate to find the logarithm of a number whose mantissa is not listed in the table. This means that we need to estimate the value of the mantissa.

Logarithms do not behave in any extremely simple pattern because mantissas increase rapidly when n is small, but the increase is relatively small for large n. Observe, for example, that log 3 is not halfway between log 2 and log 4, but log 717 is halfway between log 716 and log 718 because we find from Table 3 that

$$\log 716 = 2.8549$$
$$\log 717 = 2.8555$$
$$\log 718 = 2.8561$$

The method of interpolation that we shall use is based on the assumption that the relationship between two successive values in Table 3 is linear.

Example 14.34

Find the approximate value of log 3.456.

SOLUTION

The characteristic is 0. The following form is used to compute the mantissa.

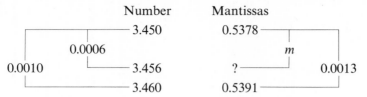

Because the relationship between two successive values in Table 3 is assumed to be linear, we need to solve the following proportion:

$$\frac{m}{0.0013} = \frac{0.0006}{0.0010}$$

$$\frac{m}{0.0013} = \frac{6}{10}$$

or

$$m = 0.00078$$

Thus,

$$\log 3.456 = 0.5378 + 0.00078$$

which, when rounded off to four decimal places, is 0.5386. ■

Graphically, the method of linear interpolation amounts to replacing a section of the graph of $y = \log x$ with a line segment. Figure 14.9 illustrates graphically Example 14.34. Notice that we are interested in the y coordinate of the point P on the curve but what we obtained is the y coordinate of the point Q on the line. This value is a good approximation of the y coordinate of the point P assuming that the line segment MN is a good approximation to the logarithmic curve. Note that the triangles MQR and MNS are similar.

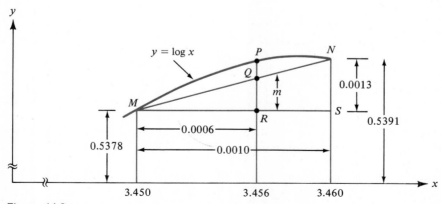

Figure 14.9

As another illustration, consider the following example.

Example 14.35
Find the approximate value of log 0.07427.

SOLUTION
Because $0.07427 = 7.427 \times 10^{-2}$, the characteristic is $c = -2$ and $n = 7.427$. Thus,

$$\log 0.07427 = (\log 7.427) + (-2)$$

From Table 3, we have

$$\log 7.42 = 0.8704$$
$$\log 7.43 = 0.8710$$

Because 7.427 is $\frac{7}{10}$ of the way from 7.42 to 7.43, we assume that log 7.427 is also $\frac{7}{10}$ of the way from log 7.42 to log 7.43. Thus,

$$\log 7.427 = 0.8704 + \frac{7}{10}(0.8710 - 0.8704)$$
$$= 0.8704 + 0.00042$$

Rounding to four decimal places, we have

$$\log 7.427 = 0.8708$$

Because the characteristic is -2, it follows that

$$\log 0.07427 = 0.8708 - 2 \qquad \blacksquare$$

The method of linear interpolation is equally useful in finding a number whose logarithm is known. If we wish to find the number n such that log $n = 0.4695$, we find the two mantissas in Table 3 such that 0.4695 lies between them. We find that

$$\log 2.94 = 0.4683$$
$$\log 2.95 = 0.4698$$

We then proceed as follows:

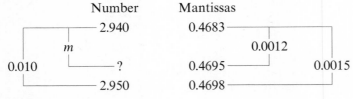

From the proportion

$$\frac{m}{0.010} = \frac{0.0012}{0.0015}$$

we find that

$$m = 0.008$$

Thus,

$$n = 2.94 + 0.008 = 2.948$$ ■

Example 14.36
Find x if $\log x = 2.3867$.

SOLUTION
Clearly,

$$\log x = 0.3867 + 2$$

so that the characteristic $c = 2$ and the mantissa is 0.3867. From Table 3, we find that

$$\log 2.43 = 0.3856$$
$$\log 2.44 = 0.3874$$

We need to find n such that $\log n = 0.3867$. Notice that $n = 2.43 + m$. Proceeding as before, we find that

$$\frac{m}{0.010} = \frac{0.3867 - 0.3856}{0.3874 - 0.3856}$$

$$\frac{m}{0.010} = \frac{11}{18}$$

or

$$m = 0.006$$

Thus,

$$n = 2.43 + 0.006 = 2.436$$

Now,

$$x = n \times 10^c$$
$$= 2.436 \times 10^2$$
$$= 243.6$$ ■

EXERCISE 14.5

1. Find the common logarithms of the following numbers.
   a. 5230
   b. 523
   c. 52.3
   d. 5.23
   e. 0.523
   f. 0.0523
2. Using linear interpolation, find the common logarithms of the following numbers.
   a. 5723
   b. 57.23
   c. 0.5723
   d. 2.317
   e. 26.97
   f. 0.7382

3. Use common logarithms to solve for x.
   a. $10^x = 84$ **b.** $10^x = 34.6$
   c. $10^x = 3.46$ **d.** $10^x = 0.00346$

4. Find the value of x in each of the following problems.
   a. $\log x = 0.4048$ **b.** $\log x = 1.6972$
   c. $\log x = 3.1614$ **d.** $\log x = -1.0783$
   e. $\log x = -2.3420$ **f.** $\log x = 8.3820 - 10$
   g. $\log x = 1.4556$ **h.** $\log x = 3.9286$

5. Using properties of common logarithms, find the value of the following.
   a. 837×124 **b.** $258 \times 37 \times 451$
   c. 9.238×0.9152 **d.** 83.2×42.6

   e. $\dfrac{24.8 \times 16.2}{37.3}$ **f.** $\dfrac{0.0074 \times 0.0137}{0.0252}$

6. Using properties of common logarithms, evaluate the following.
   a. $(20)^{1/4}$ **b.** $(0.2)^{1/5}$
   c. $(0.003)^{1/2}$ **d.** $(0.34)^{1/2} \times (1.21)^2$

7. Use common logarithms to solve for x.
   a. $2^x = 15$ **b.** $3^x = 4$
   c. $5^x = 27$ **d.** $(0.01)^x = 8$
   e. $x^5 = 12$ **f.** $(2x)^3 = 14$

8. Solve the following for x.

   a. $x = \dfrac{(71.4)(23.6)^{1/2}}{35.1}$ **b.** $10^x = \dfrac{123}{231}$

   c. $10^{-x} = \dfrac{123}{231}$ **d.** $3^{2x-1} = 26$

   e. $3^{1-2x} = 49$ **f.** $5^{x+2} = 8^{2x-3}$

9. Using common logarithms, find the value of each of the following.

   a. $\dfrac{(435)\sqrt{0.056}}{(3.80)^3}$ **b.** $\dfrac{(6.45)^3(0.00034)^{1/3}}{(9.37)^2(8.93)^{1/4}}$

10. Using common logarithms, find the value of each of the following.

   a. $\dfrac{(125)^{1/4}(10)^{1/5}}{(8.47)^3(0.0024)^{1/3}}$ **b.** $\dfrac{(270)^{1/5}(1.06)^{2/3}(0.089)^{4/5}}{\sqrt{2430}(49.80)^{1/3}}$

14.9 NATURAL LOGARITHMS

Logarithms to the base e are called natural logarithms. For brevity, we shall interpret $\ln x$ to mean logarithm of x to the base e. Tables of natural logarithms are available in most handbooks of mathematical tables, but we consider it instructive to be able to evaluate such logarithms by using Table 3 of common logarithms.

The relation between $\ln x$ and $\log x$ is given by the following proposition.

Proposition 14.9.1: Let x be any positive real number, then

$$\ln x = \frac{\log x}{\log e}$$

PROOF

To prove this relationship, we observe that $y = \ln x$ if and only if $x = e^y$. Taking common logarithms of $x = e^y$, we obtain

$$\log x = \log e^y$$
$$= y \log e \qquad \text{(Proposition 14.6.2)}$$

Dividing both sides by $\log e$, we have

$$y = \frac{\log x}{\log e}$$

as asserted. ∎

Assuming that $e = 2.718$, it can be shown that $\log 2.718 = 0.4343$. Thus, we have

Corollary: $\ln x = \dfrac{\log x}{0.4343} = 2.3025 \log x$

Example 14.37
Evaluate $\ln 4$.

SOLUTION

$$\ln 4 = (2.3025) \log 4$$
$$= (2.3025)(0.6021) \qquad \text{(From Table 3)}$$
$$= 1.3863 \qquad\qquad ∎$$

Recall that an exponential function is of the form $f(x) = b^x$, where $b > 0$, $b \neq 1$, and x is any real number. Because most exponential functions have base e, we shall indicate briefly how to change $f(x) = b^x$ to an exponential function with base e. In other words, we need to determine z such that

$$b^x = e^z$$

Taking natural logarithms of the both sides, we have

$$\ln b^x = \ln e^z$$

or

$$x \ln b = z \ln e \qquad \text{(Proposition 14.6.2)}$$

Because $\ln e = \log_e e = 1$, we conclude that

$$z = x \ln b$$

Hence, we can write $f(x) = b^x$ also as

$$f(x) = e^{x \ln b}$$

Example 14.38

The quantity of radium, $Q(t)$, measured in milligrams, at time t is given by $Q(t) = 1000(0.95)^t$, where t is measured in centuries. Express $Q(t)$ as an exponential function with base e and then determine the quality present at $t = 10$. [Use $e^{-0.513} = 0.5987$.]

SOLUTION

The quantity $Q(t)$ given by the equation

$$Q(t) = 1000(0.95)^t$$

can also be expressed as

$$Q(t) = 1000e^{t(\ln 0.95)}$$

Note that

$$\begin{aligned}
\ln 0.95 &= 2.3025 \log 0.95 &\quad &\text{(Corollary)} \\
&= 2.3025(0.9777 - 1) &\quad &\text{(Table 3)} \\
&= -0.0513
\end{aligned}$$

Thus,

$$Q(t) = 1000e^{-0.0513t}$$

and

$$\begin{aligned}
Q(10) &= 1000e^{-0.513} \\
&= 1000(0.5987) \\
&= 598.7
\end{aligned}$$

EXERCISE 14.6

1. Find the natural logarithms of the following numbers.

    a. 4500   **b.** 450   **c.** 45

    d. 4.5   **e.** 0.45   **f.** 0.0045

2. Find the natural logarithms of each of the following.

    a. 125   **b.** 263   **c.** $(2.73)^4$

    d. $(1.89)^{5.6}$ **e.** $(3.16)^{3.4}$ **f.** $(0.23)^{2.3}$

    g. $\frac{57}{23}$ **h.** $\frac{1350}{482}$

3. The monthly sales of a new product is approximated by the equation $s(t) = 20,000(0.75)^t$, where t is the number of months the product remains in the market. Express $s(t)$ as an exponential function with base e and then determine the sales at $t = 8$.

4. The decline in sales of a product is approximated by the equation $s(t) = 10,000(0.82)^t$, where t is the number of months the product was not advertised due to rising material and labor costs. Express $s(t)$ as an exponential function with base e and then calculate $s(t)$ for $t = 5$ and $t = 10$.

5. Show that $e^{\ln x} = x$.

15

Sequences and Mathematics of Finance

15.1 INTRODUCTION

A sequence is a real-valued function whose domain consists of sets of positive integers. Traditionally, sequences have played an important role in advanced mathematics and have several applications in installment buying, simple and compound interest problems, annuities and their present values, monthly payments for automobiles, mortgage payments, and so on. Consider, for example, that a saleswoman in a shoe store sold five pairs of shoes on a certain day and sold three more pairs each day thereafter than she had sold the day before. What would be her sale on the tenth day? Suppose further that she is entitled to a bonus after she has sold a total of at least 1455 pairs of shoes. How long will it take her to earn the bonus?

Mr. Brown borrows $2500 to finance his new car and agrees to pay the amount with finance charges in 24 equal monthly installments. What will be his monthly payment if the current rate of interest is 12 percent compounded monthly? Steve wishes to have $10,000 available for his daughter, who is to enter college 10 years from now. How much money should he deposit monthly in a bank if the interest rate is 5 percent compounded quarterly? As another illustration, suppose that the management of a factory wishes to install new equipment for $10,000. The profits from this equipment will be $3000 a year for the next four years, after which the equipment will have no market value. If the money could be invested elsewhere at 6 percent compounded monthly, should the management be advised to purchase this equipment or invest the money elsewhere?

The mathematics of finance, which deals in general with questions of the type given above, has a wide range of applications in the insurance and financial industries. In business, this branch of mathematics is a powerful tool widely used to analyze the current status of the money market in an effort to predict its impact on such areas as the automobile industry, the construction industry, and other important segments of the national and international economy.

15.2 SEQUENCES

Intuitively, an infinite sequence is an ordered set of numbers such as

$$2, 5, 8, 11, 14, \ldots$$

The equation $a_2 = 5$ is interpreted to mean that the second element of the sequence is 5. That the third element in the sequence is 8 is represented by the equation $a_3 = 8$. In other words,

$$a_1 = 2, a_2 = 5, a_3 = 8, a_4 = 11, \ldots$$

The subscripts of the symbols $a_1, a_2, a_3, a_4, \ldots$ are called indices and serve only to locate the numbers in the sequence. Thus, the above sequence is a real-valued function that consists of ordered pairs

$$(1, 2), (2, 5), (3, 8), (4, 11), \ldots$$

with the set of counting numbers as the domain of the function. Note that for an integer n in the domain of the function a, the corresponding element in the range is denoted by $a(n)$ if we use functional notation. In sequence notation, we represent this element by a_n. Thus, a sequence may be represented by a set of ordered pairs

$$(n, a_n)$$

whose first components are always positive integers. We shall abbreviate this notation further and denote this sequence by $\{a_n\}$. The numbers $a_1, a_2, a_3, \ldots$ are called the terms of the sequence $\{a_n\}$.

Definition 15.2.1: An infinite sequence, $\{a_n\}$, is a real-valued function that has the set of positive integers as its domain.

Example 15.1

Find the first six terms in each of the following sequences:

    a. $a_n = 2n + 3$
    b. $a_n = n^2 + 1$
    c. $a_n = 3^n - 1$

SOLUTION

    a. If we set $n = 1, 2, 3, 4, 5$, and 6, in the general term

$$a_n = 2n + 3$$

we obtain

$$a_1 = 5, a_2 = 7, a_3 = 9, a_4 = 11, a_5 = 13, a_6 = 15$$

    b. In the sequence

$$a_n = n^2 + 1$$

if we let $n = 1, 2, \ldots, 6$, we have

$$a_1 = 1^2 + 1 = 2; a_2 = 2^2 + 1 = 5; a_3 = 3^2 + 1 = 10;$$
$$a_4 = 4^2 + 1 = 17; a_5 = 5^2 + 1 = 26; a_6 = 6^2 + 1 = 37$$

Thus, the first six terms of the sequence are

2, 5, 10, 17, 26, 37

c. In the sequence $a_n = 3^n - 1$, we have

$$a_1 = 3^1 - 1 = 2; a_2 = 3^2 - 1 = 8; a_3 = 3^3 - 1 = 26;$$
$$a_4 = 3^4 - 1 = 80; a_5 = 3^5 - 1 = 242; a_6 = 3^6 - 1 = 728 \qquad \blacksquare$$

Another equally acceptable way to specify a sequence is to list the first few terms and then guess the general pattern of this sequence. Consider, for example, the first few terms

$$a_1 = 1, a_2 = \tfrac{1}{2}, a_3 = \tfrac{1}{4}, a_4 = \tfrac{1}{8}, a_5 = \tfrac{1}{16}$$

Does it seem reasonable to guess that $a_6 = \tfrac{1}{32}$? If that is the number that comes to your mind, you have an insight into this problem. Can you determine the general term a_n? Notice that

$$a_1 = (\tfrac{1}{2})^0, a_2 = (\tfrac{1}{2})^1, a_3 = (\tfrac{1}{2})^2, a_4 = (\tfrac{1}{2})^3, \text{ and } a_5 = (\tfrac{1}{2})^4$$

Observe that the power of $(\tfrac{1}{2})$ in each of the terms is one less than the index of the symbol $a_1, a_2, \ldots$. Thus, $a_n = (\tfrac{1}{2})^{n-1}$. Once the general term a_n is known, we can find any term in the sequence $\{a_n\}$ for a given value of n.

With each sequence $\{a_n\}$, we can associate another sequence $\{S_n\}$ defined by the equation

$$S_n = \sum_{j=1}^{j=n} a_j$$
$$= a_1 + a_2 + a_3 + \cdots + a_n$$

This sequence is called the sequence of partial sums of the sequence $\{a_n\}$. Evidently,

$$S_1 = a_1$$
$$S_2 = a_1 + a_2$$
$$S_3 = a_1 + a_2 + a_3$$
$$\vdots$$
$$S_n = a_1 + a_2 + a_3 + \cdots + a_n$$

Example 15.2

Find $S_1, S_2, S_3, S_4, S_5,$ and S_6 for the following sequences:

a. $a_n = 3n + 2$
b. $a_n = (\tfrac{1}{2})^{n-1}$

SOLUTION

a. Let $n = 1, 2, 3, 4, 5$, and 6. Then

$a_1 = 5, a_2 = 8, a_3 = 11, a_4 = 14, a_5 = 17$, and $a_6 = 20$

Thus,

$S_1 = a_1 = 5$

$S_2 = a_1 + a_2$

$\quad = 5 + 8 = 13$

$S_3 = a_1 + a_2 + a_3 = S_2 + a_3$

$\quad = 13 + 11 = 24$

Using the relation that

$S_n = S_{n-1} + a_n$

we obtain

$S_4 = S_3 + a_4 = 24 + 14 = 38$

$S_5 = S_4 + a_5 = 38 + 17 = 55$

and

$S_6 = S_5 + a_6 = 55 + 20 = 75$

b. In the sequence $a_n = (\frac{1}{2})^{n-1}$, we have

$S_1 = 1$

$S_2 = 1 + \frac{1}{2} = \frac{3}{2}$

$S_3 = S_2 + a_3 = \frac{3}{2} + \frac{1}{4} = \frac{7}{4}$

$S_4 = S_3 + a_4 = \frac{7}{4} + \frac{1}{8} = \frac{15}{8}$

$S_5 = S_4 + a_5 = \frac{15}{8} + \frac{1}{16} = \frac{31}{16}$

$S_6 = S_5 + a_6 = \frac{31}{16} + \frac{1}{32} = \frac{63}{32}$

EXERCISE 15.1

1. Find the first five terms for each of the following sequences.

a. $a_n = 3n - 2$ **b.** $a_n = n^2 - 1$

c. $a_n = (-1)^n$ **d.** $a_n = n(n + 2)$

e. $a_n = 2^n - 1$ **f.** $a_n = \dfrac{(-1)^n}{n + 1}$

2. Find the first seven terms for each of the following sequences.

a. $a_n = \dfrac{n(n + 1)}{2}$ **b.** $a_n = \dfrac{n(n + 1)(2n + 1)}{6}$

c. $a_n = (-1)^n + n$ **d.** $a_n = 1 + (-1)^n$

3. Determine the general term a_n in each of the following sequences.
   a. 4, 7, 10, 13, 16, . . . , a_n, . . .
   b. 3, 9, 27, 81, 243, . . . , a_n, . . .
   c. 1, $\frac{1}{2}$, $\frac{1}{3}$, $\frac{1}{4}$, $\frac{1}{5}$, . . . , a_n, . . .
   d. 1, -1, 1, -1, 1, . . . , a_n, . . .
   e. $\frac{1}{2}$, $\frac{2}{3}$, $\frac{3}{4}$, $\frac{4}{5}$, $\frac{5}{6}$, . . . , a_n, . . .
   f. $\frac{1}{2}$, $\frac{1}{4}$, $\frac{1}{6}$, $\frac{1}{8}$, $\frac{1}{10}$, . . . , a_n, . . .

4. Find the partial sum S_4 in each of the following sequences.

   a. $a_n = \dfrac{1}{n}$

   b. $a_n = (-1)^n$

   c. $a_n = n(n + 1)$

   d. $a_n = (n + 1)(n - 1)$

15.3 ARITHMETIC PROGRESSIONS

Consider the sequence

$$5, 9, 13, 17, 21, \ldots$$

Each term in the sequence after the first is obtained by adding 4 to the term that precedes it; the first few terms of the sequence are

$$a_1 = 5$$
$$a_2 = 5 + 4 = 9$$
$$a_3 = 9 + 4 = 13$$
$$a_4 = 13 + 4 = 17$$

and so on. Any such sequence in which the difference obtained by subtracting any term from the succeeding term is constant is called an arithmetic sequence or arithmetic progression. The constant difference is called the common difference.

Notice that an arithmetic progression is completely determined if the first term a_1 and the common difference d is known. In general, an arithmetic progression is of the form

$$a_1, a_2, a_3, \ldots$$

where

$$a_2 = a_1 + d$$
$$a_3 = a_2 + d = (a_1 + d) + d = a_1 + 2d$$
$$a_4 = a_3 + d = (a_1 + 2d) + d = a_1 + 3d$$
$$a_5 = a_4 + d = (a_1 + 3d) + d = a_1 + 4d$$

The coefficient of d in any term is one less than the number of terms in the sequence. Thus the general term in an arithmetic progression is

(15.1) $a_n = a_1 + (n - 1)d$

where a_1 is the first term in the sequence and d is the common difference.

Example 15.3

Find the tenth term of the sequence

   $4, 7, 10, 13, 16, \ldots$

SOLUTION

Here

   $a_1 = 4 \qquad d = 3 \qquad n = 10$

Hence

   $a_{10} = 4 + (10 - 1) \cdot 3 = 31$ ■

Example 15.4

Find the 23rd term in an arithmetic sequence whose 5th and 11th terms are 41 and 23.

SOLUTION

If a_1 is the first term and d is the common difference, then

   $a_5 = a_1 + 4d = 41$
   $a_{11} = a_1 + 10d = 23$

Subtracting the first equation from the second, we get $6d = -18$ or $d = -3$. Substituting $d = -3$ in the equation $a_1 + 4d = 41$, we have $a_1 = 53$. Hence,

   $a_{23} = a_1 + 22d$
   $\quad\;\; = 53 + 22(-3)$
   $\quad\;\; = -13$ ■

Example 15.5

Determine three consecutive numbers in an arithmetic sequence such that their sum is 24 and their product is 480.

SOLUTION

Let $a - d$, a, and $a + d$ be three consecutive numbers in a sequence. Then

   $(a - d) + a + (a + d) = 24$
   $\qquad\qquad\qquad 3a = 24$
   $\qquad\qquad\qquad\; a = 8$

Also,

   $a(a - d)(a + d) = 480$
   $\qquad a(a^2 - d^2) = 480$

Because $a = 8$, it follows that $d^2 = 4$ or $d = \pm 2$. Thus, the numbers are

   $6, 8, 10 \quad \text{or} \quad 10, 8, 6$ ■

Proposition 15.3.1: The sum of the first n terms of an arithmetic progression with a_1 as the first term and d the common difference is given by

$$S_n = \frac{n}{2}[2a_1 + (n-1)d]$$

PROOF
Note that each term in an arithmetic progression is obtained by adding the common difference d to the term that precedes it or by subtracting d from the term that follows it. Thus,

(15.2) $S_n = a_1 + (a_1 + d) + (a_1 + 2d) + \cdots + (a_n - d) + a_n$

Writing S_n in reverse order, we have

(15.3) $S_n = a_n + (a_n - d) + (a_n - 2d) + \cdots + (a_1 + d) + a_1$

Adding (15.2) and (15.3), we have

(15.4) $2S_n = (a_1 + a_n) + (a_1 + a_n) + \cdots + (a_1 + a_n)$
$$= n(a_1 + a_n)$$

or

$$S_n = \frac{n}{2}(a_1 + a_n)$$

$$= \frac{n}{2}[a_1 + a_1 + (n-1)d] \qquad \text{Eq. (15.1)}$$

$$= \frac{n}{2}[2a_1 + (n-1)d]$$
∎

Example 15.6
A saleswoman in a shoe store sold five pairs of shoes the day she was hired and each day thereafter she sold three more shoes than she sold the day before. Determine her sale on the 20th day. What are her total sales after 20 days?

SOLUTION
The numbers of pairs of shoes sold each day constitute an arithmetic sequence whose first term $a_1 = 5$ and whose common difference $d = 3$. Using the formula (15.1), we obtain

$$a_{20} = 5 + (20 - 1) \cdot 3 = 62$$

The total sales after 20 days is given by

$$S_{20} = \frac{20}{2}[2 \cdot 5 + (20 - 1) \cdot 3]$$

$$= 670$$
∎

Example 15.7

Susan deposited $1000 in her checking account at the beginning of the semester. She withdraws $25 the first week, $30 the second week, $35 the third week, and so on until her money runs out. How much money is in the checking account after 12 weeks? How long will the initial deposit of $1000 last?

SOLUTION

Since

$$S_n = \frac{n}{2}\left[2a_1 + (n-1)d\right]$$

and $a_1 = 25$, $d = 5$, and $n = 12$, the total withdrawal during the first 12 weeks is given by

$$S_{12} = \frac{12}{2}\left[2 \cdot 25 + (12-1)5\right] = \$630$$

Thus, the amount on deposit is $1000 - \$630 = \$370$.

To determine how long the deposit of $1000 will suffice, suppose that n is the number of weeks the money will last. Then $S_n = \$1000$. Hence

$$S_n = \frac{n}{2}\left[50 + (n-1)5\right]$$

or

$$\frac{n}{2}(5n + 45) = 1000$$

$$n(n + 9) = 400$$

$$n^2 + 9n - 400 = 0$$

$$(n + 25)(n - 16) = 0$$

It follows that $n = 16$ or $n = -25$. Because n must be positive, we conclude that $n = 16$. ∎

EXERCISE 15.2

1. Find the 23rd term of the arithmetic sequence

$$4, 7, 10, 13, \ldots$$

2. Find the 28th term in each of the following arithmetic sequences.
   a. $3, 7, 11, 15, \ldots$ **b.** $15, 13, 11, 9, \ldots$
   c. $-8, -4, 0, 4, \ldots$ **d.** $-6, -1, 4, 9, \ldots$

3. The 3rd and 16th terms of an arithmetic sequence are 13 and 78, respectively. Determine the first term and the common difference. What are the formulas for a_n and S_n?

4. There are 60 terms in an arithmetic sequence of which the first is 9 and the last is 127. Determine a_{31} and S_{10}.

5. The sum of three numbers in an arithmetic progression is 15 and the sum of their squares is 83. Find the numbers.

6. The sum of three numbers in an arithmetic sequence is 33 and the sum of the squares of two extremes is 244. Find the numbers.

7. Find the sum of the
   a. first 40 odd positive integers
   b. first 25 even positive integers
   c. first 60 positive integers

8. Susan runs 2 miles the first day, and increases her daily run by $\frac{1}{2}$ mile every day. How many miles will she run on the 10th day? How far has she run from the beginning to the end of the 15th day?

9. Sunil starts a savings account by depositing $2 the first week and on each subsequent week he deposits $0.50 more than the week before. How much money will he have in his account (without interest) after 10 weeks?

10. A salesman in a department store had sales of $200 on his first day on the job. On each subsequent working day, he had sales of $20 more than he had a day before. Determine his total sales at the end of 15 working days.

11. A salesman starts a savings account by depositing $100. Each month thereafter he deposits $25 more than a month before. What are his total savings (without interest) at the end of one year?

12. Tracey has stacked 20 blocks in the bottom row, 19 in the second row, 18 in the third row, and so on. Determine the number of rows if she has a stack of 155 blocks.

13. Judy stacks 25 blocks in the bottom row, 23 in the second row, 21 in the third row, and so on. Determine the total number of blocks if there are only three blocks in the uppermost row.

14. Anita's father has deposited $4050 in her checking account at the beginning of her school year. She withdraws $25 the first week, $30 the second week, $35 the third week, and so on until her money runs out.
   a. How much money does she withdraw from her account in the 10th week?
   b. How much money is in her checking account after 18 weeks?
   c. What is the balance in her account at the end of 36 weeks?

15. Show that
   a. the sum of the first n positive numbers is $\frac{1}{2}n(n + 1)$
   b. the sum of the first n odd positive number is n^2

15.4 GEOMETRIC PROGRESSIONS

Consider the sequences

   (a) 1, 2, 4, 8, 16, . . .
   (b) 3, 9, 27, 81, 243, . . .
   (c) 2, $-\frac{1}{2}$, $\frac{1}{8}$, $-\frac{1}{32}$, $\frac{1}{128}$, . . .

Each term after the first is the product of the preceding number and a constant. This constant is 2 in the first sequence, 3 in the second sequence, and $-\frac{1}{4}$ in the third sequence. Any such sequences in which the ratio of any term to the preceding term is constant is called a geometric progression. The constant is called the common ratio. Thus, if a_1 is the first number and r is the common ratio, then

$$a_2 = a_1 r$$
$$a_3 = a_2 r = a_1 r^2$$
$$a_4 = a_3 r = a_1 r^3$$

In general, the nth term in a geometric sequence is given by

(15.5) $\quad a_n = a_1 r^{n-1}$

Example 15.8

Find the seventh term of a geometric sequence whose first term is 18 and whose common ratio is $\frac{1}{3}$.

SOLUTION

Here $a_1 = 18$, $r = \frac{1}{3}$, and $n = 7$. Thus,

$$a_7 = a_1 r^6$$
$$= (18)(\tfrac{1}{3})^6 = \tfrac{2}{81}$$ ∎

Example 15.9

Find the eleventh term in a sequence whose fourth term is 24 and whose ninth term is 768.

SOLUTION

We have

$$a_4 = a_1 r^3 = 24$$

and

$$a_9 = a_1 r^8 = 768$$

Thus,

$$\frac{a_1 r^8}{a_1 r^3} = \frac{768}{24} = 32$$

that is,

$$r^5 = 32 \quad \text{or} \quad r = 2$$

Because

$$a_1 r^3 = 24 \quad \text{and} \quad r = 2$$

it follows that

$$a_1 = 3$$

Hence,

$$a_{11} = a_1 r^{10} = 3(2^{10}) = 3072$$ ◼

Example 15.10

Find three consecutive numbers of a geometric sequence that have product 125 and sum 31.

SOLUTION

Let a/r, a, and ar be three consecutive numbers in a sequence. Then

$$\frac{a}{r} \cdot a \cdot ar = 125$$

$$a^3 = 125$$

$$a = 5$$

Also,

$$\frac{5}{r} + 5 + 5r = 31$$

or

$$\frac{5}{r} + 5r = 26$$

$$5r^2 - 26r + 5 = 0$$

$$(5r - 1)(r - 5) = 0$$

$$r = \tfrac{1}{5} \quad \text{or} \quad r = 5$$

Thus, if $r = \tfrac{1}{5}$, then the numbers a/r, a, and ar are

$$25, 5, 1$$

but if $r = 5$, then the numbers are

$$1, 5, 25$$ ◼

Proposition 15.4.1: The sum of the first n terms in a geometric sequence with a_1 as the first term and r the common ratio is given by

$$S_n = \begin{cases} \dfrac{a_1(1 - r^n)}{1 - r} & \text{for } r \neq 1 \\ na_1 & \text{for } r = 1 \end{cases}$$

PROOF

Let

(15.6) $\quad S_n = a_1 + a_1 r + a_1 r^2 + \cdots + a_1 r^{n-2} + a_1 r^{n-1}$

Multiplying this equation by r, we obtain

(15.7) $\quad rS_n = a_1 r + a_1 r^2 + \cdots + a_1 r^{n-1} + a_1 r^{n-1} + a_1 r^n$

Subtracting (15.7) from (15.6), we have

$$S_n(1 - r) = a_1(1 - r^n)$$

or

$$S_n = \frac{a_1(1 - r^n)}{1 - r} \qquad r \neq 1$$

If $r = 1$, then from (15.6), we have

$$S_n = \underbrace{a_1 + a_1 + \cdots + a_1}_{n \text{ times}}$$

$$= na_1 \qquad \blacksquare$$

Example 15.11
Find the sum of the first eight terms of the geometric sequence

$$3, 6, 12, 24, \ldots$$

SOLUTION
Because $a_1 = 3, r = 2$, and $n = 8$, the required sum

$$S_8 = \frac{3(1 - 2^8)}{1 - 2}$$

$$= 765 \qquad \blacksquare$$

Example 15.12
The profit of a department store has shown an annual increase of 4 percent. Assuming that current market trends continue, what will be the store's annual profit in the fifth year, given that the first year profit was \$20,000? Determine also the total profit for the first 5 years.

SOLUTION
Here,

$$a_1 = \$20{,}000 \quad \text{and} \quad n = 5$$

Because the profit increases at an annual rate of 4 percent, we have $r = 1.04$. Thus, the profit in the fifth year is given by

$$a_5 = \$20{,}000(1.04)^4$$

Using Table 4 at the end of the book, we obtain

$$(1.04)^4 = 1.16986$$

Thus,

$$a_5 = \$20,000(1.16986)$$
$$= \$23,397.20$$

The total profit for the 5-year period is given by

$$S_5 = \$20,000 \left[\frac{(1.04)^5 - 1}{(1.04) - 1} \right]$$

$$= \$20,000 \left(\frac{1.21665 - 1}{0.04} \right)$$

$$= \$108,325$$

EXERCISE 15.3

1. Find the 10th term in each of the following sequences.
   a. 2, 6, 18, 54, . . .
   b. 1, 4, 16, 64, . . .
   c. $1, \frac{1}{2}, \frac{1}{4}, \frac{1}{8}, \ldots$
   d. $1, \frac{2}{3}, \frac{4}{9}, \frac{8}{27}, \ldots$
   e. $1, 1.05, (1.05)^2, (1.05)^3, \ldots$
   f. 1, 0.9, 0.81, 0.729, . . .
2. Determine the geometric sequence whose fifth term is 80 and whose eighth term is 640.
3. Determine the geometric sequence whose third term is the square of the first, and whose fifth term is 64.
4. Find three numbers in a geometric progression whose product is 27 and whose sum is 13.
5. Find three numbers in a geometric progression such that their sum is 21 and their product is 216.
6. Find the sum of the first six terms in each of the following sequences.
   a. 2, 10, 50, 250, . . .
   b. 3, 9, 27, 81, . . .
   c. 16, 8, 4, 2, . . .
   d. $6, 3, \frac{3}{2}, \frac{3}{4}, \ldots$
   e. $9, 3, 1, \frac{1}{3}, \ldots$
7. Find a_8 and S_8 given the first term and common ratio as follows:
   a. $a_1 = 3, r = 2$
   b. $a_1 = 2, r = 3$
   c. $a_1 = 27, r = \frac{1}{3}$
   d. $a_1 = 1, r = 1.05$
8. The profit of a grocery store has shown an annual increase of 5 percent. Assuming that current market trends continue, what will be the store's annual profit in the third year, given that the first-year profit was \$15,000? Determine also the total profit for the first 5 years.
9. The expenditures of the Clinton Smelting Company to control air pollution were \$12,500 in 1970. Assuming that the expenditures increase 6 percent annually, what will be the company's annual expenditure in 1975? Determine also the total amount expended from 1970 to 1975.
10. Determine n and S_n in the geometric sequence whose first term is 3, whose common ratio is 2 and whose nth term is 384.

15.5 SIMPLE INTEREST AND SIMPLE DISCOUNT

Consider the investment of P dollars. If i is the annual rate of interest, then the interest earned at the end of the first year is Pi so that the accumulated value of P is $P + Pi$; at the end of 2 years, the accumulated value is $P + P(2i)$; at the end of 3 years, the accumulated value of P is $P + P(3i)$; and so on. Thus, in general, the accumulated value of P at the end of t years is given by

(15.8)
$$A = P + P(it)$$
$$= P(1 + ti)$$

Interest earned according to this method is called simple interest and is given by the formula

$$I = Pit$$

where P is the principal (or the amount invested), i is the annual rate of interest, and t is the number of years.

Example 15.13

Calculate the simple interest and the accumulated value of $800 invested for 4 years at 5 percent per annum.

SOLUTION

Here $P = \$800$, $t = 4$ years, and $i = 5$ percent. The simple interest is

$$I = \$800(0.05) \cdot 4$$
$$= \$160$$

The accumulated value is

$$A = \$800 + \$160$$
$$= \$960$$

The effective rate of interest is the interest paid at the end of the year on the balance at the beginning of the year. The effective rate of discount, denoted by d, on the other hand, is the interest paid at the beginning of the year on the balance at the end of the year. Suppose, for example, that Mr. Brown borrows $100 from a bank for 1 year at an effective rate of interest of 10 percent. He receives $100 from the bank and pays the bank the original loan of $100 plus interest of $10, or a total of $110 at the end of the year. However, if $100 is borrowed for 1 year at an effective rate of discount of 10 percent, then the bank collects the interest in advance and pays Mr. Brown only $90 with the understanding that Mr. Brown will pay $100 at the end of the year. The interest is $10 in both cases. However, if the interest is paid at the end of the year, the customer has the use of the original loan of $100 for the year, but if the interest is collected in advance, then the customer has the use of only $90 for the year. Thus, an effective rate of interest is not the same as an effective rate of discount. However, there is a definite relationship between effective rates of discount and effective rates of interest.

Suppose that Mr. Brown borrows P dollars for t years from the bank at an effective rate of discount d. Because the bank collects its interest of Pdt in advance, the money actually paid to Mr. Brown is $P - Pdt$. If i is the effective rate of interest, then the simple interest earned on the principal of $(P - Pdt)$ for t years is given by

$$(P - Pdt) \cdot t \cdot i$$

Because $(P - Pdt) \cdot t \cdot i = Pdt$, it follows that

$$(15.9) \quad i = \frac{d}{1 - dt}$$

Thus, if an interest of 10 percent is collected in advance when the loan is given for 1 year, then the effective rate of interest is

$$i = \frac{0.10}{1 - 0.10} = 11.11 \text{ percent}$$

Example 15.14

A man has signed a promisory note for $5000 payable 2 years hence. If the money is discounted at 8 percent, how much actual money has he received in cash? What is the effective rate of interest?

SOLUTION

The interest collected in advance is

$$\$5000(0.08) \cdot 2 = \$800$$

Thus, the original principal, in effect, is

$$\$5000 - \$800 = \$4200$$

The effective rate of interest is

$$i = \frac{0.08}{1 - 0.16} = \frac{0.08}{0.84} = 9.52 \text{ percent}$$

EXERCISE 15.4

1. Calculate the simple interest in each of the following cases.
   a. $P = \$200$, $t = 2$ years, $i = 5$ percent
   b. $P = \$500$, $t = 18$ months, $i = 6$ percent
   c. $P = \$450$, $t = 3$ years, $i = 4\frac{1}{2}$ percent
   d. $P = \$275$, $t = 6$ months, $i = 7$ percent
   e. $P = \$300$, $t = 8$ months, $i = 7\frac{1}{2}$ percent
2. Calculate the simple interest and the accumulated amount in each of the following short-term loans.
   a. $P = \$150$, $t = 6$ months, $i = 12$ percent
   b. $P = \$425$, $t = 8$ months, $i = 15$ percent
   c. $P = \$600$, $t = 4$ months, $i = 10$ percent
   d. $P = \$50$, $t = 3$ months, $i = 18$ percent

3. Determine the principal P in each of the following short-term loans.
   a. $A = \$220$, $t = 8$ months, $i = 15$ percent
   b. $A = \$537.50$, $t = 9$ months, $i = 10$ percent
   c. $A = \$88.50$, $t = 18$ months, $i = 12$ percent
   d. $A = \$445.00$, $t = 18$ months, $i = 7\frac{1}{2}$ percent

4. Tracey has deposited \$300 in a savings account that pays 6 percent interest. How much money is in the account after 3 years?

5. Sunil borrows \$500 from the bank for 3 months. If he paid \$11.25 as interest in advance, what is the effective rate of interest?

6. A man borrows money from the bank for 6 months. If he signed a promisory note for \$200 but actually received \$192, what is the effective rate of interest?

7. Marilyn needs \$525 immediately. How much money should she borrow from the bank for 1 year at 12.50 percent if the bank collects the interest in advance? Determine also the effective rate of interest.

8. Anita needs \$300 immediately. How much money should she borrow for 6 months at 15 percent if the interest is collected in advance?

9. Determine the effective rate of interest if the effective rate of discount is
   a. 6 percent   **b.** 15 percent
   c. 18 percent   **d.** 20 percent

10. Determine the effective rate of discount if the effective rate of interest is
   a. 5 percent   **b.** $7\frac{1}{2}$ percent
   c. 8 percent   **d.** 10 percent

15.6 COMPOUND INTEREST AND COMPOUND DEPRECIATION

Consider, for instance, that Mr. Brown opens a savings account with \$500 for 2 years and the bank pays him simple interest at the rate of 6 percent. If he withdraws the interest earned each year, he will have an annual income of

$$\$500(0.06) = \$30$$

and the balance in the account remains at \$500. If he does not withdraw the interest, then the interest for the second year is computed on the \$530 that was in the account at the beginning of the second year. The interest for the second year would then be

$$\$530(0.06) = \$31.80$$

instead of \$30. The practice of reinvesting the interest to earn additional interest is called compound interest. Thus, the theory of compound interest assumes that the principal and the interest earned thereon continue to be reinvested each year.

To develop a basic formula for compound interest, consider an investment of P dollars at the rate of interest i per year. Because the interest during the first year is Pi, the balance at the end of 1 year will be

$$P + Pi = P(1 + i)$$

This balance considered as principal at the beginning of the second year earns interest

$$P(1 + i)i$$

during the second year, so that the balance at the end of the second year is

$$P(1 + i) + P(1 + i)i = P(1 + i)(1 + i) = P(1 + i)^2$$

Now the balance of $P(1 + i)^2$ is considered as principal at the beginning of the third year and earns interest

$$P(1 + i)^2 i$$

during the third year, bringing the total on deposit to

$$P(1 + i)^2 + P(1 + i)^2 i = P(1 + i)^2(1 + i) = P(1 + i)^3$$

Thus, in this manner the general formula for the continued growth of P dollars can be shown to be

(15.10) $A(t) = P(1 + i)^t$

where $A(t)$ is the accumulation of the principal P at the end of t years. Recall from Chapter 9 that we can use the binomial theorem to calculate $(1 + i)^t$ for a given value of i and t.

Example 15.15

If \$500 is deposited at 6 percent compounded annually, what will be the total on deposit at the end of 6 years? How much is the interest?

SOLUTION

Here, $P = \$500$, $i = 0.06$, and $t = 6$. Using (15.10), we have

$$A(6) = \$500(1 + 0.06)^6$$

The values of $(1 + i)^t$ are given in Table 4 at the back of the book for some values of i and t. From Table 4, we obtain

$$(1.06)^6 = 1.41852$$

Thus,

$$A(6) = \$500(1.41852) = \$709.26$$

The interest is $\$709.26 - \$500 = \$209.26$

We have shown that an investment of P dollars will accumulate to $P(1 + i)^t$ at the end of t years at an annual interest rate of i. Sometimes it is necessary to determine how much money a person must invest so as to have a specified sum at the end of t years. Solving (15.10) for P, we obtain

(15.11) $P = A(t)(1 + i)^{-t}$

The values of $(1 + i)^{-t}$ for some values of i and t are available in Table 5 at the back of the book.

Example 15.16

Mrs. Berman wishes to have $2000 available for a European tour she is planning to undertake 3 years hence. What sum of money must she invest now that will accumulate to $2000 in 3 years if interest is 6 percent compounded annually?

SOLUTION

Using the formula (15.11), we have

$$P = \$2000(1.06)^{-3}$$

From Table 5, we obtain

$$(1.06)^{-3} = 0.839619$$

Thus,

$$P = \$2000(0.839619)$$
$$= \$1679.24$$

In recent years, it has become an established practice among commercial banks, savings and loan institutions, credit unions, and other approved financial companies to pay interest more frequently than once a year. Generally, the rate of interest often quoted on an annual basis is, in practice, compounded quarterly, monthly, or even daily. The frequency with which interest is compounded and paid or reinvested to earn additional interest is called the conversion period.

The term effective rate of interest is the rate that, compounded annually, would produce the same dollar amount as the quoted or published rate compounded m times a year. An interest rate of 6 percent per year compounded quarterly, for instance, does not mean that 6 percent is credited to an account at each quarter but rather that an interest of $\frac{1}{4} \cdot 6$ percent $= 1.50$ percent is credited each quarter to the existing balance. The 6 percent is called the nominal rate of interest. That the effective annual rate of interest is 6.14 percent is explained by the fact that each $1 of principal compounded quarterly at 6 percent yields

$$\$(1 + 0.015)^4 = \$1.061364$$

so that annual interest earned is

$$\$1.061364 - \$1 = \$0.061364$$

or 6.14 percent approximately. As another illustration, recall the savings bank advertisement that $1000 deposited with the bank for a period of 4 or more years at 7.50 percent compounded quarterly results in an actual annual yield of 7.90 percent. The effective rate of interest is thus 7.90 percent as compared to the nominal rate of 7.50 percent.

Let i_m denote a nominal rate of interest that is compounded m times a year. What is the equivalent effective rate of interest i compounded annually? Clearly, (i_m/m) is the interest paid at the end of each of the m conversion periods. By an argument similar to the one used in developing (15.10), we can show that the accumulated value of P dollars at the end of t years is given by

(15.12) $$P\left(1 + \frac{i_m}{m}\right)^{mt}$$

Because this must be equal to $P(1 + i)^t$, we have

$$1 + i = \left(1 + \frac{i_m}{m}\right)^{m}$$

Thus, the effective rate of interest is

(15.13) $$i = \left(1 + \frac{i_m}{m}\right)^{m} - 1$$

Example 15.17

Determine the effective rate of interest at a rate of 9 percent compounded
  a. semiannually
  b. monthly

SOLUTION

  a. We have $m = 2$, $i_m = 0.09$. Using (15.13), we obtain

  $i = (1.045)^2 - 1$
  $\quad = 1.092025 - 1 \quad$ (Table 4)
  $\quad = 0.092025$

  b. Here $m = 12$ and $i_m = 0.09$. Thus,

  $i = (1.0075)^{12} - 1$
  $\quad = 1.093807 - 1 \quad$ (Table 4)
  $\quad = 0.093807$

Example 15.18

Find the accumulated amount after 10 years if $1500 is invested at 6 percent per annum compounded
  a. annually   b. semiannually
  c. quarterly   d. monthly

SOLUTION

  a. Here $P = \$1500$, $i = 0.06$, and $t = 10$. Using (15.10), we obtain

  $A = \$1500(1.06)^{10}$
  $\quad = \$1500(1.790848)$
  $\quad = \$2686.27$

b. Here $P = \$1500$, $i_m = 0.06$, $m = 2$, and $i_m/m = 0.06/2 = 0.03$. There are 20 conversion periods. Using (15.12), we have

$$A = \$1500(1.03)^{20}$$
$$= \$1500(1.806111)$$
$$= \$2709.17$$

c. Again, $P = \$1500$, $i_m = 0.06$, $m = 4$, and $i_m/m = 0.06/4 = 0.015$. There are 40 conversion periods. Hence, using (15.12), we obtain

$$A = \$1500(1.015)^{40}$$
$$= \$1500(1.814018)$$
$$= \$2721.03$$

d. $P = \$1500$, $i_m = 0.06$, $m = 12$, and $i_m/m = 0.06/12$. There are 120 conversion periods. Hence,

$$A = \$1500(1.005)^{120}$$

The value of $(1.005)^{120}$ is not given in Table 4. However, observe that

$$(1.005)^{60} = 1.348850 \qquad \text{(Table 4)}$$

and

$$(1.005)^{120} = [(1.005)^{60}]^2$$
$$= (1.348850)^2$$
$$= 1.819396$$

Thus,

$$A = \$1500(1.005)^{120}$$
$$= \$1500(1.819396)$$
$$= \$2729.09$$

■

Example 15.19
Determine the accumulated amount after 10 years if $1500 is invested at 6 percent compounded daily.

SOLUTION
$P = \$1500$, $i_m = 0.06$, $m = 365$, and

$$\frac{i_m}{m} = \frac{0.06}{365} = 0.000164384$$

We are assuming that there are 365 days in a year; thus, there are $10 \times 365 = 3650$ conversion periods. Hence,

$$A = \$1500(1 + 0.000164384)^{3650}$$
$$= \$1500(1.000164384)^{3650}$$

Using an electronic calculator, we observe that

$$(1.000164384)^{3650} = 1.82202895$$

Thus,

$$A = \$1500(1.82202895)$$

$$= \$2733.04$$

The information obtained in the preceding two examples is summarized in the following table.

$$P = \$1500, i_m = 0.06, t = 10 \text{ years}$$

Compounded	Value of m	Accumulated Value of P	Successive Differences
Annually	1	$2686.27	
Semiannually	2	2709.17	$22.90
Quarterly	4	2721.03	11.86
Monthly	12	2729.09	8.06
Daily	365	2733.04	3.95

Note that the more often the interest is compounded, the greater the accumulated value of the principal invested. However, the differences in the accumulated value gets smaller and smaller with every increase in the compounding frequency. This observation suggests that if interest is compounded continuously, the accumulated value of P would be slightly more than the one obtained by daily compounding.

We observed earlier that if (i_m/m) is an interest paid at the end of each of the m conversion periods, then the accumulated value of P dollars at the end of t years is given by (15.12). It can be shown that if interest is compounded continuously, then the accumulated value

$$(15.14) \quad P\left(1 + \frac{i_m}{m}\right)^{mt} \rightarrow Pe^{i_m t}$$

Thus, if $P = \$1500$, $i_m = 0.06$, and $t = 10$ years, then

$$A = \$1500e^{(0.06)10}$$

$$= \$1500e^{0.6}$$

$$= \$1500(1.82212)$$

$$= \$2733.18$$

which is slightly more than the amount obtained by daily compounding.

Example 15.20

Determine how much money should be deposited in the bank if the money is to accumulate to $3000 in 5 years at 6 percent interest compounded
    a. semiannually   b. quarterly
    c. monthly   d. continuously

SOLUTION

a. Here $m = 2$, $i_m = 0.06$, and $i_m/m = 0.06/2 = 0.03$. Because there are 10 conversion periods in 5 years, we have

$P = \$3000(1.03)^{-10}$
$\quad = \$3000(0.744094)$ \quad (Table 5)
$\quad = \$2232.28$

b. Now $m = 4$, $i_m = 0.06$ and $i_m/m = 0.06/4 = 0.015$. Note that there are 20 compounding periods. Thus,

$P = \$3000(1.015)^{-20}$
$\quad = \$3000(0.74247)$ \quad (Table 5)
$\quad = \$2227.41$

c. Here $m = 12$, $i_m = 0.06$, and $i_m/m = 0.06/12 = 0.005$. Because there are 60 conversion periods, we obtain

$P = \$3000(1.005)^{-60}$
$\quad = \$3000(0.741372)$ \quad (Table 5)
$\quad = \$2224.12$

d. From (15.14), we have

$A = Pe^{i_m t}$

or

$P = Ae^{-i_m t}$

Here $A = \$3000$, $i_m = 0.06$, and $t = 5$ years. Hence,

$P = \$3000e^{-(0.06)5}$
$\quad = \$3000e^{-0.3}$
$\quad = \$3000(0.74082)$ \quad (Table 2)
$\quad = \$2222.46$ ■

Compound Depreciation

Linear depreciation assumes that the equipment, machinery, and other items in business depreciate equally for each year of life. However, the value of automobiles, office furniture, household appliances, televisions, and several other business assets drops rapidly at first and then less rapidly as time passes. Several methods are used to determine the market value of an asset after it has been in use for some years. However, we shall limit our discussion to the double declining-balance method approved by the Internal Revenue Service for depreciating business property. According to this method, the depreciation of a business asset for the first year is $2c/n$, where c is the original cost of the asset and n (>1) is the number of years of the life of the asset. Thus, the value of the asset after 1 year of its life is

$$c - \frac{2c}{n} = c\left(1 - \frac{2}{n}\right)$$

The depreciation for each year thereafter is $2/n$ of the value of the asset at the beginning of that year. This implies that the value of the asset after 2 years is

$$c\left(1 - \frac{2}{n}\right) - c\left(1 - \frac{2}{n}\right)\frac{2}{n} = c\left(1 - \frac{2}{n}\right)\left(1 - \frac{2}{n}\right)$$

$$= c\left(1 - \frac{2}{n}\right)^2$$

Thus, the value of the asset after t years is

(15.15) $V(t) = c\left(1 - \frac{2}{n}\right)^t \qquad t \le n$

and the total depreciation after t years is

(15.16) $D(t) = c\left[1 - \left(1 - \frac{2}{n}\right)^t\right]$

Example 15.21

An automobile costs $4000 and has a useful life of 8 years. Determine the amount by which the automobile is depreciated after each of the first 5 years. What is the value of the car after 5 years?

SOLUTION
Here $c = \$4000$. Because $n = 8$,

$$1 - \frac{2}{n} = \frac{3}{4}$$

Thus,

$$D(t) = \$4000\left[1 - (\tfrac{3}{4})^t\right]$$

Let $t = 1, 2, 3, 4$, and 5; we obtain

$$D(1) = \$4000(\tfrac{1}{4}) = \$1000$$
$$D(2) = \$4000(\tfrac{7}{16}) = \$1750$$
$$D(3) = \$4000(\tfrac{37}{64}) = \$2312.50$$
$$D(4) = \$4000(\tfrac{175}{256}) = \$2734.37$$

and

$$D(5) = \$4000(\tfrac{781}{1024}) = \$3050.78$$

The value of the automobile after 5 years is

$$\$4000 - \$3050.78 = \$949.22$$

EXERCISE 15.5

1. Find the accumulated amount $A(t)$ and the compound interest if $300 is deposited for 2 years at 4 percent compounded
   a. annually   **b.** semiannually   **c.** quarterly

2. Find the accumulated amount $A(t)$ and the compound interest if $2000 is invested for 5 years at 6 percent compounded
   a. annually   **b.** semiannually   **c.** quarterly
   d. monthly   **e.** continuously

3. Determine the accumulated amount for each of the following.
   a. $500 for 3 years at 5 percent compounded annually
   b. $1500 for 2 years at 6 percent compounded monthly
   c. $2500 for 5 years at 5 percent compounded semiannually
   d. $1000 for 10 years at 5 percent compounded quarterly
   e. $2000 for 4 years at 6 percent compounded continuously

4. Mr. Smith borrows $800 at 8 percent compounded quarterly. How much does he owe if he borrows funds for
   a. 6 months   **b.** 9 months   **c.** 1 year
   d. 2 years   **e.** $2\frac{1}{2}$ years

5. Mrs. Hawkes deposits $5000 in a savings account at 6 percent compounded quarterly. How much money will she have in her account 10 years from now?

6. At 5 percent compounded quarterly, how long will it take for an investment to double in value?

7. A commercial bank A pays 6 percent interest for savings and compounds it quarterly, whereas another bank B pays $6\frac{1}{2}$ percent simple interest. If a customer wants to deposit $5000 for 5 years, in which bank should he make the deposit?

8. Determine the effective rate of interest at a rate of 9 percent compounded
   a. quarterly   **b.** semiannually

9. Determine the effective rate of interest at a rate of 12 percent compounded
   a. semiannually   **b.** quarterly   **c.** monthly

10. Find the amount that must be invested at 8 percent in order to accumulate $2000 at the end of 3 years if interest is compounded
   a. annually   **b.** semiannually   **c.** quarterly   **d.** continuously

11. Find the amount that must be deposited so as to accumulate to $5000 five years from now at 6 percent compounded
   a. annually   **b.** semiannually   **c.** quarterly
   d. monthly   **e.** continuously

12. Mr. Charles has a loan of $1500 from a bank due in 2 years. How much money must he pay now if the bank is willing to settle for the present value of the loan if the current rate of interest is 10 percent compounded quarterly?

13. Steve wishes to have $5000 available for his daughter, who will enter college in 8 years. What sum of money must he invest now if the current rate of interest is 7 percent compounded quarterly?

14. Determine the rate of interest compounded quarterly if $1000 amounts to $1282.04 in 5 years.

15. Mr. Kaplan needs to borrow $400 for a period of 3 years. He has a choice of borrowing money from bank A, which lends at $5\frac{1}{2}$ percent simple interest, or another bank B, which lends at 5 percent compounded quarterly. At what bank is it cheaper to borrow money?

16. The general level of inflation in the domestic economy averages 6 percent per year. Determine the number of years it will take for the general cost of living to double. (Hint: Use tables of logarithms.)

17. An electric typewriter costs $400 and has a useful life of 10 years. Determine by how much the typewriter has depreciated after each of its first 6 years. What is the resale value of this typewriter in the sixth year of its use?

18. A color television set costs $750 and has a useful life of 5 years. Determine its market value after each of the first 3 years of its use.

19. An automobile costs $3000 and has a useful life of 6 years.
    a. What is its first-year depreciation?
    b. Determine its trade-in value after 3 years of its use.

20. A refrigerator costs $600 and has a useful life of 5 years. Determine by how much it has depreciated after each of its first 3 years.

15.7 ANNUITIES

Let us return to Example 15.16 regarding Mrs. Berman and her trip to Europe. We agreed that she must set aside $1679.24, which would accumulate to $2000 after 3 years at 6 percent compounded annually. Generally, it is not true that people are in a position to deposit a single large sum of money at a given time for a future purpose or obligation. It is far more reasonable to expect lesser amounts of money deposited at the end of each regular interval and the money allowed to grow to a fixed amount after a certain number of years. This leads us to ask how much money Mrs. Berman must deposit at the end of each month assuming that the interest is compounded monthly. Suppose that she makes equal deposits of P dollars each month. Clearly, her first payment, which earns interest for 35 months, would accumulate to $P(1.005)^{35}$; the second monthly payment of P dollars earns interest for 34 months and accumulates to $P(1.005)^{34}$; the accumulated value of her third payment of P dollars is $P(1.005)^{33}$, and so on. Note that her last payment of P dollars made at the end of the thirty-sixth month would not earn interest. The total accumulated value after 36 months, which is denoted by s_{36}, must equal the sum of accumulated values of each monthly payment; that is,

$$P(1.005)^{35} + P(1.005)^{34} + \cdots + P(1.005)^2 + P(1.005) + P$$

Using Proposition 15.4.1 for the sum of n terms of a geometric progression with $a_1 = P$ and $r = 1.005$, we have

$$s_{\overline{36|}} = P\left[\frac{(1.005)^{36} - 1}{0.005}\right]$$

$$= P(39.336104) \qquad \text{(from Table 6 at the back of the book)}$$

Because these deposits must equal $2000, we have

$$P(39.336104) = \$2000$$

or

$$P = \frac{\$2000}{39.336104}$$

$$= \$50.84$$

This is the amount Mrs. Berman must set aside at the end of each month for a period of 3 years.

Definition 15.7.1: A sequence of payments made at regular intervals over a fixed period of time is called an annuity.

The premium paid on a life insurance policy, an interest payment on money borrowed, installment payments on loans, household appliances, automobiles, and mortgage payments on real estate property are all examples of annuities. Consider an annuity under which equal deposits of $1 are made at the end of each year for n years. The first payment of $1, which earns interest for $(n - 1)$ years, accumulates to $(1 + i)^{n-1}$ dollars, where i is the rate of interest per annum. The accumulated value of second payment of $1 at the end of the second year is $(1 + i)^{n-2}$ dollars, and so on. The total accumulated value of this annuity, denoted by $s_{\overline{n}|i}$, is the sum of accumulated values of each payment. Thus,

$$s_{n\,i} = 1 + (1 + i) + (1 + i)^2 + \cdots + (1 + i)^{n-2} + (1 + i)^{n-1}$$

Using Proposition 15.4.1, we obtain

(15.17) $s_{\overline{n}|i} = \left[\dfrac{(1 + i)^n - 1}{i} \right]$

The values of $s_{\overline{n}|i}$ for some values of n and i are given in Table 6 at the back of the book. Thus, if equal deposits of P dollars are made at the end of each interval, then the total accumulated value of the annuity after n payment periods is

(15.18) $A = P \cdot s_{\overline{n}|i}$

where i is the interest allowed for each conversion period.

Example 15.22

George is planning to make a deposit of $50 at the end of every month for 8 years in a bank. Determine the accumulated value of this annuity if the rate of interest is 6 percent compounded
  a. monthly
  b. quarterly

SOLUTION
    a. The interest conversion period and the payment period are both 1 month. Because $P = \$50$, the accumulated value of the annuity is

$A = \$50 s_{\overline{96}|0.005}$

$= \$50(122.828550)$ (from Table 6)

$= \$6141.43$

b. Because the interest is compounded quarterly, it is clear that no funds are on deposit at the beginning of the first quarter, $150 is on deposit at the beginning of the second quarter, and so on. The interest per quarter is $0.06/4 = 0.015$. Thus, the accumulated value of the annuity is

$$A = \$150 \left[\frac{(1 + 0.015)^{32} - 1}{0.015} \right]$$

$$= \$150(40.688288) \quad \text{(Table 6)}$$

$$= \$6103.24$$

Note that the money was compounded less frequently than it was deposited. ■

Example 15.23

Steve wants to buy a stereo 2 years from now. He deposits an equal amount at the end of each month in a bank that pays 9 percent compounded monthly. What should be his monthly deposit if the stereo will cost him $1000?

SOLUTION

From (15.17), we have

$$\$1000 = Ps_{\overline{24}|0.0075}$$

From Table 6, we see that

$$s_{\overline{24}|0.0075} = 26.188469$$

Thus,

$$P = \frac{\$1000}{26.188469}$$

$$= \$38.18$$

■

EXERCISE 15.6

1. Determine the accumulated value of the following annuities, assuming that payments are made at the end of each compounding period.
   a. $2000 deposited annually at 5 percent after 5 years
   b. $1500 deposited semiannually at 6 percent compounded semiannually after 10 years
   c. $1000 deposited quarterly at 7 percent compounded quarterly after 8 years
   d. $1000 deposited monthly at 7 percent compounded quarterly after 8 years
   e. $200 deposited monthly at 6 percent compounded quarterly after 5 years
   f. $200 deposited monthly at 6 percent compounded monthly after 5 years
2. Mr. Smith deposits $40 at the end of each month in a bank for the next 5 years. Determine the accumulated value of this annuity if the rate of interest is 5 percent compounded
   a. annually   b. semiannually   c. quarterly

3. Mr. Peterson is making a monthly deposit of $200 at the end of each month in a special account. The bank pays 5 percent interest compounded quarterly and raises its rate to 6 percent after 4 years. Determine the accumulated value of this annuity after 8 years.

4. Determine the accumulated value of an annuity after 10 years if $500 is deposited at the end of each quarter and the bank pays 6 percent interest compounded quarterly and then raises the rate of interest to 7 percent compounded quarterly after 5 years.

5. Determine the accumulated value of a 15-year annuity if $100 is deposited at the end of each month and the bank pays 6 percent interest compounded monthly for the first 5 years, 9 percent for the next 5 years, and 12 percent for the last 5 years.

6. Marilyn wants to buy a color television 3 years from now. She wants to deposit an equal amount at the end of each month in a bank that pays interest at 9 percent compounded monthly. What should be her monthly deposit if the television set costs $1000?

7. Roger is planning to buy an expensive engagement ring for Jeannie 2 years from now. He wants to make monthly deposits of an equal amount at the end of each month in a bank that pays 8 percent interest compounded quarterly. What should be his monthly deposit if the engagement diamond will cost $1500?

8. Mr. Spark is planning to buy an expensive graduation gift for his daughter 3 years from now. How much money should he deposit at the end of each month if the gift costs $7200 and the bank pays 6 percent interest compounded
   a. monthly   **b.** quarterly

9. Dr. Grant intends to have $20,000 in a special account at the end of 15 years for his daughter's college education. How much money should he deposit at the end of each month if the bank pays 9 percent interest compounded monthly? {Hint: $(1.0075)^{180} = [(1.0075)^{90}]^2 = 3.838041$].}

10. Refer to Exercise 9. What should be the monthly deposit if the bank pays 9 percent interest compounded monthly for the first 10 years and then raises its interest to 12 percent?

11. Mr. Peterson intends to have $25,000 in a special account at the end of 25 years. He deposits $50 in the bank at the end of each month for the first 10 years. What should be his monthly deposit for the last 15 years if the bank pays interest at 6 percent compounded monthly?

12. Refer to Exercise 11. What should be the monthly deposit for the last 15 years if the bank pays 6 percent interest compounded monthly for the first 10 years and then raises the rate of interest to 9 percent?

13. A loan of $1000 is to be repaid 1 year from now by regular monthly payments. How much money must be set aside at the end of each month if interest is 12 percent compounded
    a. quarterly   **b.** monthly

14. Mr. Peterson has borrowed $2000 for 2 years at 10 percent compounded quarterly. How much money must he set aside each month if his deposits earn 6 percent interest compounded monthly?

15. Prugg has borrowed $3000 for 5 years at 12 percent interest compounded monthly. He deposits $40 each month for the first 2 years. What should be his monthly deposits for the next 3 years if the bank pays interest at 5 percent compounded quarterly?

15.8 PRESENT VALUE OF AN ANNUITY

Having determined the accumulated value of the annuity and the periodical payment P for an annuity, we now consider the present value of an annuity. Suppose, for example, that Mr. Smith wants to provide for his daughter's college education by depositing enough money in a savings bank the day she enters college so that she can withdraw $750 at the end of each quarter for the next 4 years. How much money should be deposited in the bank in one lump sum if interest is 5 percent compounded quarterly?

In order to provide the first payment of $750 at the end of the first 3-month period, we must have its present value, that is, $750(1 + 0.0125)^{-1}$ on deposit with the bank at the outset. Similarly, to provide $750 at the end of the second quarter, we must have $750(1.0125)^{-2}$ on deposit at the start, and so on. Because the present value of an annuity must equal the sum of the present values of each periodical payment, we obtain

$$750(1.0125)^{-1} + 750(1.0125)^{-2} + \cdots + 750(1.0125)^{-16}$$
$$= 750(1.0125)^{-16}[1 + (1.0125) + (1.025)^2 + \cdots + (1.025)^{15}]$$
$$= 750(1.0125)^{-16}\left[\frac{(1.0125)^{16} - 1}{0.0125}\right]$$
$$= 750\left[\frac{1 - (1.0125)^{-16}}{0.0125}\right]$$

From Table 5 at the back of the book, we see that $(1.0125)^{-16} = 0.81975$. Thus, the present value of the annuity is

$$750\left(\frac{1 - 0.819746}{0.125}\right) = 750(14.42)$$
$$= \$10,815$$

Thus, a deposit of $10,815 will enable Mr. Smith's daughter to withdraw $750 at the end of each 3-month period for the next 4 years.

We now develop a general formula for the present value of an annuity.

Definition 15.8.1: The present value of an annuity, denoted by $a_{\overline{n}|}$ is the sum of the present values of each payment.

Consider an annuity under which payments of $1 are made at the end of each year for n years. The present value of the first payment at the end of the first year is $(1 + i)^{-1}$; the present value of the second payment at the end of the second year is $(1 + i)^{-2}$; the present value of the third payment at the end of the third year is $(1 + i)^{-3}$; and so on. Because the present value of an annuity is the sum of the present value of each payment,

$$a_{\overline{n}} = (1 + i)^{-1} + (1 + i)^{-2} + \cdots + (1 + i)^{-n}$$
$$= (1 + i)^{-n}[1 + (1 + i) + (1 + i)^2 + \cdots + (1 + i)^{n-1}]$$
$$= (1 + i)^{-n}\left[\frac{(1 + i)^n - 1}{i}\right] \qquad \text{(Proposition 15.4.1)}$$

Hence,

(15.19) $\quad a_{\overline{n}} = \dfrac{1 - (1 + i)^{-n}}{i}$

Thus, if P represents the payment made in dollars, the present value V of the annuity for n payment periods is

(15.20) $\quad V = Pa_{\overline{n}i}$

where i is the rate of interest for each conversion period. Values of $a_{\overline{n}i}$ at several rates of interest and for different values of n are given in Table 7 at the back of the book.

Example 15.24

Determine the present value of an annuity that pays \$500 at the end of each 6-month period for 15 years if interest is 5 percent compounded semiannually.

SOLUTION
Here $P = \$500$. Thus,

$$V = \$500a_{\overline{30}|0.025}$$
$$= \$500(20.930292) \qquad \text{(from Table 7)}$$
$$= \$10,465.15$$

Example 15.25

Susan wants to finance her new car for \$3000 and wants to pay it off in 30 equal monthly payments. How much money should she set aside at the end of each month if the current rate of interest is 15 percent compounded monthly?

SOLUTION
Let R be the amount of each monthly payment. Then

$$Ra_{\overline{30}|0.0125} = \$3000$$
$$R = \frac{\$3000}{a_{\overline{30}|0.0125}}$$
$$= \frac{\$3000}{24.888905} \qquad \text{(from Table 7)}$$
$$= \$124.96$$

Example 15.26

A house is offered for sale for $25,000. The buyer has $5000 for a down payment. What will be his mortgage payment if he borrows $20,000 for 25 years at an annual rate of 9 percent compounded monthly? Determine also the total interest paid on this loan.

SOLUTION

Let R be the amount of his monthly mortgage payment. Then

$$Ra_{\overline{300}|0.0075} = \$20,000$$

Values of $a_{\overline{300}|0.0075}$ are not given in Table 7. However, because

$$a_{\overline{300}|0.0075} = \frac{1 - (1.0075)^{-300}}{0.0075}$$

and $(1.0075)^{-100} = 0.473690$ from Table 5, we have

$$(1.0075)^{-300} = (0.47369)^3 = 0.106287$$

Thus,

$$a_{\overline{300}|0.0075} = 119.161$$

and

$$R = \frac{\$20,000}{119.161} = \$167.84$$

The total money paid to the lending institution is $300(167.84) = \$50,352$, so that

$$\$50,352 - \$25,000 = \$27,352$$

is the interest, which is more than the principal originally borrowed. ■

EXERCISE 15.7

1. Assuming that payments are made at the end of each conversion period, determine the present value of each of the following annuities.
   a. $1000 payable annually for 5 years at 5 percent interest
   b. $1500 payable semiannually for 10 years at 6 percent compounded semiannually
   c. $500 payable quarterly for 20 years at 8 percent compounded quarterly
   d. $200 payable monthly for 15 years at 6 percent compounded quarterly
   e. $200 payable monthly for 15 years at 6 percent compounded monthly
2. Determine the periodic payment derived from the following established annuities:

	Present Value	Term	Annual Rate	To Be Paid
a.	$ 5,000	5 years	5 percent	annually
b.	$10,000	10 years	8 percent	semiannually
c.	$10,000	6 years	6 percent	quarterly
d.	$20,000	15 years	9 percent	monthly

3. Mr. Robinson wishes to retire at the end of this year. He plans to withdraw $250 at the end of each month for the next 10 years. Determine the amount that must be deposited in the bank if interest is at 6 percent compounded monthly.

4. Mr. Johnson wishes to retire at age 60 and plans to withdraw $600 at the end of each quarter for the next 15 years. How much money should he deposit in the bank in one lump sum if the bank pays interest at 7 percent compounded quarterly?

5. Kathy is the beneficiary of a life insurance policy of $20,000. She wishes to receive a steady income at the end of each quarter for the next 10 years. If money is worth 8 percent compounded quarterly, what amount will she receive at the end of each quarter?

6. Refer to Exercise 5. What is the amount of her monthly withdrawals for the next 10 years if money is worth 9 percent compounded monthly?

7. Mr. Dorman wants to provide for his daughter's college education by depositing enough money in a savings bank the day she enters college so that she can withdraw $200 at the end of each month for the next 4 years. Determine the amount that must be on deposit in a bank if interest is 6 percent compounded monthly.

8. In Exercise 7, suppose that withdrawals of $500 are scheduled at the end of each quarter for the next 4 years. What amount should Mr. Dorman deposit in the bank if interest is 7 percent compounded quarterly?

9. An executive secretary aged 50 wishes to establish his retirement fund by depositing $300 at the end of each quarter for the next 15 years. Starting at 65, he decides to make quarterly withdrawals from his fund for 10 years after retirement. Determine how much money he can withdraw at the end of each quarter if money is worth 5 percent compounded quarterly.

10. Mr. Goodrich plans to borrow $5000 for a period of 5 years. If money is worth 12 percent compounded monthly, what is his monthly payment? Determine also the total finance charge.

11. Jeannie wants to finance her new car for $4000. Determine her monthly payment if the current rate of interest is 12 percent compounded monthly and she plans to pay off the loan with finance charges in
    a. 24 months   b. 30 months   c. 36 months   d. 48 months

12. Mike wants to finance his new color television set for $750. Determine his monthly payment if the current rate of interest is 18 percent compounded monthly and he plans to pay off in
    a. 12 months   b. 18 months   c. 24 months

13. A house is offered for sale for $25,000. The seller agrees to accept $150 at the end of each month for 10 years. Assuming that the interest rate is 9 percent compounded monthly, what should be the down payment?

14. In Exercise 13, suppose that a down payment of $10,000 is made. What is the monthly payment if the house is to be paid off in 15 years?

15. A newly wed couple is planning to buy a $40,000 home and wishes to make a down payment of $10,000. What is their mortgage monthly payment if the house is to be paid off in 20 years and the current rate of interest is 6 percent compounded monthly?

16
Limits and Continuity

16.1 INTRODUCTION

The limit concept is the single most important concept of calculus that sets it apart from the other branches of mathematics. In many cases, the concept examines the behavior of a function, say, $f(x)$, as x approaches but is never allowed to equal a given number in its domain. Because a precise understanding of the limit is essential for a good grasp of what follows in the next few chapters, we shall introduce the limit concept in relation to the sequences. Later we shall extend this concept to more general functions which, in turn, lead to the basic ideas of continuity.

16.2 LIMIT OF A SEQUENCE

In the preceding chapter, we discussed arithmetic and geometric sequences. Now, we shall study the behavior of the general term a_n of an infinite sequence when n becomes large.

Example 16.1

Consider the infinite geometric sequence

$$\tfrac{1}{2}, \tfrac{1}{4}, \tfrac{1}{8}, \tfrac{1}{16}, \ldots, (\tfrac{1}{2})^n, \ldots$$

In this sequence,

$$a_1 = \tfrac{1}{2}, a_2 = \tfrac{1}{4}, a_3 = \tfrac{1}{8}, \ldots, a_n = (\tfrac{1}{2})^n, \ldots$$

Because a sequence is a special type of function, we can graph it in the usual coordinate system as shown in Figure 16.1. Note that the successive terms in the sequence get smaller and smaller; they come closer and closer to zero despite the fact that no term in the sequence is actually zero. Accordingly, we write

$$(\tfrac{1}{2})^n \to 0 \quad \text{or} \quad \lim_{n \to \infty} (\tfrac{1}{2})^n = 0$$

and say that as n gets larger and larger or as n approaches infinity, the sequence $(\tfrac{1}{2})^n$ converges to 0 or has limit 0.

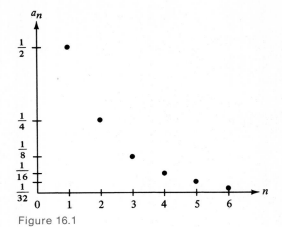

Figure 16.1

Example 16.2

Consider the infinite sequence

$$1, \frac{1}{2}, \frac{1}{3}, \frac{1}{4}, \ldots, \frac{1}{n}, \ldots$$

Here,

$$a_1 = 1, a_2 = \frac{1}{2}, a_3 = \frac{1}{3}, \ldots, a_n = \frac{1}{n}, \ldots$$

Again, as n gets larger and larger, the terms of the sequence come closer and closer to zero (yet no term in the sequence is actually zero). Intuitively, it appears that the terms of the sequence converge to zero as n approaches infinity. Thus,

$$\lim_{n \to \infty} \left(\frac{1}{n} \right) = 0$$

Example 16.3

Consider the infinite sequence

$$3, \frac{7}{2}, \frac{11}{3}, \frac{15}{4}, \ldots, \frac{4n-1}{n}, \ldots$$

Here,

$$a_1 = 3, a_2 = \frac{7}{2}, a_3 = \frac{11}{3}, a_4 = \frac{15}{4}, a_5 = \frac{19}{5}, \ldots,$$

$$a_{10} = \frac{39}{10}, \ldots, a_{50} = \frac{199}{50}, \ldots, a_{100} = \frac{399}{100}, \ldots, a_{1000} = \frac{3999}{1000}, \ldots$$

As n takes on larger and larger values, the terms of the sequence get closer and closer to 4. Thus,

$$\lim_{n \to \infty} \left(\frac{4n - 1}{n} \right) = 4$$ ∎

Example 16.4

Consider the infinite sequence with the general term

$$a_n = \frac{3n + 1}{2n - 1}$$

We wish to examine whether or not this infinite sequence has a limit when $n \to \infty$. Substituting $n = 1, 2, 3, \ldots$, we see that

$$a_1 = 4, a_2 = \frac{7}{3} = 2.333, a_3 = 2,$$

$$a_4 = \frac{13}{7} = 1.857, a_5 = \frac{16}{9} = 1.777, a_6 = \frac{19}{11} = 1.727, \ldots$$

$$a_{13} = \frac{8}{5} = 1.6, \ldots, a_{51} = \frac{154}{101} = 1.524, \ldots$$

$$a_{101} = \frac{304}{201} = 1.512, \ldots, a_{501} = \frac{1504}{1001} = 1.502, \ldots$$

Figure 16.2 represents the graph of the first six terms of this sequence. Note that as n becomes larger and larger, the terms of this sequence come closer and closer to a particular number. This observation suggests that a limit may exist. Can you guess this number? If not, let us look at the problem a little differently. Because $n \neq 0$, we can divide both numerator and denominator of the general term a_n by n. Thus,

$$\frac{3n + 1}{2n - 1} = \frac{3 + 1/n}{2 - 1/n}$$

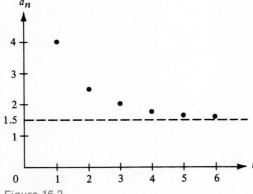

Figure 16.2

Using the fact that

$$\lim_{n \to \infty} \frac{1}{n} = 0$$

we observe that

$$\lim_{n \to \infty} \left(3 + \frac{1}{n} \right) = 3 \quad \text{and} \quad \lim_{n \to \infty} \left(2 - \frac{1}{n} \right) = 2$$

Thus, it is reasonable to suggest that

$$\lim_{n \to \infty} \left(\frac{3n + 1}{2n - 1} \right) = \lim_{n \to \infty} \left(\frac{3 + 1/n}{2 - 1/n} \right) = \frac{3}{2} \qquad \blacksquare$$

Now we attempt to make the concept of the limit of a sequence more precise. When we say that the sequence $\{a_n\}$ approaches a particular number, say L, when n is very large, we mean that after a certain stage in the sequence $\{a_n\}$ is reached, say for $n = N$, all the remaining terms of the sequence $a_{N+1}, a_{N+2}, \ldots$, lie in the interval $(L - \varepsilon, L + \varepsilon)$, where ε is any given positive integer.

These considerations lead to the following precise definition of the limit of a sequence.

Definition 16.2.1: The infinite sequence $\{a_n\}$ approaches L or has limit L as $n \to \infty$ if and only if for any preassigned positive number ε, there exists a positive integer N such that

$$L - \varepsilon < a_n < L + \varepsilon$$

That is,

$$-\varepsilon < a_n - L < \varepsilon \qquad \text{for } n \geq N$$

We must emphasize that N depends on the size of ε. To illustrate this important point, let us return to the sequence $a_n = 1/n$ in Example 16.2. Because we have already suggested that this sequence has the limit zero, we should be able to demonstrate the existence of a positive integer N (depending on ε) such that all terms of the sequence a_n for $n \geq N$ lie in the open interval $(-\varepsilon, \varepsilon)$, where ε is a preassigned positive number. In other words, we need to show that for any given $\varepsilon > 0$, there exists a positive integer N such that

$$\frac{1}{n} < \varepsilon \qquad \text{for } n \geq N$$

which in turn implies that

$$n > \frac{1}{\varepsilon}$$

This means that we can let N be the first positive integer greater than $1/\varepsilon$. If $\varepsilon = 1/5$, then $N = 6$ satisfies the definition, because $n \geq 6$ implies that $1/n < 1/5$. If $\varepsilon = 1/100$, then $N = 101$, because $n \geq 101$ is equivalent to $1/n < 1/100$. Thus, given any positive number ε, we can always find an integer N that satisfies Definition 16.2.1.

As another illustration, let us return to the sequence $a_n = (3n - 1)/(2n + 1)$ in Example 16.4. We suggested earlier that this sequence has the limit $L = \frac{3}{2}$. Now we can prove it. How can we choose N for a given $\varepsilon > 0$? Note that

$$a_n - L = \frac{3n + 1}{2n - 1} - \frac{3}{2}$$

$$= \frac{6n + 2 - 6n + 3}{2(2n - 1)}$$

$$= \frac{5}{2(2n - 1)}$$

Further, $a_n - L < \varepsilon$ implies that

$$\frac{5}{2(2n - 1)} < \varepsilon$$

Taking reciprocals of both sides, we obtain

$$\frac{2(2n - 1)}{5} > \frac{1}{\varepsilon}$$

which on simplification yields

$$n > \frac{1}{2} + \frac{5}{4\varepsilon}$$

so that if $\varepsilon = \frac{1}{4}$, the term on the right-hand side equals $5\frac{1}{2}$ and thus $N = 6$. If $\varepsilon = \frac{1}{20}$, then

$$\frac{1}{2} + \frac{5}{4\varepsilon} = 25\frac{1}{2}$$

and we can choose $N = 26$; and if $\varepsilon = 1/1000$, then

$$\frac{1}{2} + \frac{5}{4\varepsilon} = 1250\frac{1}{2}$$

and $N = 1251$. In all such cases, we choose N as the first positive integer greater than $[(1/2) + (5/4\varepsilon)]$.

We must caution the reader that Definition 16.2.1 is not to be used as a tool for finding the limit of an infinite sequence, nor is it of any help in determining whether or not the limit exists. Its only aim is to make the intuitive idea precise and consequently provide the basic machinery to find a positive integer N, if the limit exists, so that all terms in the sequence from that point onward lie in an interval of the form $(L - \varepsilon, L + \varepsilon)$.

We do not wish to leave the impression that all sequences approach a particular number if we go far enough out in the sequence. We illustrate this in the following examples.

Example 16.5

Consider the infinite sequence

$$3, 5, 7, 9, \ldots, (2n + 1), \ldots$$

As n increases, the terms of the sequence $a_n = 2n + 1$ get larger and larger but do not approach any particular number. Intuitively, the sequence does not have a limit. Accordingly, we say that the sequence $a_n = 2n + 1$ diverges. ■

Example 16.6

Consider the infinite sequence

$$-1, 1, -1, 1, \ldots, (-1)^n, \ldots$$

Apparently,

$$a_n = \begin{cases} 1 & \text{if } n \text{ is even} \\ -1 & \text{if } n \text{ is odd} \end{cases}$$

This sequence does not tend to a limit, because there are two numbers to which the terms of the sequence approach. ■

This example leads us to the following proposition, which we state without proof.

Propostion 16.2.1: The limit of an infinite sequence, if it exists, is unique. ■

Limits of sequences have several useful properties that may be used to evaluate the limit of many sequences. If $\{a_n\}$ and $\{b_n\}$ are two infinite sequences, and c is a constant, we can form new sequences $\{ca_n\}$, $\{a_n \pm b_n\}$, and $\{a_n b_n\}$. The sequence $\{a_n/b_n\}$ can be formed if and only if $b_n \neq 0$ for each n.

We now state the following propositions (without proof). Note that in each case, L, L_1, and L_2 are finite.

Proposition 16.2.2: $\lim_{n \to \infty} c = c$ where c is constant. ■

Proposition 16.2.3: If $\lim_{n \to \infty} a_n = L$, then

$$\lim_{n \to \infty} (ca_n) = c \lim_{n \to \infty} a_n = cL,$$

where c is a constant. ■

Proposition 16.2.4: If $\lim_{n \to \infty} a_n = L_1$ and $\lim_{n \to \infty} b_n = L_2$, then

$$\lim_{n \to \infty} (a_n \pm b_n) = \lim_{n \to \infty} a_n \pm \lim_{n \to \infty} b_n = L_1 \pm L_2$$

■

Proposition 16.2.5: If $\lim_{n \to \infty} a_n = L_1$ and $\lim_{n \to \infty} b_n = L_2$, then

$$\lim_{n \to \infty} (a_n b_n) = \left(\lim_{n \to \infty} a_n \right) \left(\lim_{n \to \infty} b_n \right) = L_1 L_2$$

Proposition 16.2.6: If $\lim_{n \to \infty} a_n = L_1$ and $\lim_{n \to \infty} b_n = L_2$, then

$$\lim_{n \to \infty} \left(\frac{a_n}{b_n} \right) = \frac{\lim_{n \to \infty} a_n}{\lim_{n \to \infty} b_n} = \frac{L_1}{L_2}$$

where $L_2 \neq 0$ and $b_n \neq 0$ for each n.

In other words, the limit of the sum (difference), product, and quotient of two sequences equals, respectively, the sum (difference), product, and quotient of their limits.

To illustrate these propositions, let us consider the following examples.

Example 16.7

Evaluate $\lim_{n \to \infty} a_n$, where

$$a_n = \frac{n + 1}{2n}$$

SOLUTION

Because

$$\frac{n + 1}{2n} = \frac{1}{2} \left(1 + \frac{1}{n} \right)$$

it is easy to see that

$$\lim_{n \to \infty} a_n = \lim_{n \to \infty} \left(\frac{n + 1}{2n} \right)$$

$$= \frac{1}{2} \lim_{n \to \infty} \left(1 + \frac{1}{n} \right) \qquad \text{(Proposition 16.2.3)}$$

$$= \frac{1}{2} \left(\lim_{n \to \infty} 1 + \lim_{n \to \infty} \frac{1}{n} \right) \qquad \text{(Proposition 16.2.4)}$$

$$= \frac{1}{2} (1 + 0) \qquad \text{because } \lim_{n \to \infty} \frac{1}{n} = 0 \qquad \text{(Proposition 16.2.2)}$$

$$= \frac{1}{2}$$

Example 16.8

Evaluate $\lim_{n \to \infty} b_n$, where

$$b_n = \frac{3n - 2}{2n + 1}$$

SOLUTION

Note that because

$$\frac{3n - 2}{2n + 1} = \frac{3 - 2/n}{2 + 1/n}$$

we have

$$\lim_{n \to \infty} b_n = \lim_{n \to \infty} \left(\frac{3n - 2}{2n + 1} \right) = \lim_{n \to \infty} \left(\frac{3 - 2/n}{2 + 1/n} \right)$$

Dealing with numerator and denominator separately, we have

$$\lim_{n \to \infty} \left(3 - \frac{2}{n} \right) = \lim_{n \to \infty} 3 - \lim_{n \to \infty} \frac{2}{n} \qquad \text{(Proposition 16.2.4)}$$

Because

$$\lim_{n \to \infty} 3 = 3 \qquad \text{(Proposition 16.2.2)}$$

and

$$\lim_{n \to \infty} \left(\frac{2}{n} \right) = 2 \lim_{n \to \infty} \left(\frac{1}{n} \right) \qquad \text{(Proposition 16.2.3)}$$

$$= 2 \cdot 0$$

$$= 0$$

we conclude that

$$\lim_{n \to \infty} \left(3 - \frac{2}{n} \right) = \lim_{n \to \infty} 3 - \lim_{n \to \infty} \frac{2}{n} = 3 - 0 = 3$$

Similarly,

$$\lim_{n \to \infty} \left(2 + \frac{1}{n} \right) = \lim_{n \to \infty} 2 + \lim_{n \to \infty} \frac{1}{n}$$

$$= 2 + 0$$

$$= 2$$

Thus,

$$\lim_{n \to \infty} \frac{(3 - 2/n)}{(2 + 1/n)} = \frac{\lim_{n \to \infty} (3 - 2/n)}{\lim_{n \to \infty} (2 + 1/n)} \qquad \text{(Proposition 16.2.6)}$$

$$= \frac{3}{2}$$

Example 16.9

Evaluate $\lim_{n \to \infty} a_n$, where

$$a_n = \frac{2n^2 + 1}{n^2 - 1}$$

SOLUTION

Because

$$\frac{2n^2 + 1}{n^2 - 1} = \frac{2 + 1/n^2}{1 - 1/n^2}$$

we have

$$\lim_{n \to \infty} a_n = \lim_{n \to \infty} \left(\frac{2n^2 + 1}{n^2 - 1} \right)$$

$$= \lim_{n \to \infty} \left(\frac{2 + 1/n^2}{1 - 1/n^2} \right)$$

$$= \frac{\lim_{n \to \infty} (2 + 1/n^2)}{\lim_{n \to \infty} (1 - 1/n^2)} \qquad \text{(Proposition 16.2.6)}$$

Because

$$\lim_{n \to \infty} \left(\frac{1}{n^2} \right) = \lim_{n \to \infty} \left(\frac{1}{n} \cdot \frac{1}{n} \right) = \left(\lim_{n \to \infty} \frac{1}{n} \right) \left(\lim_{n \to \infty} \frac{1}{n} \right) = 0 \cdot 0 = 0$$

we have

$$\lim_{n \to \infty} a_n = \frac{2 + 0}{1 - 0}$$

$$= 2$$

■

Example 16.10

Let

$$a_n = \frac{n + 1}{2n} \quad \text{and} \quad b_n = \frac{3n - 2}{2n + 3}$$

Verify that

$$\lim_{n \to \infty} (a_n b_n) = \left(\lim_{n \to \infty} a_n \right) \left(\lim_{n \to \infty} b_n \right)$$

SOLUTION

We have already established that

$$\lim_{n \to \infty} \left(\frac{n + 1}{2n} \right) = \frac{1}{2} \quad \text{and} \quad \lim_{n \to \infty} \frac{3n - 2}{2n + 3} = \frac{3}{2}$$

Now

$$a_n b_n = \left(\frac{n+1}{2n}\right)\left(\frac{3n-2}{2n+3}\right)$$

$$= \frac{3n^2 + n - 2}{4n^2 + 6n}$$

$$= \frac{3 + 1/n - 2/n^2}{4 + 6/n}$$

Because

$$\lim_{n \to \infty} \frac{1}{n} = 0 \quad \text{and} \quad \lim_{n \to \infty} \frac{1}{n^2} = 0$$

it is easy to see that

$$\lim_{n \to \infty}(a_n b_n) = \frac{\displaystyle\lim_{n \to \infty}(3 + 1/n - 2/n^2)}{\displaystyle\lim_{n \to \infty}(4 + 6/n)}$$

$$= \frac{3 + 0 - 0}{4 + 0}$$

$$= \frac{3}{4}$$

$$= \frac{1}{2} \cdot \frac{3}{2}$$

$$= \left(\lim_{n \to \infty} a_n\right)\left(\lim_{n \to \infty} b_n\right)$$

and this illustrates Proposition 16.2.5. ∎

EXERCISE 16.1

In each of the following, the nth term of a sequence $\{a_n\}$ is given. Evaluate $\lim_{n \to \infty} a_n$ if it exists.

1. $a_n = \dfrac{n}{n+1}$

2. $a_n = \dfrac{n-1}{n+2}$

3. $a_n = \dfrac{2n+1}{3n+2}$

4. $a_n = \dfrac{3n+4}{4n+3}$

5. $a_n = \dfrac{n}{n^2+1}$

6. $a_n = \dfrac{n^2}{3n^2+5}$

7. $a_n = \dfrac{2n-1}{n^2+n+2}$

8. $a_n = \dfrac{6-2n^2}{8+3n^2}$

9. $a_n = \dfrac{(-1)^n}{n^2+2}$

10. $a_n = \dfrac{(-1)^n(n+1)}{n}$

11. $a_n = n^n$

12. $a_n = n!$

13. $a_n = \dfrac{2n + 1}{3n - 4}$

14. $a_n = \dfrac{3n + 1}{n^2}$

15. $a_n = \dfrac{(-1)^n(n + 1)}{2n}$

16. $a_n = \dfrac{n^2}{3n + 8}$

17. $a_n = \dfrac{n^2 + 3}{n + 1}$

18. $a_n = \dfrac{n^2 - 3n + 1}{4n^2 + 3n + 5}$

19. $a_n = \dfrac{2^n - 1}{2^n}$

20. $a_n = \dfrac{3^n - 1}{3^n}$

In each of the following sequences, the nth term of a sequence $\{a_n\}$ is given. Evaluate $\lim_{n \to \infty} a_n$ and find a positive integer N corresponding to the given ε to satisfy Definition 16.2.2.

21. $a_n = \dfrac{n + 1}{2n}; \varepsilon = \dfrac{1}{50}$

22. $a_n = \dfrac{2n + 1}{3n + 1}; \varepsilon = \dfrac{1}{10}$

23. $a_n = \dfrac{3n + 1}{4n}; \varepsilon = \dfrac{1}{100}$

24. $a_n = \dfrac{1}{n^2}; \varepsilon = \dfrac{1}{25}$

25. Given two infinite sequences

$$a_n = \frac{2n + 3}{3n - 4} \qquad b_n = \frac{n - 1}{2n}$$

Verify that

a. $\lim\limits_{n \to \infty} (a_n b_n) = \left(\lim\limits_{n \to \infty} a_n \right)\left(\lim\limits_{n \to \infty} b_n \right)$

b. $\lim\limits_{n \to \infty} \left(\dfrac{a_n}{b_n} \right) = \dfrac{\lim\limits_{n \to \infty} a_n}{\lim\limits_{n \to \infty} b_n}, b_n \neq 0$

26. Given two infinite sequences

$$a_n = \frac{5n}{2n + 1} \qquad b_n = \frac{3n + 4}{2n}$$

Verify that

a. $\lim\limits_{n \to \infty} (a_n + b_n) = \lim\limits_{n \to \infty} a_n + \lim\limits_{n \to \infty} b_n$

b. $\lim\limits_{n \to \infty} (a_n \cdot b_n) = \left(\lim\limits_{n \to \infty} a_n \right) \cdot \left(\lim\limits_{n \to \infty} b_n \right)$

c. $\lim\limits_{n \to \infty} \left(\dfrac{a_n}{b_n} \right) = \dfrac{\lim\limits_{n \to \infty} a_n}{\lim\limits_{n \to \infty} b_n}, b_n \neq 0$

16.3 LIMIT OF A FUNCTION

Consider a function $y = f(x)$ and a line $x = a$ as in Figure 16.3. What is the value of $f(x)$ as x approaches a through values of x less than a? Does it, in some sense, get closer and closer to some particular number, say L_1? If so, we say that the left-hand limit exists, and we write

$$\lim_{x \to a^-} f(x) = L_1$$

The symbol $x \to a^-$ means that x approaches a through values of x less than a. Now consider the analogous situation and ask what is the value of $f(x)$ as x approaches a through values of x greater than a as shown in Figure 16.4. If $f(x)$ approaches some particular number, say L_2, then we say that the right-hand limit of $f(x)$ exists, and we write

$$\lim_{x \to a^+} f(x) = L_2$$

The symbol $x \to a^+$ implies that x approaches a through values of x greater than a.

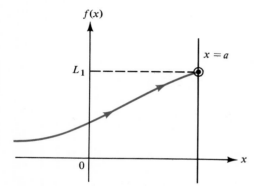

Figure 16.3

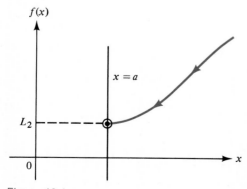

Figure 16.4

If $L_1 = L_2 = L$ (say), then we say that the limit of $f(x)$, as x approaches a, exists, and we write

$$\lim_{x \to a} f(x) = L$$

Note that the value of the function $f(x)$ at $x = a$ has no effect on the existence or nonexistence of the limit. This means that in order for the limit of $f(x)$ to exist (as $x \to a$) and be equal to L, it is necessary that both the left-hand and the right-hand limits at a exist and are equal to L. Thus, $\lim_{x \to a} f(x)$ does not exist if either the right-hand or left-hand limit fails to exist at a or both these limits exist but are not equal.

We now consider several examples and find the limit by computing the values of $f(x)$ as x approaches a through values of $x < a$ and through values of $x > a$.

Example 16.11
Evaluate $\lim_{x \to 1} f(x)$, where

$$f(x) = (x + 2)^2 \qquad -2 \leq x \leq 2$$

SOLUTION
First, we investigate the behavior of the function $f(x)$ for values of x less than 1. Note that

$f(0.6) = 6.76$	$f(0.95) = 8.7025$
$f(0.7) = 7.29$	$f(0.99) = 8.9401$
$f(0.8) = 7.84$	$f(0.995) = 8.970025$
$f(0.9) = 8.41$	$f(0.999) = 8.994001$

Thus, as x approaches 1 through the values of $x < 1$, $f(x)$ gets closer and closer to 9. This is equivalent to the statement that the left-hand limit of $f(x)$ equals 9; that is,

$$\lim_{x \to 1^-} f(x) = 9$$

Now consider the values of $f(x)$ as x approaches 1 through values of x greater than 1. Observe that

$f(1.5) = 12.25$	$f(1.1) = 9.61$
$f(1.4) = 11.56$	$f(1.05) = 9.3025$
$f(1.2) = 10.24$	$f(1.01) = 9.0601$
$f(1.15) = 9.9225$	$f(1.001) = 9.006001$

and so on. It is clear that as x gets closer and closer to 1 through values of $x > 1$, $f(x)$ gets closer and closer to 9. This suggests that the right-hand limit of $f(x)$ is 9; that is,

$$\lim_{x \to 1^+} f(x) = 9$$

Because both right- and left-hand limits exist and are equal, we conclude that

$$\lim_{x \to 1} (x + 2)^2 = 9$$

Example 16.12

Evaluate $\lim_{x \to 1} f(x)$, where

$$f(x) = \frac{x^2 - 1}{x - 1} \qquad x \neq 1$$

SOLUTION

Again, we need to study the behavior of the function $f(x)$ for values of $x < 1$. We see that

$$f(0.8) = 1.8 \qquad f(0.98) = 1.98$$
$$f(0.85) = 1.85 \qquad f(0.99) = 1.99$$
$$f(0.9) = 1.9 \qquad f(0.995) = 1.995$$
$$f(0.95) = 1.95 \qquad f(0.999) = 1.999$$

and so on. The values of $f(x)$ get closer and closer to 2 as x moves through values of $x < 1$. Thus, the left-hand limit of $f(x)$ exists and equals 2. In other words,

$$\lim_{x \to 1^-} f(x) = 2$$

Similarly, we observe that

$$f(1.2) = 2.2 \qquad f(1.05) = 2.05$$
$$f(1.15) = 2.15 \qquad f(1.01) = 2.01$$
$$f(1.1) = 2.1 \qquad f(1.001) = 2.001$$

Note that as x approaches 1 through values of $x > 1$, $f(x)$ gets closer and closer to 2. This means that

$$\lim_{x \to 1^+} f(x) = 2$$

Because

$$\lim_{x \to 1^-} f(x) = \lim_{x \to 1^+} f(x)$$

it follows that

$$\lim_{x \to 1} f(x) = 2$$

The same result could have been derived more quickly by using elementary algebra. Note that for $x \neq 1$,

$$f(x) = \left(\frac{x^2 - 1}{x - 1} \right) = \frac{(x + 1)(x - 1)}{(x - 1)} = x + 1, \quad x \neq 1$$

and this provides a simpler device to calculate the values of $f(x)$ as x approaches 1. The graph of $f(x)$ is shown in Figure 16.5. The circle at the point (1, 2) indicates that this point is not a part of the graph.

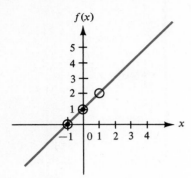

Figure 16.5

Example 16.13

Evaluate $\lim_{x \to 3} f(x)$, where

$$f(x) = \begin{cases} x + 1 & x < 3 \\ 7 - x & x > 3 \end{cases}$$

SOLUTION

First, we determine the values of $f(x)$ as x approaches 3 through values of $x < 3$. Note that $f(x) = x + 1$ for $x < 3$, and we have

$f(-1) = 0$	$f(2.8) = 3.8$
$f(0) = 1$	$f(2.9) = 3.9$
$f(1.5) = 2.5$	$f(2.99) = 3.99$
$f(2) = 3$	$f(2.999) = 3.999$
$f(2.5) = 3.5$	$f(2.9999) = 3.9999$

This means that as x approaches 3 from the left, $f(x)$ gets closer and closer to 4. Thus, the left-hand limit of $f(x)$ equals 4. Now observe the values of $f(x)$ as x approaches 3 through values of $x > 3$. Clearly, if $f(x) = 7 - x$ for $x > 3$, then

$f(7) = 0$	$f(3.5) = 3.5$
$f(6) = 1$	$f(3.1) = 3.9$
$f(5) = 2$	$f(3.05) = 3.95$
$f(4.5) = 2.5$	$f(3.005) = 3.995$
$f(4) = 3$	$f(3.0005) = 3.9995$

As x gets closer and closer to 3 from the right, $f(x)$ gets closer and closer to the number 4. This means that right-hand limit of $f(x)$ is 4. Because both the left-hand and the right-hand limits of $f(x)$ exist and are equal, it follows that

$$\lim_{x \to 3} f(x) = 4$$

Example 16.14

Graph the function

$$f(x) = \begin{cases} x^2 & x < 0 \\ x & x > 0 \end{cases}$$

and use the graph to determine $\lim_{x \to 0} f(x)$ if it exists.

SOLUTION

The graph of $f(x)$ is shown in Figure 16.6. As x approaches 0 through values of $x < 0$, $f(x)$ gets closer and closer to 0. Hence, the left-hand limit of $f(x)$ equals 0. In other words,

$$\lim_{x \to 0^-} f(x) = 0$$

Now consider the values of $f(x)$ as $x \to 0$ through values of $x > 0$. Observe that as x gets closer and closer to 0 from the right, $f(x)$ approaches the number 0. This means that

$$\lim_{x \to 0^+} f(x) = 0$$

Thus,

$$\lim_{x \to 0^-} f(x) = \lim_{x \to 0^+} f(x)$$

Hence, the limit $\lim_{x \to 0} f(x) = 0$.

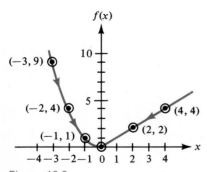

Figure 16.6

We now consider situations in which the limit of a function does not exist.

Example 16.15

Consider the graph of the function

$$f(x) = \begin{cases} 1 & x \leq 2 \\ 2 & x > 2 \end{cases}$$

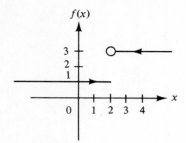

Figure 16.7

in Figure 16.7. Clearly, the left-hand limit exists and equals 1. However, we see that as x approaches 2 through values of $x > 2$, the right-hand limit exists and equals 2. Thus,

$$\lim_{x \to 2^-} f(x) = 1 \quad \text{and} \quad \lim_{x \to 2^+} f(x) = 2$$

Because $f(x)$ approaches two different numbers depending on whether $x \to 2$ from the left or from the right, we conclude that

$$\lim_{x \to 2} f(x)$$

does not exist. ∎

Example 16.16

Evaluate $\lim_{x \to 0} f(x)$, where

$$f(x) = \frac{|x|}{x} \qquad x \neq 0$$

SOLUTION
Note that for $x > 0$, $|x|^* = x$ and thus

$$f(x) = \frac{x}{x} = 1$$

If $x < 0$, $|x|^* = -x$, and we have

$$f(x) = -\frac{x}{x} = -1$$

This means that as x approaches 0 through the values of $x < 0$, $f(x)$ approaches -1, and when x approaches 0 through values of $x > 0$, $f(x) \to +1$. Thus,

$$\lim_{x \to 0^-} f(x) = -1$$

---

* Definition A.3.1 in Appendix A.

and

$$\lim_{x \to 0^+} f(x) = 1$$

Because

$$\lim_{x \to 0^-} f(x) \neq \lim_{x \to 0^+} f(x)$$

we conclude that

$$\lim_{x \to 0} f(x)$$

does not exist.

Example 16.17

Evaluate $\lim_{x \to 2} f(x)$, where

$$f(x) = \frac{1}{(x-2)^2} \qquad x \neq 2$$

SOLUTION

To investigate the behavior of $f(x)$ for values of $x < 2$, we note that

$$f(-0.5) = 0.16 \qquad f(1.8) = 25$$
$$f(0) = 0.25 \qquad f(1.9) = 100$$
$$f(1) = 1 \qquad f(1.99) = 10^4$$
$$f(1.5) = 4 \qquad f(1.999) = 10^6$$

and so on. Now observe the values of $f(x)$ for $x > 2$. Clearly,

$$f(4) = 0.25 \qquad f(2.1) = 100$$
$$f(3) = 1 \qquad f(2.01) = 10^4$$
$$f(2.5) = 4 \qquad f(2.001) = 10^6$$
$$f(2.2) = 25 \qquad f(2.0001) = 10^8$$

The graph of $f(x)$ is shown in Figure 16.8.

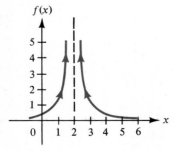

Figure 16.8

Note that as $x \to 2$ from values of $x < 2$, $f(x)$ becomes larger and larger but does not approach any particular number. Thus, the left-hand limit fails to exist. Similarly, as x approaches 2 through values of $x > 2$, again $f(x)$ gets larger and larger. This means that the right-hand limit does not exist. Hence, it follows that

$$\lim_{x \to 2} f(x)$$

does not exist.

■

EXERCISE 16.2

Determine the limit, if it exists, in each of the following problems. (Do not graph the function.)

1. $\lim_{x \to 2}(2x + 3)$

2. $\lim_{x \to 3}(3x + 1)$

3. $\lim_{x \to 3}(4x^2 + 3)$

4. $\lim_{x \to 1}(x + 2)^2$

5. $\lim_{x \to 2}\left(\dfrac{1}{x - 2}\right)$

6. $\lim_{x \to 1}\left(\dfrac{1}{x - 1}\right)^2$

7. $\lim_{x \to 2}\left(\dfrac{x^2 - 4}{x - 2}\right)$

8. $\lim_{x \to 1}\left(\dfrac{x^3 - 1}{x - 1}\right)$

9. $\lim_{x \to -1}\left(\dfrac{x^2 - 1}{x + 1}\right)$

10. $\lim_{x \to 2}\left(\dfrac{x^2 - x - 2}{x - 2}\right)$

11. $\lim_{x \to 3}\left(\dfrac{x^2 - 5x + 6}{x - 3}\right)$

12. $\lim_{x \to 4}\left(\dfrac{x^2 - 7x + 12}{x - 4}\right)$

13. $\lim_{x \to 1}\dfrac{|x - 1|}{x - 1}$

14. $\lim_{x \to 3}\dfrac{|x - 3|}{3(x - 3)}$

15. $\lim_{x \to 2}\dfrac{x - 2}{3|x - 2|}$

16. $\lim_{x \to 2}\left(\dfrac{1}{x^2}\right)$

17. $\lim_{x \to 2} f(x)$, where

$$f(x) = \begin{cases} 2x - 1 & x > 2 \\ 9 - 3x & x < 2 \end{cases}$$

18. $\lim_{x \to 1} f(x)$, where

$$f(x) = \begin{cases} 2x & x > 1 \\ x^2 + 1 & x < 1 \end{cases}$$

19. $\lim_{x \to 2} f(x)$, where

$$f(x) = \begin{cases} 2x + 1 & x > 2 \\ 9 - 2x & x < 2 \end{cases}$$

20. $\lim_{x \to 1} f(x)$, where

$$f(x) = \begin{cases} x + 1 & x < 1 \\ 3 - x & x > 1 \end{cases}$$

Graph the functions specified in each of the following and use the graphs to determine the limit of $f(x)$, if it exists.

21. $\lim_{x \to -1} f(x)$, where

$$f(x) = \begin{cases} 3 + x^2 & x < -1 \\ 3x & x > -1 \end{cases}$$

22. $\lim_{x \to 3} f(x)$, where

$$f(x) = \begin{cases} x - 1 & x < 3 \\ 9 - 2x & x > 3 \end{cases}$$

23. $\lim_{x \to 2} f(x)$, where

$$f(x) = \begin{cases} |x| & -2 \le x < 2 \\ 2 & x > 2 \end{cases}$$

24. $\lim_{x \to 3} f(x)$, where

$$f(x) = \begin{cases} |x - 2| & -2 \le x < 0 \\ x + 2 & x > 0 \end{cases}$$

25. $\lim_{x \to 0} f(x)$, where

$$f(x) = \begin{cases} \dfrac{1}{x} & x > 0 \\ 1 + x & x < 0 \end{cases}$$

16.4 PROPERTIES OF LIMITS

The methods for evaluating the limit for values of x near a but not at a were time-consuming, cumbersome, and somewhat awkward. After discussing several examples to illustrate the limit concept, one wonders whether it is really necessary to repeat the arguments for the existence of the limit in each problem. A good deal of repetition can perhaps be avoided if we use some general properties of limits. These properties, which can reduce calculations, are presented in the form of propositions. Their proofs, however, are omitted.

Proposition 16.4.1: If $f(x) = mx + b$, where m and b are constants, then

$$\lim_{x \to a} f(x) = ma + b$$

As an immediate consequence of this proposition, we have the following special cases:

(i) If $f(x) = b$, where b is a constant, then

$$\lim_{x \to a} f(x) = b$$

(ii) If $f(x) = x$, then

$$\lim_{x \to a} f(x) = a$$ ∎

Proposition 16.4.2: If $\lim_{x \to a} f(x) = L$, then for any constant c,

$$\lim_{x \to a} [cf(x)] = c[\lim_{x \to a} f(x)] = cL$$ ∎

Proposition 16.4.3: If $\lim_{x \to a} f(x) = L$ and $\lim_{x \to a} g(x) = M$, then

$$\lim_{x \to a} [f(x) \pm g(x)] = \lim_{x \to a} f(x) \pm \lim_{x \to a} g(x) = L \pm M$$

This proposition states that the limit of the sum (difference) of two functions is the sum (difference) of their limits. ∎

Proposition 16.4.4: If $\lim_{x \to a} f(x) = L$ and $\lim_{x \to a} g(x) = M$, then

$$\lim_{x \to a}[f(x)g(x)] = \left[\lim_{x \to a} f(x)\right]\left[\lim_{x \to a} g(x)\right] = LM$$

In other words, the limit of the product of two functions is equal to the product of their limits.   ▪

Corollary: If $\lim_{x \to a} f(x) = L$, then for a positive integer n, $\lim_{x \to a}[f(x)]^n = L^n$. Note that

$$\lim_{x \to a}[f(x)]^n = \lim_{x \to a}\left[\underbrace{f(x) \cdot f(x) \cdots \cdot f(x)}_{n \text{ times}}\right]$$

$$= \lim_{x \to a} f(x) \cdot \lim_{x \to a}[f(x)] \cdots \cdot \lim_{x \to a}[f(x)]$$

$$= \underbrace{L \cdot L \cdots \cdot L}_{n \text{ times}}$$

$$= L^n$$ ▪

Proposition 16.4.5: If $\lim_{x \to a} f(x) = L$ and $\lim_{x \to a} g(x) = M \neq 0$, then

$$\lim_{x \to a}\left[\frac{f(x)}{g(x)}\right] = \frac{\lim_{x \to a} f(x)}{\lim_{x \to a} g(x)} = \frac{L}{M}$$ ▪

Note how closely Propositions 16.4.2 through 16.4.5 resemble Propositions 16.2.3 through 16.2.6.

To illustrate these propositions, let us consider the following examples.

Example 16.18
Evaluate $\lim_{x \to 2}(3x + 4)$.

SOLUTION
Using Proposition 16.4.1 we have

$$\lim_{x \to 2}(3x + 4) = 3(2) + 4$$
$$= 10$$ ▪

Example 16.19
Evaluate $\lim_{x \to 3}(2x^2 + 3x + 7)$.

SOLUTION

$$\lim_{x \to 3}(2x^2 + 3x + 7) = \lim_{x \to 3}(2x^2) + \lim_{x \to 3}(3x) + \lim_{x \to 3} 7 \qquad \text{(Proposition 16.4.3)}$$

Note that

$$\lim_{x \to 3}(2x^2) = 2 \lim_{x \to 3} x^2 \qquad \text{(Proposition 16.4.2)}$$

$$= 2 \lim_{x \to 3}(x \cdot x)$$

$$= 2 \left(\lim_{x \to 3} x\right)\left(\lim_{x \to 3} x\right) \qquad \text{(Corollary to Proposition 16.4.4)}$$

$$= 2 \cdot 3 \cdot 3$$

$$= 18;$$

$$\lim_{x \to 3}(3x) = 3 \lim_{x \to 3} x = 3(3) = 9 \qquad \text{(Proposition 16.4.2)}$$

and

$$\lim_{x \to 3} 7 = 7 \qquad \text{(Proposition 16.4.1(i))}$$

Thus,

$$\lim_{x \to 3}(2x^2 + 3x + 7) = 18 + 9 + 7 = 34 \qquad \blacksquare$$

Example 16.20
Evaluate $\lim_{x \to 4}[(x^2 + 3)(x + 1)]$.

SOLUTION
By Proposition 16.4.4, we have

$$\lim_{x \to 4}[(x^2 + 3)(x + 1)] = \lim_{x \to 4}(x^2 + 3) \cdot \lim_{x \to 4}(x + 1)$$

Now, by using Proposition 16.4.2 and 16.4.1(i), respectively, we obtain

$$\lim_{x \to 4}(x^2 + 3) = \lim_{x \to 4} x^2 + \lim_{x \to 3} 3$$

$$= 16 + 3 = 19$$

and

$$\lim_{x \to 4}(x + 1) = \lim_{x \to 4} x + \lim_{x \to 4} 1$$

$$= 4 + 1 = 5$$

Thus,

$$\lim_{x \to 4}[(x^2 + 3)(x + 1)] = (19)(5) = 95 \qquad \blacksquare$$

Example 16.21
Evaluate

$$\lim_{x \to 2}\left(\frac{4x^2 + 7x + 6}{2x^2 + x - 1}\right)$$

SOLUTION

$$\lim_{x \to 2} \left(\frac{4x^2 + 7x + 6}{2x^2 + x - 1} \right) = \frac{\lim_{x \to 2}(4x^2 + 7x + 6)}{\lim_{x \to 2}(2x^2 + x - 1)} \qquad \text{(Proposition 16.4.5)}$$

$$= \frac{\lim_{x \to 2}(4x^2) + \lim_{x \to 2}(7x) + \lim_{x \to 2} 6}{\lim_{x \to 2}(2x^2) + \lim_{x \to 2}(x) - \lim_{x \to 2} 1} \qquad \text{(Proposition 16.4.3)}$$

$$= \frac{4 \lim_{x \to 2} x^2 + 7 \lim_{x \to 2} x + \lim_{x \to 2} 6}{2 \lim_{x \to 2} x^2 + \lim_{x \to 2} x - \lim_{x \to 2} 1} \qquad \text{(Proposition 16.4.2)}$$

$$= \frac{4(4) + 7(2) + 6}{2(4) + 2 - 1} \qquad \text{(Proposition 16.4.1(i))}$$

$$= \frac{16 + 14 + 6}{8 + 2 - 1}$$

$$= 4 \qquad \blacksquare$$

16.5 LIMITS AS *x* APPROACHES INFINITY

We have so far evaluated $\lim_{x \to a} f(x)$, where *a* is a fixed real number. What is the limit of

$$f(x) = \frac{2x + 3}{x + 4}$$

when $x \to \infty$? Clearly, the domain of *f* is the set of all reals except $x = -4$. We can show intuitively that $f(x)$ can be made as close to 2 as we desire by choosing *x* large enough. Consider, for example, the values of $f(x)$ as *x* increases without bound. Note that

$f(10) = 1.6428571$	$f(1{,}000) = 1.9950199$
$f(50) = 1.9074074$	$f(5{,}000) = 1.9990007$
$f(100) = 1.951923$	$f(10{,}000) = 1.9995001$
$f(500) = 1.9900793$	$f(100{,}000) = 1.999950$

Thus, as *x* gets larger and larger, $f(x)$ approaches the number 2. Hence, we conclude that

$$\lim_{x \to \infty} f(x) = 2$$

We now state a proposition that is useful in evaluating $\lim f(x)$ when *x* approaches infinity.

Proposition 16.5.1: Let *c* be a constant and *n* any positive real number. Then

$$\lim_{x \to \infty} \left(\frac{c}{x^n} \right) = 0 \qquad \blacksquare$$

To apply this proposition, consider again the function

$$f(x) = \frac{2x + 3}{x + 4}$$

Dividing both the numerator and the denominator by x, we see that

$$\lim_{x \to \infty} \left(\frac{2x + 3}{x + 4} \right) = \lim_{x \to \infty} \frac{2 + 3/x}{1 + 4/x}$$

$$= \frac{\lim_{x \to \infty} (2 + 3/x)}{\lim_{x \to \infty} (1 + 4/x)} \qquad \text{(Proposition 16.4.5)}$$

$$= \frac{2 + 0}{1 + 0} \qquad \text{(Proposition 16.5.1)}$$

$$= 2$$

Example 16.22

Evaluate $\lim_{x \to \infty} f(x)$, where

$$f(x) = \frac{ax^2 + bx + c}{dx^2 + ex + f}$$

and a, b, c, d, e, and f are real numbers, and $d \neq 0$.

SOLUTION
Dividing both the numerator and the denominator by the highest power of x in the fraction, that is, x^2, we obtain

$$\lim_{x \to \infty} f(x) = \lim_{x \to \infty} \left(\frac{a + b/x + c/x^2}{d + e/x + f/x^2} \right)$$

$$= \frac{\lim_{x \to \infty} (a + b/x + c/x^2)}{\lim_{x \to \infty} (d + e/x + f/x^2)}$$

$$= \frac{a + 0 + 0}{d + 0 + 0} \qquad \text{(Proposition 16.5.1)}$$

$$= \frac{a}{d} \qquad d \neq 0$$

EXERCISE 16.3

Using the limit propositions, evaluate each of the following.

1. $\lim_{x \to 1} (4x + 3)$

2. $\lim_{x \to -2} (3x + 11)$

3. $\lim_{x \to 3} (2x - 6)$

4. $\lim_{x \to 1} (2x + 5)$

5. $\lim\limits_{x\to 2}(3x^2 + 2x + 1)$

6. $\lim\limits_{x\to 4}(x^2 - 2x + 3)$

7. $\lim\limits_{x\to -1}(x^3 + x^2 + x + 1)$

8. $\lim\limits_{x\to -2}(2x^3 - 8x^2 + 3x + 4)$

9. $\lim\limits_{x\to 2}[(2x + 3)(3x + 4)]$

10. $\lim\limits_{x\to 3}[(x^2 + x + 1)(x + 2)]$

11. $\lim\limits_{x\to 1}[(x^2 + 2x + 1)(2x + 3)]$

12. $\lim\limits_{x\to 2}[(x^3 + x - 2)(4x - 1)]$

13. $\lim\limits_{x\to 1}\left(\dfrac{4x + 5}{2x + 1}\right)$

14. $\lim\limits_{x\to -2}\left(\dfrac{x}{3x + 8}\right)$

15. $\lim\limits_{x\to 0}\left(\dfrac{2x^2 - 3x}{x}\right)$

16. $\lim\limits_{x\to 0}\left(\dfrac{x^3 + x^2 + x}{2x}\right)$

17. $\lim\limits_{x\to 2}\left(\dfrac{x^3 - 8}{x - 2}\right)$

18. $\lim\limits_{x\to 3}\left(\dfrac{3x^3 - 81}{x - 3}\right)$

19. $\lim\limits_{x\to 3}\left(\dfrac{x^2 - 7x + 12}{x - 3}\right)$

20. $\lim\limits_{x\to -2}\left(\dfrac{x^2 - 4}{x + 2}\right)$

21. $\lim\limits_{x\to 2}\dfrac{|x - 2|}{x - 2}$

22. $\lim\limits_{x\to 1}\dfrac{x - 2}{|x - 2|}$

23. $\lim\limits_{x\to 2}\left(\dfrac{x^2 - 6x + 8}{x - 2}\right)$

24. $\lim\limits_{x\to 2}\left(\dfrac{x + 3}{x + 2}\right)$

Using the limit proposition 16.5.1, evaluate the limit, if it exists, in each case.

25. $\lim\limits_{x\to\infty}\left(\dfrac{x + 3}{x - 2}\right)$

26. $\lim\limits_{x\to\infty}\left(\dfrac{2x}{3x + 1}\right)$

27. $\lim\limits_{x\to\infty}\left(\dfrac{3x + 2}{2x + 3}\right)$

28. $\lim\limits_{x\to\infty}\left(\dfrac{3x + 2}{2x^2 + 3}\right)$

29. $\lim\limits_{x\to\infty}\left(\dfrac{2x^2 + 3}{3x + 2}\right)$

30. $\lim\limits_{x\to\infty}\left(\dfrac{x^2 + x + 1}{3x^2 + 4x + 8}\right)$

31. $\lim\limits_{x\to\infty}\left(\dfrac{x + 1}{2x^2 + 3x + 1}\right)$

32. $\lim\limits_{x\to\infty}\left(\dfrac{x^2}{x^3 + 1}\right)$

33. $\lim\limits_{x\to\infty}\left(\dfrac{x^2 + 4}{x + 4}\right)$

34. $\lim\limits_{x\to\infty}\left(\dfrac{x + 4}{x^2 + 2x + 1}\right)$

35. $\lim\limits_{x\to\infty}\left(\dfrac{x + 1}{x + 2}\right)^2$

36. $\lim\limits_{x\to\infty}\left(\dfrac{2x - 1}{3x + 2}\right)^2$

37. $\lim\limits_{x\to\infty}\left(\dfrac{4x + 3}{2x + 1}\right)^3$

38. $\lim\limits_{x\to\infty}\left(\dfrac{x^2 - x + 3}{2x^2 + 5x + 1}\right)^2$

39. $\lim\limits_{x\to\infty}\left(\dfrac{4x^3 + 3x^2 + 2x + 5}{8x^3 + 16x^2 - x + 21}\right)^2$

40. $\lim\limits_{x\to\infty}\left(\dfrac{2x^2 - x + 4}{x^4 + x^2 + 1}\right)^3$

16.6 CONTINUITY

In Sections 16.3 and 16.4 we analyzed the meaning of

$$\lim_{x \to a} f(x) = L$$

and in so doing we paid no attention to the value of the function at $x = a$. In fact, for several expressions, the function was not even defined at $x = a$. In this section, the limit of $f(x)$ as x approaches a and the value of the function at $x = a$ both play a significant role.

An airline, for instance, charges full fare for passengers over 12 years of age, half-fare for those under 12, and one-tenth of regular fare for infants under 2. In other words,

$$f(x) = \begin{cases} \frac{1}{10} & 0 < x < 2 \\ \frac{1}{2} & 2 \le x < 12 \\ 1 & x \ge 12 \end{cases}$$

The graph of $f(x)$ is shown in Figure 16.9. Note that

$$\lim_{x \to 2^-} f(x) = \tfrac{1}{10} \quad \text{and} \quad \lim_{x \to 2^+} f(x) = \tfrac{1}{2}$$

Hence, we conclude that $\lim_{x \to 2} f(x)$ does not exist. Similarly, $\lim_{x \to 12} f(x)$ does not exist. Further, Figure 16.9 shows that there is a jump or a break in the graph both at $x = 2$ and $x = 12$. Formally, we say that the function is discontinuous at these points. Intuitively we say that the function is continuous if we can draw its graph without taking the pencil off the paper.

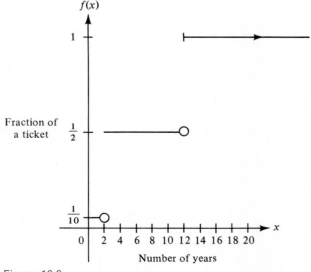

Figure 16.9

Another example of a discontinuous function is given by the following:

$$f(x) = \frac{x^2 - 4}{x - 2} \qquad x \neq 2$$

Note that the function is not defined at 2. Using the methods explained in earlier sections, we find that

$$\lim_{x \to 2} \left(\frac{x^2 - 4}{x - 2} \right) = \lim_{x \to 2} \frac{(x + 2)(x - 2)}{(x - 2)}$$

$$= \lim_{x \to 2} (x + 2)$$

$$= 4$$

Thus, the limit of $f(x)$ exists at $x = 2$. However, the function is discontinuous at $x = 2$, because its graph (see Figure 16.10) has a break at this point and the function is not defined at $x = 2$. But if we define $f(2) = 4$, then the function is continuous at $x = 2$, and if we define $f(2)$ to have any value other than 4, the function will be discontinuous at $x = 2$. This discussion leads us to the following definition.

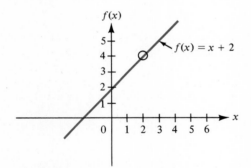

Figure 16.10

Definition 16.6.1: A function f is continuous at $x = a$ if and only if

$$\lim_{x \to a} f(x) = f(a)$$

This means that in order for a function $f(x)$ to be continuous at $x = a$, the following conditions must be satisfied:

1. $f(a)$ is defined;
2. $\lim_{x \to a} f(x)$ exists; and
3. $\lim_{x \to a} f(x)$ and $f(a)$ are equal.

If $f(x)$ is not continuous at $x = a$, we say $f(x)$ is discontinuous at $x = a$ or that there is a discontinuity at point a.

Definition 16.6.2: A function f is said to be continuous over an open interval if it is continuous at every point in that interval.

Let us consider a few more examples to reinforce the continuity concept.

Example 16.23

Let

$$f(x) = \begin{cases} 3x + 2 & x \neq 2 \\ 8 & x = 2 \end{cases}$$

Determine whether or not $f(x)$ is continuous at $x = 2$.

SOLUTION

Note that

$$\lim_{x \to 2}(3x + 2) = 3(2) + 2 = 8 \qquad \text{(Proposition 16.4.1)}$$

Because $f(2)$ is defined and also equals 8, we conclude that the function is continuous at $x = 2$. ∎

Example 16.24

Let $f(x)$ be defined as follows:

$$f(x) = \begin{cases} 6x & 0 < x < 5 \\ 25 + 2x & x \geq 5 \end{cases}$$

Is $f(x)$ continuous at $x = 5$?

SOLUTION

If x approaches 5 through values of $x < 5$, $f(x)$ gets closer and closer to 30. This means that

$$\lim_{x \to 5^-} f(x) = 30$$

If x approaches 5 through values of $x > 5$, $f(x)$ gets closer and closer to 35. That is,

$$\lim_{x \to 5^+} f(x) = 35$$

Because

$$\lim_{x \to 5^-} f(x) \neq \lim_{x \to 5^+} f(x)$$

We conclude that $\lim_{x \to 5} f(x)$ does not exist. The second condition is violated and hence $f(x)$ is discontinuous at $x = 5$. ∎

Example 16.25

Let $f(x)$ be defined as follows.

$$f(x) = \begin{cases} x + 1 & x < 2 \\ 1 & x = 2 \\ 5 - x & x > 2 \end{cases}$$

Graph $f(x)$ and determine whether or not $f(x)$ is continuous at $x = 2$.

SOLUTION

The graph of $f(x)$ is shown in Figure 16.11. Note that

$$\lim_{x \to 2^-} (x + 1) = 3 \quad \text{and} \quad \lim_{x \to 2^+} (5 - x) = 3$$

Thus, $\lim_{x \to 2} f(x) = 3$. Because $f(2) \neq 3$, the function is discontinuous at $x = 2$. But if we change the definition of $f(x)$ so that $f(2) = 3$, then

$$\lim_{x \to 2} f(x) = f(2)$$

and the function is continuous at $x = 2$.

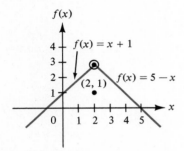

Figure 16.11

In the preceding sections, we encountered several examples of continuous functions. These functions have certain properties, which we state below. Their proofs are, however, omitted.

Proposition 16.6.1: If $f(x) = c$, where c is a constant, then $f(x)$ is continuous for all x.

Proposition 16.6.2: If $f(x) = x^n$, where n is any positive integer, then $f(x)$ is continuous for all x.

Proposition 16.6.3: If $f(x)$ is continuous at any point x_0 in its domain and c is a constant, then $cf(x)$ is also continuous at x_0.

Proposition 16.6.4: If $f(x)$ and $g(x)$ are continuous at any point x_0, where x_0 is in the domain of both f and g, then the functions $F(x)$, $G(x)$, and $H(x)$ defined by

$$F(x) = f(x) + g(x)$$
$$G(x) = f(x) - g(x)$$
$$H(x) = f(x) \cdot g(x)$$

are also continuous at x_0.

This means that the sum, difference, and product of two continuous functions are continuous.

Proposition 16.6.5: Any polynomial function

$$p(x) = a_n x^n + a_{n-1}x^{n-1} + \cdots + a_2 x^2 + a_1 x + a_0$$

where n is a positive integer and $a_0, a_1, \ldots, a_n$ are real numbers, is continuous for all x. ∎

Consider, for example, the polynomial functions

$$f(x) = x^3 + 3x^2 + 8x + 1$$

and

$$g(x) = x^4 + 2x^3 + 4x^2 + x + 3$$

then

$$f(x) + g(x) = x^4 + 3x^3 + 7x^2 + 9x + 4$$
$$f(x) - g(x) = -x^4 - x^3 - x^2 + 7x - 2$$

and

$$f(x)g(x) = x^7 + 5x^6 + 18x^5 + 30x^4 + 40x^3 + 21x^2 + 25x + 3$$

are all polynomial functions and hence continuous for all x.

Proposition 16.6.6: If $p(x)$ and $q(x)$ are polynomial functions of x, then the rational expression

$$\frac{p(x)}{q(x)}$$

is continuous at x_0 if and only if $q(x_0) \neq 0$. ∎

As a simple illustration, recall that $f(x) = 1/x$ is not defined at $x = 0$ and hence is discontinuous at that point.

EXERCISE 16.4

Determine in each of the following problems whether or not the function is continuous at all points in its domain.

1. $f(x) = \begin{cases} 2x + 3 & x \neq 3 \\ 9 & x = 3 \end{cases}$

2. $f(x) = \begin{cases} x^2 + 2 & x \neq 1 \\ 3 & x = 1 \end{cases}$

3. $f(x) = \begin{cases} 9 - 3x & x < 2 \\ 2 & x = 2 \\ 2x + 1 & x > 2 \end{cases}$

4. $f(x) = \begin{cases} 3x + 2 & x \leq 1 \\ 5x & x > 1 \end{cases}$

5. $f(x) = \begin{cases} 3x - 2 & x \leq 5 \\ x^2 + x + 1 & x > 5 \end{cases}$

6. $f(x) = \begin{cases} 2x + 6 & x \leq 3 \\ x^3 - 15 & x > 3 \end{cases}$

7. $f(x) = \begin{cases} x^2 - 3 & x < 1 \\ 2x - 4 & 1 \le x < 2 \\ 5 - 3x & x \ge 2 \end{cases}$

8. $f(x) = \begin{cases} 2x^2 + 5 & x < 2 \\ 6x + 1 & 2 \le x < 4 \\ x^3 - 4x^2 & x \ge 4 \end{cases}$

9. $f(x) = \begin{cases} \dfrac{x^2 - 1}{x - 1} & x \ne 1 \\ 6 & x = 1 \end{cases}$

10. $f(x) = \begin{cases} \dfrac{x^2 - 3x + 2}{x - 2} & x \ne 2 \\ 2 & x = 2 \end{cases}$

11. $f(x) = \begin{cases} \dfrac{x^2 - x - 6}{x - 3} & x \ne 3 \\ 5 & x = 3 \end{cases}$

12. $f(x) = \begin{cases} \dfrac{x - 4}{x^2 - 6x + 8} & x \ne 4 \\ \frac{1}{2} & x = 4 \end{cases}$

13. $f(x) = \begin{cases} \dfrac{x - 1}{|x - 1|} & \text{for } x \ne 1 \\ 1 & \text{for } x = 1 \end{cases}$

14. $f(x) = \begin{cases} \dfrac{|x - 2|}{x - 2} & \text{for } x \ne 2 \\ 0 & \text{for } x = 2 \end{cases}$

15. $f(x) = |x|$ for all values of x

16. $f(x) = |x - 3|$ for all values of x

Determine all values of x for which each of the following functions is discontinuous.

17. $f(x) = \dfrac{1}{x - 2}$

18. $f(x) = \dfrac{x^2 - 1}{x^2 - 7x + 12}$

19. $f(x) = \dfrac{x - 3}{x^2 + 5x + 6}$

20. $f(x) = \dfrac{x + 3}{x^2 - x - 6}$

21. A cost function is described by

$$C(x) = \begin{cases} \$5x & 0 < x < 5 \\ \$20 + x & 5 \le x < 10 \\ \$15 + \frac{3}{2}x & 10 < x \end{cases}$$

where x is the number of pounds of a certain material sold. Determine whether or not $C(x)$ is continuous at $x = 5$ and $x = 10$.

22. A cost function is described by

$$C(x) = \begin{cases} \$0.60x & 0 < x \le 100 \\ \$0.50x & 100 < x \le 500 \\ \$0.40x & 500 < x \end{cases}$$

where x is the number of pounds of goods shipped and $C(x)$ is the cost of shipping. Graph $C(x)$ and determine the points where $C(x)$ is discontinuous.

23. A moving van line offers a discount in freight rates on a large shipment. The cost function is

$$C(x) = \begin{cases} \$0.80x & 0 < x \le 250 \\ \$10 + 0.03x & 250 < x \le 500 \\ \$12 + 0.02x & 500 < x \end{cases}$$

where x is the number of pounds of goods shipped and $C(x)$ is the cost of shipping. Determine the points where $C(x)$ is discontinuous.

24. The current postage rate is $0.13 up to and including 1 ounce and $0.11 for each additional ounce or fraction thereof up to 10 ounces. Sketch a graph showing the postage for a letter weighing up to 10 ounces and determine the points at which the graph is discontinuous.

25. An attendant in a parking lot charges $1.00 for the first hour and $0.50 for each additional hour or part thereof subject to a maximum of $4.00. Sketch a graph showing the parking rates and determine the points at which the graph is discontinuous.

CHAPTER 17 Differential Calculus

17.1 INTRODUCTION

In this chapter we shall apply the concept of limit to introduce the idea of derivative, which is useful in constructing mathematical models that can be translated into some meaningful applications. If the criterion is to select the course of action that may yield the highest return on our financial investment, we shall develop a model that may tell us what the return is likely to be if certain action is taken. The same rationale applies to problems involving the optimum selling price or the minimum production cost.

17.2 INSTANTANEOUS RATE OF CHANGE

The derivative measures the rate at which changes are taking place—the rate at which the purchasing power of the dollar is dwindling, the rate at which the price of gold is fluctuating in the international market, the rate at which unemployment is rising in the private sector of the economy, the rate at which the enrollment is dropping in liberal arts colleges, the rate at which the sale of automobiles is improving in the economic recovery, the rate at which the stock market is showing an upward trend, and so on.

Consider, for example, a manufacturer whose revenue (in millions of dollars) is given by the function

$$(17.1) \quad f(x) = 20x - x^2 \qquad 0 \le x \le 20$$

where x is the number of articles (in thousands) that the firm produces. The graph of $f(x)$ is shown in Figure 17.1.

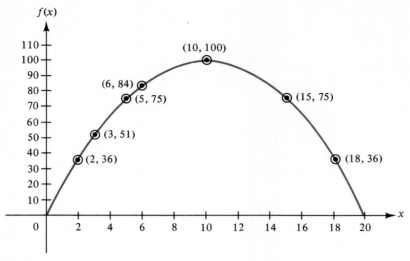

Figure 17.1

That x cannot exceed 20 is an indication of the production capacity of the plant. We wish to study the behavior of this function in the vicinity of some particular value of x, say $x = 5$, that is, whether or not the revenue is increasing or decreasing at this particular level of production. This kind of information is essential for the industry planning to expand its operations to its optimum level of production beyond which any further expansion is uneconomic. Note that

$$f(5) = 20(5) - 5^2 = 75$$

If the production is increased to $x = 10$, then the corresponding revenue is

$$f(10) = 20(10) - 10^2 = 100$$

Thus, the revenue increases by $100 - 75 = 25$ when the production level is increased from $x = 5$ to $x = 10$. We say that the average rate of increase in revenue is

$$\frac{f(10) - f(5)}{10 - 5} = \frac{100 - 75}{5} = 5 \text{ units per level of production}$$

Because we are interested primarily in the behavior of $f(x)$ in the neighborhood of the point $P(5, 75)$, it may be instructive to see what happens when the production level increases by a smaller amount, say from $x = 5$ to $x = 6$. Note that

$$f(6) = 20(6) - 36 = 84$$

Thus, when production increases from $x = 5$ to $x = 6$, the average rate of increase in revenue is

$$\frac{f(6) - f(5)}{6 - 5} = \frac{84 - 75}{6 - 5} = 9 \text{ units per level of production}$$

What is the average rate of increase in revenue when production increases from $x = 5$ to $x = 5.5$? Because $f(5) = 75$, we need only compute $f(5.5)$. Substituting $x = 5.5$ in (17.1), we obtain

$$f(5.5) = 20(5.5) - (5.5)^2 = 79.75$$

Thus, the average rate of increase for this interval is

$$\frac{f(5.5) - f(5)}{5.5 - 5.0} = \frac{79.75 - 75}{0.5} = 9.50 \text{ units per level of production}$$

We have observed that an increase in production from $x = 5$ to $x = 10$ is associated with an average rate of increase in revenue of 5 units; an increase from $x = 5$ to $x = 6$ results in an average increase in revenue of 9 units, whereas an increase from $x = 5$ to $x = 5.5$ corresponds to an average increase in revenue of 9.5 units. To get a still better approximation, we let production increase from $x = 5$ to $x = 5 + \delta x$, where $\delta x > 0$, and examine the corresponding average rate of increase in revenue as $\delta x \to 0$ as shown in the following table.

$$f(x) = 20x - x^2$$

δx	$5 + \delta x$	$f(5 + \delta x)$	$\delta y = $ $f(5 + \delta x) - f(5)$	$\dfrac{\delta y}{\delta x}$
5	10	100	25	5
1	6	84	9	9
0.5	5.5	79.75	4.75	9.50
0.1	5.1	75.99	0.99	9.90
0.01	5.01	75.0999	0.0999	9.99
0.001	5.001	75.009999	0.009999	9.999
0.0001	5.0001	75.00099999	0.00099999	9.9999

The ratio $\delta y / \delta x$ in the last column reflects the average rate of increase in revenue corresponding to an increase in the production level from $x = 5$ to $x = 5 + \delta x$. As the increase δx in the production level gets smaller and smaller, so does the corresponding increase in revenue, δy, and the difference quotient

$$\frac{\delta y}{\delta x} = \frac{f(5 + \delta x) - f(5)}{\delta x}$$

approaches the limit 10 as δx approaches 0. In other words,

$$\lim_{\delta x \to 0} \frac{\delta y}{\delta x} = \lim_{\delta x \to 0} \left[\frac{f(5 + \delta x) - f(5)}{\delta x} \right] = 10$$

and this represents the instantaneous rate of change in revenue function $f(x)$ at $x = 5$. To determine the instantaneous rate of change in $f(x)$ at some other level of production, say $x = 8$, we need to repeat the above steps using $x = 8$ instead of $x = 5$. However, we shall develop a general definition of the instantaneous rate of change at any arbitrary point $(x, f(x))$. When the production level increases from the level x to $x + \delta x$, the corresponding increase in revenue is

$$\delta y = f(x + \delta x) - f(x)$$

and the average rate of increase in revenue is

$$\frac{\delta y}{\delta x} = \frac{f(x + \delta x) - f(x)}{\delta x}$$

To get the instantaneous rate of change in revenue, we take the limit of the above quantity as δx approaches 0. The following is a formal definition.

Definition 17.2.1: The derivative of the function f at the point x is defined by

$$(17.2) \quad \lim_{\delta x \to 0} \left[\frac{f(x + \delta x) - f(x)}{\delta x} \right]$$

The limit is generally denoted by $f'(x)$, read f prime of x, or dy/dx where $y = f(x)$. If the limit does not exist, the function does not have a derivative for that particular value of x. Note that dy/dx is a symbol representing

$$\lim_{\delta x \to 0} \left(\frac{\delta y}{\delta x} \right)$$

and is not to be regarded as the quotient of dy by dx. Other notations in common use are

$$D_x(y) \qquad D_x[f(x)] \qquad \frac{d}{dx} f(x)$$

To apply this definition to the revenue function $f(x) = 20x - x^2$, we proceed as follows:

$$f(x) = 20x - x^2$$
$$f(x + \delta x) = 20(x + \delta x) - (x + \delta x)^2$$
$$= 20x + 20(\delta x) - x^2 - 2x(\delta x) - (\delta x)^2$$

Then,

$$\delta y = f(x + \delta x) - f(x)$$
$$= 20x + 20(\delta x) - x^2 - 2x(\delta x) - (\delta x)^2 - 20x + x^2$$
$$= 20(\delta x) - 2x(\delta x) - (\delta x)^2$$
$$\frac{\delta y}{\delta x} = \frac{20(\delta x) - 2x(\delta x) - (\delta x)^2}{\delta x}$$
$$= 20 - 2x - (\delta x)$$

Proceeding to the limit when $\delta x \to 0$, we have

$$\frac{dy}{dx} = \lim_{\delta x \to 0} \left(\frac{\delta y}{\delta x} \right)$$
$$= \lim_{\delta x \to 0} (20 - 2x - \delta x)$$
$$= 20 - 2x$$

Thus, the instantaneous rate of change in the revenue at $x = 8$, is given by

$$\left(\frac{dy}{dx}\right)_{x=8} = 20 - 2(8) = 4$$

At $x = 10$, the instantaneous rate of change is

$$\left(\frac{dy}{dx}\right)_{x=10} = 20 - 2(10) = 0$$

whereas at $x = 12$, the instantaneous rate of change is

$$\left(\frac{dy}{dx}\right)_{x=12} = 20 - 2(12) = -4$$

This suggests that the revenue function $f(x)$ can be increased to its maximum by the optimum level of production at $x = 10$. Any increase in production beyond that level results in reduced revenue and is no longer economically feasible. Later on, we shall be able to verify that this is indeed the case.

Example 17.1

Consider a commodity, such as the amount of crude oil that may be produced in the Gulf Coast in a given year. The total cost of production, $c(x)$, is associated with the output level x. Then the marginal cost at the production level x is defined to be the derivative $c'(x)$.

To take a specific case, suppose that

(17.3) $c(x) = ax^2 + bx + d \qquad x > 0$

where a, b, and d are constants. Then the marginal cost at level x is

$$\begin{aligned}
c'(x) &= \lim_{\delta x \to 0} \left[\frac{c(x + \delta x) - c(x)}{\delta x} \right] \\
&= \lim_{\delta x \to 0} \left[\frac{a(x + \delta x)^2 + b(x + \delta x) + d - ax^2 - bx - d}{\delta x} \right] \\
&= \lim_{\delta x \to 0} \frac{a[x^2 + 2x\,\delta x + (\delta x)^2 - x^2] + b[x + (\delta x) - x]}{\delta x} \\
&= \lim_{\delta x \to 0} \frac{a[2x(\delta x) + (\delta x)^2] + b(\delta x)}{\delta x} \\
&= \lim_{\delta x \to 0} [2ax + a(\delta x) + b]
\end{aligned}$$

Thus,

(17.4) $c'(x) = 2ax + b$

We have assumed that the amount of crude oil is a continuous variable and that the change in this amount from x to $(x + \delta x)$ may be infinitesimal. But in the case of a product that has discrete units (positive integers only), a change of one unit is the smallest change possible. Consider, for example, that a firm produces x color television sets in one week. This level of production depends on several factors, such as the capital invested, the number of workers available, the frequency of breakdown of the equipment in the plant, and so on. Assume that the cost of production for producing x color television sets is given by the cost function

(17.5) $\quad c(x) = 10,000 + 200x - \dfrac{x^2}{2}$

The term $10,000 is the total fixed cost of the firm and generally includes rent, executive salaries, interest on investments, taxes, insurance, advertising, and allowances for equipment and machinery depreciation. If 100 color television sets come off the assembly line in one week, the cost is

$$c(100) = \$\left[10,000 + 200(100) - \frac{(100)^2}{2} \right] = \$25,000$$

but if 101 color television sets are produced, the cost is

$$c(101) = \$\left[10,000 + 200(101) - \frac{(101)^2}{2} \right] = \$25,099.50$$

Thus, the cost of an additional set is

$c(101) - c(100) = \$99.50$

Let us now calculate the marginal cost by differentiating $c(x)$ at $x = 100$. Comparing (17.3) and (17.5), we observe that

$a = -\frac{1}{2} \qquad b = 200 \qquad d = 10,000$

From (17.4), we have

$c'(x) = 2ax + b$

$\qquad = 2(-\frac{1}{2})x + 200$

$\qquad = 200 - x$

and

$c'(100) = 100$

which is approximately the same as $c(101) - c(100)$. Note that, in general,

$$c'(x) = \lim_{\delta x \to 0} \left[\frac{c(x + \delta x) - c(x)}{\delta x} \right]$$

but in the case of a product that has discrete units, $\delta x = 1$ is the smallest change possible. Hence,

$$c'(x) \approx \frac{c(x + 1) - c(x)}{1}$$

Thus, whenever a commodity is produced in discrete units, the marginal cost $c'(x)$ gives the approximate cost of the $(x + 1)$st item produced. ∎

Another marginal concept in economics is that of marginal revenue, defined as the change in total revenue resulting from the sale of an additional unit. It can be shown that the marginal revenue $R'(x)$ is approximately the revenue received for the $(x + 1)$st item, assuming that the first x items have already been sold. In other words,

$$R'(x) \approx R(x + 1) - R(x)$$

Similarly, the marginal profit $P'(x)$ is approximately the profit realized from the sale of an additional unit. That is,

$$P'(x) \approx P(x + 1) - P(x)$$

Example 17.2
The profit function of a department store is given by

(17.6) $\quad P(x) = \$\left(200x + \dfrac{x^2}{5} \right)$

where x is the number of articles sold in one day. Find the marginal profit at $x = 50$ and at $x = 95$.

SOLUTION
To find the marginal profit, we use the derivative $P'(x)$. Comparing (17.6) with (17.3), we note that

$$a = \tfrac{1}{5} \qquad b = 200 \qquad d = 0$$

From (17.4), we have

$$P'(x) = 2ax + b$$
$$= \tfrac{2}{5}x + 200$$

The marginal profit at $x = 50$ is

$$P'(50) = \tfrac{2}{5}(50) + 200 = \$220$$

Similarly, the marginal profit at $x = 95$ is

$$P'(95) = \tfrac{2}{5}(95) + 200 = \$238 \qquad\qquad\quad \blacksquare$$

We now discuss a systematic procedure for obtaining derivatives—a method we call the five-step rule.

Example 17.3
Given $f(x) = x^3$, find $f'(x)$ by the five-step rule.

SOLUTION

Step 1: Write the function f at x; that is,

$$f(x) = x^3$$

Step 2: Find $f(x + \delta x)$; that is,

$$f(x + \delta x) = (x + \delta x)^3$$
$$= x^3 + 3x^2(\delta x) + 3x(\delta x)^2 + (\delta x)^3$$

Step 3: Subtract $f(x)$ from $f(x + \delta x)$.

$$f(x + \delta x) - f(x) = 3x^2(\delta x) + 3x(\delta x)^2 + (\delta x)^3$$

Step 4: Form the difference quotient,

$$\frac{f(x + \delta x) - f(x)}{\delta x}$$

and simplify.

$$\frac{f(x + \delta x) - f(x)}{\delta x} = 3x^2 + 3x(\delta x) + (\delta x)^2$$

Step 5: Find

$$\lim_{\delta x \to 0} \frac{f(x + \delta x) - f(x)}{\delta x}$$

Thus,

$$\lim_{\delta x \to 0} \frac{f(x + \delta x) - f(x)}{\delta x} = \lim_{\delta x \to 0} \left[3x^2 + 3x(\delta x) + (\delta x)^2 \right]$$
$$= 3x^2$$

Example 17.4
Given $f(x) = 1/x$, find $f'(x)$ by the five-step rule.

SOLUTION

1. $f(x) = \dfrac{1}{x}$

2. $f(x + \delta x) = \dfrac{1}{x + \delta x}$

3. $f(x + \delta x) - f(x) = \dfrac{1}{x + \delta x} - \dfrac{1}{x} = \dfrac{x - x - \delta x}{x(x + \delta x)}$

$$= -\dfrac{\delta x}{x(x + \delta x)}$$

4. $\dfrac{f(x + \delta x) - f(x)}{\delta x} = -\dfrac{1}{x(x + \delta x)}$

$$5.\ f'(x) = \lim_{\delta x \to 0} \frac{f(x + \delta x) - f(x)}{\delta x}$$

$$= \lim_{\delta x \to 0} \left[-\frac{1}{x(x + \delta x)} \right]$$

$$= -\frac{1}{x^2}$$

The reader will note that the first three steps are purely mechanical and are carried out in a routine manner. It is the last two steps that frequently require some skill in algebraic manipulation. ∎

Example 17.5
Given $f(x) = 1/\sqrt{x}$, find $f'(x)$.

SOLUTION

1. $f(x) = \dfrac{1}{\sqrt{x}}$

2. $f(x + \delta x) = \dfrac{1}{\sqrt{x + \delta x}}$

3. $f(x + \delta x) - f(x) = \dfrac{1}{\sqrt{x + \delta x}} - \dfrac{1}{\sqrt{x}}$

$$= \frac{\sqrt{x} - \sqrt{x + \delta x}}{\sqrt{x}\sqrt{x + \delta x}}$$

4. $\dfrac{f(x + \delta x) - f(x)}{\delta x} = \dfrac{\sqrt{x} - \sqrt{x + \delta x}}{(\delta x)\sqrt{x}\sqrt{x + \delta x}}$

Now we rationalize the numerator, and observe that

$$\frac{\sqrt{x} - \sqrt{x + \delta x}}{(\delta x)\sqrt{x}\sqrt{x + \delta x}} \cdot \frac{\sqrt{x} + \sqrt{x + \delta x}}{\sqrt{x} + \sqrt{x + \delta x}} = \frac{1}{(\delta x)\sqrt{x}\sqrt{x + \delta x}} \cdot \frac{x - (x + \delta x)}{\sqrt{x} + \sqrt{x + \delta x}}$$

$$= \frac{-1}{\sqrt{x}\sqrt{x + \delta x}(\sqrt{x} + \sqrt{x + \delta x})}$$

5. $f'(x) = \lim_{\delta x \to 0} \dfrac{f(x + \delta x) - f(x)}{\delta x} = \lim_{\delta x \to 0} \dfrac{-1}{\sqrt{x}\sqrt{x + \delta x}(\sqrt{x} + \sqrt{x + \delta x})}$

$$= \frac{-1}{\sqrt{x}\sqrt{x}(\sqrt{x} + \sqrt{x})}$$

$$= -\frac{1}{2x^{3/2}}$$

Thus,

$$f'(x) = -\frac{1}{2x^{3/2}}$$

■

EXERCISE 17.1

Find the derivatives of each of the following functions using the five-step rule.

1. $f(x) = 3x$ **2.** $f(x) = 3x^2$

3. $f(x) = 10 - 5x$ **4.** $f(x) = x^2 + 5x + 6$

5. $f(x) = x^3 + 8$ **6.** $f(x) = 8$

7. $f(x) = \dfrac{1}{x^2}$ **8.** $f(x) = \dfrac{1}{x + 4}$

9. $f(x) = \dfrac{1}{x - 4}$ **10.** $f(x) = \dfrac{1}{4 - x}$

11. $f(x) = \dfrac{1}{x^3}$ **12.** $f(x) = \dfrac{1}{x^2 + 1}$

13. $f(x) = \dfrac{x}{x + 1}$ **14.** $f(x) = \dfrac{x}{x - 1}$

15. $f(x) = \sqrt{x}$ **16.** $f(x) = \sqrt{x + 2}$

17. $f(x) = \dfrac{1}{\sqrt{x + 2}}$ **18.** $f(x) = \dfrac{2}{\sqrt{x + 3}}$

19. $f(x) = \dfrac{1}{\sqrt{x + 1}}$ **20.** $f(x) = \dfrac{3}{\sqrt{x - 1}}$

21. The production function for a firm producing a certain commodity is given by

$$f(x) = 100 + 80x - 5x^2$$

where $f(x)$ denotes total cost in thousands of dollars and x represents hundreds of units per week. Determine the instantaneous rate of change at

    a. $x = 5$ **b.** $x = 7$ **c.** $x = 8$ **d.** $x = 10$

22. The profits of a department store are determined approximately by the function

$$P(x) = \$(60x - 3x^2)$$

where x is the number of products sold in units of hundreds. Determine the instantaneous rate of change in $P(x)$ at

    a. $x = 4$ **b.** $x = 6$ **c.** $x = 8$

    d. $x = 10$ **e.** $x = 12$ **f.** $x = 15$

23. Assume that the market demand function for unskilled labor in the United States is given by

$$f(x) = \frac{400}{x}$$

where $f(x)$ represents thousands of labor hours per month and x denotes the wage rate per hour in dollars. Determine the marginal demand at

a. $x = 5$ **b.** $x = 10$ **c.** $x = 15$ **d.** $x = 20$

24. The manager of a chain of bookstores has determined that the supply of certain paperbacks is given approximately by

$$S(p) = 320 - \frac{64}{p - 1}$$

where $S(p)$ denotes the supply at the price p (in dollars) per carton of books. Determine the marginal supply at

a. $p = 2$ **b.** $p = 3$ **c.** $p = 5$ **d.** $p = 9$

25. The market demand function for a certain commodity is given by

$$f(p) = 400 - 20\sqrt{p}$$

where $f(p)$ is the quantity demanded at price p. Determine the marginal demand at

a. $p = 9$ **b.** $p = 16$

17.3 GEOMETRIC INTERPRETATION OF THE DERIVATIVE

In this section, we shall develop the concept of a tangent to the curve $y = f(x)$ at a point P. Because we have not yet formally defined this concept, it seems natural to do this first. Intuitively, the tangent line should touch the curve at one and only one point. Consider, for example, a tangent line to a circle at a point P on the circle as shown in Figure 17.2. From geometry we know that the line drawn perpendicular to the radius of the circle at the point P is the tangent to the circle at that point. Let us now find the tangent line to the curve $f(x) = x^2 + 1$ at a point P in Figure 17.3. Because point P is (0, 1), it seems intuitively reasonable to consider the line $y = 1$ as the tangent line, but is it really? If so, how do we find the tangent line to this curve at point Q? The intuitive definition that the tangent is simply a line that touches the curve at point Q and nowhere else is clearly unsuitable, because there may be several such lines, and in fact a vertical line through Q has only one point in common with the curve. Although the definition of tangent to a circle at point P is elementary, this definition requires the sophisticated notion of limit for other kinds of curves.

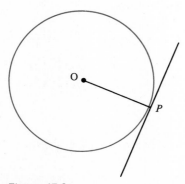

Figure 17.2

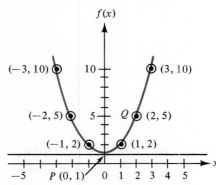

Figure 17.3

Suppose that $P(x_0, f(x_0))$ is a fixed point on the curve $y = f(x)$ at which we wish to find the tangent. (See Figure 17.4.) Let $Q(x_0 + \delta x, f(x_0 + \delta x))$ be another point on the curve. The line drawn through two points P and Q is called a secant line. The slope of the line PQ is

$$\frac{\delta y}{\delta x} = \frac{f(x_0 + \delta x) - f(x_0)}{(x_0 + \delta x) - x_0} = \frac{f(x_0 + \delta x) - f(x_0)}{\delta x}$$

As δx moves closer and closer to zero, point Q moves closer to point P, and line PQ rotates about point P. Intuitively, it seems that the secant PQ approaches a limiting line as δx tends to zero and this limiting line is the tangent to the curve $y = f(x)$ at point P. Figure 17.5 shows several positions for secant PQ and its limiting position as $\delta x \to 0$. Thus, if the function $f(x)$ possesses a derivative at $x = x_0$, then

$$\lim_{\delta x \to 0} \left[\frac{f(x_0 + \delta x) - f(x_0)}{\delta x} \right] = \left(\frac{dy}{dx} \right)_{x = x_0} = f'(x_0)$$

suggests that $f'(x_0)$ or $(dy/dx)_{x=x_0}$ is the slope of the tangent to the curve $y = f(x)$ at the point $P(x_0, f(x_0))$.

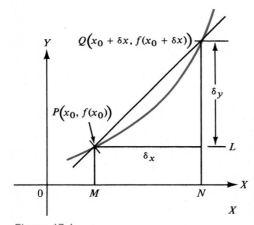

Figure 17.4

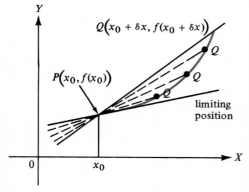

Figure 17.5

Definition 17.3.1: Let $y = f(x)$ be a function differentiable at a point x_0. The tangent to the curve $y = f(x)$ at $P(x_0, f(x_0))$ is the line through P with slope $f'(x_0)$.

Thus, the equation of the tangent to the curve $y = f(x)$ at $P(x_0, f(x_0))$ is

$$y - y_0 = m(x - x_0)$$

where $y_0 = f(x_0)$ and $m = f'(x_0)$ is the slope at point P.

Example 17.6

Find the equation of the line that is tangent to the curve $f(x) = x^2 + 1$ at the point $(3, f(3))$.

SOLUTION

In the problem $f(x) = x^2 + 1$, $x_0 = 3$. Thus, $f(x_0) = 10$. We need to determine whether or not $f(x) = x^2 + 1$ is differentiable at $x = 3$. In other words, does

$$\lim_{\delta x \to 0} \left[\frac{f(3 + \delta x) - f(3)}{\delta x} \right]$$

exist? Note that

$$\frac{f(3 + \delta x) - f(3)}{\delta x} = \frac{(3 + \delta x)^2 + 1 - 10}{\delta x}$$

$$= \frac{6\,\delta x + (\delta x)^2}{\delta x}$$

$$= 6 + \delta x$$

Hence,

$$\lim_{\delta x \to 0} \left[\frac{f(3 + \delta x) - f(3)}{\delta x} \right] = \lim_{\delta x \to 0} (6 + \delta x) = 6$$

and $f(x)$ is differentiable at $x = 3$. Thus, the slope of the tangent is $f'(3) = 6$ and the equation of the tangent is

$$y - 10 = 6(x - 3)$$

That is,

$$y = 6x - 8$$

∎

EXERCISE 17.2

Find the equation of the tangent to each of the following curves at the point $(x_0, f(x_0))$.

1. $f(x) = x^2 - x$; $x_0 = 2$
2. $f(x) = x^2 + 2x + 1$; $x_0 = -1$
3. $f(x) = x^2 - x + 1$; $x_0 = 0$

4. $f(x) = x^2 - 2x + 3; x_0 = 2$
5. $f(x) = x^3; x_0 = 1$
6. $f(x) = x^3 + x^2 + x - 1; x_0 = -1$
7. $f(x) = \sqrt{x}, x \geq 0; x_0 = 4$
8. $f(x) = \sqrt{x + 2}, x \geq -2; x_0 = 7$ [Hint: Use the five-step to find $f'(x)$]
9. $f(x) = \sqrt{2x}, x \geq 0; x_0 = 2$ [Hint: $\sqrt{2x} = \sqrt{2}\sqrt{x}$]
10. $f(x) = x + \sqrt{x}, x \geq 0; x_0 = 4$

17.4 DIFFERENTIABILITY AND CONTINUITY

It would be convenient at this point to relate the concept of continuity with that of differentiability. To say that a function $f(x)$ is continuous at $x = a$ means that

$$\lim_{x \to a} f(x) = f(a)$$

To say that a function $f(x)$ is differentiable at $x = a$ implies that

$$f'(a) = \lim_{\delta x \to 0} \left[\frac{f(a + \delta x) - f(a)}{\delta x} \right]$$

exists. Note that these two concepts are different.

Proposition 17.4.1: If the function $f(x)$ is differentiable at $x = a$, then $f(x)$ is continuous at that point.

PROOF
If $f(x)$ has a derivative at $x = a$, then

$$\lim_{\delta x \to 0} \left[\frac{f(a + \delta x) - f(a)}{\delta x} \right]$$

exists and equals $f'(a)$. We need to show that

$$\lim_{\delta x \to 0} f(a + \delta x) = f(a)$$

which is equivalent to showing that

$$\lim_{\delta x \to 0} [f(a + \delta x) - f(a)] = 0$$

Note that we can write

$$f(a + \delta x) - f(a) = \left[\frac{f(a + \delta x) - f(a)}{\delta x} \right] \cdot \delta x$$

Thus,

$$\lim_{\delta x \to 0} [f(a + \delta x) - f(a)] = \lim_{\delta x \to 0} \left[\frac{f(a + \delta x) - f(a)}{\delta x} \cdot \delta x \right]$$

$$= \lim_{\delta x \to 0} \left[\frac{f(a + \delta x) - f(a)}{\delta x} \right] \lim_{\delta x \to 0} (\delta x)$$

$$= f'(a) \cdot 0$$

$$= 0$$

as asserted. ∎

We have established that differentiability implies continuity. The converse, however, is not true, as is shown in the following example.

Example 17.7

The function

$$f(x) = |x|$$

is continuous at $x = 0$. (Why?) The graph of $f(x)$ is shown in Figure 17.6. That $f(x)$ is not differentiable at $x = 0$ follows from the fact that

$$\frac{f(0 + \delta x) - f(0)}{\delta x} = \frac{f(\delta x)}{\delta x} = \frac{|\delta x|}{\delta x} = \begin{cases} 1 & \text{for } \delta x > 0 \\ -1 & \text{for } \delta x < 0 \end{cases}$$

and

$$\lim_{\delta x \to 0} \left[\frac{f(0 + \delta x) - f(0)}{\delta x} \right] = \lim_{\delta x \to 0} \frac{|\delta x|}{\delta x}$$

does not exist.

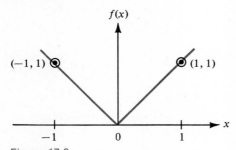

Figure 17.6 ∎

Example 17.8

Let

$$f(x) = \begin{cases} x + 2 & \text{if } x \neq 2 \\ 5 & \text{if } x = 2 \end{cases}$$

a. Is $f(x)$ continuous at $x = 2$?
b. Is $f(x)$ differentiable at $x = 2$?

SOLUTION

a. Note that

$$\lim_{x \to 2} f(x) = \lim_{x \to 2}(x + 2) = 2 + 2 = 4 \qquad \text{(Proposition 16.4.1)}$$

Because $f(2) \neq 4$, we conclude that $f(x)$ is discontinuous at $x = 2$.

b. The function is not differentiable at $x = 2$, because $f(x)$ is not continuous at that point. We could also see this by observing that

$$\lim_{\delta x \to 0} \frac{f(2 + \delta x) - f(2)}{\delta x}$$

does not exist. Note that

$$f(2 + \delta x) = (2 + \delta x) + 2 = 4 + x \quad \text{and} \quad f(2) = 5$$

Thus,

$$\lim_{\delta x \to 0} \frac{f(2 + \delta x) - f(2)}{\delta x} = \lim_{\delta x \to 0} \left(\frac{4 + \delta x - 5}{\delta x} \right)$$

$$= \lim_{\delta x \to 0} \left(1 - \frac{1}{\delta x} \right)$$

This limit does not exist, because $(1 - 1/\delta x)$ gets large and negative as δx approaches 0 from the right and large and positive as δx approaches 0 from the left. ∎

EXERCISE 17.3

Determine in each of the following problems whether or not the function is (a) continuous, (b) differentiable at all points in the domain.

1. $f(x) = \begin{cases} x + 5 & x \neq 5 \\ 10 & x = 5 \end{cases}$

2. $f(x) = \begin{cases} 2x + 1 & x \neq 4 \\ 9 & x = 4 \end{cases}$

3. $f(x) = \begin{cases} 3x + 4 & x \neq 2 \\ 10 & x = 2 \end{cases}$

4. $f(x) = \begin{cases} 2x + 7 & x \neq 1 \\ 9 & x = 1 \end{cases}$

5. $f(x) = |x - 1|$

6. $f(x) = |2x - 1|$

7. Let $f(x)$ be defined as follows:

$$f(x) = \begin{cases} x + 1 & 0 \leq x < 3 \\ 1 & x = 3 \\ 7 - x & 3 < x \leq 5 \end{cases}$$

Is $f(x)$ differentiable at $x = 3$? Explain.

8. Let $f(x)$ be defined as follows:

$$f(x) = \begin{cases} \dfrac{x^2 - 4}{x - 2} & 0 \le x < 2 \\ 4 & x = 2 \\ 6 - x & 2 < x \le 4 \end{cases}$$

a. Is $f(x)$ continuous at $x = 2$?
b. Is $f(x)$ differentiable at $x = 2$?

17.5 SOME FUNDAMENTAL RULES OF DIFFERENTIATION

The use of the five-step rule for finding the derivative of a function frequently involves a lengthy and complicated process. Certain simple functions and their combinations occur repeatedly, and the derivatives of most of these can be written down at sight. In this section, we use the basic Definition 17.2.1 to develop some simple rules of differentiation.

Proposition 17.5.1: If $f(x) = c$, where c is a constant, then $f'(x) = 0$ for all x.

PROOF
Note that the function $f(x)$ always takes on the same value c for all values of x. This means that $f(x) = c$ and $f(x + \delta x) = c$. Using Definition 17.2.1, we obtain

$$f'(x) = \lim_{\delta x \to 0} \frac{f(x + \delta x) - f(x)}{\delta x}$$

$$= \lim_{\delta x \to 0} \frac{c - c}{\delta x}$$

$$= 0$$

Next, we use the definition to differentiate some special cases. Let $f(x) = x$. Then

$$f'(x) = \lim_{\delta x \to 0} \frac{f(x + \delta x) - f(x)}{\delta x}$$

$$= \lim_{\delta x \to 0} \frac{(x + \delta x) - x}{\delta x}$$

$$= \lim_{\delta x \to 0} (1)$$

$$= 1$$

Next, if $f(x) = x^2$, then $f(x + \delta x) = (x + \delta x)^2 = x^2 + 2x(\delta x) + (\delta x)^2$, and

$$f'(x) = \lim_{\delta x \to 0} \frac{f(x + \delta x) - f(x)}{\delta x}$$

$$= \lim_{\delta x \to 0} \frac{(x + \delta x)^2 - x^2}{\delta x}$$

$$= \lim_{\delta x \to 0} \frac{2x(\delta x) + (\delta x)^2}{\delta x}$$

$$= \lim_{\delta x \to 0} [2x + (\delta x)]$$

$$= 2x$$

Using the definition of derivative, we have shown in Example 17.3 that if $f(x) = x^3$, then

$$f'(x) = 3x^2$$

This pattern suggests the following proposition.

Proposition 17.5.2: If $f(x) = x^n$, where n is a positive integer, then $f'(x) = nx^{n-1}$.

PROOF
Note that if

$$f(x) = x^n$$

then

$$f(x + \delta x) = (x + \delta x)^n$$

$$= x^n + nx^{n-1}\,\delta x + \frac{n(n - 1)}{2}\,x^{n-2}(\delta x)^2 + \cdots$$

$$+ (\delta x)^n \qquad \text{(Proposition 9.4.1)}$$

and hence

$$\frac{f(x + \delta x) - f(x)}{\delta x} = nx^{n-1} + \frac{n(n - 1)}{2}\,x^{n-2}(\delta x) + \cdots + (\delta x)^{n-1}$$

Using Definition 17.2.1, we have

$$f'(x) = \lim_{\delta x \to 0} \left[\frac{f(x + \delta x) - f(x)}{\delta x} \right]$$

$$= \lim_{\delta x \to 0} \left[nx^{n-1} + \frac{n(n - 1)}{2}\,x^{n-2}(\delta x) + \cdots + (\delta x)^n \right]$$

$$= nx^{n-1}$$

Thus, if $f(x) = x^5$, then we can immediately write down that $f'(x) = 5x^4$ and if $f(x) = x^{20}$, then $f'(x) = 20x^{19}$. What is even more interesting is that Proposition 17.5.2 holds for any real number n. For example, if

$$f(x) = \frac{1}{x} = x^{-1}(x \neq 0), \text{ then } f'(x) = (-1)x^{-1-1} = -x^{-2} = -\frac{1}{x^2} \qquad \text{(Example 17.4)}$$

Furthermore, if $x > 0$ and if

$$f(x) = \frac{1}{\sqrt{x}} = x^{-1/2}, \text{ then } f'(x) = -\frac{1}{2}x^{-(1/2)-1} = -\frac{1}{2}x^{-3/2} = -\frac{1}{2x^{3/2}}$$

$$\text{(Example 17.5)}$$

Proposition 17.5.3: If $g(x) = c \cdot f(x)$, where c is a constant, then $g'(x) = c \cdot f'(x)$.

PROOF

Note that if $g(x) = c \cdot f(x)$, then

$$g(x + \delta x) = c \cdot f(x + \delta x)$$

Then

$$\frac{g(x + \delta x) - g(x)}{\delta x} = \frac{cf(x + \delta x) - cf(x)}{\delta x}$$

$$= c \cdot \left[\frac{f(x + \delta x) - f(x)}{\delta x} \right]$$

and finally,

$$g'(x) = \lim_{\delta x \to 0} \frac{g(x + \delta x) - g(x)}{\delta x} = \lim_{\delta x \to 0} c \left[\frac{f(x + \delta x) - f(x)}{\delta x} \right]$$

$$= c \cdot \lim_{\delta x \to 0} \left[\frac{f(x + \delta x) - f(x)}{\delta x} \right]$$

$$= c \cdot f'(x)$$

as asserted. ∎

Thus, if $f(x) = 8x^5$, then $f'(x) = 8(5x^4) = 40x^4$.

Next, we consider the derivative of the sum (difference) of any finite number of functions.

We have seen many propositions relating to the sum, difference, product, and quotient functions. Judging from our past experiences, one might intuitively suggest that because the limit of the sum (difference) of two functions is the sum (difference) of the limit, it seems reasonable to state that the derivative of the sum (difference) is equal to the sum (difference) of their derivatives.

Proposition 17.5.4: Assuming that $f(x)$ and $g(x)$ have derivatives, if $h(x) = f(x) + g(x)$, then

$$h'(x) = f'(x) + g'(x)$$

PROOF

To prove this proposition, we use Definition 17.2.1. Then

$$h'(x) = \lim_{\delta x \to 0} \frac{h(x + \delta x) - h(x)}{\delta x}$$

$$= \lim_{\delta x \to 0} \frac{[f(x + \delta x) + g(x + \delta x)] - [f(x) + g(x)]}{\delta x}$$

$$= \lim_{\delta x \to 0} \frac{[f(x + \delta x) - f(x)] + [g(x + \delta x) - g(x)]}{\delta x}$$

$$= \lim_{\delta x \to 0} \frac{f(x + \delta x) - f(x)}{\delta x} + \lim_{\delta x \to 0} \frac{g(x + \delta x) - g(x)}{\delta x}$$

$$= f'(x) + g'(x) \qquad \blacksquare$$

Corollary: Let $f(x)$ and $g(x)$ be two differentiable functions and if $k(x) = f(x) - g(x)$, then $k'(x) = f'(x) - g'(x)$.

We leave the proof as an exercise for the reader.

Example 17.9

Find the derivative of

$$f(x) = 3x^4 + 4x^3 + 2x^2 + 7x$$

SOLUTION

The quantity x^4 has the derivative $4x^3$, as we know from Proposition 17.5.2. Using this fact and Proposition 17.5.3, we find that

$$\frac{d}{dx}(3x^4) = 12x^3, \quad \frac{d}{dx}(4x^3) = 12x^2,$$

$$\frac{d}{dx}(2x^2) = 4x, \qquad \frac{d}{dx}(7x) = 7$$

Using Proposition 17.5.4, we have

$$f'(x) = 12x^3 + 12x^2 + 4x + 7 \qquad \blacksquare$$

EXERCISE 17.4

Find the derivatives of each of the following functions without using the five-step rule.

1. $f(x) = x^4$

2. $f(x) = 3x^5$

3. $f(x) = 4x^8$

4. $f(x) = 5\sqrt{x}$

5. $f(x) = 2x^{3/2}$

6. $f(x) = 8x^{2/3}$

7. $f(x) = \dfrac{1}{x}$

8. $f(x) = \dfrac{1}{x^2}$

9. $f(x) = x^3 + \dfrac{1}{x^3}$

10. $f(x) = x^2 + \dfrac{1}{x^2} + 2$

11. $f(x) = x^3 + 6x^2 + 7$

12. $f(x) = x^5 + 3x^3 + 2x + 1$

13. $f(x) = \sqrt{x} + \dfrac{1}{\sqrt{x}}$

14. $f(x) = x^3 + 8x^2 + \sqrt{x} + \dfrac{1}{2x}$

15. $f(x) = 4x^3 + 7x^2 + 6x + \dfrac{1}{x}$

16. $f(x) = x^4 + 6x^3 + 8x^2 + \dfrac{3}{\sqrt{x}}$

17. $f(x) = 2x^4 + 3x^2 + 5x + \dfrac{7}{\sqrt{x}}$

18. $f(x) = x^5 + 8x^3 + 7\sqrt{x} + \dfrac{1}{\sqrt{x}}$

19. $f(x) = x^{5/4} + x^{3/2} + x^{1/2}$

20. $f(x) = x^{2/3} + x^{1/3} + x^{-1/2}$

For each of the following functions, find

    a. $f'(x)$ **b.** $f'(2)$ **c.** $f'(3)$

21. $f(x) = x^2 + 5x$

22. $f(x) = x^3$

23. $f(x) = \sqrt{x}$

24. $f(x) = x + \sqrt{x}$

25. $f(x) = \dfrac{1}{\sqrt{2x}}$ $\left(\text{Hint:} \dfrac{1}{\sqrt{2x}} = \dfrac{1}{\sqrt{2}} \dfrac{1}{\sqrt{x}} \right)$

26. $f(x) = \sqrt{x} - \dfrac{1}{\sqrt{x}}$

27. The total cost of production of an industry is given as

$$c(x) = 0.03x^2 + 10x + 1200$$

where $c(x)$ denotes the total cost associated with the production level x. Find the marginal cost of production.

28. The total cost of production of a plant is given by

$$c(x) = 0.005x^3 - 0.02x^2 + 30x + 3000$$

where $c(x)$ is the total cost associated with the total output x. Determine the marginal cost of production.

29. The marginal propensity to consume is defined as the instantaneous change in total consumption with respect to a change in income. The aggregate consumption function for the economy as a whole is given by

$$c(x) = 300 + 40\sqrt{x}$$

where $c(x)$ denotes total consumption and x denotes the national income. Determine the marginal propensity to consume for

    a. $x = 100$ **b.** $x = 196$ **c.** $x = 289$

30. The investment function for the building industry as a whole is given by

$$I(r) = 200 - 10{,}000r^3$$

where $I(r)$ denotes the total investment in millions of dollars and r denotes the rate of interest. Determine the instantaneous change in investment with respect to the interest rate when

a. $r = 0.07$ **b.** $r = 0.08$ **c.** $r = 0.10$

17.6 PRODUCT AND QUOTIENT RULES

Thus far, we have limited ourselves to the derivatives of the sum, difference, and constant multiples of functions. We have shown that the derivative of the sum (difference) of two functions is the sum (difference) of their derivatives. Is the derivative of the product of two differentiable functions equal to the product of their derivatives? In other words, does

$$(17.7) \quad \frac{d}{dx}[f(x)g(x)] \overset{?}{=} \frac{d}{dx}[f(x)] \cdot \frac{d}{dx}[g(x)]$$

Suppose, for instance, that $f(x) = 2x + 3$ and $g(x) = x + 2$. Then

$$f(x) \cdot g(x) = (2x + 3)(x + 2)$$
$$= 2x^2 + 7x + 6$$

and

$$\frac{d}{dx}[f(x) \cdot g(x)] = \frac{d}{dx}(2x^2 + 7x + 6)$$

$$= \frac{d}{dx}(2x^2) + \frac{d}{dx}(7x) + \frac{d}{dx}(6)$$

$$= 4x + 7$$

whereas

$$\frac{d}{dx}[f(x)] = \frac{d}{dx}(2x + 3) = \frac{d}{dx}(2x) + \frac{d}{dx}(3) = 2$$

$$\frac{d}{dx}[g(x)] = \frac{d}{dx}(x + 2) = \frac{d}{dx}(x) + \frac{d}{dx}(2) = 1$$

and

$$\frac{d}{dx}[f(x)] \cdot \frac{d}{dx}[g(x)] = 2$$

Thus, it follows that (17.7) does not hold. What sort of equality does hold? The answer lies in the following proposition.

Proposition 17.6.1: Let $f(x)$ and $g(x)$ be two differentiable functions and $h(x) = f(x) \cdot g(x)$. Then

$(17.8) \quad h'(x) = f(x)g'(x) + g(x)f'(x)$

PROOF

We use the five-step rule.

Step 1. $\qquad\qquad\qquad h(x) = f(x) \cdot g(x)$

Step 2. $\qquad\qquad h(x + \delta x) = f(x + \delta x) \cdot g(x + \delta x)$

Step 3. $h(x + \delta x) - h(x) = f(x + \delta x)g(x + \delta x) - f(x)g(x)$

At this point, we use a standard trick for this type of problem. We add and subtract simultaneously the term $f(x + \delta x)g(x)$. This enables us to write step 3 as follows:

$$\begin{aligned}
\delta h &= f(x + \delta x)g(x + \delta x) - f(x + \delta x)g(x) + f(x + \delta x)g(x) - f(x)g(x) \\
&= f(x + \delta x)[g(x + \delta x) - g(x)] + g(x)[f(x + \delta x) - f(x)] \\
&= f(x + \delta x)\,\delta g + g(x)\,\delta f
\end{aligned}$$

Step 4. $\qquad\qquad \dfrac{\delta h}{\delta x} = f(x + \delta x)\dfrac{\delta g}{\delta x} + g(x)\dfrac{\delta f}{\delta x}$

Step 5. $\displaystyle \lim_{\delta x \to 0}\left(\frac{\delta h}{\delta x}\right) = \lim_{\delta x \to 0}\left[f(x + \delta x)\frac{\delta g}{\delta x} + g(x)\frac{\delta f}{\delta x}\right]$

$$h'(x) = \lim_{\delta x \to 0} f(x + \delta x)\lim_{\delta x \to 0}\frac{\delta g}{\delta x} + g(x)\lim_{\delta x \to 0}\frac{\delta f}{\delta x}$$

Because $f(x)$ is differentiable and therefore continuous (Proposition 17.4.1), we have

$$\lim_{\delta x \to 0} f(x + \delta x) = f(x)$$

Using this fact, we conclude that

$$h'(x) = f(x)g'(x) + g(x)f'(x) \qquad\qquad\qquad\qquad ■$$

Example 17.10

If $h(x) = (x^2 + 5)(x^3 + 7x^2 + 8)$, find $h'(x)$.

SOLUTION

Let $f(x) = x^2 + 5$ and $g(x) = x^3 + 7x^2 + 8$. Then

$$f'(x) = 2x \quad \text{and} \quad g'(x) = 3x^2 + 14x$$

Using the product rule, we have

$$\begin{aligned}
h'(x) &= f(x)g'(x) + g(x)f'(x) \\
&= (x^2 + 5)(3x^2 + 14x) + (x^3 + 7x^2 + 8)(2x) \\
&= (3x^4 + 14x^3 + 15x^2 + 70x) + (2x^4 + 14x^3 + 16x) \\
&= 5x^4 + 28x^3 + 15x^2 + 86x \qquad\qquad\qquad ■
\end{aligned}$$

Example 17.11

If $h(x) = x^2(\sqrt{x} + 2)$, find $h'(x)$.

SOLUTION

Let $f(x) = x^2$ and $g(x) = \sqrt{x} + 2$. Then

$$f'(x) = \frac{d}{dx}(x^2) = 2x \qquad g'(x) = \frac{d}{dx}(\sqrt{x} + 2)$$

$$= \frac{d}{dx}(\sqrt{x}) + \frac{d}{dx}(2)$$

$$= \frac{1}{2\sqrt{x}} \qquad x > 0$$

Using the product rule, we obtain

$$h'(x) = f(x)g'(x) + g(x)f'(x)$$

$$= x^2 \left(\frac{1}{2\sqrt{x}}\right) + (\sqrt{x} + 2)(2x)$$

$$= \tfrac{1}{2}x^{3/2} + 2x(\sqrt{x} + 2)$$

Proposition 17.6.2: If $g(x) \neq 0$ and $g(x)$ is differentiable, then

$$h(x) = \frac{1}{g(x)}$$

is differentiable and

(17.9) $\quad h'(x) = -\dfrac{g'(x)}{[g(x)]^2}$

PROOF

We proceed by the five-step rule.

Step 1. $\qquad\qquad h(x) = \dfrac{1}{g(x)}$

Step 2. $\qquad h(x + \delta x) = \dfrac{1}{g(x + \delta x)}$

Step 3. $h(x + \delta x) - h(x) = \dfrac{1}{g(x + \delta x)} - \dfrac{1}{g(x)}$

$$= \frac{g(x) - g(x + \delta x)}{g(x + \delta x) \cdot g(x)}$$

$$= -\left(\frac{g(x + \delta x) - g(x)}{g(x + \delta x)g(x)}\right)$$

Step 4. $\qquad \dfrac{\delta h}{\delta x} = -\left(\dfrac{g(x + \delta x) - g(x)}{\delta x}\right) \cdot \left(\dfrac{1}{g(x + \delta x) \cdot g(x)}\right)$

Step 5.
$$\lim_{\delta x \to 0} \left(\frac{\delta h}{\delta x} \right) = \lim_{\delta x \to 0} \left[-\left(\frac{g(x + \delta x) - g(x)}{\delta x} \right) \cdot \left(\frac{1}{g(x + \delta x) \cdot g(x)} \right) \right]$$

$$= -\frac{1}{g(x)} \lim_{\delta x \to 0} \left(\frac{g(x + \delta x) - g(x)}{\delta x} \right) \lim_{\delta x \to 0} \left(\frac{1}{g(x + \delta x)} \right)$$

$$= -\frac{1}{g(x)} \cdot g'(x) \cdot \frac{1}{g(x)} \qquad \left[\lim_{\delta x \to 0} g(x + \delta x) = g(x) \right]$$

$$= -\frac{g'(x)}{[g(x)]^2} \qquad \qquad \blacksquare$$

Example 17.12

Given that

$$h(x) = \frac{1}{3x + 2} \qquad x \neq -\frac{2}{3}$$

find $h'(x)$.

SOLUTION

Let $g(x) = 3x + 2$. Then $g'(x) = 3$. Using Proposition 17.6.2, we have

$$h'(x) = \frac{-3}{(3x + 2)^2} \qquad \qquad \blacksquare$$

Next, we use the product rule (Proposition 17.6.1) to generalize Proposition 17.6.2 and develop what is commonly known as the quotient rule.

Proposition 17.6.3: Let $f(x)$ and $g(x)$ be two differentiable functions such that $g(x) \neq 0$. Then the function

$$h(x) = \frac{f(x)}{g(x)}$$

is differentiable, and

(17.10) $\quad h'(x) = \dfrac{g(x)f'(x) - f(x)g'(x)}{[g(x)]^2}$

PROOF

Observe that

$$h(x) = \frac{f(x)}{g(x)} = f(x) \cdot \frac{1}{g(x)}$$

Using Proposition 17.6.1, we get

$$h'(x) = f(x) \cdot \frac{d}{dx} \left(\frac{1}{g(x)} \right) + f'(x) \cdot \frac{1}{g(x)}$$

Note that

$$\frac{d}{dx}\left(\frac{1}{g(x)}\right) = -\frac{g'(x)}{[g(x)]^2} \qquad \text{(Proposition 17.6.2)}$$

Thus,

$$h'(x) = f(x)\left(-\frac{g'(x)}{[g(x)]^2}\right) + \frac{f'(x)}{g(x)}$$

$$= \frac{-f(x)g'(x) + f'(x)g(x)}{[g(x)]^2}$$

$$= \frac{g(x)f'(x) - f(x)g'(x)}{[g(x)]^2}$$

Example 17.13
Given that

$$h(x) = \frac{x + 1}{x + 2}$$

find $h'(x)$.

SOLUTION
Let $f(x) = x + 1$ and $g(x) = x + 2$. Then

$$f'(x) = 1 \qquad g'(x) = 1$$

Using Proposition 17.6.3, we have

$$h'(x) = \frac{(x + 2) \cdot 1 - (x + 1) \cdot 1}{(x + 2)^2}$$

$$= \frac{1}{(x + 2)^2}$$

Example 17.14
Given that

$$h(x) = \frac{x^2 - 3x + 4}{2x^2 + 7x + 1}$$

find $h'(x)$.

SOLUTION
Let $f(x) = x^2 - 3x + 4$ and $g(x) = 2x^2 + 7x + 1$. Then

$$f'(x) = 2x - 3 \quad \text{and} \quad g'(x) = 4x + 7$$

Applying the quotient rule (17.10), we obtain

$$h'(x) = \frac{(2x^2 + 7x + 1)(2x - 3) - (x^2 - 3x + 4)(4x + 7)}{(2x^2 + 7x + 1)^2}$$

$$= \frac{(4x^3 - 6x^2 + 14x^2 - 21x + 2x - 3) - (4x^3 + 7x^2 - 12x^2 - 21x + 16x + 28)}{(2x^2 + 7x + 1)^2}$$

$$= \frac{(4x^3 + 8x^2 - 19x - 3) - (4x^3 - 5x^2 - 5x + 28)}{(2x^2 + 7x + 1)^2}$$

$$= \frac{13x^2 - 14x - 31}{(2x^2 + 7x + 1)^2}$$

Example 17.15

Given that

$$h(x) = \frac{\sqrt{x} + 1}{x + 3}$$

find $h'(x)$.

SOLUTION

If $f(x) = \sqrt{x} + 1$ and $g(x) = x + 3$, then

$$f'(x) = \frac{1}{2\sqrt{x}} \quad \text{and} \quad g'(x) = 1$$

Using Proposition 17.6.3, we obtain

$$h'(x) = \frac{(x + 3)(1/2\sqrt{x}) - (\sqrt{x} + 1) \cdot 1}{(x + 3)^2}$$

$$= \frac{(x + 3) - 2\sqrt{x}(\sqrt{x} + 1)}{2\sqrt{x}(x + 3)^2}$$

$$= \frac{(x + 3) - 2x - 2\sqrt{x}}{2\sqrt{x}(x + 3)^2}$$

$$= \frac{3 - x - 2\sqrt{x}}{2\sqrt{x}(x + 3)^2} \quad \text{if } x > 0$$

EXERCISE 17.5

Differentiate each of the following functions using the product rule.

1. $f(x) = (x + 3)(x + 4)$
2. $f(x) = (2x + 1)(2x - 1)$
3. $f(x) = (3x + 4)(2x - 1)$
4. $f(x) = (4x + 5)(2x + 1)$
5. $f(x) = (2x + 5)(3x + 7)$
6. $f(x) = (5x + 7)(2x - 3)$
7. $f(x) = (3x + 2)(2x - 3)$
8. $f(x) = (x + 4)\sqrt{x}$

9. $f(x) = (x^2 + 4)(3x^2 + 7)$

10. $f(x) = (x^2 + x - 1)(x^2 + x + 1)$

11. $f(x) = (x + 1)\sqrt{x}$

12. $f(x) = (3x + 2)(2\sqrt{x} + 1)$

13. $f(x) = \sqrt{x}(\sqrt{x} + 2)$

14. $f(x) = (\sqrt{x} + 1)(\sqrt{x} - 1)$

Using the quotient rule, find dy/dx for each of the following functions.

15. $y = \dfrac{1}{x}$

16. $y = \dfrac{1}{2x + 3}$

17. $y = \dfrac{x}{3x + 2}$

18. $y = \dfrac{x}{2x + 1}$

19. $y = \dfrac{2x - 1}{2x + 1}$

20. $y = \dfrac{1 + x}{1 - x}$

21. $y = \dfrac{1 - x^2}{1 + x^2}$

22. $y = \dfrac{1 + \sqrt{x}}{1 - \sqrt{x}}$

23. $y = \dfrac{1 - x + x^2}{1 + x + x^2}$

24. $y = \dfrac{2x}{1 + x^2}$

For each of the following functions, find

a. $f'(0)$ **b.** $f'(2)$ **c.** $f'(4)$

25. $f(x) = \dfrac{1}{x + 1}$

26. $f(x) = \dfrac{x^2 + 2x + 3}{x + 1}$

27. $f(x) = \dfrac{x - 1}{x + 1}$

28. $f(x) = \dfrac{x}{2x + 1}$

29. $f(x) = \dfrac{3x + 1}{4x - 2}$

30. $f(x) = \dfrac{x^2}{3x + 1}$

17.7 THE CHAIN RULE

The preceding sections in this chapter have enlarged considerably different types of functions that we are able to differentiate. However, we still are unable to find derivatives of such functions as

$$\sqrt{x^2 + 1} \quad \text{or} \quad (3x^2 + 4x + 8)^{60} \quad \text{or} \quad \left(\frac{2x - 5}{4x + 3}\right)^8$$

and so on. We shall, therefore, develop in this section what is commonly known as the chain rule. This rule is one of the useful tools in differentiation of composite functions. Recall from Chapter 2 that when $f(x)$ and $g(x)$ are two functions, we can obtain another function $h(x)$ and denote it by

$$h(x) = (g \circ f)x = g[f(x)]$$

Thus, if g is a function of u, and $u = f(x)$, then a combination of these functional relationships make $g[f(x)]$ as a function of x. For example, if

$$g(u) = u^{1/2} \quad \text{and} \quad u = f(x) = x^2 + 1$$

then, by substitution,

$$g[f(x)] = (x^2 + 1)^{1/2}$$

Similarly, if

$$g(u) = u^2 + 1 \quad \text{and} \quad u = f(x) = \frac{2x - 1}{3x + 2}$$

then

$$g[f(x)] = \left(\frac{2x - 1}{3x + 2}\right)^2 + 1$$

To find the derivative of the composite function, $g[f(x)]$, we need the following proposition. A proof of this proportion is beyond our current scope.

Proposition 17.7.1: If $g(x)$ and $f(x)$ are differentiable, then $h(x) = g[f(x)]$ is differentiable and

(17.11) $h'(x) = g'[f(x)]f'(x)$

In d/dx notation, we may express (17.11) as

(17.12) $\dfrac{dy}{dx} = \dfrac{dy}{du} \cdot \dfrac{du}{dx}$

where $y = g(u)$ and $u = f(x)$. ■

Before illustrating the proposition by examples, we state below one of the most important special cases.

Corollary: If $y = [f(x)]^n$, then

(17.13) $\dfrac{dy}{dx} = n[f(x)]^{n-1}f'(x)$

Example 17.16
Find dy/dx if $y = (3x^2 + 4x + 8)^7$.

SOLUTION
Note that we can write y as

$$y = [f(x)]^7 \qquad \text{where } f(x) = 3x^2 + 4x + 8$$

Then

$$f'(x) = 6x + 4$$

Applying (17.13), with $n = 7$, we have

$$\frac{dy}{dx} = 7(3x^2 + 4x + 8)^6(6x + 4) \qquad ■$$

Example 17.17
Find dy/dx if $y = \sqrt{x^2 + 1}$.

SOLUTION

Here $y = \sqrt{u}$, where $u = x^2 + 1$. Then

$$\frac{dy}{du} = \frac{1}{2\sqrt{u}} \quad \text{and} \quad \frac{du}{dx} = 2x$$

Applying (17.12), we have

$$\frac{dy}{dx} = \frac{1}{2\sqrt{u}} \, 2x = \frac{x}{\sqrt{x^2 + 1}}$$

Example 17.18

Find dy/dx if

$$y = \left(\frac{2x - 5}{4x + 3}\right)^8$$

SOLUTION

We write y as

$$y = [f(x)]^8 \qquad \text{where } f(x) = \frac{2x - 5}{4x + 3}$$

Then using (17.13), with $n = 8$, we obtain

$$\frac{dy}{dx} = 8[f(x)]^7 \frac{d}{dx}\left(\frac{2x - 5}{4x + 3}\right)$$

To find the derivative of $(2x - 5)/(4x + 3)$, we use the quotient formula. Thus,

$$\frac{d}{dx}\left(\frac{2x - 5}{4x + 3}\right) = \frac{(4x + 3)\dfrac{d}{dx}(2x - 5) - (2x - 5)\dfrac{d}{dx}(4x + 3)}{(4x + 3)^2}$$

$$= \frac{(4x + 3) \cdot 2 - (2x - 5) \cdot 4}{(4x + 3)^2}$$

$$= \frac{26}{(4x + 3)^2} \qquad \left(x \neq -\frac{3}{4}\right)$$

Hence,

$$\frac{dy}{dx} = 8\left(\frac{2x - 5}{4x + 3}\right)^7 \frac{26}{(4x + 3)^2}$$

$$= \frac{208(2x - 5)^7}{(4x + 3)^9} \qquad \left(x \neq -\frac{3}{4}\right)$$

Example 17.19

Find the derivative of

$$y = (3x + 4)^6(2x + 7)^8$$

SOLUTION

Note that if $u(x) = (3x + 4)^6$ and $v(x) = (2x + 7)^8$, then by the product formula (17.8), we have

$$\frac{dy}{dx} = u(x)v'(x) + v(x)u'(x)$$

To find $u'(x)$ and $v'(x)$, we use (17.11):

$$u'(x) = 6(3x + 4)^5 \cdot 3$$

and

$$v'(x) = 8(2x + 7)^7 \cdot 2$$

Substituting in the formula for dy/dx, we obtain

$$\frac{dy}{dx} = (3x + 4)^6 \cdot 16(2x + 7)^7 + (2x + 7)^8 \cdot 18(3x + 4)^5$$

$$= 2(3x + 4)^5(2x + 7)^7[8(3x + 4) + 9(2x + 7)]$$

$$= 2(3x + 4)^5(2x + 7)^7(42x + 95)$$

Example 17.20

The demand for a product is given by the function

$$D(p) = \frac{10}{\sqrt{4p + 1}}$$

where $D(p)$ represents the demand at the price p. Find the marginal demand at $p = 6$.

SOLUTION

$$D(p) = 10(4p + 1)^{-1/2}$$

$$D'(p) = \frac{d}{dp}\left[10(4p + 1)^{-1/2}\right]$$

$$= 10(-\tfrac{1}{2})(4p + 1)^{-3/2}(4)$$

$$= -20(4p + 1)^{-3/2}$$

At $p = 6$,

$$D'(p) = -20(4p + 1)^{-3/2}\Big|_{p=6}$$

$$= -\frac{20}{125} = -\frac{4}{25} = -0.16$$

The fact that $D'(6)$ is negative reflects the fact that the demand for a product is decreasing.

EXERCISE 17.6

Find dy/dx in each of the following.

1. $y = (2x + 3)^4$

2. $y = (4x + 7)^5$

3. $y = (6 - 3x^2)^3$

4. $y = (x^2 + 2x + 5)^4$

5. $y = (2x^2 + 3x + 1)^{-2}$

6. $y = (x^2 - 2x - 1)^{-3}$

7. $y = \sqrt{3x + 8}$

8. $y = \sqrt{5x - 3}$

9. $y = \sqrt{x^2 + 1}$

10. $y = \sqrt{x^2 - 2x - 1}$

11. $y = x\sqrt{2x + 1}$

12. $y = x^2\sqrt{3x + 2}$

13. $y = (x^2 + 2)\sqrt{x}$

14. $y = (x^2 + 1)\sqrt{x^2 + 2}$

15. $y = x^2(3x + 7)^{10}$

16. $y = x^3(2x + 3)^{12}$

17. $y = (x^2 + 1)(2x - 1)^8$

18. $y = (x^3 + 2)(4x^2 + 7)^4$

19. $y = (2x + 3)^4(3x + 2)^5$

20. $y = (3x - 1)^4(3x + 1)^6$

21. $y = (x^2 + x + 1)^3(x^2 - x + 1)^4$

22. $y = (1 - x - x^2)^8(1 - x + x^2)^5$

23. $y = \left(\dfrac{2x - 1}{3x + 2}\right)^3$

24. $y = \left(\dfrac{2x + 1}{2x - 1}\right)^4$

25. $y = \left(\dfrac{x + 1}{x - 1}\right)^{1/2}$

26. $y = \left(\dfrac{4x - 5}{3x + 1}\right)^{1/3}$

27. The demand for a certain product is given by

$$D(p) = \sqrt{25 - 5p + 2p^2}$$

where p is the price in cents per unit. Find the marginal demand at $p = 5$ cents.

28. The demand $D(p)$ for a new product is given by

$$D(p) = \frac{500}{\sqrt{4p + 5}}$$

where p is the price in dollars per unit. Find the marginal demand at $p = 5$.

29. The revenue from the sale of x items is given by

$$R(x) = 25x + \frac{x^2}{50}$$

Find the marginal revenue when

a. $x = 25$　　　　　　　　　　**b.** $x = 75$

30. The revenue from the sale of x items is given by

$$R(x) = 5x + \frac{10}{(2x + 1)}$$

Find the marginal revenue when

a. $x = 4$　　　　　　　　　　**b.** $x = 12$

17.8 DERIVATIVES OF EXPONENTIAL FUNCTIONS

In Chapter 14, we studied exponential functions, which provided the necessary means for solving many new applied problems. In Chapter 15, we have shown yet another application of the exponential function involving the base e. In this section, we shall discuss the differentiation of these functions.

Proposition 17.8.1: If $y = e^x$, then $dy/dx = e^x$. Using the five-step rule, we have

Step 1. $y = e^x$
Step 2. $y + \delta y = e^{x + \delta x}$
Step 3. $(y + \delta y) - y = e^{x + \delta x} - e^x$

That is,

$$\delta y = e^x(e^{\delta x} - 1)$$

Step 4. $\dfrac{\delta y}{\delta x} = e^x \left(\dfrac{e^{\delta x} - 1}{\delta x} \right)$

Step 5. $\dfrac{dy}{dx} = \lim_{\delta x \to 0} \left(\dfrac{\delta y}{\delta x} \right)$

$$= \lim_{\delta x \to 0} \left[\frac{e^x(e^{\delta x} - 1)}{\delta x} \right]$$

$$= e^x \lim_{\delta x \to 0} \left(\frac{e^{\delta x} - 1}{\delta x} \right)$$

The evaluation of the expression

$$\lim_{\delta x \to 0} \left(\frac{e^{\delta x} - 1}{\delta x} \right)$$

is undoubtedly beyond our present scope. We shall simply note that this limit does exist and that

$$\lim_{\delta x \to 0} \left(\frac{e^{\delta x} - 1}{\delta x} \right) = 1$$

Thus, if $y = e^x$, then

(17.14) $\qquad \dfrac{dy}{dx} = e^x$

■

Corollary: If $y = e^{u(x)}$, then

(17.15) $\qquad \dfrac{dy}{dx} = e^{u(x)}u'(x)$

This follows from Proposition 17.8.1 and the chain rule.

Proposition 17.8.2: If $y = a^x$, then

$$\frac{dy}{dx} = a^x \ln a \qquad a > 0$$

PROOF

Note that we can write

(17.16) $\quad a^x = e^{x \ln a}$

Thus,

$$y = e^{u(x)} \qquad \text{where } u(x) = x \ln a$$

Applying (17.15), we have

(17.17) $\quad \dfrac{dy}{dx} = e^{x \ln a} \dfrac{d}{dx}(x \ln a)$

$$= e^{x \ln a} \cdot \ln a$$

$$= a^x \ln a \qquad\qquad \blacksquare$$

Corollary: If $y = a^{u(x)}$, then

(17.18) $\quad \dfrac{dy}{dx} = a^{u(x)} u'(x) \ln a$

This follows from Proposition 17.8.2 and the chain rule.

Example 17.21

Find dy/dx if $y = e^{\sqrt{x}}$.

SOLUTION

Here, $u(x) = \sqrt{x}$. Differentiating $u(x)$, we have

$$u'(x) = \dfrac{1}{2\sqrt{x}}$$

From (17.15), we get

$$\dfrac{dy}{dx} = e^{u(x)} \cdot u'(x)$$

$$= e^{\sqrt{x}} \cdot \dfrac{1}{2\sqrt{x}} \qquad\qquad \blacksquare$$

Example 17.22

Find dy/dx if $y = x^2 e^{2x}$. Using the product rule, we get

$$\dfrac{dy}{dx} = x^2 \cdot \dfrac{d}{dx}(e^{2x}) + e^{2x} \cdot \dfrac{d}{dx}(x^2)$$

$$= x^2 \cdot e^{2x} \dfrac{d}{dx}(2x) + e^{2x} \cdot (2x)$$

$$= x^2 e^{2x} \cdot 2 + 2x e^{2x}$$

$$= 2x e^{2x}(x + 1) \qquad\qquad \blacksquare$$

EXERCISE 17.7

Find dy/dx in each of the following cases.

1. $y = e^{3x}$
2. $y = 4e^{5x}$
3. $y = e^{x^2}$
4. $y = e^{x^2 + 2x}$
5. $y = e^{2x^2 + 3x + 1}$
6. $y = e^{3x^2 - 4x}$

7. $y = e^x + e^{-x}$
8. $y = \dfrac{e^x - e^{-x}}{2}$

9. $y = e^{\sqrt{x+1}}$
10. $y = e^{\sqrt{2x+3}}$
11. $y = e^{x\sqrt{x-1}}$
12. $y = e^{x\sqrt{x+1}}$
13. $y = e^{\sqrt{x^2-1}}$
14. $y = e^{\sqrt{2x^2+1}}$
15. $y = x(10)^x$
16. $y = (x + 2)e^{-x}$
17. $y = x^2 e^{\sqrt{x}}$
18. $y = x^2(8)^{3x}$
19. $y = (x^2 + 1)a^{4x}$
20. $y = (x + 1)^2(10)^{4x}$

21. $y = \dfrac{e^x}{1 + e^x}$
22. $y = \dfrac{e^{3x}}{1 + e^{3x}}$

23. $y = \dfrac{200}{1 + 10e^{0.3x}}$
24. $y = \dfrac{5000}{1 + 30e^{0.5x}}$

25. The annual profit of a publisher from the sales of a certain book is given by

$$P(t) = \$6000 + 8000e^{-0.5t}$$

where t is the number of years the product is on the market. Find the instantaneous rate of change in profit when
a. $t = 2$ years **b.** $t = 4$ years **c.** $t = 5$ years

26. The demand for a product (in thousands of units) is given by the equation

$$D(t) = 1000(6 - 5e^{-0.6t})$$

where t is measured in months. Find the instantaneous rate of change in the demand of this product when
a. $t = 1$ **b.** $t = 3$ **c.** $t = 5$

27. The monthly sales of a new model of an automobile in the New England states is approximated by

$$S(t) = 5000e^{-0.2t}$$

where t is the number of months that this model remains in production. Determine the instantaneous rate of change in the sales at $t = 4$.

28. If $y = Ae^{kx}$, where A and k are constants, show that the instantaneous rate of change of y with respect to x is proportional to y itself.

17.9 DERIVATIVES OF LOGARITHMIC FUNCTIONS

We recall an observation in Chapter 2 that the logarithmic function is the inverse of the exponential function and that the graph of the logarithmic function can be obtained directly from the exponential curve. Now we are ready to show that the derivative of the logarithmic function can be obtained by using Proposition 17.8.2.

Proposition 17.9.1: If $y = \log_a x$, then

$$\frac{dy}{dx} = \frac{1}{x} \log_a e$$

PROOF

Note that

$$y = \log_a x \quad \text{and} \quad x = a^y$$

are equivalent equations. Using (17.18), we differentiate

$$a^y = x$$

with respect to x and obtain

$$a^y \cdot \frac{dy}{dx} \cdot \ln a = 1$$

Therefore,

$$\frac{dy}{dx} = \frac{1}{a^y \ln a}$$

$$= \frac{1}{x} \frac{1}{\ln a}$$

$$= \frac{1}{x} \log_a e \qquad (\log_e a \cdot \log_a e = 1)$$

as asserted.

Corollary 1: If $y = \log_a u(x)$, $u(x) > 0$, then

$$(17.19) \qquad \frac{dy}{dx} = \frac{u'(x)}{u(x)} \log_a e$$

This assertion follows directly from Proposition 17.9.1 and the chain rule.

Corollary 2: If $y = \ln u(x)$, then

$$(17.20) \qquad \frac{dy}{dx} = \frac{u'(x)}{u(x)}$$

because $\log_e e = 1$. Thus, if $y = \ln x$, when $x > 0$, then

$$(17.21) \qquad \frac{dy}{dx} = \frac{1}{x}$$

Example 17.23

Find dy/dx if $y = \ln(1 + x^2)$.

SOLUTION

This function is of the form $\ln u(x)$, where

$$u(x) = (1 + x^2)$$

Differentiating $u(x)$, we get

$$u'(x) = 2x$$

Now applying (17.20), we have

$$\frac{dy}{dx} = \frac{u'(x)}{u(x)} = \frac{2x}{1 + x^2}$$

Example 17.24
Find dy/dx if $y = \ln\sqrt{x}$.

SOLUTION
First, we apply Proposition 14.6.2 and simplify the original expression.

$$\begin{aligned} y &= \ln\sqrt{x} \\ &= \ln x^{1/2} \\ &= \tfrac{1}{2}\ln x \end{aligned}$$

Now, differentiating y, we obtain

$$\frac{dy}{dx} = \frac{1}{2}\frac{d}{dx}(\ln x) \qquad x > 0$$

$$= \frac{1}{2x}$$

Example 17.25
Find dy/dx if

$$y = \frac{\ln x}{x} \qquad x > 0$$

SOLUTION
Using the quotient rule, we have

$$\frac{dy}{dx} = \frac{x \cdot \dfrac{d}{dx}(\ln x) - (\ln x) \cdot \dfrac{d}{dx}(x)}{x^2}$$

$$= \frac{x \cdot (1/x) - \ln x}{x^2} \qquad x > 0$$

$$= \frac{1 - \ln x}{x^2}$$

Example 17.26
Find dy/dx if

$$y = \ln\left[\frac{x(x + 1)}{(x + 2)^2}\right] \qquad x > 0$$

SOLUTION

$$y = \ln\left[\frac{x(x + 1)}{(x + 2)^2}\right]$$

$$= \ln(x) + \ln(x + 1) - \ln(x + 2)^2 \qquad \text{(Proposition 14.6.1)}$$

$$= \ln(x) + \ln(x + 1) - 2\ln(x + 2) \qquad \text{(Proposition 14.6.2)}$$

Now we differentiate y with respect to x. Thus,

$$\frac{dy}{dx} = \frac{1}{x} + \frac{1}{x + 1} - \frac{2}{x + 2}$$

$$= \frac{3x + 2}{x(x + 1)(x + 2)} \qquad x > 0 \qquad ■$$

Example 17.27
Find dy/dx if $y = \ln(1 + e^{3x})$.

SOLUTION
Here,

$$u(x) = 1 + e^{3x}$$

$$u'(x) = \frac{d}{dx}(1 + e^{3x}) = 3e^{3x}$$

Using (17.20), we obtain

$$\frac{dy}{dx} = \frac{u'(x)}{u(x)} = \frac{3e^{3x}}{1 + e^{3x}} \qquad ■$$

Example 17.28
Find dy/dx if

$$y = \frac{x\sqrt{x + 1}}{\sqrt{x + 3}}$$

SOLUTION
First, we take logarithms of both sides and obtain

$$\ln y = \ln\left(\frac{x\sqrt{x + 1}}{\sqrt{x + 3}}\right)$$

$$= \ln x + \ln\sqrt{x + 1} - \ln\sqrt{x + 3} \qquad \text{(Proposition 14.6.1)}$$

$$= \ln x + \tfrac{1}{2}\ln(x + 1) - \tfrac{1}{2}\ln(x + 3) \qquad \text{(Proposition 14.6.2)}$$

Now we differentiate both sides with respect to x. Note that the derivative of $\ln y$ is

$$\frac{1}{y}\frac{dy}{dx}$$

Thus,

$$\frac{1}{y}\frac{dy}{dx} = \frac{1}{x} + \frac{1}{2}\frac{1}{x+1} - \frac{1}{2}\frac{1}{x+3}$$

$$= \frac{x^2 + 5x + 3}{2x(x+1)(x+3)}$$

Hence,

$$\frac{dy}{dx} = y \cdot \frac{(x^2 + 5x + 3)}{2x(x+1)(x+3)}$$

$$= \frac{x\sqrt{x+1}}{\sqrt{x+3}} \frac{(x^2 + 5x + 3)}{2x(x+1)(x+3)}$$

$$= \frac{(x^2 + 5x + 3)}{2\sqrt{x+1}(x+3)^{3/2}}$$

Example 17.29
Find dy/dx if $y = x^x$.

SOLUTION
Taking logarithms of both sides, we get

$$\ln y = \ln(x^x)$$
$$= x \ln x \qquad \text{(Proposition 14.6.2)}$$

Differentiating both sides with respect to x, we obtain

$$\frac{1}{y}\frac{dy}{dx} = x\frac{d}{dx}(\ln x) + \ln x \frac{d}{dx}(x)$$

$$= x \cdot \frac{1}{x} + \ln x$$

$$= 1 + \ln x$$

Hence,

$$\frac{dy}{dx} = y(1 + \ln x)$$

$$= x^x(1 + \ln x)$$

EXERCISE 17.8

Find dy/dx in each of the following.

1. $y = \ln(x + 1)$

2. $y = \ln(2x + 3)$

3. $y = \ln\sqrt{x+1}$

4. $y = \ln\sqrt{2x+3}$

5. $y = \ln(x\sqrt{x-1})$

6. $y = \ln\sqrt{x^2+1}$

7. $y = \ln(\ln x)$

8. $y = \ln(\ln\sqrt{x+1})$

9. $y = x^2 \ln 3x$

10. $y = x^3 \ln\sqrt{x + 2}$

11. $y = \ln(xe^x)$

12. $y = \ln(x^2 e^{2x})$

13. $y = \ln(x^x)$

14. $y = \ln(1 + e^{2x})$

15. $y = \ln\left(\dfrac{e^x}{1 + e^x}\right)$

16. $y = \ln\left(\dfrac{e^{2x}}{1 + x}\right)$

17. $y = \dfrac{e^x - 1}{2 \ln x}$

18. $y = \dfrac{a}{1 + \ln kx}$

19. $y = x^3(x + 1)^6$

20. $y = x^2(x - 4)^3(x + 2)^4$

21. $y = \left(\dfrac{1 + x}{1 - x}\right)^5$

22. $y = \left(\dfrac{3 + x + x^2}{x + 4}\right)^6$

23. $y = \dfrac{\sqrt{x + 1}}{x + 2}$

24. $y = \dfrac{\sqrt{x + 4}(x - 2)}{\sqrt{x^3 + 8}}$

25. $y = (x + 3)^x$

26. $y = (x + 1)^{x + 2}$

27. $y = (\ln x)^{\ln x}$

28. $y = (\sqrt{x})^{\sqrt{x}}$

29. $y = \dfrac{\sqrt{x + 1}}{\sqrt{x + 2}}$

30. Prove Proposition 17.9.1 using the five-step rule.

17.10 HIGHER DERIVATIVES

The function $f'(x)$ defined by

$$\lim_{\delta x \to 0} \left[\frac{f(x + \delta x) - f(x)}{\delta x}\right]$$

in Definition 17.2.1 is also called the first derivative of the function $y = f(x)$. If $f'(x)$ has a derivative at a point x, then this derivative is called the second derivative of y or $f(x)$ at that point, and is denoted by $f''(x)$ or d^2y/dx^2. In other words,

(17.22) $f''(x) = \lim_{\delta x \to 0} \dfrac{f'(x + \delta x) - f'(x)}{\delta x}$

provided that this limit exists. If this new derivative has a derivative, then it is called the third derivative of y or $f(x)$. Various notations are used to denote the higher derivatives of a function $y = f(x)$. Thus, the first, second, third, ... , nth derivative of $y = f(x)$ are represented by

$y', y'', y''', \ldots, y^{(n)}$

or by

$f'(x), f''(x), f'''(x), \ldots, f^n(x)$

or by

$\dfrac{dy}{dx}, \dfrac{d^2y}{dx^2}, \dfrac{d^3y}{dx^3}, \ldots, \dfrac{d^ny}{dx^n}$

or by

$$Dy, D^2y, D^3y, \ldots, D^ny$$

Example 17.30
Let $y = x^4$. Then

$$\frac{dy}{dx} = 4x^3$$

$$\frac{d^2y}{dx^2} = \frac{d}{dx}\left(\frac{dy}{dx}\right) = \frac{d}{dx}(4x^3) = 12x^2$$

$$\frac{d^3y}{dx^3} = \frac{d}{dx}\left(\frac{d^2y}{dx^2}\right) = \frac{d}{dx}(12x^2) = 24x$$

and

$$\frac{d^4y}{dx^4} = \frac{d}{dx}\left(\frac{d^3y}{dx^3}\right) = \frac{d}{dx}(24x) = 24$$

Note that if $y = x^4$, then all derivatives of the function higher than the fourth derivative are equal to zero. ∎

Example 17.31
Find d^3y/dx^3 if $y = \ln(x + 1)$, $x > -1$.

SOLUTION
Note that if

$$y = \ln(x + 1)$$

then

$$\frac{dy}{dx} = \frac{1}{x + 1} = (x + 1)^{-1}$$

$$\frac{d^2y}{dx^2} = (-1)(x + 1)^{-2}$$

and

$$\frac{d^3y}{dx^3} = (-1)(-2)(x + 1)^{-3}$$

$$= \frac{2}{(x + 1)^3}$$

∎

Example 17.32
Find d^4y/dx^4 if

$$y = \frac{x + 3}{x + 2} \qquad x \neq -2$$

SOLUTION

If we write

$$y = \frac{x + 3}{x + 2} = 1 + \frac{1}{x + 2} = 1 + (x + 2)^{-1}$$

then

$$\frac{dy}{dx} = (-1)(x + 2)^{-2}$$

$$\frac{d^2y}{dx^2} = (-1)(-2)(x + 2)^{-3} = 2(x + 2)^{-3}$$

$$\frac{d^3y}{dx^3} = 2(-3)(x + 2)^{-4} = -6(x + 2)^{-4}$$

and

$$\frac{d^4y}{dx^4} = (-6)(-4)(x + 2)^{-5} = 24(x + 2)^{-5} = \frac{24}{(x + 2)^5} \qquad \blacksquare$$

We shall encounter several interpretations of the second derivative in the next chapter. However, we may state in passing that the second derivative is the instantaneous rate of change of the first derivative. If, for example, the first derivative represents the marginal revenue, then the second derivative gives the rate of change in the marginal revenue.

EXERCISE 17.9

Find the first two derivatives of each of the following functions.

1. $y = x^7$

2. $y = \dfrac{1}{x}$

3. $y = 50x + \dfrac{x^2}{200}$

4. $y = 4x^3 - 7x^2 + 6x + 12$

5. $y = x^4 + 3x^3 + 6x^2$

6. $y = x^5 + 8x^4 + 2x^3 + 4x^2$

7. $y = \dfrac{x}{1 - x}$

8. $y = \dfrac{x^2}{1 - x^2}$

9. $y = \dfrac{3x^2}{1 + x^2}$

10. $y = \dfrac{x^2}{1 + x}$

Find the first four derivatives of each of the following functions.

11. $y = (ax + b)^5$

12. $y = \dfrac{1}{x + 2}$

13. $y = \sqrt{x + 1}$

14. $y = \dfrac{1}{\sqrt{2x + 3}}$

15. $y = e^{5x}$

16. $y = e^{nx}$

17. $y = \ln(x + 3)$

18. $y = \ln(2x + 5)$

19. $y = \ln(3x + 4)$

20. $y = \ln(ax + b)$

17.11 IMPLICIT FUNCTIONS

We have considered so far functions that can be expressed in terms of the independent variable. Such functions are called explicit functions. Sometimes it happens that x and y are both involved in an equation and it is not possible to determine y uniquely in terms of x. Consider, for example, the equations

$$b^2 x^2 + a^2 y^2 = a^2 b^2$$
$$x^2 + 2xy + 3y^2 + 5y = 8$$

or

$$y^3 + 3y^2 x + 6yx^2 + x^3 = 57$$

None of the expressions can be solved for y uniquely. Further, all these expressions are of the general form

$$f(x, y) = 0$$

In these cases, y is defined implicitly in terms of x.

Returning to the equation

$$b^2 x^2 + a^2 y^2 = a^2 b^2$$

we solve for y and obtain

$$y = \frac{b}{a}\sqrt{a^2 - x^2} \quad \text{and} \quad y = -\frac{b}{a}\sqrt{a^2 - x^2}$$

Thus, there are two functions of x, each restricted to the range $-a \le x \le a$ to keep y a real number. Geometrically, the first of these corresponds to the upper half and the second to the lower half of the ellipse. (See Figure 17.7.) We would

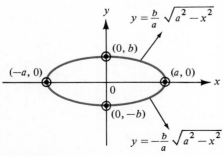

Figure 17.7

certainly need additional information to determine which half of the ellipse we need to use in a particular problem. However, it is possible to differentiate without first solving for y in terms of x, as illustrated in the following examples.

Example 17.33

Find dy/dx without solving for y if

$$b^2x^2 + a^2y^2 = a^2b^2$$

SOLUTION

We differentiate each term in the equation $b^2x^2 + a^2y^2 = a^2b^2$ with respect to x. Now

$$\frac{d}{dx}(b^2x^2) = 2b^2x$$

$$\frac{d}{dx}(a^2y^2) = 2a^2y\frac{dy}{dx} \qquad \text{(Chain Rule)}$$

$$\frac{d}{dx}(a^2b^2) = 0$$

Thus, we have

$$2b^2x + 2a^2y \cdot \frac{dy}{dx} = 0$$

Solving for dy/dx, we find that

$$\frac{dy}{dx} = -\frac{b^2x}{a^2y} \qquad y \neq 0$$

∎

Example 17.34

Find dy/dx if $x^{2/3} + y^{2/3} - a^{2/3} = 0$.

SOLUTION

Differentiating each term with respect to x, we have

$$\frac{2}{3}x^{-1/3} + \frac{2}{3}y^{-1/3} \cdot \frac{dy}{dx} = 0 \qquad x, y \neq 0$$

which on simplification yields

$$\frac{dy}{dx} = -\left(\frac{y}{x}\right)^{1/3} \qquad x, y \neq 0$$

∎

Example 17.35

Find d^2y/dx^2 if $x^2 + 2xy - y^2 + 32 = 0$.

SOLUTION

First, we find dy/dx by implicit differentiation. That is,

$$2x + 2x\frac{dy}{dx} + 2y - 2y\frac{dy}{dx} = 0$$

$$\frac{dy}{dx}(2x - 2y) + (2x + 2y) = 0$$

$$\frac{dy}{dx} = \frac{y + x}{y - x}, \quad y - x \neq 0$$

Differentiating both sides of this equation, we obtain

$$\frac{d^2y}{dx^2} = \frac{d}{dx}\left(\frac{y + x}{y - x}\right) = \frac{(y - x)\dfrac{d}{dx}(y + x) - (y + x)\dfrac{d}{dx}(y - x)}{(y - x)^2}$$

$$= \frac{(y - x)\left(\dfrac{dy}{dx} + 1\right) - (y + x)\left(\dfrac{dy}{dx} - 1\right)}{(y - x)^2}$$

$$= \frac{\left(y\dfrac{dy}{dx} + y - x\dfrac{dy}{dx} - x\right) - \left(y\dfrac{dy}{dx} - y + x\dfrac{dy}{dx} - x\right)}{(y - x)^2}$$

which on simplification yields

$$\frac{d^2y}{dx^2} = \frac{2y - 2x\dfrac{dy}{dx}}{(y - x)^2}$$

$$= \frac{2y - 2x\left[(y + x)/(y - x)\right]}{(y - x)^2}$$

$$= \frac{2(y^2 - 2xy - x^2)}{(y - x)^3} = \frac{64}{(y - x)^3}, x \neq y \quad (y^2 - 2xy - x^2 = 32) \quad \blacksquare$$

Example 17.36

Find the equation of the tangent to the circle $x^2 + y^2 = a^2$ at the point (x_0, y_0).

SOLUTION

Differentiating with respect to x, we have

$$2x + 2y\frac{dy}{dx} = 0$$

or

$$\frac{dy}{dx} = -\frac{x}{y} \quad y \neq 0$$

The slope of the tangent line to the curve at (x_0, y_0) is given by

$$\left(\frac{dy}{dx}\right)(x_0, y_0) = -\frac{x_0}{y_0}$$

The equation of the tangent line through (x_0, y_0) is

$$y - y_0 = m(x - x_0)$$

$$y - y_0 = -\frac{x_0}{y_0}(x - x_0)$$

This yields

$$yy_0 - y_0^2 = -xx_0 + x_0^2$$

or

$$yy_0 + xx_0 = x_0^2 + y_0^2$$

Because (x_0, y_0) is a point on the circle, it follows that $x_0^2 + y_0^2 = a^2$. Thus, the equation of the tangent to the circle is

$$yy_0 + xx_0 = a^2$$ ■

EXERCISE 17.10

Find dy/dx by implicit differentiation in each of the following.

1. $y^2 = 4x$
2. $xy = 16$
3. $x^2 + 4y^2 = 24$
4. $9x^2 + 4y^2 = 36$
5. $x^2 - 3y^2 = 18$
6. $x^3 + y^3 = 15$
7. $x^3 + y^3 = 18xy$
8. $x^2 + 2xy = 25$
9. $x^2 + xy + y^2 = 4$
10. $2x^2 - xy + 3y^2 = 24$
11. $x + \sqrt{xy} = y^2$
12. $xy^2 - 2x^2y = 12$
13. $y^2(x^2 + y^2) = 64$
14. $y^3 = 4(x^2 + y^2)$
15. $x^4 - x^2y^2 + y^4 = a^4$
16. $\sqrt{x} + \sqrt{y} = \sqrt{a}$
17. $\sqrt{x} + \sqrt{xy} + \sqrt{y} = 25$
18. $x^{1/3} + y^{1/3} = 27$
19. $x^5 - 2x^3y^2 + 4x^2y^4 + y^5 = 10$
20. $x^6 + 5x^4y^2 + 3x^2y^4 + y^6 = 32$

Find dy/dx and d^2y/dx^2 by implicit differentiation in each of the following.

21. $x^2 + y^2 = a^2$
22. $3x^2 + 4y^2 = 12$
23. $25x^2 - 16y^2 = 400$
24. $xy + y^2 = 16$
25. $x^{2/3} + y^{2/3} = a^{2/3}$
26. $x^2 + xy + y^2 = 25$

Find the equation of the tangent to each of the following curves at the point specified.

27. $x^2 + y^2 = 25; (4, 3)$
28. $xy = 8; (2, 4)$
29. $x^{2/3} + y^{2/3} = 2; (1, 1)$
30. $x^3 - 2axy + y^3 = 0; (a, a)$
31. $2x^2 - xy + 3y^2 = 18; (3, 1)$
32. $x^2 + xy + y^2 = 4; (2, -2)$
33. $x^3 - 3axy + y^3 = 0; \left(\dfrac{3a}{2}, \dfrac{3a}{2}\right)$
34. $x^3 + y^3 = 18xy; (8, 4)$
35. $y + \sqrt{x^2 + y^2} - x = 6; (3, 4)$

18
Differential Calculus—Applications

18.1 INTRODUCTION

The concept of maximization of profit runs through the basic literature of any firm or industry. Behind the conditions of market equilibrium can be found the general assumption that the management of a firm, industry, or a factory explores different avenues to maximize profit or the rate of growth of its operations and to minimize the cost of its products. This basic assumption helps to explain the behavior of practically all economic institutions in the society and forms the basis for a consumer who seeks to maximize the utility of the goods and services he buys. Consequently, the mathematical tools that assist the management in obtaining a maximum or minimum value of a function are of vital importance in business.

Consider, for example, a travel agency that advertises a five-day all-expenses-paid trip to Nova Scotia and has reserved space for 50 couples on a boat. The charge is $600 plus $20 for each subsequent cancellation. What is the number of cancellations that will maximize the travel agency's total receipts? Consider, as another example, a real estate office that handles an apartment complex with 150 units. Past experience shows that all units are occupied if the rent is $200 per month, but for each $10 increase per month in rent, five units become vacant. Assuming that the cost of servicing each rented apartment is $40 per month, what rent should the management charge each tenant so as to maximize the profit? Consider the classic problem of a farmer who wishes to fence off a rectangular pasture along a straight river, the side along the river requiring no fence. He has barbed wire enough to build a fence 1 mile long. How long should the sides of the rectangle be so as to enclose the largest possible area?

The theory of optimization, which deals in general with questions of this nature, has a wide range of applications in physics, engineering, marketing, and many other related areas of economics.

18.2 MAXIMA AND MINIMA

To begin with, we present some background material necessary to define the maximum and minimum value of a function. We shall make a distinction between a relative maximum and an absolute maximum and a similar distinction between a relative minimum and an absolute minimum value. We note that a closed interval $[a, b]$ is the set of real numbers* $\{x|a \leq x \leq b\}$, that an open interval (a, b) is the set of real numbers $\{x|a < x < b\}$, and that the semiclosed intervals $(a, b]$ and $[a, b)$ are the sets of real numbers $\{x|a < x \leq b\}$ and $\{x|a \leq x < b\}$, respectively. These intervals, which are of finite length, are called finite intervals.

The notations for a point in a plane and for an open interval are the same, but it is easy to distinguish them by the context.

Definition 18.2.1: Let $f(x)$ be a function defined on a closed interval $[a, b]$ or an open interval (a, b) and let $x_0 \in (a, b)$. Then $f(x_0)$ is a relative maximum of $f(x)$ if there exists a $\delta > 0$ such that

$$f(x_0) \geq f(x)$$

for all $x \in (x_0 - \delta, x_0 + \delta)$.

This statement implies that the function $f(x)$ has a relative maximum at x_0 if the value of the function at x_0 is greater than or equal to $f(x)$ evaluated at any other point in the interval $(x_0 - \delta, x_0 + \delta)$ as shown in Figure 18.1.

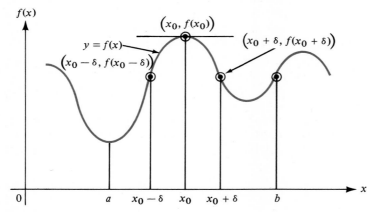

Figure 18.1

Definition 18.2.2: Let $f(x)$ be a function defined on a closed interval $[a, b]$ or an open interval (a, b) and let $x_0 \in (a, b)$. Then $f(x_0)$ is a relative minimum of $f(x)$ if there exists a $\delta > 0$ such that

$$f(x_0) \leq f(x)$$

for all $x \in (x_0 - \delta, x_0 + \delta)$.

This is equivalent to saying that the function $f(x)$ has a relative minimum at x_0 if the value of the function at x_0 is less than or equal to $f(x)$ evaluated at any other point in the interval $(x_0 - \delta, x_0 + \delta)$ as shown in Figure 18.2.

---

* An elementary discussion on the real number system is given in Appendix A.

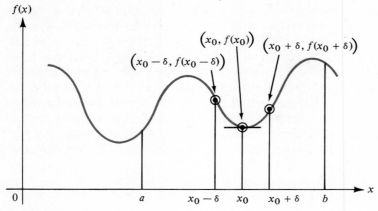

Figure 18.2

It should be emphasized that the function $y = f(x)$ whose graph we have shown in Figures 18.1 and 18.2 is differentiable for all $x \in (a, b)$ and $f'(x) = 0$ at the points of relative maxima or relative minima. It is possible that the derivative may fail to exist at a point x_0 even though the function $f(x)$ has a relative maximum or relative minimum at that point.

Consider, for example, the graph of

$$f(x) = \begin{cases} 3 - x & -2 \leq x \leq 1 \\ x + 1 & 1 < x \leq 4 \end{cases}$$

in Figure 18.3. Note that the function $f(x)$ has a relative minimum at $x = 1$ even though $f'(x)$ does not exist at that point. (Why?) Thus, for locating points of relative maxima or relative minima, it is essential that we check carefully any point x_0 in (a, b) at which $f'(x_0) = 0$ and we also consider points in (a, b) at which the derivative does not exist.

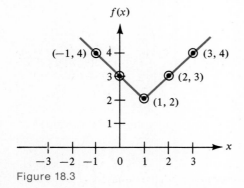

Figure 18.3

Definition 18.2.3: **Points where $f'(x) = 0$ or where $f'(x)$ does not exist are called critical points of the function $f(x)$.**

Proposition 18.2.1: If the function $f(x)$ has a relative maximum or relative minimum at a point x_0 in the open interval (a, b), then x_0 is a critical point of the function $f(x)$. ∎

The converse of Proposition 18.2.1 is not true, because the existence of a critical point $x_0 \in (a, b)$ does not necessarily imply that the function has a relative maximum or relative minimum at x_0. The function $f(x) = x^3$, for example, has a derivative $f'(x) = 3x^2$ which is zero at $x = 0$ (see Figure 18.4), but $(0, 0)$ is neither a relative maximum nor a relative minimum of the function $f(x)$. Thus, the knowledge that $f(x)$ has a critical point $x = x_0$ is not enough to conclude that a relative maximum or minimum exists at x_0.

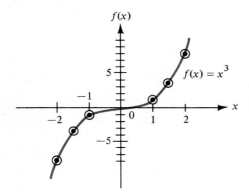

Figure 18.4

Example 18.1
Discuss the function

$$f(x) = 20 + 60x - 5x^2 \qquad 0 \le x \le 12$$

with regard to relative maxima.

SOLUTION
Note that the function is differentiable everywhere in the open interval $(0, 12)$ and hence the solutions of $f'(x) = 0$ are the only critical points. Differentiating $f(x)$, we obtain

$$f'(x) = 60 - 10x$$

Setting $f'(x) = 0$, we get $x = 6$.
The following table shows the values of $f(x)$ corresponding to some values of $x \in [0, 12]$.

x	0	1	2	4	6	8	10	11	12
$f(x)$	20	75	120	180	200	180	120	75	20

Plotting the ordered pairs $(0, 20)$, $(1, 75)$, $(2, 120)$, ..., $(12, 20)$, we have the graph of $f(x)$ as shown in Figure 18.5.

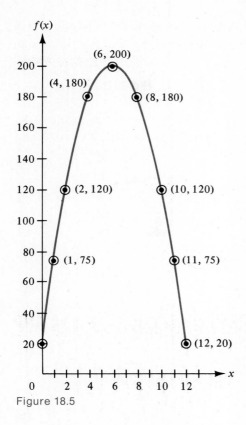

Figure 18.5

The function $f(x)$ has a relative maximum at $x = 6$, and this relative maximum is given by $f(6) = 200$.

Example 18.2

Discuss the function

$$f(x) = x^3 - 3x^2 - 9x + 15 \qquad -4 \le x \le 6$$

with regard to relative maxima and relative minima.

SOLUTION

The derivative $f'(x)$ exists for all values of $x \in (-4, 6)$, and hence the solutions of $f'(x) = 0$ are the only critical points we need to examine for relative maxima or relative minima. Observe that the derivative

$$\begin{aligned} f'(x) &= 3x^2 - 6x - 9 \\ &= 3(x^2 - 2x - 3) \\ &= 3(x - 3)(x + 1) \end{aligned}$$

and $f'(x) = 0$ if and only if $x = 3$ and $x = -1$.

The following table shows the values of $f(x)$ corresponding to some values of x in the closed interval $[-4, 6]$.

x	-4	-3	-2	-1	0	1	2	3	4	5	6
$f(x)$	-61	-12	13	20	15	4	-7	-12	-5	20	69

Plotting some of the ordered pairs $(-3, -12)$, $(-2, 13)$, ..., $(5, 20)$, we have the graph of $f(x)$. (See Figure 18.6.) Thus, $f(x)$ has a relative maximum at $x = -1$ and a relative minimum at $x = 3$. These values are given by $f(-1) = 20$ and $f(3) = -12$, respectively.

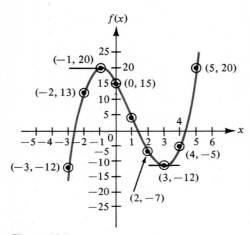

Figure 18.6

EXERCISE 18.1

Discuss the relative maxima and the relative minima for each of the following functions.

1. $f(x) = x^2 + 2x + 6 \qquad -4 \leq x \leq 4$
2. $f(x) = x^2 - 6x + 13 \qquad -6 \leq x \leq 5$
3. $f(x) = 4x - x^2 \qquad -2 \leq x \leq 4$
4. $f(x) = 8x - x^2 \qquad -1 \leq x \leq 6$
5. $f(x) = x^3 - 3x^2 \qquad -3 \leq x \leq 4$
6. $f(x) = x^3 - 12x^2 + 8 \qquad -4 \leq x \leq 4$
7. $f(x) = x^3 - 6x^2 + 9x \qquad -1 \leq x \leq 5$
8. $f(x) = x^3 - 9x^2 + 24x + 1 \qquad 0 \leq x \leq 5$

Thus far, we have determined the points that are relative maxima or minima partly by graphing the functions. Because graphing some functions is time-consuming, we must explore more efficient methods to determine whether or not a critical point is a point of relative maximum, relative minimum, or neither. We begin with a study of increasing and decreasing functions.

Definition 18.2.4: Suppose that a function $f(x)$ is defined on the interval (a, b). Then $f(x)$ is said to be increasing on (a, b) if for any x_1 and $x_2 \in (a, b)$, $x_1 < x_2$ implies that $f(x_1) < f(x_2)$. If for any x_1 and $x_2 \in (a, b)$, $x_1 < x_2$ implies that $f(x_1) > f(x_2)$, then $f(x)$ is said to be a decreasing function on the interval (a, b).

Consider, for instance, a demand curve in economics. (See Figure 18.7.) The demand for a certain product depends largely on its price. Generally speaking, as the price increases, the quantity of items demanded by customers decreases. On the other hand, if a department store reduces the price of a certain item, the demand of that product increases. Thus, the demand of a product is a decreasing function of its price. Note that the supply of a product in the market also depends on the price that customers are charged. Any increase in the price of a product is an incentive for an increase in production, and consequently large supplies in the market results in more profits for the suppliers. Thus, the supply of a product is an increasing function of its price. The graph of a supply curve is shown in Figure 18.8.

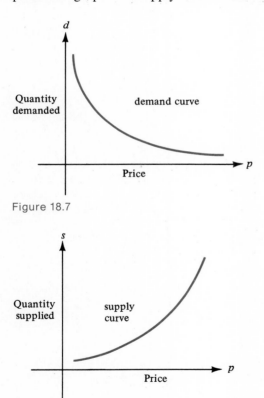

Figure 18.7

Figure 18.8

It seems that if a curve is rising as we go from left to right across the interval (a, b), then the function is increasing on (a, b). In such cases the curve has a positive slope at each point in the interval; that is, $f'(x_0) > 0$ for each $x_0 \in (a, b)$. If a curve is falling as we go from left to right, we have a decreasing function on (a, b) and the curve has a negative slope at each point in the interval (a, b); that is, $f'(x_0) < 0$ for each $x_0 \in (a, b)$. Thus, we have the following statement.

Proposition 18.2.2: Let $f(x)$ be differentiable over the interval (a, b). If $f'(x) > 0$ for each $x \in (a, b)$, then $f(x)$ is an increasing function on (a, b). If $f'(x) < 0$ for each $x \in (a, b)$, then $f(x)$ is a decreasing function on the interval (a, b). ∎

This proposition is of significance in determining on what interval a function is increasing and on what interval a function is decreasing. Let us consider the following examples.

Example 18.3
Find the intervals on which

$$f(x) = x^3 - 3x + 16$$

is increasing and those in which it is decreasing.

SOLUTION
First, we find that

$$f'(x) = 3x^2 - 3 = 3(x - 1)(x + 1)$$

Thus, $x = -1$ and $x = 1$ are the only points at which the slope is zero. To see where $f'(x)$ is positive and negative, we look at the open intervals $(-\infty, -1)$, $(-1, 1)$, and $(1, \infty)$. If $x \in (-\infty, -1)$, then both $(x - 1)$ and $(x + 1)$ are negative so that $f'(x) > 0$. If $x \in (-1, 1)$, then $(x - 1)$ is negative and $(x + 1)$ is positive so that $f'(x) < 0$. Finally, if $x \in (1, \infty)$, then $(x - 1)$ and $(x + 1)$ are both positive; consequently, $f'(x) > 0$. Now, applying Proposition 18.2.2 to each of the three intervals, we conclude that $f(x)$ is increasing on the intervals $(-\infty, -1)$ and $(1, \infty)$ and decreasing on $(-1, 1)$. ∎

EXERCISE 18.2

In Exercises 1 through 10, determine the intervals on which the function $f(x)$ is increasing and those on which the function is decreasing.

1. $f(x) = x^2 - 4x$ **2.** $f(x) = x^2 - 8x + 12$
3. $f(x) = x^2 + 6x + 1$ **4.** $f(x) = 6x - x^2$
5. $f(x) = x^3 - 3x$ **6.** $f(x) = 3x^2 - 2x^3$
7. $f(x) = x^3 - 3x^2 - 9x$ **8.** $f(x) = 3 - x - 2x^2 - x^3$
9. $f(x) = 2x^3 - 9x^2 + 12x$ **10.** $f(x) = x^3 - 9x^2 + 24x$

18.3 THE FIRST DERIVATIVE TEST

The behavior of the derivative of a function is a powerful tool in analyzing whether a given critical point is a point of relative maximum, relative minimum, or neither. Consider, for example, the graph of $f(x)$ in Figure 18.9. Note that at the far left $f(x)$

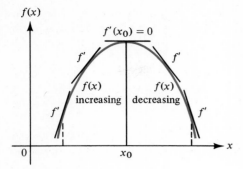

Figure 18.9

increases rapidly, the slope of the curve is steep, and the first derivative $f'(x)$ is large but positive. As x increases further, $f(x)$ also increases but now more and more slowly until, finally, the graph has a horizontal tangent at x_0. Thus, $f'(x)$ becomes smaller and smaller until it reaches zero at $x = x_0$. Thereafter, $f(x)$ decreases, slowly at first, then rapidly, and the corresponding value of $f'(x)$, which starts from zero at $x = x_0$, becomes negative for all values of $x \in (x_0, x_0 + \delta)$, $\delta > 0$. Thus, $f(x)$ has a relative maximum at x_0 if there exists an interval $(x_0 - \delta, x_0)$ on which $f'(x) > 0$ and an interval $(x_0, x_0 + \delta)$ on which $f'(x) < 0$.

Now let us examine the graph of $f(x)$ in Figure 18.10. To begin with, $f(x)$ is decreasing rapidly, the derivative $f'(x)$ is large but negative. As x increases, $f(x)$ continues to decrease but at a slower rate until the graph has a horizontal tangent at x_0. Then $f(x)$ increases slowly and then rapidly for all values of $x \in (x_0, x_0 + \delta)$, $\delta > 0$. The corresponding value of $f'(x)$ is negative for values of $x \in (x_0 - \delta, x_0)$, becomes zero at $x = x_0$, and finally becomes positive for values of $x \in (x_0, x_0 + \delta)$. Note that the function attains a relative minimum at x_0 if $f'(x)$ changes its sign from negative to positive while passing through the point $(x_0, f(x_0))$.

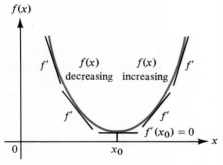

Figure 18.10

Finally, the function $f(x)$ in Figure 18.11 attains neither a maximum nor a minima, because $f(x)$ decreases on both sides of the critical point x_0 and $f'(x)$ does not change its sign when the curve passes through $(x_0, f(x_0))$. These facts lead to the following proposition, which we state without proof.

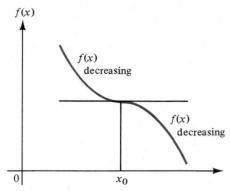

Figure 18.11

Proposition 18.3.1: Let $f(x)$ be differentiable on (a, b) and $f'(x_0) = 0$ for $x_0 \in (a, b)$. Then the function $f(x)$ has a

(a) relative maximum at x_0 if there exists an interval $(x_0 - \delta, x_0)$ on which $f'(x) > 0$ and an interval $(x_0, x_0 + \delta)$ on which $f'(x) < 0$.

(b) relative minimum at x_0 if there exists an interval $(x_0 - \delta, x_0)$ on which $f'(x) < 0$ and an interval $(x_0, x_0 + \delta)$ on which $f'(x) > 0$.

(c) neither a relative maximum nor a relative minimum at x_0 if there exists an interval $(x_0 - \delta, x_0 + \delta)$ centered at x_0 and $f'(x)$ has the same sign for $x \in (x_0 - \delta, x_0)$ and $x \in (x_0, x_0 + \delta)$. ■

Let us look at some examples.

Example 18.4

Discuss the function

$$f(x) = x^4 - 8x^2 \qquad -3 \le x \le 3$$

with regard to relative maxima and relative minima.

SOLUTION

The function is differentiable everywhere in the open interval $(-3, 3)$ and so the solutions of $f'(x) = 0$ are the only critical points we shall examine for relative maxima and relative minima. Note that

$$\begin{aligned} f'(x) &= 4x^3 - 16x \\ &= 4x(x^2 - 4) \\ &= 4x(x - 2)(x + 2) \end{aligned}$$

Clearly, $f'(x) = 0$ for $x = 0$, $x = 2$, and $x = -2$. Further,

$$\begin{aligned} f'(x) &< 0 \quad \text{for} \quad -3 < x < -2 \\ f'(x) &> 0 \quad \text{for} \quad -2 < x < 0 \\ f'(x) &< 0 \quad \text{for} \quad 0 < x < 2 \end{aligned}$$

and

$$f'(x) > 0 \quad \text{for} \quad 2 < x < 3$$

This means that as x goes from left to right, the derivatives of the function $f'(x)$ is negative in a neighborhood to the left of $x = -2$, becomes zero at $x = -2$, and then becomes positive in a neighborhood to the right of $x = -2$. Consider, for instance, two values of x in the neighborhood $x = -2.5$ to the left of $x = -2$ and $x = -1.5$ to the right of $x = -2$. Note that these values under consideration do not surround another critical point.

For $x = -2.5$, we have

$$f'(-2.5) = 4(-2.5)^3 - 16(-2.5)$$
$$= -62.5 + 40$$
$$= -22.5 < 0$$

But for $x = -1.5$,

$$f'(-1.5) = 4(-1.5)^3 - 16(-1.5)$$
$$= -13.5 + 24$$
$$= 10.5 > 0$$

Hence, by Proposition 18.3.1, $f(x)$ has a relative minimum at $x = -2$. Now observe that

$$f'(1.5) = 4(1.5)^3 - 16(1.5)$$
$$= 13.5 - 24$$
$$= -10.5 < 0$$

Because $f'(x) > 0$ for $x \in (-2, 0)$ and $f'(x) < 0$ for $x \in (0, 2)$, it follows that $f(x)$ has a relative maximum at $x = 0$. Similarly, we observe that $x = 2$ is a point at which a relative minimum occurs. ∎

Example 18.5
Find the points at which

$$f(x) = x^3 - 9x^2 + 24x \qquad 0 < x < 5$$

has a relative maximum or relative minimum.

SOLUTION
The function $f(x)$ is differentiable for all $x \in (0, 5)$ and

$$f'(x) = 3x^2 - 18x + 24$$
$$= 3(x^2 - 6x + 8)$$
$$= 3(x - 2)(x - 4)$$

Thus, $f'(x) = 0$ for $x = 2$ and 4. Further,

$$f'(x) > 0 \quad \text{for} \quad 0 < x < 2$$
$$f'(x) < 0 \quad \text{for} \quad 2 < x < 4$$
$$f'(x) > 0 \quad \text{for} \quad 4 < x < 5$$

The analysis reveals that as x increases from left to right, the derivative $f'(x)$ is positive on the interval $(0, 2)$, zero at $x = 2$, and negative on the interval $(2, 4)$. Hence, by Proposition 18.3.1, the function has a relative maximum at $x = 2$. Because the derivative $f'(x)$ changes sign from negative on the interval $(2, 4)$ to positive on the interval $(4, 5)$, we conclude that the function $f(x)$ has a relative minimum at $x = 4$. ∎

Example 18.6

Discuss the function

$$g(x) = \begin{cases} -x & -3 < x \le 0 \\ x^3 - 9x^2 + 24x & 0 < x < 5 \\ -2x + 30 & 5 \le x < 9 \end{cases}$$

with regard to relative maxima and relative minima.

SOLUTION

Note that the function $g(x)$ is defined over the open interval $(-3, 9)$ and agrees with the function $f(x)$ of Example 18.5 defined over $(0, 5)$. The function $g(x)$ is continuous at $x = 0$ and $x = 5$ but is not differentiable at these points. (Why?) Further,

$$g'(x) = \begin{cases} -1 & -3 < x \le 0 \\ 3x^2 - 18x + 24 & 0 < x < 5 \\ -2 & 5 \le x < 9 \end{cases}$$

Clearly, $3x^2 - 18x + 24 = 0$ if and only if $x = 2$ and 4. Thus, the critical points are $x = 0$ and 5, where $g'(x)$ does not exist and $x = 2$ and 4 where $g'(x) = 0$. Observe that

$g'(x) < 0$ for $x \in (-3, 0)$
$g'(x) > 0$ for $x \in (0, 2)$
$g'(x) < 0$ for $x \in (2, 4)$
$g'(x) > 0$ for $x \in (4, 5)$
$g'(x) < 0$ for $x \in (5, 9)$

Hence, $g(x)$ has relative minima at $x = 0$ and $x = 4$ and relative maxima at $x = 2$ and $x = 5$. ∎

We have studied methods for locating relative maxima and relative minima of a function. The functions exhibited have relative maxima and minima at the interior points in an open interval. If the function has a closed interval $[a, b]$ as its domain, then a function may attain the largest or smallest functional value at the end points of the domain of the function. The function whose graph is sketched in Figure 18.12, for example, has a relative maximum at C but attains its largest functional value at the end point b. Similarly, the function has a relative minimum at D but the smallest functional value occurs at a and is $f(a)$. If $[a, b^*]$ were the interval of interest, then the largest and smallest functional value would occur at the point C and the end point a, respectively. This discussion enables us to define the maximum and minimum of a function over a closed interval. These are also called the absolute maximum and absolute minimum, respectively.

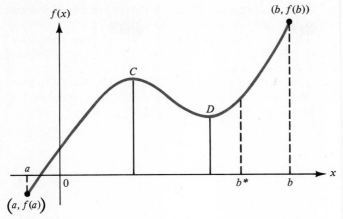

Figure 18.12

Definition 18.3.1: A function $f(x)$ has an absolute maximum at x_0 if

$$f(x) \leq f(x_0)$$

for all x in the domain of the function. The function has an absolute minimum at x_0 if

$$f(x) \geq f(x_0)$$

for all x in the domain of the function.

This definition implies that if a function $f(x)$ is defined over $[a, b]$, then an absolute maximum and minimum (if it exists) are attained either at some points in (a, b) or at the end points of the interval.

Example 18.7

Determine the absolute maximum and absolute minimum of the function

$$f(x) = x^3 - 12x^2 + 21x + 5$$

where the domain of the function is $[-1, 8]$.

SOLUTION

Note that $f'(x)$ exists for all $x \in (-1, 8)$ and

$$f'(x) = 3x^2 - 24x + 21$$
$$= 3(x^2 - 8x + 7)$$
$$= 3(x - 1)(x - 7)$$

The absolute maximum and the absolute minimum value of the function occur either at the end points $x = -1$, $x = 8$ or the points $x = 1$ and $x = 7$, at which $f'(x) = 0$. Evaluating $f(x)$ at each of these points, we observe that

$$f(-1) = -29 \qquad f(1) = 15$$
$$f(7) = -93 \qquad f(8) = -83$$

Hence, the absolute maximum occurs at $x = 1$ and the absolute minimum at $x = 7$. ∎

In summary, we use the following methods to locate maximum and minimum points of a continuous function $f(x)$ defined on the closed interval $[a, b]$.

1. Determine $f'(x)$ and locate all points for which $f'(x) = 0$. Also list points for which $f'(x)$ fails to exist.
2. Calculate the values of $f(x)$ at these points. Find also the value of the function at the end points. The largest of the values is the absolute maximum, and the smallest of these values is the absolute minimum.

EXERCISE 18.3

Examine each of the following functions for relative maxima and relative minima in the intervals specified.

1. $f(x) = x^2 - 6x + 8; (1, 6)$ **2.** $f(x) = 3x^2 - 6x + 10; (-1, 4)$
3. $f(x) = 2x^3 - 9x^2 + 12x + 8; (-4, 4)$
4. $f(x) = x^3 + x^2 - x + 1; (-3, 3)$
5. $f(x) = x^4 - 2x^2 + 6; (-3, 5)$ **6.** $f(x) = 3x^4 - 8x^3 - 18x^2 + 9; (-4, 6)$

7. $f(x) = \begin{cases} 3x + 18 & -6 < x < -3 \\ x^4 - 8x^2 & -3 \le x \le 3 \\ -3x + 18 & 3 < x < 6 \end{cases}$

8. $f(x) = \begin{cases} x + 2 & -5 < x < -1 \\ x^2 & -1 \le x \le 1 \\ -2x + 3 & 1 < x < 4 \end{cases}$

In Exercises 9 through 16, find the absolute maxima and the absolute minima of the given functions on the closed interval indicated.

9. $f(x) = x^2 - 4x + 5; [0, 5]$ **10.** $f(x) = 3x^2 + 6x - 5; [-3, 2]$
11. $f(x) = 2x^2 - 8x + 1; [-1, 4]$ **12.** $f(x) = x^3 - 12x + 8; [-3, 4]$
13. $f(x) = 2x^3 + 3x^2 - 12x; [-3, 4]$ **14.** $f(x) = x^3 - 2x^2 + x - 1; [-3, 3]$
15. $f(x) = x^4 - 2x^2 + 1; [-2, 3]$
16. $f(x) = x^4 + 4x^3 + 6x^2 + 4x + 1; [-3, 2]$
17. The daily profit function of a firm producing hair dryers is given by

$$p(x) = \$(30x - x^2 - 50)$$

where x denotes the output of the firm in hundreds of units per month. Determine the value of x that will maximize profits. What will be the total profit of the firm at that level of production?

18. The Alexander Baking Company finds that the profit is related directly to the number of wedding cakes it sells in a month. Experience has shown that the profit function is given approximately by

$$P(x) = 70x - x^2$$

where x represents the number of cakes sold. Determine the number of wedding cakes that must be sold so as to maximize profits.

19. The total profits of a firm producing a single product are determined approximately by the function

$$p(x) = 135x + 18x^2 - x^3 - 250$$

where x is the number of units sold. Determine the number of units that must be sold so as to maximize the profit.

20. The concentration of anesthesia x seconds after injection is given by the function

$$D(x) = \frac{x}{x^2 + 400} \qquad 0 \le x \le 50$$

Determine how many seconds must elapse before the concentration will reach its maximum level.

18.4 THE SECOND DERIVATIVE TEST

In the preceding sections, we used the first derivative to determine the critical points and the intervals over which a function is increasing or decreasing. This information enabled us to locate relative maxima and minima. Now we examine how the second derivative can be used in conjunction with the first derivative to discriminate among critical values. To begin with, let us return to the graph of the function $f(x)$ in Figure 18.9. Recall that the first derivative, which is associated with the slope of the tangent, is positive for all $x \in (x_0 - \delta, x_0)$, zero at $x = x_0$, and then becomes negative for all $x \in (x_0, x_0 + \delta)$. Thus, the second derivative, which determines the rate of change of the slope, is negative near a point of relative maxima. In Figure 18.10, the first derivative is negative for all $x \in (x_0 - \delta, x_0)$, is zero at $x = x_0$, and then positive for all $x \in (x_0, x_0 + \delta)$. Thus, the rate of change of the slope is positive near a point of relative minima. Returning to the graph of the function in Figure 18.11, we note that the first derivative is negative for all $x \in (x_0 - \delta, x_0)$, is zero at $x = x_0$, and then again becomes negative for all $x \in (x_0, x_0 + \delta)$. Hence, there is no change in the rate of change of the slope near x_0 and thus the second derivative is zero. These observations lead to the following proposition, which we state without proof.

Proposition 18.4.1: Let $f(x)$ be differentiable at a point x_0 for which $f'(x_0) = 0$ and for which $f''(x_0)$ exists for $x_0 \in (a, b)$. Then

(i) $f(x_0)$ is a relative maximum of $f(x)$ if $f''(x_0) < 0$
(ii) $f(x_0)$ is a relative minimum of $f(x)$ if $f''(x_0) > 0$

The test fails if $f''(x_0) = 0$. ■

Let us now consider some examples.

Example 18.8
The function

$$f(x) = x^3 - 9x^2 + 24x \qquad 0 < x < 5$$

has a first derivative

$$f'(x) = 3x^2 - 18x + 24$$
$$= 3(x - 2)(x - 4)$$

Note that the function is differentiable for all $x \in (0, 5)$ and $f'(x) = 0$ if and only if $x = 2$ and $x = 4$. Thus, the critical points are $x = 2$ and $x = 4$. Now we apply the second derivative test. Note that

$$f''(x) = 6x - 18$$
$$= 6(x - 3)$$

Thus,

$$f''(2) = -6 < 0 \quad \text{and} \quad f''(4) = 6 > 0$$

Hence, $x = 2$ corresponds to a relative maximum and $x = 4$ corresponds to a relative minimum. ∎

Example 18.9

Using the second derivative test, examine the following function

$$f(x) = x^4 - 2x^2 + 5$$

for relative maxima or relative minima.

SOLUTION
Differentiating $f(x)$, we have

$$f'(x) = 4x^3 - 4x$$
$$= 4x(x^2 - 1)$$
$$= 4x(x - 1)(x + 1)$$

Setting $f'(x) = 0$, we obtain $x = 0$, $x = 1$, and $x = -1$ as critical points. The second derivative of $f(x)$ is

$$f''(x) = 12x^2 - 4$$
$$= 4(3x^2 - 1)$$

At the critical points, we have

$$f''(-1) = 8 \qquad f''(0) = -4 \qquad f''(1) = 8$$

Consequently, $f(0)$ is a relative maximum, whereas $f(-1)$ and $f(1)$ are relative minimum values of $f(x)$. ∎

Example 18.10

An automobile dealer has determined that commercial advertisements on the local television channel has an appreciable impact on the sales of new model cars. It is estimated that the number of cars, $s(x)$, sold and the expenditure x (in thousands of dollars) are related by the function

$$s(x) = 50 + 36x - 3x^2$$

Determine the amount that must be spent on television commercials so as to maximize sales.

SOLUTION

Differentiating $s(x)$, we obtain

$$s'(x) = 36 - 6x$$

The critical points are the solutions of $s'(x) = 0$; that is, $x = 6$ is a point that needs to be examined for relative maximum. Note that $s''(x) = -6$; hence, $x = 6$ yields maximum sales. ∎

Example 18.11

The cost of fuel in running a truck per mile is given by

$$c(x) = \$(\tfrac{1}{25}x^2 + 25x + 100)$$

where x is the speed of the truck in miles. Determine the speed that will minimize the cost per mile.

SOLUTION

The average cost in dollars per mile is

$$A(x) = \frac{c(x)}{x} = \frac{(\tfrac{1}{25})x^2 + 25x + 100}{x} = \frac{x}{25} + 25 + \frac{100}{x}$$

Thus,

$$A'(x) = \frac{1}{25} - \frac{100}{x^2}$$

and $A'(x) = 0$ implies that $x^2 = 2500$ or $x = 50$. It is clear that

$$A''(x) = \frac{200}{x^3}$$

and $A''(50) = 1/625 > 0$. Thus, the most economical speed for the truck is 50 miles per hour. ∎

EXERCISE 18.4

Using the second derivative test, examine each of the following functions for relative maxima and relative minima in the intervals specified.

1. $f(x) = x^2 - 4x + 3; (0, 6)$ **2.** $f(x) = 2x^2 - 5x + 8; (-1, 5)$

3. $f(x) = x^3 - 6x^2 + 9x + 5; (-1, 5)$

4. $f(x) = 2x^3 + 3x^2 - 36x + 8; (-4, 4)$

5. $f(x) = x^4 - 2x^2 + 6; (-3, 5)$ **6.** $f(x) = x^4 - 4x^3 + 4x^2; (-5, 4)$

7. $f(x) = x + \dfrac{1}{x}; (0, 3)$ **8.** $f(x) = x + \dfrac{4}{x}; (1, 5)$

In each of Exercises 9 through 12, determine the production level x for which the cost is minimum.

9. $c(x) = x^2 - 12x + 25$ **10.** $c(x) = x^3 - 6x^2 - 15x + 30$

11. $c(x) = 100 - 30x - \frac{7}{2}x^2 + \frac{1}{3}x^3$ **12.** $c(x) = \frac{1}{3}x^3 - 5x^2 + 24x + 75$

13. Find the output x that maximizes the profit function

$$P(x) = 200x - \tfrac{1}{2}x^2$$

14. The total profit made by selling x units of a single product is given by

$$P(x) = 160x - x^2 - 300$$

Determine the number of units that will maximize the profit.

15. The number of air conditioners expected to be sold next summer in the ABC Department Store is given by the function

$$s(x) = 15 + 20x - x^2 \qquad 0 \le x \le 15$$

where x is the number of hot days in a given summer. Determine the number of hot days that will maximize the sales of air conditioners next summer.

16. A station wagon uses gasoline at the rate of

$$\frac{1}{12}\left(\frac{25}{x} + \frac{x}{100}\right)$$

gallons per mile while traveling x miles per hour on an interstate highway. If gasoline costs $0.55 a gallon, determine the speed of the station wagon that will minimize fuel costs for a 600-mile trip. Find the minimum fuel cost.

17. The total cost function of a product is given by

$$c(x) = x^3 - 120x^2 + 2100x + 1000$$

where x is the number of units produced. Determine the value of x that would minimize the total cost.

18. The total cost function of a product is given by

$$c(x) = x^3 - 315x^2 + 27{,}000x + 20{,}000$$

where x is the number of units produced. Determine the number of units that should be produced to minimize the total cost.

19. The cost function of a product in a certain industry is given by

$$c(x) = \tfrac{1}{2}x^2 + 10x + 200 \qquad 0 < x \le 25$$

where x is the number of products the industry produces in one month. Determine the value of x for which the average cost $c(x)/x$ is minimum.

20. The cost function of a product in an industry is given by

$$c(x) = \frac{x^2}{100} + 50x + 900 \qquad 0 < x \le 500$$

Determine the number of units that should be produced so as to minimize the average cost.

18.5 APPLICATIONS OF MAXIMA AND MINIMA

So far we have encountered functions in the form of polynomials and rational functions. Once these functions were given, we determined various points of relative maxima and relative minima and also calculated the values of the function at the end points. Now, we discuss some problems in which we must set up the function before we proceed to find the lowest cost, the maximum profit, or the largest area of a certain figure and the like.

Example 18.12

Find two positive integers that have a sum of 30 and are such that their product is as large as possible.

SOLUTION

Let x be one of the positive integers; then the other integer is $(30 - x)$. Thus, the function to be maximized is

$$f(x) = x(30 - x) \qquad 0 < x < 30$$
$$= 30x - x^2$$

The derivative

$$f'(x) = 30 - 2x$$

is zero if and only if $x = 15$. Because $f''(x) = -2 < 0$, it follows that $f(x)$ attains its maximum at $x = 15$. ∎

Example 18.13

A farmer has 3000 feet of barbed wire with which to enclose a rectangular pasture. His plan includes fencing the entire area and then subdividing it by running a fence across the width as shown in Figure 18.13. Determine the dimensions of the pasture that would enclose the maximum area.

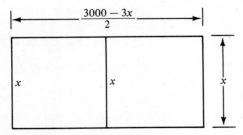

Figure 18.13

SOLUTION

Let x feet be the width of the pasture. Then the length of the field to be fenced is $(3000 - 3x)/2$. The area to be maximized is

$$A(x) = x\left(\frac{3000 - 3x}{2}\right)$$
$$= \tfrac{3}{2}(1000x - x^2)$$

Then

$$A'(x) = \tfrac{3}{2}(1000 - 2x)$$

and $A'(x) = 0$ if and only if $x = 500$. Because $A''(x) < 0$, it follows that a pasture with length 750 feet and width 500 feet would enclose the maximum area. ■

Example 18.14

An open box is to be made from a rectangular sheet of tin by cutting equal squares out of each corner and folding up the sides. If the sheet is 21 inches long and 16 inches wide, what should be the size of the squares cut out if the box is to have the maximum volume?

SOLUTION

We let x inches be the size of the square cut out from each corner of the sheet as shown in Figure 18.14. Then, the box obtained by folding up the sides along the dotted line is $(21 - 2x)$ inches in length, $(16 - 2x)$ in width, and x inches in depth. (See Figure 18.15.) Thus, the volume of this box is

$$V(x) = x(21 - 2x)(16 - 2x)$$
$$= 336x - 74x^2 + 4x^3$$

Note that there are restrictions on x. First, $x > 0$, and second, $x < 8$ for if $x = 8$, the width of the base is zero and we have no box at all. Differentiating $V(x)$, we have

$$V'(x) = 336 - 148x + 12x^2$$
$$= 4(84 - 37x + 3x^2)$$
$$= 4(3x - 28)(x - 3)$$

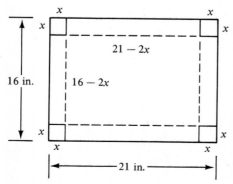

Figure 18.14

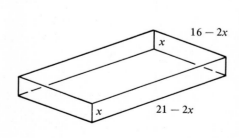

Figure 18.15

Solving $V'(x) = 0$, we obtain $x = 3$ and $x = \frac{28}{3}$. The only critical value worth further consideration is $x = 3$, for if a segment of $\frac{28}{3}$ inches is cut out from each corner, there remains no tin sheet to make a box. Further,

$$V''(x) = -148 + 24x$$

and $V''(3) < 0$. Thus, we conclude that the critical value $x = 3$ maximizes the volume of the box at 450 cubic inches. ■

Example 18.15
A travel agency has chartered a flight to Paris for high school students. The charge is $200 with an additional charge of $2.50 for each subsequent cancellation. The plane has a seating capacity of 100 passengers. Determine the total revenue, $R(x)$, as a function of x, the number of cancellations received prior to the departure date. What is the value of x for which $R(x)$ is maximum?

SOLUTION
Let x be the number of cancellations received prior to the departure of the flight; then $(100 - x)$ passengers are on the plane and each pays $200 plus $2.50x$. Thus, the total receipts of the travel agency are

$$R(x) = \$(100 - x)(200 + 2.50x)$$
$$= \$20,000 + 50x - 2.50x^2 \qquad 0 \le x \le 100$$

Hence, the derivative

$$R'(x) = 50 - 5x$$

is zero if and only if $x = 10$. We claim that the receipts of the travel agency are maximum if 10 cancellations are received. We need to evaluate $R(x)$ at $x = 10$ and the end point $x = 0$ but not at the other end point, because if 100 cancellations are received, the chartered flight will not take off. Note that $R''(x) < 0$ for all x and

$$R(0) = \$20,000 \quad \text{and} \quad R(10) = \$20,250$$

Thus, each passenger pays $200 + 10(\$2.50) = \$225$ and the travel agency receives a maximum of $20,250. ■

The behavior of the revenue or profit function is typical in the sense that these functions usually have a maximum point. Consider, for example, a firm that produces a certain quantity x of a single product that generates a revenue of $R(x)$ upon selling these units. If $C(x)$ is the total cost of producing these units, then the profit function is

$$P(x) = R(x) - C(x)$$

Assuming that M is the production capacity of the plant, the management must decide the quantity x $(0 \le x \le M)$ that it should produce so as to maximize the profit function $P(x)$. If $R(x)$ and $C(x)$ are both differentiable on a closed interval $[0, M]$, then the maximum profit, if it exists, occurs either at the end points or at those points for which $P'(x) = 0$.

Differentiating $P(x)$, we obtain

$$P'(x) = R'(x) - C'(x)$$

and $P'(x) = 0$ implies that

$$R'(x) = C'(x)$$

Thus, for a profit function to attain its maximum, the production of the plant should be adjusted to the point where the marginal revenue $R'(x)$ is equal to the marginal cost $C'(x)$. ∎

Example 18.16

The total cost and revenue functions for a certain product are given by

$$C(x) = \$(\tfrac{1}{5}x^2 - 29x + 150) \qquad 0 \le x \le 100$$

$$R(x) = \$\left(50 - \frac{x}{10}\right)$$

Determine the value of x for which the profit will be maximum.

SOLUTION

The cost and the revenue functions are both differentiable on the closed interval $[0, 100]$. Differentiating $C(x)$ and $R(x)$, we obtain

$$C'(x) = \tfrac{2}{5}x - 29$$

and

$$R'(x) = -\tfrac{1}{5}$$

We seek the value of x at which the marginal cost and the marginal revenue are equal. Solving the equation

$$C'(x) = R'(x)$$

that is,

$$\tfrac{2}{5}x - 29 = -\tfrac{1}{5}$$

we obtain $x = 72$. ∎

Example 18.17

A manufacturer determines that the selling price per unit of his product is given approximately by

$$p(x) = 100 - \frac{x}{2} - \frac{x^2}{12} \qquad 0 \le x \le 30$$

whereas the total cost function is

$$C(x) = 50 + 20x$$

Determine how many units should be produced so as to maximize profit.

SOLUTION

If x represents the number of units produced and sold, then the total revenue received is

$$R(x) = x \cdot p$$

$$= 100x - \frac{x^2}{2} - \frac{x^3}{12}$$

The profit function is

$$P(x) = R(x) - C(x)$$

$$= 80x - \frac{x^2}{2} - \frac{x^3}{12} - 50$$

$$P'(x) = 80 - x - \frac{x^2}{4}$$

Note that $P'(x) = 0$ implies that

$$320 - 4x - x^2 = 0$$
$$(20 + x)(16 - x) = 0$$

That is,

$$x = 16 \quad \text{or} \quad x = -20$$

Clearly, $x = -20$ is not admissible. (Why?) Because

$$P''(x) = -4 - 2x$$

and

$$P''(16) = -36$$

we conclude that the profit is maximum when 16 units are produced and sold. ■

EXERCISE 18.5

1. Two identical 50-centimeter rods are to be bent into the shape of an L and then put together to enclose a rectangular space. Where should the bends occur if the space is to have as large an area as possible?

2. To provide material for a large commercial-sized window, a jobber takes a 60-foot steel brace and cuts it into two parts. One of the parts he cuts into three equal pieces. One of these latter pieces and the longer piece left from the first cut will form two sides of the rectangular window. What is the maximum glass area that the window could enclose?

3. A printed poster is to have a margin 1 inch along the sides and $1\frac{1}{2}$ inches at the top and the bottom. What are the most economical dimensions for a page if the printed area must be 96 square inches?

4. A printed poster is to have a margin of $1\frac{1}{4}$ inches on the sides and $1\frac{1}{2}$ inches at the top and bottom. What are the most economical dimensions for a page if the printed area must be 30 square inches?

5. A tray is to be made of a rectangular piece of sheet metal by cutting out equal squares from each corner and turning up the sides. If the sheet is 32 inches long and 12 inches wide, determine the dimensions of the tray of largest possible volume.

6. A box is to be made from a cardboard 15 inches square by cutting a square from each corner and folding up the edges. Determine the dimensions of the box of largest volume that can be made.

7. A rancher has 2800 feet of fence to enclose a pasture. One side of his rectangular land needs no fence. Determine the dimensions of this pasture so as to enclose the maximum area.

8. A high school is planning to build a rectangular playground that must contain 423,200 square feet. Find the minimum length of fence required and the dimensions of the playground if one side needs no fence.

9. A farmer wants to fence in 1,280,000 square feet of land in a rectangular plot and then subdivide it into three equal plots with the fence running across the width as shown in Figure 18.16. What is the smallest amount of fence required to enclose this area?

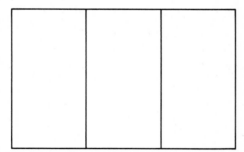

Figure 18.16

10. A rectangular building must contain 405,600 square feet of floor space. The front is to be all glass, and the other three walls are of block construction. Assuming that glass construction costs twice as much per foot as block, find the dimensions of the building that would minimize the cost.

11. A rental agency needs to determine the rent to charge for each of the 200 apartments in order to attain the maximum income. Experience shows that if the rent is set at $150 a month, all units are occupied, but for each $5 per month increase in rent, five units become vacant. What rent should be fixed so as to maximize the revenue? Determine also the maximum revenue.

12. A high school has arranged a dance for the senior class. The charge is $5.00 per couple if 40 couples attend the dance and then decrease by $0.05 for each additional couple above the minimum of 40 couples. Determine the number of couples that would maximize the revenue. What is the maximum revenue?

13. A travel agency makes plans for a trip to Washington, D.C., for a senior class. The fare is $60 per student if 30 students sign up and the fare decreases by $1 for each additional student above 30 who go. Determine the number of students that will generate maximum revenue for the travel agency.

14. An alumni group makes plans for a charter flight to Key West, Florida. The plane fare is $100 a person if at least 40 persons go and will decrease by $0.50 for every additional person above the minimum of 40 who go. Find the number of passengers that will maximize the revenue for the alumni group. What is the maximum revenue?

15. A department store estimates that if it charges x dollars for an electric shaver, it can sell $(380 - 10x)$ shavers. What selling price should the store fix in order to maximize its total revenue?

16. A restaurant owner plans to build a new restaurant with a seating capacity of between 90 and 125. The owner has estimated that his profit will average $12 per week per chair if the seating capacity is 90, then decrease by $0.10 per chair for each additional seat in excess of 90. Determine the number of seats that must be planned so as to maximize the profit. What is the maximum profit per week?

17. The total cost and revenue functions for a certain product are given by

$$C(x) = \$\left(\frac{x^2}{20} + 29x + 100\right)$$

$$R(x) = \$(50x - x^2)$$

Determine the value of x for which the profit will be maximum.

18. A product can be manufactured at a total cost

$$C(x) = \$(1000 + 20x)$$

where x is the number manufactured. The price, p dollars, at which each unit is sold is given by

$$p(x) = 50 - \frac{x}{10}$$

What production level will maximize the profit? What is the total profit and the price per unit at this level of production?

19. A manufacturer finds that his product can be assembled at a total cost

$$C(x) = \$200 + 30x$$

where x is the number manufactured. Assume that the price at which he can sell each unit is given by

$$p(x) = \$\left(150 - \frac{x}{5}\right)$$

What level of production will maximize the total profit? What is the corresponding selling price per unit? What is the total profit at this level of production?

20. A given product can be manufactured at a total cost

$$C(x) = \$\left(\frac{x^2}{50} + 50x + 4000\right)$$

where x is the number produced. The price at which each unit can be sold is given by

$$p(x) = \$\left(100 - \frac{x}{200}\right)$$

Determine the production level x at which the profit is maximum. What is the price per unit and the total profit at this level of production?

19
Integral Calculus

19.1 INTRODUCTION

Up to this point in calculus, our work has centered on finding the derivative, some of whose properties and applications we have discussed in the preceding chapters. We now turn to another branch of the subject, namely, the integral calculus, whose meaning we propose to illustrate by finding the area under a given curve. We shall exploit the relation between the concept of the derivative and the integral of a function as expressed in the fundamental theorem of calculus. We shall also discuss, later in the chapter, some applications of integration to business and economics and explain how integration techniques aid in problems related to the social and biological sciences.

19.2 THE DEFINITE INTEGRAL

The concept of a definite integral arises from the idea of finding the area bounded by the lines $x = a$, $x = b$, the x axis, and the graph of $y = f(x)$, where $f(x)$ is a continuous function of x on the closed interval $a \leq x \leq b$. The fact that three sides of the region are straight lines facilitates our intuitive approach to the problem. We shall assume that $f(x) \geq 0$ for all $x \in [a, b]$.

A plausible procedure for approximating the area would be to divide the closed interval $[a, b]$ into n equal parts, each of length $h = (b - a)/n$, so that $x_1, x_2, x_3, \ldots, x_{n-1}$ are the points of the subdivision with the stipulation that $a = x_0$ and $b = x_n$. Note that

$$x_1 = a + h, x_2 = a + 2h, \ldots, x_n = a + nh$$

We shall use here the inscribed rectangles (see Figure 19.1) to approximate the area in each subinterval. Note that the height of each inscribed rectangle is the value of the function evaluated at the left end point of the corresponding interval. Thus,

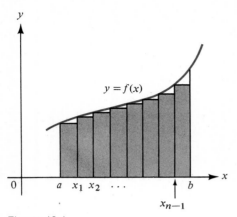

Figure 19.1

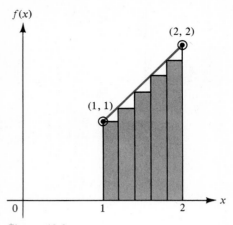

Figure 19.2

we have

$$\text{area of first rectangle} = h \cdot f(a)$$
$$\text{area of second rectangle} = h \cdot f(a + h)$$
$$\text{area of third rectangle} = h \cdot f(a + 2h)$$
$$\vdots \qquad \qquad \vdots$$
$$\text{area of last rectangle} = h \cdot f[a + (n - 1)h]$$

Adding the area of these rectangles, we have the sum

(19.1) $\quad S_n = h \cdot f(a) + h \cdot f(a + h) + h \cdot f(a + 2h) + \cdots + h \cdot f[a + (n - 1)h]$

as an approximation for the area under the given curve. Consider, for example, the function $f(x) = x$ over the interval $[1, 2]$ and $n = 5$. There are four intermediate points that divide the closed interval $[1, 2]$ into $n = 5$ equal parts, each of length $h = 0.2$. (See Figure 19.2.) The inscribed rectangles are of height

1, 1.2, 1.4, 1.6, and 1.8

units. The corresponding sum of areas is given by

$$S_5 = (0.2) \cdot 1 + (0.2)(1.2) + (0.2)(1.4) + (0.2)(1.6) + (0.2)(1.8)$$
$$= 1.40$$

We must underscore the fact that any construction of this type will give an approximation, which can be improved by dividing the interval into a larger number of subintervals each of smaller length. If $n = 10$, then we have nine intermediate points that divide the segment into 10 equal parts, each of length $h = 0.1$. (See Figure 19.3.) The inscribed rectangles are of height

$$f(1) = 1, f(1 + h) = 1.1, f(1 + 2h) = 1.2, \ldots, f(1 + 9h) = 1.9$$

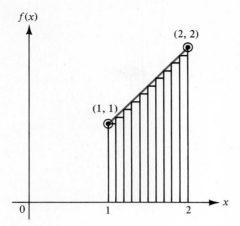

Figure 19.3

The corresponding sum of areas is given by

$$S_{10} = (0.1)1 + (0.1)(1.1) + (0.1)(1.2) + \cdots + (0.1)(1.9)$$
$$= (0.1)(1 + 1.1 + 1.2 + \cdots + 1.9)$$

Note that the quantity in the second parentheses is an arithmetic progression with 1 as the first term and (0.1) as the common difference. Applying Proposition 15.3.1, we obtain

$$S_{10} = (0.1)(\tfrac{10}{2})[2 + (10 - 1)(0.1)]$$
$$= 1.45$$

If $n = 100$, then we have 99 intermediate points that divide $[1, 2]$ into 100 subintervals, each of length 0.01, whereas the rectangles are of height

$$f(1) = 1, f(1 + h) = 1.01, f(1 + 2h) = 1.02, \ldots, f(1 + 99h) = 1.99$$

The sum of the areas of the rectangles is

$$S_{100} = (0.01)(1 + 1.01 + 1.02 + \cdots + 1.99)$$
$$= (0.01)(\tfrac{100}{2})[2 + 99(0.01)] \qquad \text{(Proposition 15.3.1)}$$
$$= 1.495$$

Thus, it seems reasonable to expect that as we divide the interval $[1, 2]$ into more but smaller subintervals, the corresponding sum of the area of the inscribed rectangles will approximate more and more closely the area of the bounded region. This involves the concept of a limit because we are now concerned with the behavior of the sum S_n as the process of subdivision is continued indefinitely and the length of the subinterval approaches zero. If the interval $[1, 2]$ is divided into n subintervals each of length $h = 1/n$, then the inscribed rectangles are of height

$$f(1) = 1, f(1 + h) = 1 + h, f(1 + 2h) = 1 + 2h, \ldots, f[1 + (n - 1)h]$$
$$= 1 + (n - 1)h$$

The sum of areas of the rectangles is

$$
\begin{aligned}
S_n &= 1 \cdot h + (1 + h)h + (1 + 2h)h + \cdots + [1 + (n - 1)h]h \\
&= h\{1 + (1 + h) + (1 + 2h) + \cdots + [1 + (n - 1)h]\} \\
&= h\{\underbrace{(1 + 1 + \cdots + 1)}_{n \text{ times}} + h[1 + 2 + 3 + \cdots + (n - 1)]\}
\end{aligned}
$$

The quantity in the second parentheses is an arithmetic progression whose sum, by Proposition 15.3.1, is

$$
\frac{n(n - 1)}{2}
$$

Thus,

$$
\begin{aligned}
S_n &= h\left[n + h\,\frac{n(n - 1)}{2} \right] \\
&= nh\left(1 + \frac{nh - h}{2} \right)
\end{aligned}
$$

Because $nh = 1$, we obtain

$$
S_n = 1\left[1 + \frac{1}{2}\left(1 - \frac{1}{n} \right) \right]
$$

Recall that when $n \to \infty$, $1/n \to 0$. Thus,

$$
\lim_{n \to \infty} S_n = \tfrac{3}{2}
$$

This limiting value is called the definite integral of $f(x)$ from $x = 1$ to $x = 2$ and we write

$$
\int_1^2 x\, dx = \tfrac{3}{2}
$$

where 1 and 2 are, respectively, the lower and upper limits of integration.

Now we return to Eq. (19.1) and generalize how the above procedure is used, at least in theory, to obtain the area bounded by the lines $x = a$, $x = b$, the x axis, and the graph of $y = f(x)$, where f is an arbitrary continuous function and $f(x) \geq 0$ over the closed interval $[a, b]$. We have observed that as the subdivisions become finer and finer, the number of rectangles increases, the width of each rectangle approaches zero, and consequently the sum of areas of the rectangles (19.1) approaches a limit. This limiting value is called the definite integral of $f(x)$ from $x = a$ to $x = b$. In symbols, we write

$$
(19.2) \quad \int_a^b f(x)\, dx = \lim_{n \to \infty} \{hf(a) + hf(a + h) + \cdots + hf[a + (n - 1)h]\}
$$

where $h = (b - a)/n$, a and b are the lower and upper limits of the integration, respectively, and $f(x)$ is referred to as the integrand. Note that the letter x in (19.1) and (19.2) merely identifies the variable being used in evaluating the area of the function and

$$\int_a^b f(x)\, dx,\ \int_a^b f(t)\, dt,\ \int_a^b f(u)\, du,\ \dots$$

have exactly the same meaning.

Let us look at a few examples.

Example 19.1

Calculate by summation

$$\int_2^4 x^2\, dx$$

SOLUTION

We divide, as before, the interval $[2, 4]$ into n equal parts, each of length $h = (4 - 2)/n = 2/n$. The inscribed rectangles thus formed are of height

$$f(2) = 2^2 = 4$$
$$f(2 + h) = (2 + h)^2 = 4 + 4h + h^2$$
$$f(2 + 2h) = (2 + 2h)^2 = 4 + 8h + (2h)^2$$
$$f(2 + 3h) = (2 + 3h)^2 = 4 + 12h + (3h)^2$$
$$\vdots$$
$$f[2 + (n - 1)h] = [2 + (n - 1)h]^2 = 4 + 4(n - 1)h + (n - 1)^2 h^2$$

The sum of the areas of n rectangles is

$$S_n = h(\underbrace{4 + 4 + \cdots + 4}_{n \text{ times}}) + 4h(1 + 2 + \cdots + (n - 1))$$
$$+ h^2[1^2 + 2^2 + 3^2 + \cdots + (n - 1)^2]$$

Note that the expression in the second parentheses is

$$1 + 2 + 3 + \cdots + (n - 1) = \frac{n(n - 1)}{2} \qquad \text{(Proposition 15.3.1)}$$

Further, we need the formula

(19.3) $\quad 1^2 + 2^2 + \cdots + k^2 = \dfrac{k(k + 1)(2k + 1)}{6}$

which for $k = n - 1$ becomes

$$1^2 + 2^2 + \cdots + (n - 1)^2 = \frac{(n - 1)n(2n - 1)}{6}$$

Thus,

$$S_n = h\left[4n + 4h\,\frac{n(n - 1)}{2} + h^2\,\frac{n(n - 1)(2n - 1)}{6}\right]$$
$$= 4nh + 2nh(nh - h) + \frac{nh(nh - h)(2nh - h)}{6}$$

Substituting $h = 2/n$, we obtain

$$S_n = 4 \cdot 2 + 2 \cdot 2 \left(2 - \frac{2}{n} \right) + \frac{2(2 - 2/n)(4 - 2/n)}{6}$$

$$= 8 + 8 \left(1 - \frac{1}{n} \right) + \frac{4(1 - 1/n)(2 - 1/n)}{3}$$

Proceeding to the limit, we observe that as $n \to \infty$, $1/n \to 0$. Thus,

$$\lim_{n \to \infty} S_n = 8 + 8 + \tfrac{8}{3} = \tfrac{56}{3}$$

Hence,

$$\int_2^4 x^2 \, dx = \tfrac{56}{3}$$

Example 19.2

Calculate, by summation,

$$\int_a^b e^x \, dx$$

SOLUTION

Because $f(x) = e^x$, we have

$$f(a) = e^a$$
$$f(a + h) = e^{a+h}$$
$$f(a + 2h) = e^{a+2h}$$
$$\vdots$$
$$f[a + (n - 1)h] = e^{a+(n-1)h}$$

Then the sum of the areas of the rectangles is

$$S_n = h(e^a + e^{a+h} + e^{a+2h} + \cdots + e^{a+(n-1)h})$$

The quantity in parentheses is a geometric progression with e^a as the first term and e^h as the common ratio. Thus, using Proposition 15.4.1, we have

$$S_n = h \cdot e^a \left(\frac{e^{nh} - 1}{e^h - 1} \right)$$

Using the fact that

$$h = \frac{b - a}{n}$$

we obtain

$$S_n = h \cdot e^a \left(\frac{e^{b-a} - 1}{e^h - 1} \right) = (e^b - e^a) \cdot \left(\frac{h}{e^h - 1} \right)$$

Note that when $n \to \infty$, $h \to 0$. Recall from Chapter 17 that

(19.4) $$\lim_{h \to 0} \left(\frac{e^h - 1}{h} \right) = 1$$

Hence,

$$\int_a^b e^x \, dx = e^b - e^a$$ ∎

19.3 PROPERTIES OF THE DEFINITE INTEGRAL

We note from (19.2) that if $f(x)$ is an arbitrary continuous function and $f(x) \geq 0$ over a closed interval $[a, b]$, then

$$\int_a^b f(x) \, dx = \lim_{h \to 0} \{h \cdot f(a) + h \cdot f(a + h) + \cdots + h \cdot f[a + (n - 1)h]\}$$

where h, the length of each subinterval, approaches zero in the limiting process. In forming the above sum, we have assumed that the lower limit of integration a is less than the upper limit of integration b. If $a > b$, we apply basically the same procedure but label the points of subdivision so that $a = x_0 > x_1 > x_2 > \cdots > x_{n-1} > x_n = b$, as shown in Figure 19.4. As before, $h = x_{i+1} - x_i$ for $i = 1, 2, \ldots, n$. Since $x_{i+1} < x_i$ in this case, h is negative for all subintervals. Thus, if the limits a and b are reversed, the sign of integral is changed. Hence, we have the following proposition, which we state without proof.

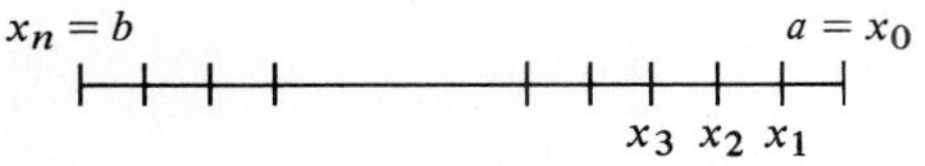

Figure 19.4

Proposition 19.3.1: If $f(x)$ is a continuous function and $f(x) \geq 0$ in the closed interval $[a, b]$, then

$$\int_a^b f(x) \, dx = - \int_b^a f(x) \, dx$$ ∎

We also agree that if $b = a$, then the area is zero, because the base $h = 0$ for each rectangle. Thus, we have the following proposition.

Proposition 19.3.2: $\int_a^a f(x) \, dx = 0$ ∎

It seems reasonable that if $f(x)$ is a continuous function and $f(x) \geq 0$ over the closed interval $[a, b]$ and $a < c < b$, as shown in Figure 19.5, then we may add the integral of $f(x)$ from a to c to the definite integral from c to b and obtain the definite integral of $f(x)$ over the entire interval $[a, b]$. Thus, we have the following proposition.

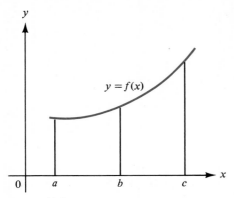

Figure 19.5

Proposition 19.3.3: If $f(x)$ is a continuous function and $f(x) \geq 0$ in the interval $[a, b]$ and $a < c < b$, then

$$\int_a^b f(x)\, dx = \int_a^c f(x)\, dx + \int_c^b f(x)\, dx \qquad \blacksquare$$

The following results (stated without proof) will be used frequently in evaluating integrals of polynomial and other functions.

Proposition 19.3.4: If $f(x)$ is a continuous function and $f(x) \geq 0$ in the interval $[a, b]$ and c is any constant, then

$$\int_a^b cf(x)\, dx = c \int_a^b f(x)\, dx \qquad \blacksquare$$

Proposition 19.3.5: If $f(x)$ and $g(x)$ are continuous functions, $f(x) \geq 0$ and $g(x) \geq 0$ in the interval $[a, b]$, then

$$\int_a^b [f(x) + g(x)]\, dx = \int_a^b f(x)\, dx + \int_a^b g(x)\, dx$$

EXERCISE 19.1

Evaluate the following integrals by dividing the closed intervals $[a, b]$ into n subintervals of equal length.

1. $\int_2^4 2x\, dx$

2. $\int_1^3 (x + 2)\, dx$

3. $\int_0^2 (3x + 4)\, dx$

4. $\int_0^5 (2t + 3)\, dt$

5. $\int_2^4 (4x + 5)\, dx$

6. $\int_2^3 (mx + c)\, dx$

7. $\int_0^2 x^2\, dx$

8. $\int_1^3 (x^2 + 2)\, dx$

9. $\int_1^2 (x^2 + 2x)\, dx$

10. $\int_2^4 (x^2 + 3x + 2)\, dx$

11. $\int_2^3 (x + 1)^2\, dx$

12. $\int_1^3 (3 + x + x^2)\, dx$

13. $\int_1^2 e^x\, dx$

14. $\int_1^3 e^{-t}\, dt$

15. $\int_2^4 e^{2x}\, dx$

16. $\int_1^5 (e^{3x} + 3)\, dx$

17. Prove that if c is constant, then

$$\int_a^b c\, dx = c(b - a)$$

18. By making a separate calculation of each of the integrals, show that

$$\int_1^3 (2x + 3)\, dx = -\int_3^1 (2x + 3)\, dx$$

19. By making a separate calculation of each of the integrals, show that

a. $\int_0^1 x^2\, dx + \int_1^3 x^2\, dx = \int_0^3 x^2\, dx$

b. $\int_1^4 (2x^2 + 3x)\, dx = 2\int_1^4 x^2\, dx + 3\int_1^4 x\, dx$

c. $\int_2^5 (x + 1)^2\, dx = \int_2^5 x^2\, dx + 2\int_2^5 x\, dx + \int_2^5 dx$

20. Using the fact that

$$1^3 + 2^3 + 3^3 + \cdots + k^3 = \left[\frac{k(k + 1)}{2}\right]^2$$

find the area under the curve $y = x^3$ by dividing the closed interval $[0, 3]$ into n subintervals each of length $3/n$.

19.4 EVALUATION OF DEFINITE INTEGRALS

It is apparent that the concept of the definite integral is intimately connected with the idea of area. Specifically, if $f(x)$ is continuous and non-negative over a closed interval $[a, b]$, then

$$\int_a^b f(x)\, dx$$

represents the area bounded by the lines $x = a$, $x = b$, the x axis, and the curve $y = f(x)$. We now state an important theorem, known as the fundamental theorem of calculus, which serves as a connecting link between integration and differentiation.

Theorem 19.4.1: If $f(x)$ is a continuous function on the closed interval $[a, b]$ and $F(x)$ is another function on $[a, b]$ such that $F'(x) = f(x)$, then

$$\int_a^b f(x)\, dx = F(b) - F(a)$$

The fundamental theorem states that given a continuous function $f(x)$, we can compute the definite integral over $[a, b]$ by finding another function $F(x)$ whose derivative is $f(x)$ and then evaluating $F(x)$ at $x = b$ and at $x = a$, and then subtracting. This process of finding $F(x)$ is called antidifferentiation or the inverse process of differentiation.

Definition 19.4.1: $F(x)$ is called an antiderivative of the continuous function $f(x)$ on an interval $[a, b]$ if and only if $F'(x) = f(x)$ for all x in that interval.

A given function $f(x)$ may have more than one antiderivative; in fact, it has infinitely many of them. Consider, for instance, the function $f(x) = x^2$; then the functions given by $F_1(x) = x^3/3$, $F_2(x) = (x^3/3) + 4$, and $F_3(x) = (x^3/3) - 50$ are all antiderivatives of $f(x)$. The following proposition, which we state without proof, guarantees that any two antiderivatives differ only by a constant.

Proposition 19.4.1: If $F_1(x)$ and $F_2(x)$ are continuous and are antiderivatives of the same function $f(x)$ in the interval $[a, b]$, then

$$F_1(x) = F_2(x) + \text{constant}$$ ■

Note that if $f(x) = e^x$, then an antiderivative of $f(x)$ is $F(x) = e^x + c$, because the derivative of $e^x + c$ is e^x. We shall further illustrate this procedure with some examples.

Example 19.3

Evaluate

$$\int_2^3 x^2 \, dx$$

SOLUTION

Note that an antiderivative of x^2 is

$$F(x) = \frac{x^3}{3}$$

Evaluating $F(x)$ at $x = 3$ and $x = 2$, respectively, we have

$$F(3) = \tfrac{27}{3}$$
$$F(2) = \tfrac{8}{3}$$

Applying Proposition 19.4.1, we have

$$\int_2^3 x^2 \, dx = F(3) - F(2) = \tfrac{19}{3}$$ ■

Example 19.4

Evaluate

$$\int_1^4 (x^3 + 3x^2 + 4) \, dx$$

SOLUTION

In this case, $f(x) = x^3 + 3x^2 + 4$ and thus to apply the fundamental theorem of calculus, we need to work backward from our knowledge of derivatives to get $F(x)$ such that $F'(x) = f(x)$. Observe that

$$\int_1^4 (x^3 + 3x^2 + 4)\, dx = \int_1^4 x^3\, dx + \int_1^4 3x^2\, dx + \int_1^4 4\, dx \qquad \text{(Proposition 19.3.5)}$$

$$= \int_1^4 x^3\, dx + 3\int_1^4 x^2\, dx + 4\int_1^4 1\, dx \qquad \text{(Proposition 19.3.4)}$$

That an antiderivative of x^3 is $x^4/4$, that one of x^2 is $x^3/3$, and that one of 1 is x follows from the fact that

$$\frac{d}{dx}\left(\frac{x^4}{4}\right) = x^3 \qquad \frac{d}{dx}\left(\frac{x^3}{3}\right) = x^2 \qquad \frac{d}{dx}(x) = 1$$

Thus, we may write

$$F(x) = \frac{x^4}{4} + x^3 + 4x$$

Evaluating $F(x)$ at $x = 1$ and at $x = 4$, we obtain

$$F(1) = \tfrac{21}{4}$$
$$F(4) = 144$$

Thus,

$$\int_1^4 (x^3 + 3x^2 + 4)\, dx = \tfrac{555}{4}$$

Example 19.5

Evaluate

$$\int_1^2 e^x\, dx$$

SOLUTION

An antiderivative of $f(x) = e^x$ is

$$F(x) = e^x$$

Thus,

$$\int_1^2 e^x\, dx = F(2) - F(1)$$
$$= e^2 - e^1$$

It is customary to use the notation

$$F(x)\, \Big]_a^b = F(b) - F(a)$$

In this notation, we formalize the fundamental theorem of calculus as

$$\int_a^b f(x)\, dx = F(x)\, \Big]_a^b \qquad \text{where } F'(x) = f(x)$$

EXERCISE 19.2

Evaluate each of the following definite integrals using the fundamental theorem of calculus.

1. $\int_1^2 x \, dx$

2. $\int_2^4 3x \, dx$

3. $\int_1^3 (2x + 3) \, dx$

4. $\int_2^4 (3x + 5) \, dx$

5. $\int_0^3 3x^2 \, dx$

6. $\int_1^2 (x^2 + 1) \, dx$

7. $\int_1^4 (x^2 - 3x + 4) \, dx$

8. $\int_0^3 (3x^2 + 2x + 1) \, dx$

9. $\int_3^5 (x^2 + x + 1) \, dx$

10. $\int_2^4 (5x^2 - 2x + 4) \, dx$

11. $\int_0^3 x(x + 1)$

12. $\int_1^4 2x(x + 4) \, dx$

13. $\int_2^3 (x + 1)(x - 1) \, dx$

14. $\int_1^2 (x + 2)(x + 3) \, dx$

15. $\int_0^2 3x^3 \, dx$

16. $\int_1^4 (x^3 + x^2 + 1) \, dx$

17. $\int_2^5 (4x^3 + 3x^2 + 2x + 1) \, dx$

18. $\int_1^3 x(x^2 + 1) \, dx$

19. $\int_2^4 x(x + 1)^2 \, dx$

20. $\int_4^6 x(x + 1)(x + 2) \, dx$

21. $\int_0^2 3e^x \, dx$

22. $\int_1^3 (2e^x + 3) \, dx$

23. $\int_{-1}^2 (4e^x + 1) \, dx$

24. $\int_0^1 (4x^3 + 3x^2 + 2e^x) \, dx$

Evaluate the area bounded by $x = a$, $x = b$, the horizontal axis, and the curve $y = f(x)$ in each of the following cases.

25. $f(x) = x^2$; $a = 3$, $b = 5$

26. $f(x) = 2x^2 + 3$; $a = 1$, $b = 4$

27. $f(x) = 2e^x$; $a = 1$, $b = 3$

28. $f(x) = (e^x + 1)$; $a = 2$, $b = 5$

29. $f(x) = \sqrt{x}$; $a = 1$, $b = 4$

30. $f(x) = \sqrt{x}$; $a = 4$, $b = 9$

19.5 INDEFINITE INTEGRALS

To evaluate the definite integral of a continuous function $f(x)$, we must first obtain its antiderivative $F(x)$ and then compute $F(b) - F(a)$, where a and b are the lower and upper limits of integration, respectively. Recall that every function has an infinite number of antiderivatives and that any two antiderivatives differ only by a constant. Thus, if two functions $f(x)$ and $F(x)$ are related by the equation $F'(x) = f(x)$, then

$$\int f(x) \, dx = F(x) + c$$

where c is a constant. The function $f(x)$ is called the integrand, $F(x)$ is an antiderivative of $f(x)$, and $F(x) + c$ is called the indefinite integral of $f(x)$.

Because integration is the inverse process of differentiation, it appears that the first requirement for developing a skill in integration is a thorough mastery of the differentiation formulas we have established in Chapter 17. Recall that the derivative of a constant is zero; therefore, the antiderivative of zero is a constant. In other words,

$$\int 0 \, dx = c$$

We now list integral formulas for certain well-known functions.

1. $\displaystyle\int x^n \, dx = \frac{x^{n+1}}{n+1} + c \qquad n \neq -1$

2. $\displaystyle\int e^x \, dx = e^x + c$

3. $\displaystyle\int a^x \, dx = \frac{a^x}{\ln a} + c \qquad (a > 0)$

4. $\displaystyle\int \frac{dx}{x} = \ln x + c \qquad (x > 0)$

Let us look at an illustrative example.

Example 19.6

a. $\displaystyle\int x^2 \, dx = \frac{x^{2+1}}{2+1} + c = \frac{x^3}{3} + c$

b. $\displaystyle\int \frac{dx}{x^3} = \int x^{-3} \, dx = \frac{x^{-3+1}}{-3+1} + c$

$$= -\frac{1}{2x^2} + c$$

c. $\displaystyle\int \sqrt{x} \, dx = \int x^{1/2} \, dx$

$$= \left(\frac{x^{1/2+1}}{\frac{1}{2}+1} \right) + c$$

$$= \tfrac{2}{3} x^{3/2} + c \qquad (x \geq 0)$$

Recall from Chapter 17 that the derivative of c times a function is c times the derivative of that function. Thus, for the inverse process of differentiation, we have

(19.5) $\displaystyle\int c \, f(x) \, dx = c \int f(x) \, dx$

which is an analog of Proposition 19.3.4. Because the derivative of a sum (difference) of two functions is the sum (difference) of their derivatives, we have

(19.6) $\displaystyle\int [f(x) \pm g(x)] \, dx = \int f(x) \, dx \pm \int g(x) \, dx$

$$= F(x) + G(x) + C$$

where $F'(x) = f(x)$ and $G'(x) = g(x)$, and C is an arbitrary constant.

Example 19.7

a. $\int 4x^2\, dx = 4 \int x^2\, dx = \frac{4}{3}x^3 + c$

b. $\int \frac{dx}{2x} = \frac{1}{2} \int \frac{dx}{x} = \frac{1}{2}\ln x + c \qquad x > 0$

c. $\int 3e^x\, dx = 3 \int e^x\, dx = 3e^x + c$ ∎

Example 19.8
Find

$$\int (3x^2 + 2x + 1)\, dx$$

SOLUTION
By (19.5),

$$\int (3x^2 + 2x + 1)\, dx = \int 3x^2\, dx + \int 2x\, dx + \int dx$$

which by (19.6) equals

$$= 3 \int x^2\, dx + 2 \int x\, dx + \int dx$$
$$= 3\left(\frac{x^3}{3}\right) + 2\left(\frac{x^2}{2}\right) + x + c$$
$$= x^3 + x^2 + x + c$$ ∎

Example 19.9
Find

$$\int \left(5x^4 + 2x^2 + 3e^x + \frac{2}{x}\right) dx$$

SOLUTION

$$\int \left(5x^4 + 2x^2 + 3e^x + \frac{2}{x}\right) dx = \int 5x^4\, dx + \int 2x^2\, dx + \int 3e^x\, dx + \int \frac{2}{x}\, dx$$
$$= 5 \int x^4\, dx + 2 \int x^2\, dx + 3 \int e^x\, dx + 2 \int \frac{dx}{x}$$
$$= 5\left(\frac{x^5}{5}\right) + 2\left(\frac{x^3}{3}\right) + 3e^x + 2\ln x + c \quad (x > 0)$$
$$= x^5 + \frac{2}{3}x^3 + 3e^x + 2\ln x + c \quad (x > 0)$$ ∎

Example 19.10
Find

$$\int \left(2a^x + \frac{1}{3x}\right) dx$$

SOLUTION

$$\int \left(2a^x + \frac{1}{3x} \right) dx = \int 2a^x \, dx + \int \frac{dx}{3x}$$

$$= 2 \int a^x \, dx + \frac{1}{3} \int \frac{dx}{x}$$

$$= 2 \left(\frac{a^x}{\ln a} \right) + \frac{1}{3} \ln x + c \qquad (a > 0, x > 0)$$

Example 19.11

Find the equation of the curve $y = f(x)$ that passes through the point $(2, 16)$ and satisfies the condition that the slope of the curve at $(x, f(x))$ is $4x^3 - 2x$.

SOLUTION

The curve $y = f(x)$ must be of the form

$$\int (4x^3 - 2x) \, dx = \int 4x^3 \, dx - \int 2x \, dx$$

that is,

$$f(x) = x^4 - x^2 + c$$

To evaluate the constant, note that $f(x)$ passes through the point $(2, 16)$. Substituting $x = 2, f(x) = 16$, we have

$$16 = 2^4 - 2^2 + c$$

$$c = 4$$

The required curve is

$$y = x^4 - x^2 + 4$$

EXERCISE 19.3

Find each of the following indefinite integrals and verify your results by differentiation.

1. $\displaystyle\int 4x^3 \, dx$

2. $\displaystyle\int \frac{dx}{x^2}$

3. $\displaystyle\int \frac{2}{x^4} \, dx$

4. $\displaystyle\int x^{2/3} \, dx$

5. $\displaystyle\int \frac{x + 1}{x^2} \, dx$

6. $\displaystyle\int \frac{dx}{x\sqrt{x}}$

7. $\displaystyle\int x(x + 1) \, dx$

8. $\displaystyle\int (x + 1)(x + 2) \, dx$

9. $\displaystyle\int (x + 2)^2 \, dx$

10. $\displaystyle\int (2x + 3)^2 \, dx$

11. $\displaystyle\int \left(x + \frac{1}{x} \right) dx$

12. $\displaystyle\int (x + \tfrac{1}{2})^2 \, dx$

13. $\displaystyle\int (x - \tfrac{1}{2})^2 \, dx$

14. $\displaystyle\int \left(x^2 + \frac{1}{x^2} \right)^2 dx$

15. $\displaystyle\int \left(x^2 + \frac{1}{x^2} + e^x \right) dx$

16. $\int (2 + x)\sqrt{x}\, dx$ **17.** $\int \left(\dfrac{e^x + e^{-x}}{2}\right) dx$ **18.** $\int \left(\dfrac{e^x - e^{-x}}{2}\right) dx$

19. $\int e^{\ln x}\, dx$ **20.** $\int \log e^x\, dx$

Evaluate the following definite integrals.

21. $\int_1^4 x\sqrt{x}\, dx$ **22.** $\int_1^8 3x^{2/3}\, dx$ **23.** $\int_3^4 \left(2x^2 + \dfrac{3}{x^2}\right) dx$

24. $\int_1^3 \left(x + \dfrac{1}{x}\right)^2 dx$ **25.** $\int_1^3 2e^x\, dx$ **26.** $\int_2^4 (e^x + e^{-x})\, dx$

27. $\int_1^e \dfrac{dx}{x}$ **28.** $\int_2^e \dfrac{3}{x}\, dx$

Find the equation of the curve $y = f(x)$ in each of the following problems.
29. $f'(x) = 2x - 3$; $f(2) = -2$
30. $f'(x) = x + 5$; $f(4) = 32$

31. $f'(x) = 3x^2 - 4x + \dfrac{1}{x^2}$; $f(2) = 9$

32. $f'(x) = 3(x + 2)^2$; $f(0) = 9$
33. $f'(x) = (x - 1)(x - 2)$; $f(1) = \frac{7}{2}$
34. $f'(x) = e^x + x^2$; $f(0) = 4$

19.6 INTEGRATION BY SUBSTITUTION

Success in the evaluation of $\int f(x)\, dx$ by using the fundamental theorem hinges on our ability to exhibit an antiderivative $F(x)$. This technique, which is thus of limited value, does not provide any systematic procedure for finding antiderivatives. Because there are several functions,

$$\int (x^3 + 2)^8\, dx, \int \frac{x\, dx}{2x^2 + 5}, \int xe^{-x^2/2}\, dx, \int \frac{(\ln x)^2}{x}\, dx$$

to name a few, that cannot be easily identified as derivatives of well-known functions, we need some additional methods of integration. One such method, which we shall discuss in this section, is "integration by substitution" or "change of variables," which may provide a partial answer to the problem of evaluating integrals. Later, we shall explain "integration by parts," which often transforms a complicated integral into a simpler one.

Let us first introduce the concept of differentials. If $y = f(x)$ where $f(x)$ is differentiable, we write

$$dy = f'(x)\, dx$$

and say that dy is the differential of f. Thus, if $y = x^3$, then $dy = 3x^2\, dx$ and if $y = e^x + \ln x$, then the differential $dy = (e^x + 1/x)\, dx$.

Proposition 19.6.1: Let $f(u)$ be a continuous function, where $u = g(x)$ and $du/dx = g'(x)$ exists. Then

$$\int f[g(x)]g'(x) \, dx = \int f(u) \, du = F(u) + c$$

where $F'(u) = f(u)$ and $du = g'(x) \, dx$. ∎

This proposition suggests that we look for the function $g(x)$ whose differential $g'(x) \, dx$ also appears in the integrand. Let us consider some examples.

Example 19.12
Find

$$\int 3x^2(x^3 + 5)^8 \, dx$$

SOLUTION
Observe that $3x^2 \, dx$ is the differential of $x^3 + 5$. Hence, if we use the substitution

$$u(x) = x^3 + 5$$

then

$$du = 3x^2 \, dx$$

Thus,

$$\int 3x^2(x^3 + 5)^8 \, dx = \int u^8 \, du$$
$$= \tfrac{1}{9}u^9 + c$$

where c is an arbitrary constant. Because $u(x) = x^3 + 5$, we have

$$\int 3x^2(x^3 + 5)^8 = \tfrac{1}{9}(x^3 + 5)^9 + c$$ ∎

Example 19.13
Find

$$\int \frac{(\ln x)^2}{x} \, dx \qquad x > 0$$

SOLUTION
Because dx/x is the differential of $\ln x$, we use the substitution

$$u(x) = \ln x$$

Then

$$du = \frac{dx}{x}$$

and

$$\int \frac{(\ln x)^2}{x} \, dx = \int u^2 \, du$$

$$= \tfrac{1}{3} u^3 + c$$

$$= \tfrac{1}{3} (\ln x)^3 + c \qquad x > 0$$

Example 19.14

Find

$$\int (2x^3 + 3x^2) e^{x^4 + 2x^3}$$

SOLUTION

Note that $(2x^3 + 3x^2) \, dx$ is closely related to the differential of $x^4 + 2x^3$. Hence, we use the substitution

$$u(x) = x^4 + 2x^3$$

Then

$$du = (4x^3 + 6x^2) \, dx$$

That is,

$$(2x^3 + 3x^2) \, dx = \tfrac{1}{2} \, du$$

Hence,

$$\int (2x^3 + 3x^2) e^{x^4 + 2x^3} \, dx = \int e^u \frac{du}{2}$$

$$= \tfrac{1}{2} e^u + c$$

$$= \tfrac{1}{2} e^{(x^4 + 2x^3)} + c$$

Example 19.15

Find

$$\int \frac{(e^x + 2x) \, dx}{e^x + x^2 + 4}$$

SOLUTION

The expression in the numerator is the differential of the expression in the denominator. This suggests a substitution

$$u(x) = e^x + x^2 + 4$$

Then

$$du = (e^x + 2x) \, dx$$

so that

$$\int \frac{(e^x + 2x)\,dx}{e^x + x^2 + 4} = \int \frac{du}{u} = \ln u + c$$

$$= \ln(e^x + x^2 + 4) + c \qquad \blacksquare$$

Example 19.16
Find

$$\int x\sqrt{x^2 + 1}\,dx$$

SOLUTION
The fact that $x\,dx$ is closely related to the differential of $x^2 + 1$ gives a clue to the substitution

$$u(x) = x^2 + 1$$

Then

$$du = 2x\,dx$$

or

$$x\,dx = \tfrac{1}{2}\,du$$

Hence,

$$\int x\sqrt{x^2 + 1}\,dx = \int \sqrt{u} \cdot \tfrac{1}{2} \cdot du$$

$$= \tfrac{1}{2} \int u^{1/2}\,du$$

$$= \tfrac{1}{2}(\tfrac{2}{3}u^{3/2}) + c$$

Because $u = x^2 + 1$, we obtain

$$\int \sqrt{x^2 + 1}x\,dx = \tfrac{1}{3}(x^2 + 1)^{3/2} + c \qquad \blacksquare$$

We wish to remind the reader that in each of the preceding examples we looked for a function $u(x)$ whose differential du or its constant multiple appeared in the integrand. This enabled us to reduce the integration to evaluating antiderivatives of the type we discussed in the preceding sections. **Remember that the choice of a substitution is best made by experience, and it takes practice to become acquainted with the suitable substitution required in each case.**

EXERCISE 19.4

Find each of the following indefinite integrals.

1. $\int \sqrt{x + 4}\,dx$ 　　　　　　**2.** $\int \sqrt{4x + 4}\,dx$

3. $\int \sqrt{3x + 2}\,dx$ 　　　　　　**4.** $\int \sqrt{4x + 3}\,dx$

5. $\int \dfrac{dx}{\sqrt{2x+3}}\, dx$

6. $\int \dfrac{dx}{\sqrt{5x+6}}$

7. $\int x(x^2+1)^8\, dx$

8. $\int x^2(x^3+5)^6\, dx$

9. $\int x\sqrt{1-x^2}\, dx$

10. $\int x^2\sqrt{x^3+1}\, dx$

11. $\int 4x^3\sqrt{x^4+2}\, dx$

12. $\int (3x^2+2x)\sqrt{x^3+x^2+1}\, dx$

13. $\int \dfrac{2x}{1+x^2}\, dx$

14. $\int \dfrac{3x^2}{x^3+8}\, dx$

15. $\int \dfrac{x\, dx}{\sqrt{x^2+1}}$

16. $\int \dfrac{x^2\, dx}{\sqrt{x^3+1}}$

17. $\int x\sqrt{x+1}\, dx$

18. $\int x^2\sqrt{x+3}\, dx$

19. $\int xe^{x^2}\, dx$

20. $\int x^2 e^{x^3}\, dx$

21. $\int \dfrac{e^{\sqrt{x}}}{\sqrt{x}}\, dx$

22. $\int \dfrac{dx}{\sqrt{x}e^{\sqrt{x}}}$

23. $\int (2x+3)e^{x^2+3x+4}\, dx$

24. $\int (e^x+x)^2(e^x+1)\, dx$

25. $\int \dfrac{dx}{x\ln x}$

26. $\int \dfrac{dx}{x(\ln x)^2}$

27. $\int \dfrac{e^x}{1+e^x}\, dx$

28. $\int \dfrac{e^{2x}}{1+e^{2x}}\, dx$

29. $\int \dfrac{(e^x-e^{-x})\, dx}{(e^x+e^{-x})^2}$

30. $\int \dfrac{(e^x+e^{-x})\, dx}{e^x-e^{-x}}$

19.7 INTEGRATION BY PARTS

The method of integration by parts transforms one integration problem into another that we hope will be easier to handle. The technique is based on the product rule

$$\frac{d}{dx}\left[u(x)v(x)\right] = u(x)v'(x) + v(x)u'(x)$$

Integrating both sides, we have

$$u(x)v(x) + c = \int u(x)v'(x)\, dx + \int v(x)u'(x)\, dx$$

or

(19.7) $\quad \displaystyle\int u(x)v'(x)\, dx = u(x)v(x) - \int v(x)u'(x)\, dx + c$

where c is a constant. This is known as the formulas for integration by parts. The success in evaluating

$$\int u(x)v'(x)\,dx$$

lies in the identification of $u(x)$ and $v'(x)\,dx$ and their manipulation into (19.7) so that the integral on the right-hand side of (19.7) is simpler than the original one. If a definite integral is involved, then we have

(19.8) $$\int_a^b u(x)v'(x)\,dx = u(x)v(x)\,\Big]_a^b - \int_a^b v(x)u'(x)\,dx$$

We shall now illustrate in the following examples how (19.7) is applied.

Example 19.17

Find

$$\int xe^x\,dx$$

SOLUTION

Let $u(x) = x$ and $v'(x) = e^x$. Then

$$u'(x) = 1 \quad \text{and} \quad v(x) = e^x + k$$

where k is a constant. Then, applying (19.7), we have

$$\int xe^x\,dx = x(e^x + k) - \int (e^x + k)\,dx$$

$$= xe^x + kx - \int e^x\,dx - \int k\,dx + c$$

$$= xe^x + kx - e^x - kx + c$$

$$= xe^x - e^x + c$$

Note that the first constant k does not appear in the final answer. Because this is always the case, we shall henceforth drop the first constant k when evaluating $\int v'(x)\,dx$.

It is worthwhile to examine what would happen if we chose $u(x)$ and $v'(x)$ differently. Suppose that

$$u(x) = e^x \quad \text{and} \quad v'(x) = x$$

Then

$$u'(x) = e^x$$

and

$$v(x) = \frac{x^2}{2}$$

Applying (19.7), we have

(19.9) $$\int xe^x\,dx = e^x \cdot \frac{x^2}{2} - \int \frac{x^2}{2}e^x\,dx$$

which is correct but does not help in the evaluation of $\int xe^x \, dx$. In fact, the integral on the right-hand side of (19.9) is harder than the original one. The choice of $u(x)$ and $v'(x)$ is, therefore, very important; the guiding principle is that the integral on the right-hand side should be simpler to work with than the one with which we started. ∎

Example 19.18
Find

$$\int x^2 e^x \, dx$$

SOLUTION
Let $u(x) = x^2$ and $v'(x) = e^x$. Then

$$u'(x) = 2x$$

and

$$v(x) = e^x$$

Using (19.7), we have

$$\int x^2 e^x \, dx = x^2 e^x - 2 \int xe^x \, dx$$

Substituting the result from Example 19.17 that

$$\int xe^x \, dx = xe^x - e^x + c$$

we have

$$\int x^2 e^x \, dx = x^2 e^x - 2(xe^x - e^x + c)$$
$$= e^x(x^2 - 2x + 2) + c_1$$

where $c_1 = -2c$. ∎

Example 19.19
Find

$$\int \ln x \, dx \qquad (x > 0)$$

SOLUTION
If $u(x) = \ln x$ and $v'(x) = 1$, then

$$u'(x) = \frac{1}{x} \quad \text{and} \quad v(x) = x$$

Thus,

$$\int \ln x \, dx = x \ln x - \int x \cdot \frac{1}{x} \, dx$$

$$= x \ln x - x + c \qquad (x > 0)$$ ∎

Example 19.20

Evaluate

$$\int_0^3 x\sqrt{1 + x}\, dx$$

SOLUTION

Let $u(x) = x$ and $v'(x) = (1 + x)^{1/2}$. Then

$$u'(x) = 1 \quad \text{and} \quad v(x) = \tfrac{2}{3}(1 + x)^{3/2}$$

Applying (19.8), we obtain

$$\int_0^3 x\sqrt{1 + x}\, dx = \tfrac{2}{3}x(1 + x)^{3/2}\, \Big]_0^3 - \tfrac{2}{3}\int_0^3 (x + 1)^{3/2}\, dx$$

$$= \tfrac{2}{3}(24) - \tfrac{2}{3}\cdot\tfrac{2}{5}(x + 1)^{5/2}\, \Big]_0^3$$

$$= 16 - \tfrac{4}{15}(31)$$

$$= 16 - \tfrac{124}{15}$$

$$= \tfrac{116}{15}$$

EXERCISE 19.5

Use integration by parts to find each of the following indefinite integrals.

1. $\int \ln(x + 1)\, dx$ **2.** $\int x \ln x\, dx$ **3.** $\int x^2 \ln x\, dx$

4. $\int (x + 1)e^x\, dx$ **5.** $\int xe^{2x}\, dx$ **6.** $\int x^2 e^{2x}\, dx$

7. $\int x^3 e^{3x}\, dx$ **8.** $\int xe^{-2x}\, dx$ **9.** $\int x(1 + x)^3\, dx$

10. $\int_5^9 x\sqrt{x - 1}\, dx$ **11.** $\int_5^9 \dfrac{x}{\sqrt{x - 1}}\, dx$ **12.** $\int_0^5 x(1 + x)^{3/2}\, dx$

19.8 APPLICATIONS

In this section we discuss a few of the many applications of integration to economics and to the social and biological sciences. These applications are intended to emphasize the fundamental relationship of integration to differentiation and to familiarize the reader with the basic value of integral calculus.

Because a marginal cost function $C'(x)$ is the derivative of the total cost function $C(x)$, the total cost function is an antiderivative or the integral of the marginal cost function. Thus,

$$C(x) = \int C'(x)\, dx$$

Recall that indefinite integration introduces an arbitrary constant, but if we know the value of $C(x)$ for some fixed value of x, we can determine the total cost function completely.

Example 19.21

The marginal cost function of a product is given by

$$C'(x) = 500 - 3x$$

where $C'(x)$ is in dollars and x denotes the output. Determine the total cost function $C(x)$ and the average cost function $A(x)$ if the fixed cost is known to be $3000.

SOLUTION

Integrating the marginal cost function $C'(x)$, we obtain

$$C(x) = \int C'(x)\, dx$$

$$= \int (500 - 3x)\, dx$$

$$= 500x - \tfrac{3}{2}x^2 + k$$

where k is a constant. From the additional information that the fixed cost is $3000, we know that

$$C(0) = 500(0) - \tfrac{3}{2}(0)^2 + k$$

Thus, $k = C(0) = \$3000$, and

$$C(x) = \$(3000 + 500x - \tfrac{3}{2}x^2)$$

Because the average cost function $A(x)$ is defined to be the total cost divided by the output, we have

$$A(x) = \frac{C(x)}{x}$$

$$= \$\left(500 + \frac{3000}{x} - \frac{3}{2}x\right)$$

The same type of reasoning applies to the revenue function. Obviously, if the marginal revenue $R'(x)$ is the derivative of the revenue function $R(x)$, then the revenue function is obtained by integrating the marginal revenue function. Thus,

$$R(x) = \int R'(x)\, dx$$

Note that indefinite integration introduces an arbitrary constant. If $R(x)$ is known for some fixed value of x, we can determine the revenue function $R(x)$ completely. Average revenue is then calculated by dividing total revenue $R(x)$ by the output x.

How do we determine the maximum profit for a firm when the information is given in terms of marginal cost and marginal revenue? Let us consider the following example.

Example 19.22

The marginal cost of production of a new product and its revenue function are given respectively by

$$C'(x) = 20 + \frac{x}{20}$$

and

$$R'(x) = 30$$

where x is the number of units produced. Determine the maximum profit assuming that the fixed cost to the firm is $200.

SOLUTION

Note that the marginal cost is an increasing function of the output [its derivative $C''(x)$ is positive], the marginal revenue is a constant function, and the profit is maximum at that level of production where marginal cost equals marginal revenue. Thus, setting $C'(x) = R'(x)$, we solve for x:

$$20 + \frac{x}{20} = 30$$

$$x = 200$$

Recall that the profit function $P(x)$ is given by

$$P(x) = R(x) - C(x)$$

Integrating the marginal revenue function $R'(x)$, we obtain

$$R(x) = \int R'(x)\, dx$$

$$= \int 30\, dx$$

$$= 30x + k_1$$

Note that the revenue $R(x) = 0$ when there is no production, thus the constant k_1 must be zero. Integrating next the marginal cost function, we have

$$C(x) = \int C'(x)\, dx$$

$$= \int \left(20 + \frac{x}{20}\right) dx$$

$$= 20x + \frac{x^2}{40} + k_2$$

Assuming that the fixed cost of the firm is $200, we find that when $x = 0$,

$$C(0) = 20(0) + \tfrac{1}{40}(0)^2 + k_2$$

$$k_2 = C(0) = \$200$$

Thus,

$$C(x) = \$\left(200 + 20x + \frac{x^2}{40}\right)$$

Hence,

$$P(x) = R(x) - C(x)$$

$$= 30x - \left(20x + \frac{x^2}{40} + 200\right)$$

$$= 10x - \frac{x^2}{40} - 200$$

When the output is 200 units, the profit

$$P(200) = \$\left[10(200) - \frac{(200)^2}{40} - 200\right]$$

$$= \$800$$ ■

Example 19.23

A corporation is contemplating opening a regional distribution center at an initial cost of $174,000. The board of directors believe that after a short period of adjustment, the cost savings resulting from increased sales will offset the cost. The rate of cost savings over 10 years is estimated to be

$$C(x) = 5000 + 8000x$$

where x represents the number of years and $C(x)$ is the savings (in dollars) at any given time. Would this regional center pay for itself in 5 years? If not, in how many years of operation would the center pay for itself?

SOLUTION

Because the rate of savings is $C(x)$, the actual savings after t years is

$$S(t) = \int_0^t (5000 + 8000x)\, dx$$

Thus, the total savings in the first 5 years is

$$S(5) = \int_0^5 (5000 + 8000x)\, dx$$

$$= 5000x + 4000x^2 \Big]_0^5$$

$$= \$105,000$$

Obviously, these savings are not enough to offset the cost of $174,000. To find how long it would take for the regional center to pay for itself we need to find t such that

$$\int_0^t (5000 + 8000x)\, dx = \$174,000$$

Thus,

$$5000x + 8000\frac{x^2}{2}\bigg]_0^t = \$174{,}000$$

$$5000t + 4000t^2 = 174{,}000$$

which reduces to

$$5t + 4t^2 = 174$$

or

$$4t^2 + 5t - 174 = 0$$
$$(t - 6)(4t + 29) = 0$$
$$t = 6 \quad \text{or} \quad t = -\tfrac{29}{4}$$

Because t cannot be negative (Why?), we conclude that the distribution center would pay for itself in 6 years. ∎

Example 19.24

Hopkin Calculating Company has recently introduced a service contract for its customers. The company has estimated that the rate of maintenance on a machine is

$$C(x) = \$20 + (0.2)e^x$$

where x is the number of years the calculator has been in use. Determine the annual charge the company must levy for each calculator for a 5-year contract.

SOLUTION

The total maintenance charge for a 5-year period is given by

$$\int_0^5 C(x)\,dx = \int_0^5 (20 + 0.2e^x)\,dx$$

$$= 20x + (0.2)e^x\bigg]_0^5$$

$$= 100 + (0.2)(147.4)$$

$$= \$129.48$$

Thus, the annual charge is $25.89. ∎

There are many situations in which a variable y changes with time according to the equation

(19.10) $$\frac{dy}{dt} = ky$$

where k is a constant. Such situations occur frequently in chemistry, physics, biology, economics, and in various other types of motion problems. Note that if

(19.11) $$y = Ae^{kt}$$

where A is some constant, then differentiating y with respect to t, one immediately gets (19.10). Conversely, if we know that y changes in accordance with (19.10), then

$$(19.12) \quad \frac{dy}{y} = k \, dt$$

and by antidifferentiation we have

$$\ln y = kt + C$$

If we suppose that $y = y_0$ at time $t = 0$, then

$$\ln y_0 = C$$

and

$$\ln y = kt + \ln y_0$$

$$\ln y - \ln y_0 = kt$$

$$\ln \frac{y}{y_0} = kt$$

This is equivalent to

$$\frac{y}{y_0} = e^{kt}$$

or

$$(19.13) \quad y = y_0 e^{kt}$$

Evidently, y decreases with increasing time if $k < 0$ and increases if $k > 0$.

Example 19.25

In 1930, the population of a city was 80,000. In 1950, it was 100,000. If the population increases according to the law

$$\frac{dy}{dt} = ky$$

what will the population be in 1980? (Use $\ln 1.25 = 0.2231$ and $e^{0.5578} = 1.7468$.)

SOLUTION

First, we must evaluate the constants y_0 and k in (19.13). Because $y = 80,000$ at $t = 0$ and $y = 100,000$ at $t = 20$, we have

$$80,000 = y_0 e^0 \quad \text{and} \quad 100,000 = y_0 e^{20k}$$

This yields $y_0 = 80,000$ and

$$80,000 e^{20k} = 100,000$$

$$e^{20k} = 1.25$$

$$20k = \ln 1.25$$

$$k = 0.011155 \qquad (\ln 1.25 = 0.2231)$$

We now have

$$y = 80,000e^{(0.011155)t}$$

When $t = 50$,

$$y = 80,000e^{(0.011155)50}$$
$$= 80,000e^{0.5578}$$
$$= 80,000(1.7468)$$
$$= 139,744$$

∎

EXERCISE 19.6

1. The marginal cost of production of a firm is given by

$$C'(x) = 6 - \frac{x}{10} + \frac{x^2}{25}$$

   where x represents the quantity produced. Determine the cost function assuming that the fixed cost is $200.

2. The management of a publishing company has estimated that the marginal cost of publishing books is given by

$$C'(x) = 20x + \frac{100}{\sqrt{x}}$$

   where x denotes the number of books published (in thousands) in a year. Determine the cost function assuming that the fixed cost of the company is $50,000.

3. The marginal cost of producing an item is given by

$$C'(x) = \frac{x}{\sqrt{x^2 + 100}}$$

   where x represents the quantity produced. Assuming that the fixed cost is $1000, determine the total cost function and the average cost function.

4. The marginal cost of production of new microwave ovens is given by

$$C'(x) = 2x\sqrt{x^2 + 100}$$

   where x is the number of units produced. If fixed costs are $25,000, what is the total cost function?

5. The marginal revenue function of a monopolist is given by

$$R'(x) = 200 - 0.0004x + 0.01x^2$$

   where x denotes the quantity produced and sold. Assuming that the total revenue is zero when $x = 0$, determine the revenue function $R(x)$.

6. The marginal revenue function of a daily newspaper is given by

$$R'(x) = 100 + 0.02x + 0.03x^2$$

   where x is the number (in thousands) of copies published. Assuming that the total revenue is zero when $x = 0$, determine the revenue function $R(x)$.

7. The marginal cost of a product and the marginal revenue function are given, respectively, by

$$C'(x) = 40 + \frac{x}{8}$$

and

$$R'(x) = 50 + \frac{x}{10}$$

where x is the number of units produced. Determine the maximum profit assuming that the fixed cost of the firm is $500.

8. The marginal cost of a new product and the marginal revenue function are given, respectively, by

$$C'(x) = 300 + x$$

and

$$R'(x) = 400 + \frac{x}{5}$$

where x is the number of units produced. What is the maximum profit if the fixed cost of the plant is known to be $1250?

9. Harpos Publishing Company is contemplating the purchase of a new computer at a cost of $28,000. The company believes that after a short period of adjustment, savings in efficiency of various departments utilizing the computer will offset the cost. The rate of cost savings over a period of 10 years is estimated to be

$$C(x) = 500 + 1000x$$

where x represents years and $C(x)$ is savings (in dollars) per year at any given time. Will the machine pay for itself in 5 years? If not, in how many years of operation would the machine pay for itself?

10. Chicos Corporation is considering the purchase of a regional distribution center at a cost of $65,000. The management believes that after a short period of adjustment, cost savings resulting from the increased sales will offset the cost. The rate of cost savings is estimated to be

$$C(x) = 3000 + 4000x$$

where x represents the number of years and $C(x)$ is the savings (in dollars per year) at any given time. Would the new setup pay for itself in 3 years? If not, in how many years of operation would the regional center pay for itself?

11. Gummos Department Store has developed a service contract for the color televisions it sells to customers. The rate of maintenance is estimated to be

$$C(x) = \$(3x^2 + 2x + 20) \qquad 0 < x \le 5$$

where x is the number of years the contract remains in force. Determine the amount the store must charge per year for
a. a 2-year contract
b. a 3-year contract

12. An automobile leasing company has developed a service contract for the new cars it leases. The management has determined that the rate of maintenance is given approximately by

$$C(x) = \$(6x^2 + 12x + 10) \qquad 0 < x \leq 3$$

where x is the number of years for which the car has been leased. How much additional charge should a customer pay per year for
a. a 2-year contract
b. a 3-year contract

13. In Exercise 12, how much should a customer pay if he leases the car for 3 years but wants to buy the maintenance contract only for the third year?

14. The bacteria in a certain culture is increasing according to the law

$$\frac{dN}{dt} = 0.02N$$

If $N = 5000$ at time $t = 0$, find N when $t = 10$.

15. The bacteria in a culture is increasing according to the law

$$\frac{dy}{dt} = ky$$

If there are 5000 bacteria at time $t = 0$ and 10,000 at $t = 2$, find the number of bacteria at $t = 5$. (Use $\ln 2 = 0.6932$, $e^{1.733} = 5.66$.)

16. The population N in a certain town is increasing according to the law

$$\frac{dN}{dt} = 400 + 100e^t$$

If $N = 500$ at $t = 0$, find N at $t = 2$. What is the size of the population at $t = 4$?

17. The demand rate for a new cologne introduced in the holiday season by a large advertising campaign is estimated to be

$$\frac{dy}{dt} = 500e^{-t}$$

where t is the time in days from the end of the advertising campaign. Determine the total sales for the cologne for
a. the first 5 days after the campaign.
b. the first 10 days after the campaign.
after the campaign.

18. The daily rate of sales for a new product is given by

$$\frac{dN}{dt} = 100te^{-0.05t}$$

where t is the number of days the product has been on the market. Determine the total sales for
a. the first 5 days
b. the first 10 days

19. The number of freshman students dropping out from a certain university is proportional to the number of students enrolled. If there were 3000 freshmen enrolled in a given semester and 10 percent dropped out after 4 weeks, what is the number of students on the roll after 12 weeks? [ln 0.9 = −0.1054, $e^{-0.3162} = 0.7289$.]

20. The population of the United States was 150 million in 1950 and 180 million in 1960. Assuming that the population increases at a rate proportional to the population itself, estimate the population for the year 1990. [ln 1.2 = 0.1823, $e^{0.7292} = 2.0734$.]

A
The Real
Number System

A.1 THE REAL NUMBERS

The system of numbers most familiar to the reader, namely

$$1, 2, 3, 4, \ldots$$

are called the natural numbers. If we add or multiply two natural numbers, we again obtain a natural number. There are certain basic rules of elementary algebra with which readers are probably so familiar that they apply them mechanically, without even thinking about them. We state some of them explicitly. If a, b, and c are natural numbers, then

(A.1)	$a + b = b + a$	Commutativity for addition
(A.2)	$ab = ba$	Commutativity for multiplication
(A.3)	$a + (b + c) = (a + b) + c$	Associativity for addition
(A.4)	$(ab)c = a(bc)$	Associativity for multiplication
(A.5)	$a(b + c) = ab + ac$	Distributive property
(A.6)	$a \cdot 1 = 1 \cdot a = a$	Multiplicative identity

Other statements about the natural numbers (also known as positive integers , which must be justified in terms of these properties, can be developed with the positive integer system as a foundation. The operation of subtraction, for example, is defined in terms of the familiar operation of addition.

Definition A.1.1: If a and b are any natural numbers and if there exists a natural number c such that $a + c = b$, then $c = b - a$.

Thus, if $a = 5$ and $b = 8$, then $8 - 5 = c$ implies the existence of a natural number c such that $c + 5 = 8$. In this case, $c = 3$. But what about $5 - 8 = c$? Clearly, no natural number satisfies this expression. Similarly, there exists no natural number that satisfies the equation $5 - 5 = c$. This demonstrates that subtraction of one natural number from another does not always produce a natural number. Fortunately, this difficulty can be overcome by introducing the negative numbers ... , $-3, -2, -1$, and the number 0, which together with the system of natural numbers form the system of all integers, namely

$$\ldots, -3, -2, -1, 0, 1, 2, 3, \ldots$$

In this system every equation of the form $5 = 8 + c$ always has a solution. Further, there exists a unique number 0 in this system with the property that for every number a

(A.7) $a + 0 = 0 + a = a$

We refer to zero as an identity element under the operation of addition. Also, for each integer a there exists another integer $(-a)$ such that

(A.8) $a + (-a) = (-a) + a = 0$

The integer $(-a)$ is called the additive inverse of a. We must reinforce the fact that we have extended the system of natural numbers to the system of integers in which subtraction is always possible. Thus, we have the following definition.

Definition A.1.2: If a and b are any integers, then there exists an integer c such that if $a + c = b$, then $b - a = c$.

This definition assures us that given any two integers a and b, we can subtract a from b; that is, we can always find an integer c such that $b = a + c$. But can we divide a by b if a and b are integers? In other words, is there an integer d such that $a = bd$? If $a = 12$ and $b = 3$, then certainly there exists an integer $d = 4$ such that $a = bd$, but what about if $a = 12$ and $b = 5$? Obviously, there is no integer d satisfying the equation $12 = 5d$. This means that if we want a number system in which exact division is always possible, we must extend the system of integers to a system that includes negative integers, zero, positive integers, and fractions of the form $-\frac{1}{2}$, $\frac{2}{3}, -\frac{3}{4}, \ldots$. This system is called the system of rational numbers.

Definition A.1.3: A rational number is a number that can be expressed in the form a/b, where a and b are integers, and $b \neq 0$.

Why do we make the restriction, $b \neq 0$? Suppose that $a \neq 0$ and a is divisible by zero. Then what is the number d such that $a/0 = d$? Note that $a/0 = d$ means that $a = 0 \cdot d$ and because $0 \cdot d = 0$ for all integers d, it follows that $a = 0$—contrary to our assumption that $a \neq 0$. This means that there exists no number d for which the statement $a/0 = d$ holds. Thus, the expression $a/0$ remains undefined, and division by zero is not permitted. This leads us to an important property in the system of rationals: that for any number $a \neq 0$, there exists another number $(1/a)$ such that

(A.9) $a \cdot \left(\dfrac{1}{a}\right) = \left(\dfrac{1}{a} \cdot a\right) = 1$

Thus, if $a = 0$, then any attempt to define $(0/0)$ is meaningless. The number $(1/a)$, also written as a^{-1}, is called the multiplicative inverse of the number a.

We now state some of the basic rules that govern the operations with rational numbers and then illustrate their use by some examples.

(A.10) $\quad \dfrac{a}{1} = a$

(A.11) $\quad \dfrac{a}{b} = \dfrac{c}{d} \qquad$ if and only if $ad = bc, b \neq 0, d \neq 0$

(A.12) $\quad \dfrac{a}{b} + \dfrac{c}{d} = \dfrac{ad + bc}{bd} \qquad b \neq 0, d \neq 0$

(A.13) $\quad \dfrac{a}{b} \cdot \dfrac{c}{d} = \dfrac{ac}{bd} \qquad b \neq 0, d \neq 0$

(A.14) $\quad \dfrac{a}{b} \div \dfrac{c}{d} = \dfrac{ad}{bc} \qquad b \neq 0, c \neq 0, d \neq 0$

(A.15) $\quad \dfrac{ac}{bc} = \dfrac{a}{b} \qquad$ for $b \neq 0, c \neq 0$

Example A.1
Perform the following addition:

$$\frac{2}{x + 2} + \frac{3}{x - 2} \qquad x \neq \pm 2$$

SOLUTION
Using the rule (A.12), we have

$$\frac{2}{x + 2} + \frac{3}{x - 2} = \frac{2(x - 2) + 3(x + 2)}{(x + 2)(x - 2)}$$

$$= \frac{2x - 4 + 3x + 6}{(x + 2)(x - 2)}$$

$$= \frac{5x + 2}{(x + 2)(x - 2)} \qquad x \neq 2, x \neq -2$$

Example A.2
Perform the following subtraction:

$$\frac{y}{x - y} - \frac{x}{x + y} \qquad x \neq \pm y$$

SOLUTION

$$\frac{y}{x-y} - \frac{x}{x+y} = \frac{y(x+y) - x(x-y)}{(x-y)(x+y)}$$

$$= \frac{xy + y^2 - x^2 + xy}{(x-y)(x+y)}$$

$$= \frac{2xy + y^2 - x^2}{(x-y)(x+y)} \qquad x \neq \pm y$$

■

Example A.3

Perform the indicated operation and simplify.

$$\frac{3x-3}{5} \cdot \frac{2x-2}{3} \cdot \frac{4}{(x-1)^3} \qquad x \neq 1$$

SOLUTION

$$\frac{3x-3}{5} \cdot \frac{2x-2}{3} \cdot \frac{4}{(x-1)^3} = \frac{3(x-1)}{5} \cdot \frac{2(x-1)}{3} \cdot \frac{4}{(x-1)^3}$$

$$= \frac{3 \cdot 2 \cdot 4(x-1)^2}{5 \cdot 3(x-1)^3} \qquad \text{(A.13)}$$

$$= \frac{8}{5(x-1)} \qquad \text{for } x \neq 1 \qquad \text{(A.15)}$$

■

Example A.4

Perform the indicated operations and simplify.

$$\left(\frac{x^2 - y^2}{x+y}\right) \div \left(\frac{x-y}{x+2}\right) \qquad x \neq \pm y, x \neq -2$$

SOLUTION
Using (A.14), we note that

$$\left(\frac{x^2 - y^2}{x+y}\right) \div \left(\frac{x-y}{x+2}\right) = \left(\frac{x^2 - y^2}{x+y}\right) \cdot \left(\frac{x+2}{x-y}\right)$$

which is further equal to

$$= \frac{(x-y)(x+y)}{(x+y)} \frac{(x+2)}{(x-y)}$$

$$= (x+2) \qquad \text{if } x \neq y, x \neq -y, \text{ and } x \neq -2 \qquad ■$$

Example A.5

Solve the following equation for the rational number x.

$$\frac{3}{x} - \frac{2}{3x} = \frac{4}{5} \qquad x \neq 0$$

SOLUTION

Note that

$$\frac{3}{x} - \frac{2}{3x} = \frac{9}{3x} - \frac{2}{3x} = \frac{7}{3x}$$

Now, if

$$\frac{7}{3x} = \frac{4}{5}$$

then by (A.11), we obtain

$$12x = 35$$

or

$$x = \tfrac{35}{12}$$

■

The rational numbers, which include positive integers, negative integers, zero, and fractions, form a system in which the operations of subtraction and division by nonzero numbers are always possible. It appears that the system of rational numbers we have developed is all that we need in mathematics; however, this is not true, because there are other numbers, for example, $-\sqrt{3}, \sqrt{5}, \pi, e$, and infinitely many more that cannot be represented in the form of a/b, but that nevertheless need to be included in the set of real numbers.

A geometric representation of the real number system is, perhaps, helpful in building an intuitive understanding and may provide better insight into what the real numbers are. On a straight line, taken to be horizontal for convenience, we choose an arbitrary point 0 as the origin and mark off an arbitrary unit length on the line segment of some convenient size. (See Figure A.1.) The unit point is usually placed to the right of the origin 0. With this unit of length, we represent positive and negative integers by a set of points equally spaced on the line, placing positive integers to the right and negative integers to the left of the origin 0. By dividing each of the segments into two equal parts, we can associate fractions such as $-\tfrac{3}{2}$, $-\tfrac{1}{2}, \tfrac{1}{2}, \tfrac{3}{2}$, with particular points. In general, to represent a fraction with denominator n, we divide each of the unit lengths into n equal parts and represent the fractions

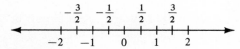

Figure A.1

with denominator n as the points of the subdivision. It appears that if this process of representing rationals by marking off the corresponding points on the line were continued, the entire line might be covered eventually. Actually, there are an infinite number of points on the line that do not correspond to any rational number. To substantiate this claim, we shall show the existence of one such point on the line.

Consider a right triangle OAB with base OA and height AB of unit length. (See Figure A.2.) Then, according to the theorem of Pythagoras, the length of hypotenuse OB is given by

$$x^2 = 1^2 + 1^2$$

or

$$x = \sqrt{2}$$

We shall now show that the distance $OC = \sqrt{2}$ cannot be represented in the form a/b, where $b \neq 0$.

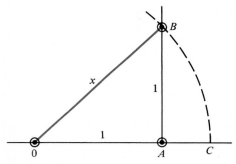

Figure A.2

Proposition A.1.1: **The number $\sqrt{2}$ is not rational.**

PROOF
Suppose that $\sqrt{2}$ is rational. Then there are positive integers a and b such that

(A.16) $$\frac{a}{b} = \sqrt{2}$$

We are assuming that a/b is in its lowest term; that is, the integers a and b have no common factors, because such factors, if any, can be cancelled to begin with. Squaring both sides, we have

(A.17) $$\left(\frac{a}{b}\right)^2 = 2 \quad \text{or} \quad a^2 = 2b^2$$

From (A.17), it is clear that a^2 is an even number. Therefore, a must itself be even because if a were odd, a^2 would also be odd. Then, let $a = 2c$, where c is an integer. Substituting this in (A.17), we have

(A.18) $$(2c)^2 = 4c^2 = 2b^2 \quad \text{or} \quad b^2 = 2c^2$$

which shows that b^2 is even and so is b. Hence, a and b are both even and have 2 as a common factor, contradicting our assumption that a and b have no common factor. Thus, the hypothesis that $\sqrt{2}$ is rational is false and the assertion follows. ■

We have demonstrated that $\sqrt{2}$ is not rational, yet it does correspond to a point on the number line, because we can construct a segment of that length (see Figure A.2). Numbers that are not rational but that can be represented on the number line are called irrationals. We shall now define the real number system.

Definition A.1.4: The collection of all rational numbers and irrational numbers is called the real number system.

Figure A.3 will, perhaps, help you picture the heirarchy of the real number system we have developed so far.

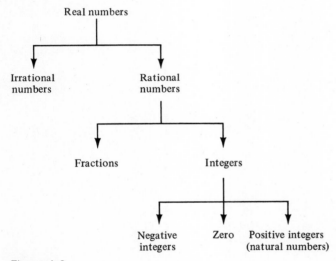

Figure A.3

We conclude this section with a brief remark that corresponding to every point on the number line we can associate one and only one real number, and conversely, to each real number corresponds one and only one point on the line representing this number. This correspondence is called a one-to-one correspondence.

EXERCISE A.1

1. Classify the following statements as true or false.
   a. Every natural number is a rational number.
   b. Every rational number is a natural number.
   c. Every rational number is an integer.
   d. Some integers are not rationals.
   e. Some rationals are not integers.

f. The sum of two rationals is rational.

g. The product of two rationals is rational.

h. The division of an integer by zero is not permitted.

i. $\sqrt{3}$ is a rational number.

Simplify each of the following expressions.

2. $\dfrac{x}{3} + \dfrac{2}{x}, x \neq 0$

3. $\dfrac{x+1}{2} + \dfrac{4}{x+2}, x \neq -2$

4. $\dfrac{1}{x+1} - \dfrac{1}{x-1}, x \neq \pm 1$

5. $\dfrac{1}{2x+1} + \dfrac{1}{2x-1}, x \neq \pm \tfrac{1}{2}$

6. $\dfrac{1}{x} - \dfrac{x}{x+1}, x \neq 0, -1$

7. $\dfrac{x+2}{x+1} + \dfrac{x+1}{x+2}, x \neq -1, -2$

8. $\dfrac{x+4}{x} \cdot \dfrac{x}{x+3}, x \neq 0, -3$

9. $\dfrac{2x-1}{x+1} \cdot \dfrac{x+3}{2x+1} \cdot \dfrac{2x+1}{2x-1}, x \neq -1, \pm\tfrac{1}{2}$

10. $\dfrac{3x+2}{2x+3} \cdot \dfrac{x+2}{3x+2} \cdot \dfrac{2x+3}{x+2}, x \neq -2, -\tfrac{2}{3}, -\tfrac{3}{2}$

11. $\dfrac{x-1}{x+1} \cdot \dfrac{2x+3}{4x+5} \cdot \dfrac{x+1}{(x-1)^2} \cdot \dfrac{x-1}{2x+3}, x \neq \pm 1, -\tfrac{4}{5}, -\tfrac{3}{2}$

12. $\dfrac{1}{x+1} \div \dfrac{2}{x+1}, x \neq -1$

13. $\dfrac{x+y}{x-y} \div \dfrac{(x+y)^2}{(x-y)^2}, x \neq \pm y$

14. $\left(1 + \dfrac{1}{x}\right) \div \left(1 - \dfrac{1}{x}\right), x \neq 0, 1$

15. $\left(\dfrac{1}{x+2} - \dfrac{1}{x-2}\right) \div \left(\dfrac{x+2}{x}\right), x \neq 0, \pm 2$

Solve each of the following equations for the rational number x.

16. $\dfrac{x}{3} + \dfrac{3}{2} = 2$

17. $\dfrac{2x-1}{3} + \dfrac{x+1}{2} = 5$

18. $\dfrac{3}{x} + \dfrac{4}{x} = \dfrac{1}{2}, x \neq 0$

19. $\dfrac{1}{x-1} + \dfrac{x}{x-1} = \dfrac{3}{2}, x \neq 1$

20. $\dfrac{2x}{3} + \dfrac{3(x+1)}{4} = 5$

21. $\dfrac{1}{2x+3} - \dfrac{3}{2x+3} = -2, x \neq -\tfrac{3}{2}$

22. $\dfrac{1}{x} + \dfrac{1}{x+1} = 0, x \neq 0, -1$

23. $\dfrac{3}{2x-3} + \dfrac{1}{2x+3} = 0, x \neq \pm\tfrac{3}{2}$

24. $\dfrac{1}{x-1} + \dfrac{1}{x+1} = 0, x \neq \pm 1$

25. $\dfrac{3x}{2x+1} - \dfrac{1}{2x+1} = \dfrac{8}{2x+1}, x \neq -\frac{1}{2}$

A.2 INEQUALITIES

In elementary algebra and geometry we study equalities almost exclusively. As we progress further in mathematics, we shall see that the study of inequalities is both interesting and useful.

Presently we are concerned with inequalities among real numbers, and we begin by recalling that positive numbers are associated with points to the right of zero whereas negative numbers are associated with those on the left of zero on the real line. A number a is greater than zero if and only if a is positive. In symbols, we write

$a > 0$

where the symbol $>$ is read as "is greater than." Similarly, a number a is less than zero if and only if a is negative. This statement is symbolized by

$a < 0$

where the symbol $<$ is interpreted as "is less than."

Definition A.2.1: Given any two real numbers a and b, we say that a is greater than b ($a > b$) and b is less than a ($b < a$) if $a - b$ is a positive number. The symbols $<$ and $>$ are called inequality signs.

Thus, $8 > 5$ means that $8 - 5 > 0$, which is a true statement. Let us now state briefly some basic facts about inequalities.

(A.19) For any real number a, one and only one of the following relations is true:

$a < 0$ or $a = 0$ or $a > 0$

(A.20) If $a > 0$ and $b > 0$, then

$a + b > 0$

and

$ab > 0$

(A.21) If $a < 0$, and $b < 0$, then

$a + b < 0$

but

$ab > 0$

(A.22) If $a < 0$ and $b > 0$, then

$ab < 0$

Other statements concerning inequalities can be justified in terms of the rules (A.19)–(A.22) and Definition A.2.1. Some of the most useful ones are as follows.

(A.23) If $a < b$ and $b < c$, then $a < c$.

(A.24) If $a < b$, then $a + c < b + c$ for any number c, positive, negative, or zero.

(A.25) If $a < b$ and c is any positive number, then

$$ac < bc$$

(A.26) If $a < b$ and c is any negative number, then

$$ac > bc$$

Thus, if $c = -1$ and $a < b$, then $-a > -b$. To prove (A.23), note that $a < b$ and $b < c$ are equivalent to the statement that $b - a$ and $c - b$ are positive numbers. That their sum

$$(b - a) + (c - b) = c - a$$

is positive follows from the statement (A.20) and the statement $c - a > 0$ means that $a < c$. The property (A.25) follows from the fact that $a < b$ implies that $b - a$ is a positive number. Because $c > 0$ and the product of two positive numbers is again a positive number (A.20), it follows that

$$(b - a)c > 0$$

or

$$bc - ac > 0$$

That is,

$$bc > ac$$

We leave the verification of properties (A.24) and (A.26) as an exercise for the reader.

The symbol $a \geq b$ means that a is greater than or equal to b. Similarly, the notation $a \leq b$ implies that a is less than or equal to b. Note that properties of $<$ may be extended to the relation $\leq$.

We shall now illustrate the use of some of the properties in the solution of an inequality involving a single unknown. Note that by a solution of an inequality we mean a number that satisfies the inequality, and the solution set is the set of all real numbers that satisfy the given inequality. Solving an inequality is thus a matter of describing the solution set of the inequality as explicitly as possible. Let us look at some examples.

Example A.6
Solve the following inequality for x:

$$5x - 3 < 12$$

SOLUTION
Let x be a number that satisfies the above inequality. Then by the property (A.24), we can add 3 to both sides of the inequality and obtain a true statement

$$5x - 3 + 3 < 12 + 3$$

or

$$5x < 15$$

Now, multiplying both sides by $\frac{1}{5}$ (Property A.25), we have

$$x < 3$$

The statement $x < 3$ is interpreted to mean that the solution set of the inequality $5x - 3 < 12$ consists of all real numbers less than 3. Thus, if we substitute any real number less than 3, say $x = 1$, into the inequality $5x - 3 < 12$, we obtain

$$5(1) - 3 < 12$$

That is,

$$2 < 12$$

which is a true statement.

Geometrically, we may represent the solution set as displayed in Figure A.4. The circle at 3 represents the fact that this number is not part of the solution set.

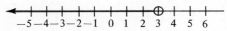

Figure A.4

Example A.7
Solve the following inequality for x,

$$2x - 7 > 5 - x$$

and represent the solution graphically.

SOLUTION
Adding x to both sides of the inequality, we obtain

$$3x - 7 > 5$$

Now we can add 7 to both sides and obtain

$$3x > 12$$

Multiplying both sides by $\frac{1}{3}$, we have

$$x > 4$$

The solution set consists of all real numbers greater than 4. Thus, if we substitute any real number greater than 4, say $x = 6$, into the inequality

$$2x - 7 > 5 - x$$

we obtain

$$2(6) - 7 > 5 - 6$$

That is,

$$5 > -1$$

which is obviously a true statement.

The solution set is represented graphically in Figure A.5. Again, the circle at 4 shows that this point is not included in the solution set.

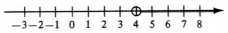

Figure A.5

Example A.8

Solve the following inequality for x,

$$5x + 16 \leq 3x + 25$$

and represent the solution set graphically.

SOLUTION

Adding $(-3x)$ to both sides of the inequality, we obtain

$$(-3x) + 5x + 16 \leq (-3x) + 3x + 25$$

or

$$2x + 16 \leq 25$$

Next, we add (-16) to both sides and get the inequality

$$2x + 16 + (-16) \leq 25 + (-16)$$

That is,

$$2x \leq 9$$

Finally, we multiply both sides by $\frac{1}{2}$, and we have

$$x \leq \frac{9}{2}$$

Thus, the solution consists of all real numbers less than or equal to $\frac{9}{2}$ and is represented graphically in Figure A.6. Note that the real number $\frac{9}{2}$ is included in the solution set.

Figure A.6

Example A.9

Solve the following inequality for x:

$$4x - 32 \leq 7x - 17$$

SOLUTION

Adding 32 to both sides, we obtain

$$4x \leq 7x + 15$$

Now we add $(-7x)$ to both sides and get

$$-3x \leq 15$$

Finally, we multiply both sides of this inequality by $(-\frac{1}{3})$. Recall from (A.26) that multiplication by a negative number reverses the direction of the inequality. Thus, we obtain

$$x \geq -5$$

representing the fact that the solution set consists of all real numbers greater than or equal to -5 as illustrated in Figure A.7.

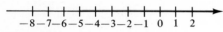

Figure A.7

We shall now consider solving inequalities of a slightly different type.

Example A.10

Solve the following inequality for x:

$$x(x - 3) > 0$$

SOLUTION

The product of two real numbers is positive if and only if both numbers have the same sign. Thus, $x(x - 3) > 0$ if and only if $x > 0$ and $x - 3 > 0$ or $x < 0$ and $x - 3 < 0$. This implies that $x > 0$ and $x > 3$ or $x < 0$ and $x < 3$. Observe that the set of all real numbers satisfying the inequality $x > 3$ also satisfies the inequality $x > 0$, because all numbers greater than 3 are also greater than 0. Similarly, the set of all real numbers satisfying the inequality $x < 0$ also satisfies the inequality $x < 3$. Hence, the inequality $x(x - 3) > 0$ holds only for those real numbers x that satisfy either $x > 3$ or $x < 0$.

Example A.11

Solve the following inequality for x:

$$x^2 - 6x + 8 < 0$$

SOLUTION

First, we factor the left side of the inequality and obtain

$$(x - 2)(x - 4) < 0$$

The product of two numbers is negative if and only if these numbers are of opposite signs. Hence, there are two cases to consider.

Case 1. $x - 2 < 0$ and $x - 4 > 0$. Using the property (A.24), we have $x < 2$ and $x > 4$. Because there are no real numbers that satisfy these inequalities simultaneously, we conclude that case 1 has no solution.

Case 2. $x - 2 > 0$ and $x - 4 < 0$. Applying (A.24), we obtain $x > 2$ and $x < 4$, or $2 < x < 4$. Thus, the solution set consists of real numbers between 2 and 4 as illustrated in Figure A.8. Note that the end points 2 and 4 are not included in the solution set.

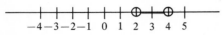

Figure A.8

EXERCISE A.2

Solve the following inequalities for x.

1. $x + 3 < 8$ 2. $x - 2 < 4$ 3. $x - 5 > -2$
4. $x + 1 > -6$ 5. $2x - 1 < 9$ 6. $3x + 2 > 4$
7. $4x - 5 \leq 7$ 8. $5x + 4 \geq -6$

Solve each of the following inequalities for x and represent the solution set graphically.

9. $\frac{1}{3}x + 2 \leq 5$ 10. $\frac{1}{2}x + 1 \geq 4$ 11. $3x - 8 < 5(2 - x)$
12. $13 - 5x < 1 + x$ 13. $3(1 - 2x) \leq 2(x + 5)$ 14. $3(5 - x) \leq 4(2 + x)$
15. $7(2 - 3x) \geq 3x + 8$ 16. $\frac{1}{3}(x - 5) \geq \frac{3}{4}(2x + 1)$

Solve each of the following inequalities for x.

17. $x(x - 1) > 0$ 18. $x(2 - x) < 0$ 19. $x(4 - x) > 0$
20. $x(2x + 1) \geq 0$ 21. $x^2 - 3x + 2 > 0$ 22. $x^2 + 3x - 4 < 0$
23. $x^2 - 5x + 6 < 0$ 24. $x^2 - 5x - 14 \geq 0$ 25. $x^2 - x - 2 \geq 0$
26. $x^2 - 2x - 8 \leq 0$

Prove each of the following statements.

27. If $a < b$ and $c > 0$, then $a/c < b/c$.
28. If $a + c < b + c$, then $a < b$.
29. If $ac < bc$ and $c < 0$, then $a > b$.
30. If a, b, c, and d are all positive numbers, and if $a < b$ and $c < d$, then $ac < bd$.

A.3 ABSOLUTE VALUE AND DISTANCE

How far is New York from Hartford on the number line in Figure A.9? The distance is obviously 75 miles. Now how far is Hartford from New York? Again, the answer is 75 miles. Thus, we are not concerned with direction in measuring distance between any two points, say A and B, and the distance from A to B is precisely the same as that from B to A. This leads us to infer that we must use a non-negative number, that is,

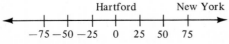

Figure A.9

a positive number or zero, to define the concept of the distance between any two points on the real line. Thus, we see the need to develop the idea of the absolute value of a number.

Definition A.3.1: For any real number a,

$$|a| = \quad a \qquad \text{if } a \geq 0$$
$$= -a \qquad \text{if } a < 0$$

From the definition, we observe that $|5| = 5$, because $5 \geq 0$, whereas $|-5| = -(-5) = 5$, because $-5 < 0$. These examples illustrate that the absolute value of a number is never negative.

We next show how the concept of absolute value is used to measure the distance between two points, say A and B, on the real line.

Definition A.3.2: If x_1 and x_2 represent two points A and B on the real number line, then the distance from A to B is $|x_1 - x_2|$.

Thus, if $x_1 = 2$ and $x_2 = 5$, then

$$|x_1 - x_2| = |2 - 5| = |-3| = 3$$

but if $x_1 = -2$ and $x_2 = 6$, then

$$|x_1 - x_2| = |-2 - 6| = |-8| = 8$$

Note that had we interchanged x_1 and x_2, our results would have been the same.

As another important consequence of absolute value, we now discuss methods of solving equations and inequalities involving absolute values.

Example A. 12
Solve for x:

$$|x - 5| = 4$$

SOLUTION
This equation expresses the fact that $x - 5$ must be equal to either 4 or -4, because in either case the absolute value is 4. If $x - 5 = 4$, then $x = 9$, and if $x - 5 = -4$, then $x = 1$. Thus, the equation $|x - 5| = 4$ is satisfied only for $x = 1$ and $x = 9$. ∎

Example A.13
Solve for x:

$$|2x - 3| = -2$$

SOLUTION
Because the absolute value of a real number is never negative, we conclude that this equation has no solution. ∎

Next, we use Definition A.3.1 to determine real numbers that satisfy $|x| < 3$. Note that if $x \geq 0$, then $|x| = x$ and $x < 3$. Thus, the numbers for which $x \geq 0$ and $x < 3$ satisfy the inequality. On the other hand, if $x < 0$, then $|x| = -x$ and $-x < 3$. Recall that the expression $-x < 3$ is equivalent to $x > -3$. (Why?) Combining these two results, we obtain

$$-3 < x < 3$$

Thus, all real numbers greater than -3 and less than 3 satisfy the inequality $|x| < 3$. This can be interpreted geometrically as shown in Figure A.10. Note that the numbers -3 and 3 are not included in the solution.

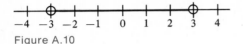

Figure A.10

The inequality $|x| \leq 3$, on the other hand, consists of all real numbers between -3 and 3, including the numbers -3 and 3, as shown in Figure A.11.

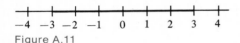

Figure A.11

Proposition A.3.1: Let a be any real number. Then the inequality $|x| \leq a$ holds if and only if $-a \leq x \leq a$. ■

Proposition A.3.2: Let a be any real number. Then the inequality $|x| \geq a$ holds if and only if $x \leq -a$ or $x \geq a$. ■

Let us now illustrate the use of these propositions in the following examples.

Example A.14

Find all real numbers x satisfying the inequality

$$|x - 4| \leq 3$$

SOLUTION

The inequality $|x - 4| \leq 3$ is satisfied if and only if

$$-3 \leq x - 4 \leq 3$$

Adding 4 to each term, we have

$$1 \leq x \leq 7$$

Thus, all real numbers between 1 and 7, inclusive, satisfy the given inequality. ■

Example A.15

Solve the following inequality for all real numbers x:

$$|4 - 5x| < 6$$

SOLUTION

This inequality is equivalent to

$$-6 < 4 - 5x < 6$$

Subtracting 4 from each term, we have

$$-10 < -5x < 2$$

Note that multiplication of each term by $(-\frac{1}{5})$ reverses the direction of each of the inequalities; that is,

$$2 > x > -\tfrac{2}{5}$$

This implies that all reals between $-\frac{2}{5}$ and 2 satisfy the inequality $\left| 4 - 5x \right| < 6$. ■

Example A.16

Solve the following inequality for all real numbers x:

$$\left| 3x - 4 \right| \geq 5$$

and represent the solution graphically.

SOLUTION

The inequality $\left| 3x - 4 \right| \geq 5$, by Proposition A.3.2, holds if and only if

$$3x - 4 \geq 5$$

or

$$3x - 4 \leq -5$$

Solving each of these for x, we have $x \geq 3$ and $x \leq -\frac{1}{3}$, respectively. This may be represented geometrically as shown in Figure A.12. All reals less than or equal to $-\frac{1}{3}$ or greater than or equal to 3 satisfy the given inequality.

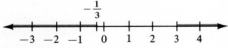

Figure A.12 ■

EXERCISE A.3

Solve for x:

1. $\left| x - 2 \right| = 3$ **2.** $\left| 2x - 3 \right| = 4$ **3.** $\left| 3x - 2 \right| = -1$

4. $\left| 3x - 2 \right| = 6$ **5.** $\left| 8 - 3x \right| = 4$ **6.** $\left| 3x - 8 \right| = 4$

Solve each of the following inequalities for x and represent the solution graphically.

7. $\left| x \right| \leq 1$ **8.** $\left| 2x \right| \leq 1$ **9.** $\left| 3x \right| > 1$

10. $\left| x - \frac{1}{2} \right| \geq 1$ **11.** $\left| x - 2 \right| \leq 3$ **12.** $\left| 2x - 3 \right| \leq 5$

13. $\left| x - 3 \right| > 2$ **14.** $\left| 3x - 6 \right| > 12$ **15.** $\left| 2x - 4 \right| > 6$

16. $|3x - 4| < 8$

17. $\left|\dfrac{x + 2}{3}\right| \le 2$

18. $\left|\dfrac{x}{2} - 3\right| < 1$

19. $\left|\dfrac{x}{3} - 2\right| \le 2$

20. $\left|\dfrac{x}{4} + 1\right| \ge 3$

B

Summation Notation

Symbols are often used to express a mathematical formula or operation. One such symbol, used frequently in the text, is the symbol for summation. It is customary to use the Greek letter $\sum$ (capital sigma) for this purpose. Following the $\sum$ is an expression representing the typical term of the summation and containing a variable, called the index of summation, that takes on successive integral values to form the different terms of the sum. The equation below the $\sum$ indicates the index of summation, and the first integral value of the index and the number above $\sum$ indicates the last value of the index.

Example B.1

$$\sum_{x=1}^{5} x = 1 + 2 + 3 + 4 + 5$$
$$= 15 \quad\blacksquare$$

Example B.2

$$\sum_{y=2}^{y=4} y^2 = 2^2 + 3^2 + 4^2$$
$$= 4 + 9 + 16$$
$$= 29 \quad\blacksquare$$

Example B.3

$$\sum_{x=2}^{x=5} (x^2 - 3) = (2^2 - 3) + (3^2 - 3) + (4^2 - 3) + (5^2 - 3)$$
$$= 1 + 6 + 13 + 22$$
$$= 42 \quad\blacksquare$$

Example B.4

$$\sum_{z=2}^{z=6} 2z = 2(2) + 2(3) + 2(4) + 2(5) + 2(6)$$

$$= 4 + 6 + 8 + 10 + 12$$
$$= 40 \qquad \blacksquare$$

Summation notation is also used frequently to represent the sum of the terms that involve subscripts. Thus, the height of n individuals in a class, for example, may be referred to as $x_1, x_2, \ldots, x_n$, where x_i represents the height of the ith individual. Obviously, the subscript i can assume any one of the values from 1 to n.

Example B.5

$$\sum_{i=1}^{i=6} x_i = x_1 + x_2 + x_3 + x_4 + x_5 + x_6 \qquad \blacksquare$$

Example B.6

$$\sum_{i=2}^{i=5} x_i^2 = x_2^2 + x_3^2 + x_4^2 + x_5^2 \qquad \blacksquare$$

Example B.7

$$\sum_{i=1}^{i=5} i \cdot x_i = x_1 + 2x_2 + 3x_3 + 4x_4 + 5x_5 \qquad \blacksquare$$

There are several useful formulas involving summation that the reader will find convenient to use.

Proposition B.1: If c is any constant, then

$$\sum_{i=1}^{n} cx_i = c \sum_{i=1}^{i=n} x_i$$

PROOF

$$\sum_{i=1}^{n} cx_i = cx_1 + cx_2 + \cdots + cx_n$$

$$= c(x_1 + x_2 + \cdots + x_n)$$

$$= c \sum_{i=1}^{i=n} x_i \qquad \blacksquare$$

Example B.8

$$\sum_{i=1}^{i=3} 4x_i = 4 \sum_{i=1}^{3} x_i$$

Let $x_1 = 3, x_2 = 5, x_3 = 7$. Then,

$$\sum_{i=1}^{3} 4x_i = 4x_1 + 4x_2 + 4x_3$$

$$= 4(3) + 4(5) + 4(7)$$
$$= 12 + 20 + 28$$
$$= 60$$

and

$$4 \sum_{i=1}^{i=3} x_i = 4(x_1 + x_2 + x_3)$$

$$= 4(3 + 5 + 7)$$
$$= 4(15)$$
$$= 60$$

Thus,

$$\sum_{i=1}^{i=3} 4x_i = 4 \sum_{i=1}^{i=3} x_i$$ ∎

Proposition B.2:

$$\sum_{i=1}^{i=n} (x_i + y_i + z_i) = \sum_{i=1}^{i=n} x_i + \sum_{i=1}^{i=n} y_i + \sum_{i=1}^{i=n} z_i$$

PROOF

$$\sum_{i=1}^{i=n} (x_i + y_i + z_i) = (x_1 + y_1 + z_1) + (x_2 + y_2 + z_2) + \cdots + (x_n + y_n + z_n)$$

Rearranging these terms, we obtain

$$\sum_{i=1}^{i=n} (x_i + y_i + z_i) = (x_1 + x_2 + \cdots + x_n) + (y_1 + y_2 + \cdots + y_n)$$

$$+ (z_1 + z_2 + \cdots + z_n)$$

$$= \sum_{i=1}^{i=n} x_i + \sum_{i=1}^{i=n} y_i + \sum_{i=1}^{i=n} z_i$$ ∎

Corollary: If c is a constant, then

$$\sum_{i=1}^{i=n} c = nc$$

Example B.9

$$\sum_{i=1}^{i=10} (x_i^2 + 15x_i + 9) = \sum_{i=1}^{i=10} x_i^2 + \sum_{i=1}^{i=10} 15x_i + \sum_{i=1}^{i=10} 9$$

$$= \sum_{i=1}^{i=10} x_i^2 + 15 \sum_{i=1}^{i=10} x_i + 9(10)$$

$$= \sum_{i=1}^{i=10} x_i^2 + 15 \sum_{i=1}^{i=10} x_i + 90$$

EXERCISE B.1

1. Express each of the following without summation sign.

a. $\sum_{i=1}^{i=3} x_i$

b. $\sum_{i=1}^{i=5} x_i y_i$

c. $\sum_{i=1}^{i=4} (x_i + y_i)$

d. $\sum_{i=1}^{i=5} c x_i$

e. $\sum_{i=2}^{i=6} (x_i + 3)$

f. $\sum_{i=1}^{i=3} (x_i + y_i + z_i)$

2. Express each of the following in summation notation.
   a. $x_1 + x_2 + x_3 + x_4 + x_5$
   b. $x_1^2 + x_2^2 + x_3^2 + x_4^2$
   c. $(x_1 + 2) + (x_2 + 2) + (x_3 + 2) + (x_4 + 2) + (x_5 + 2)$
   d. $x_2 y_2 + x_3 y_3 + x_4 y_4 + x_5 y_5 + x_6 y_6$
3. Let $x_1 = 2$, $x_2 = 4$, $x_3 = 5$, $x_4 = 1$, $x_5 = -2$. Determine the following sums.

a. $\sum_{i=1}^{i=4} x_i$

b. $\sum_{i=2}^{i=5} x_i^2$

c. $\sum_{i=1}^{i=5} (x_i + 2)^2$

d. $\sum_{i=3}^{i=5} (x_i - 3)$

e. $\sum_{i=2}^{i=4} (3x_i + 4)$

f. $\sum_{i=1}^{i=5} i \cdot x_i$

C
Tables

1. **Area Under the Normal Density Function**

2. **The Exponential Function**

3. **Common Logarithms**

4. **Compound Interest** $(1 + r)^n$

5. **Present Value of a Dollar** $(1 + r)^{-n}$

6. **Amount of an Annuity** $\left(s_{\overline{n}|r} = \dfrac{(1 + r)^n - 1}{r} \right)$

7. **Present Value of an Annuity** $\left(a_{\overline{n}|r} = \dfrac{1 - (1 + r)^{-n}}{r} \right)$

Table 1 Area Under the Normal Density Function[a]

$$\Phi(x) = \frac{1}{\sqrt{2\pi}} \int_{-\infty}^{x} e^{-y^2/2} \, dy$$

x	0.00	0.01	0.02	0.03	0.04	0.05	0.06	0.07	0.08	0.09
0.0	0.5000	0.5040	0.5080	0.5120	0.5160	0.5199	0.5239	0.5279	0.5319	0.5359
0.1	0.5398	0.5438	0.5478	0.5517	0.5557	0.5596	0.5636	0.5675	0.5714	0.5753
0.2	0.5793	0.5832	0.5871	0.5910	0.5948	0.5987	0.6026	0.6064	0.6103	0.6141
0.3	0.6179	0.6217	0.6255	0.6293	0.6331	0.6368	0.6406	0.6443	0.6480	0.6517
0.4	0.6554	0.6591	0.6628	0.6664	0.6700	0.6736	0.6772	0.6808	0.6844	0.6879
0.5	0.6915	0.6950	0.6985	0.7019	0.7054	0.7088	0.7123	0.7157	0.7190	0.7224
0.6	0.7257	0.7291	0.7324	0.7357	0.7389	0.7422	0.7454	0.7486	0.7517	0.7549
0.7	0.7580	0.7611	0.7642	0.7673	0.7704	0.7734	0.7764	0.7794	0.7823	0.7852
0.8	0.7881	0.7910	0.7939	0.7967	0.7995	0.8023	0.8051	0.8078	0.8106	0.8133
0.9	0.8159	0.8186	0.8212	0.8238	0.8264	0.8289	0.8315	0.8340	0.8365	0.8389
1.0	0.8413	0.8438	0.8461	0.8485	0.8508	0.8531	0.8554	0.8577	0.8599	0.8621
1.1	0.8643	0.8665	0.8686	0.8708	0.8729	0.8749	0.8770	0.8790	0.8810	0.8830
1.2	0.8849	0.8869	0.8888	0.8907	0.8925	0.8944	0.8962	0.8980	0.8997	0.9015
1.3	0.9032	0.9049	0.9066	0.9082	0.9099	0.9115	0.9131	0.9147	0.9162	0.9177
1.4	0.9192	0.9207	0.9222	0.9236	0.9251	0.9265	0.9279	0.9292	0.9306	0.9319
1.5	0.9332	0.9345	0.9357	0.9370	0.9382	0.9394	0.9406	0.9418	0.9429	0.9441
1.6	0.9452	0.9463	0.9474	0.9484	0.9495	0.9505	0.9515	0.9525	0.9535	0.9545
1.7	0.9554	0.9564	0.9573	0.9582	0.9591	0.9599	0.9608	0.9616	0.9625	0.9633
1.8	0.9641	0.9649	0.9656	0.9664	0.9671	0.9678	0.9686	0.9693	0.9699	0.9706
1.9	0.9713	0.9719	0.9726	0.9732	0.9738	0.9744	0.9750	0.9756	0.9761	0.9767
2.0	0.9772	0.9778	0.9783	0.9788	0.9793	0.9798	0.9803	0.9808	0.9812	0.9817
2.1	0.9821	0.9826	0.9830	0.9834	0.9838	0.9842	0.9846	0.9850	0.9854	0.9857
2.2	0.9861	0.9864	0.9868	0.9871	0.9875	0.9878	0.9881	0.9884	0.9887	0.9890
2.3	0.9893	0.9896	0.9898	0.9901	0.9904	0.9906	0.9909	0.9911	0.9913	0.9916
2.4	0.9918	0.9920	0.9922	0.9925	0.9927	0.9929	0.9931	0.9932	0.9934	0.9936
2.5	0.9938	0.9940	0.9941	0.9943	0.9945	0.9946	0.9948	0.9949	0.9951	0.9952
2.6	0.9953	0.9955	0.9956	0.9957	0.9959	0.9960	0.9961	0.9962	0.9963	0.9964
2.7	0.9965	0.9966	0.9967	0.9968	0.9969	0.9970	0.9971	0.9972	0.9973	0.9974
2.8	0.9974	0.9975	0.9976	0.9977	0.9977	0.9978	0.9979	0.9979	0.9980	0.9981
2.9	0.9981	0.9982	0.9982	0.9983	0.9984	0.9984	0.9985	0.9985	0.9986	0.9986
3.0	0.9987	0.9987	0.9987	0.9988	0.9988	0.9989	0.9989	0.9989	0.9990	0.9990
3.1	0.9990	0.9991	0.9991	0.9991	0.9992	0.9992	0.9992	0.9992	0.9993	0.9993
3.2	0.9993	0.9993	0.9994	0.9994	0.9994	0.9994	0.9994	0.9995	0.9995	0.9995
3.3	0.9995	0.9995	0.9995	0.9996	0.9996	0.9996	0.9996	0.9996	0.9996	0.9997
3.4	0.9997	0.9997	0.9997	0.9997	0.9997	0.9997	0.9997	0.9997	0.9997	0.9998
3.6	0.9998	0.9998	0.9999	0.9999	0.9999	0.9999	0.9999	0.9999	0.9999	0.9999

[a] Reproduced by permission from E. Parzen, *Modern Probability Theory and Its Applications*, Wiley, New York, 1960, p. 441.

Table 2 The Exponential Functions

x	e^x	e^{-x}	x	e^x	e^{-x}
0.0	1.0000	1.00000	5.0	148.51	0.00674
0.1	1.1052	0.90484	5.1	164.13	0.00609
0.2	1.2214	0.81873	5.2	181.39	0.00551
0.3	1.3499	0.74082	5.3	200.47	0.00498
0.4	1.4918	0.67032	5.4	221.55	0.00451
0.5	1.6487	0.60653	5.5	244.75	0.00408
0.6	1.8221	0.54881	5.6	270.40	0.00369
0.7	2.0138	0.49659	5.7	298.90	0.00334
0.8	2.2255	0.44933	5.8	330.31	0.00302
0.9	2.4596	0.40657	5.9	365.08	0.00274
1.0	2.7183	0.36788	6.0	403.45	0.00247
1.1	3.0042	0.33287	6.1	445.89	0.00224
1.2	3.3201	0.30119	6.2	492.77	0.00203
1.3	3.6693	0.27253	6.3	544.61	0.00184
1.4	4.0552	0.24660	6.4	601.86	0.00166
1.5	4.4817	0.22313	6.5	665.17	0.00150
1.6	4.9530	0.20190	6.6	735.15	0.00136
1.7	5.4739	0.18268	6.7	812.43	0.00123
1.8	6.0496	0.16530	6.8	897.89	0.00111
1.9	6.6859	0.14957	6.9	992.38	0.00100
2.0	7.3891	0.13534	7.0	1,096.69	0.00091
2.1	8.1662	0.12246	7.1	1,212.07	0.00082
2.2	9.0250	0.11080	7.2	1,339.57	0.00074
2.3	9.9742	0.10026	7.3	1,480.49	0.00068
2.4	11.023	0.09072	7.4	1,636.25	0.00061
2.5	12.182	0.08208	7.5	1,808.0	0.00055
2.6	13.464	0.07427	7.6	1,998.2	0.00050
2.7	14.880	0.06721	7.7	2,208.3	0.00045
2.8	16.445	0.06081	7.8	2,440.6	0.00041
2.9	18.174	0.05502	7.9	2,697.3	0.00037
3.0	20.086	0.04979	8.0	2,981.0	0.00034
3.1	22.198	0.04505	8.1	3,294.5	0.00030
3.2	24.533	0.04076	8.2	3,641.0	0.00027
3.3	27.113	0.03688	8.3	4,023.9	0.00025
3.4	29.964	0.03337	8.4	4,447.1	0.00022
3.5	33.115	0.03020	8.5	4,914.8	0.00020
3.6	36.598	0.02732	8.6	5,431.7	0.00018
3.7	40.447	0.02472	8.7	6,002.9	0.00017
3.8	44.701	0.02237	8.8	6,634.2	0.00015
3.9	49.402	0.02024	8.9	7,332.0	0.00014
4.0	54.598	0.01832	9.0	8,103.1	0.00012
4.1	60.340	0.01657	9.1	8,955.3	0.00011
4.2	66.686	0.01500	9.2	9,897.1	0.00010
4.3	73.700	0.01357	9.3	10,938	0.00009
4.4	81.451	0.01228	9.4	12,088	0.00008
4.5	90.017	0.01111	9.5	13,360	0.00007
4.6	99.484	0.01005	9.6	14,765	0.00007
4.7	109.95	0.00910	9.7	16,318	0.00006
4.8	121.51	0.00823	9.8	18,034	0.00006
4.9	134.29	0.00745	9.9	19,930	0.00005

Table 3 Common Logarithms

N	0	1	2	3	4	5	6	7	8	9
1.0	0.0000	0.0043	0.0086	0.0128	0.0170	0.0212	0.0253	0.0294	0.0334	0.0374
1.1	0.0414	0.0453	0.0492	0.0531	0.0569	0.0607	0.0645	0.0682	0.0719	0.0755
1.2	0.0792	0.0828	0.0864	0.0899	0.0934	0.0969	0.1004	0.1038	0.1072	0.1106
1.3	0.1139	0.1173	0.1206	0.1239	0.1271	0.1303	0.1335	0.1367	0.1399	0.1430
1.4	0.1461	0.1492	0.1523	0.1553	0.1584	0.1614	0.1644	0.1673	0.1703	0.1732
1.5	0.1761	0.1790	0.1818	0.1847	0.1875	0.1903	0.1931	0.1959	0.1987	0.2014
1.6	0.2041	0.2068	0.2095	0.2122	0.2148	0.2175	0.2201	0.2227	0.2253	0.2279
1.7	0.2304	0.2330	0.2355	0.2380	0.2405	0.2430	0.2455	0.2480	0.2504	0.2529
1.8	0.2553	0.2577	0.2601	0.2625	0.2648	0.2672	0.2695	0.2718	0.2742	0.2765
1.9	0.2788	0.2810	0.2833	0.2856	0.2878	0.2900	0.2923	0.2945	0.2967	0.2989
2.0	0.3010	0.3032	0.3054	0.3075	0.3096	0.3118	0.3139	0.3160	0.3181	0.3201
2.1	0.3222	0.3243	0.3263	0.3284	0.3304	0.3324	0.3345	0.3365	0.3385	0.3404
2.2	0.3424	0.3444	0.3464	0.3483	0.3502	0.3522	0.3541	0.3560	0.3579	0.3598
2.3	0.3617	0.3636	0.3655	0.3674	0.3692	0.3711	0.3729	0.3747	0.3766	0.3784
2.4	0.3802	0.3820	0.3838	0.3856	0.3874	0.3892	0.3909	0.3927	0.3945	0.3962
2.5	0.3979	0.3997	0.4014	0.4031	0.4048	0.4065	0.4082	0.4099	0.4116	0.4133
2.6	0.4150	0.4166	0.4183	0.4200	0.4216	0.4232	0.4249	0.4265	0.4281	0.4298
2.7	0.4314	0.4330	0.4346	0.4362	0.4378	0.4393	0.4409	0.4425	0.4440	0.4456
2.8	0.4472	0.4487	0.4502	0.4518	0.4533	0.4548	0.4564	0.4579	0.4594	0.4609
2.9	0.4624	0.4639	0.4654	0.4669	0.4683	0.4698	0.4713	0.4728	0.4742	0.4757
3.0	0.4771	0.4786	0.4800	0.4814	0.4829	0.4843	0.4857	0.4871	0.4886	0.4900
3.1	0.4914	0.4928	0.4942	0.4955	0.4969	0.4983	0.4997	0.5011	0.5024	0.5038
3.2	0.5051	0.5065	0.5079	0.5092	0.5105	0.5119	0.5132	0.5145	0.5159	0.5172
3.3	0.5185	0.5198	0.5211	0.5224	0.5237	0.5250	0.5263	0.5276	0.5289	0.5302
3.4	0.5315	0.5328	0.5340	0.5353	0.5366	0.5378	0.5391	0.5403	0.5416	0.5428
3.5	0.5441	0.5453	0.5465	0.5478	0.5490	0.5502	0.5514	0.5527	0.5539	0.5551
3.6	0.5563	0.5575	0.5587	0.5599	0.5611	0.5623	0.5635	0.5647	0.5658	0.5670
3.7	0.5682	0.5694	0.5705	0.5717	0.5729	0.5740	0.5752	0.5763	0.5775	0.5786
3.8	0.5798	0.5809	0.5821	0.5832	0.5843	0.5855	0.5866	0.5877	0.5888	0.5899
3.9	0.5911	0.5922	0.5933	0.5944	0.5955	0.5966	0.5977	0.5988	0.5999	0.6010
4.0	0.6021	0.6031	0.6042	0.6053	0.6064	0.6075	0.6085	0.6096	0.6107	0.6117
4.1	0.6128	0.6138	0.6149	0.6160	0.6170	0.6180	0.6191	0.6201	0.6212	0.6222
4.2	0.6232	0.6243	0.6253	0.6263	0.6274	0.6284	0.6294	0.6304	0.6314	0.6325
4.3	0.6335	0.6345	0.6355	0.6365	0.6375	0.6385	0.6395	0.6405	0.6415	0.6425
4.4	0.6435	0.6444	0.6454	0.6464	0.6474	0.6484	0.6493	0.6503	0.6513	0.6522
4.5	0.6532	0.6542	0.6551	0.6561	0.6571	0.6580	0.6590	0.6599	0.6609	0.6618
4.6	0.6628	0.6637	0.6646	0.6656	0.6665	0.6675	0.6684	0.6693	0.6702	0.6712
4.7	0.6721	0.6730	0.6739	0.6749	0.6758	0.6767	0.6776	0.6785	0.6794	0.6803
4.8	0.6812	0.6821	0.6830	0.6839	0.6848	0.6857	0.6866	0.6875	0.6884	0.6893
4.9	0.6902	0.6911	0.6920	0.6928	0.6937	0.6946	0.6955	0.6964	0.6972	0.6981
5.0	0.6990	0.6998	0.7007	0.7016	0.7024	0.7033	0.7042	0.7050	0.7059	0.7067
5.1	0.7076	0.7084	0.7093	0.7101	0.7110	0.7118	0.7126	0.7135	0.7143	0.7152
5.2	0.7160	0.7168	0.7177	0.7185	0.7193	0.7202	0.7210	0.7218	0.7226	0.7235
5.3	0.7243	0.7251	0.7259	0.7267	0.7275	0.7284	0.7292	0.7300	0.7308	0.7316
5.4	0.7324	0.7332	0.7340	0.7348	0.7356	0.7364	0.7372	0.7380	0.7388	0.7396

Table 3 Common Logarithms (*Continued*)

N	0	1	2	3	4	5	6	7	8	9
5.5	0.7404	0.7412	0.7419	0.7427	0.7435	0.7443	0.7451	0.7459	0.7466	0.7474
5.6	0.7482	0.7490	0.7497	0.7505	0.7513	0.7520	0.7528	0.7536	0.7543	0.7551
5.7	0.7559	0.7566	0.7574	0.7582	0.7589	0.7597	0.7604	0.7612	0.7619	0.7627
5.8	0.7634	0.7642	0.7649	0.7657	0.7664	0.7672	0.7679	0.7686	0.7694	0.7701
5.9	0.7709	0.7716	0.7723	0.7731	0.7738	0.7745	0.7752	0.7760	0.7767	0.7774
6.0	0.7782	0.7789	0.7796	0.7803	0.7810	0.7818	0.7825	0.7832	0.7839	0.7846
6.1	0.7853	0.7860	0.7868	0.7875	0.7882	0.7889	0.7896	0.7903	0.7910	0.7917
6.2	0.7924	0.7931	0.7938	0.7945	0.7952	0.7959	0.7966	0.7973	0.7980	0.7987
6.3	0.7993	0.8000	0.8007	0.8014	0.8021	0.8028	0.8035	0.8041	0.8048	0.8055
6.4	0.8062	0.8069	0.8075	0.8082	0.8089	0.8096	0.8102	0.8109	0.8116	0.8122
6.5	0.8129	0.8136	0.8142	0.8149	0.8156	0.8162	0.8169	0.8176	0.8182	0.8189
6.6	0.8195	0.8202	0.8209	0.8215	0.8222	0.8228	0.8235	0.8241	0.8248	0.8254
6.7	0.8261	0.8267	0.8274	0.8280	0.8287	0.8293	0.8299	0.8306	0.8312	0.8319
6.8	0.8325	0.8331	0.8338	0.8344	0.8351	0.8357	0.8363	0.8370	0.8376	0.8382
6.9	0.8388	0.8395	0.8401	0.8407	0.8414	0.8420	0.8426	0.8432	0.8439	0.8445
7.0	0.8451	0.8457	0.8463	0.8470	0.8476	0.8482	0.8488	0.8494	0.8500	0.8506
7.1	0.8513	0.8519	0.8525	0.8531	0.8537	0.8543	0.8549	0.8555	0.8561	0.8567
7.2	0.8573	0.8579	0.8585	0.8591	0.8597	0.8603	0.8609	0.8615	0.8621	0.8627
7.3	0.8633	0.8639	0.8645	0.8651	0.8657	0.8663	0.8669	0.8675	0.8681	0.8686
7.4	0.8692	0.8698	0.8704	0.8710	0.8716	0.8722	0.8727	0.8733	0.8739	0.8745
7.5	0.8751	0.8756	0.8762	0.8768	0.8774	0.8779	0.8785	0.8791	0.8797	0.8802
7.6	0.8808	0.8814	0.8820	0.8825	0.8831	0.8837	0.8842	0.8848	0.8854	0.8859
7.7	0.8865	0.8871	0.8876	0.8882	0.8887	0.8893	0.8899	0.8904	0.8910	0.8915
7.8	0.8921	0.8927	0.8932	0.8938	0.8943	0.8949	0.8954	0.8960	0.8965	0.8971
7.9	0.8976	0.8982	0.8987	0.8993	0.8998	0.9004	0.9009	0.9015	0.9020	0.9025
8.0	0.9031	0.9036	0.9042	0.9047	0.9053	0.9058	0.9063	0.9069	0.9074	0.9079
8.1	0.9085	0.9090	0.9096	0.9101	0.9106	0.9112	0.9117	0.9122	0.9128	0.9133
8.2	0.9138	0.9143	0.9149	0.9154	0.9159	0.9165	0.9170	0.9175	0.9180	0.9186
8.3	0.9191	0.9196	0.9201	0.9206	0.9212	0.9217	0.9222	0.9227	0.9232	0.9238
8.4	0.9243	0.9248	0.9253	0.9258	0.9263	0.9269	0.9274	0.9279	0.9284	0.9289
8.5	0.9294	0.9299	0.9304	0.9309	0.9315	0.9320	0.9325	0.9330	0.9335	0.9340
8.6	0.9345	0.9350	0.9355	0.9360	0.9365	0.9370	0.9375	0.9380	0.9385	0.9390
8.7	0.9395	0.9400	0.9405	0.9410	0.9415	0.9420	0.9425	0.9430	0.9435	0.9440
8.8	0.9445	0.9450	0.9455	0.9460	0.9465	0.9469	0.9474	0.9479	0.9484	0.9489
8.9	0.9494	0.9499	0.9504	0.9509	0.9513	0.9518	0.9523	0.9528	0.9533	0.9538
9.0	0.9542	0.9547	0.9552	0.9557	0.9562	0.9566	0.9571	0.9576	0.9581	0.9586
9.1	0.9590	0.9595	0.9600	0.9605	0.9609	0.9614	0.9619	0.9624	0.9628	0.9633
9.2	0.9638	0.9643	0.9647	0.9652	0.9657	0.9661	0.9666	0.9671	0.9675	0.9680
9.3	0.9685	0.9689	0.9694	0.9699	0.9703	0.9708	0.9713	0.9717	0.9722	0.9727
9.4	0.9731	0.9736	0.9741	0.9745	0.9750	0.9754	0.9759	0.9763	0.9768	0.9773
9.5	0.9777	0.9782	0.9786	0.9791	0.9795	0.9800	0.9805	0.9809	0.9814	0.9818
9.6	0.9823	0.9827	0.9832	0.9836	0.9841	0.9845	0.9850	0.9854	0.9859	0.9863
9.7	0.9868	0.9872	0.9877	0.9881	0.9886	0.9890	0.9894	0.9899	0.9903	0.9908
9.8	0.9912	0.9917	0.9921	0.9926	0.9930	0.9934	0.9939	0.9943	0.9948	0.9952
9.9	0.9956	0.9961	0.9965	0.9969	0.9974	0.9978	0.9983	0.9987	0.9991	0.9996

Table 4 Compound Interest[a]

$$(1 + r)^n$$

r = rate of interest per payment period; n = number of payment periods

n	$\frac{1}{4}\%$	$\frac{1}{2}\%$	$\frac{3}{4}\%$	1%	$1\frac{1}{4}\%$
1	1.002500	1.005000	1.007500	1.010000	1.012500
2	1.005006	1.010025	1.015056	1.020100	1.025156
3	1.007519	1.015075	1.022669	1.030301	1.037971
4	1.010038	1.020151	1.030339	1.040604	1.050945
5	1.012563	1.025251	1.038067	1.051010	1.064082
6	1.015094	1.030378	1.045852	1.061520	1.077383
7	1.017632	1.035529	1.053696	1.072135	1.090850
8	1.020176	1.040707	1.061599	1.082857	1.104486
9	1.022726	1.045911	1.069561	1.093685	1.118292
10	1.025283	1.051140	1.077583	1.104622	1.132271
11	1.027846	1.056396	1.085664	1.115668	1.146424
12	1.030416	1.061678	1.093807	1.126825	1.160755
13	1.032922	1.066986	1.102010	1.138093	1.175264
14	1.035574	1.072321	1.110276	1.149474	1.189955
15	1.038163	1.077683	1.118603	1.160969	1.204829
16	1.040759	1.083071	1.126992	1.172579	1.219890
17	1.043361	1.088487	1.135445	1.184304	1.235138
18	1.045969	1.093929	1.143960	1.196147	1.250577
19	1.048584	1.099399	1.152540	1.208109	1.266210
20	1.051205	1.104896	1.161134	1.220190	1.282037
21	1.053833	1.110420	1.169893	1.232392	1.298063
22	1.056468	1.115972	1.178667	1.244716	1.314288
23	1.059109	1.121552	1.187507	1.257163	1.330717
24	1.061757	1.127160	1.196414	1.269735	1.347351
25	1.064411	1.132796	1.205387	1.282432	1.364193
26	1.067072	1.138460	1.214427	1.295256	1.381245
27	1.069740	1.144152	1.223535	1.308209	1.398511
28	1.072414	1.149873	1.232712	1.321291	1.415992
29	1.075096	1.155622	1.241957	1.334504	1.433692
30	1.077783	1.161400	1.251272	1.347849	1.451613
31	1.080478	1.167207	1.260656	1.361327	1.469758
32	1.088179	1.173043	1.270111	1.374941	1.488130
33	1.085887	1.178908	1.279637	1.388690	1.506732
34	1.088602	1.184803	1.289234	1.402577	1.525566
35	1.091323	1.190727	1.298904	1.416603	1.544636
36	1.094051	1.196681	1.308645	1.430769	1.563944
37	1.096786	1.202664	1.318460	1.445076	1.583493
38	1.099528	1.208677	1.328349	1.459527	1.603287
39	1.102277	1.214721	1.338311	1.474122	1.623328
40	1.105033	1.220794	1.348349	1.488864	1.643619
41	1.107796	1.226898	1.358461	1.503752	1.664165
42	1.110565	1.233033	1.368650	1.518790	1.684967
43	1.113341	1.239198	1.378915	1.533978	1.706029
44	1.116125	1.245394	1.389256	1.549318	1.727354
45	1.118915	1.251621	1.399676	1.564811	1.748946
46	1.121712	1.257879	1.410173	1.580459	1.770808
47	1.124517	1.264168	1.420750	1.596263	1.792943
48	1.127328	1.270489	1.431405	1.612226	1.815355
49	1.130146	1.270842	1.442141	1.628348	1.818047
50	1.132972	1.283226	1.452957	1.644632	1.861022

[a] Reproduced by permission from A. Mizrahi and M. Sullivan, *Finite Mathematics with Applications*, Wiley, New York, 1973.

n	$\frac{1}{4}\%$	$\frac{1}{2}\%$	$\frac{3}{4}\%$	1%	$1\frac{1}{4}\%$
51	1.135804	1.289642	1.463854	1.661078	1.884285
52	1.138644	1.296090	1.474833	1.677688	1.907839
53	1.141490	1.302571	1.485894	1.694466	1.931687
54	1.144344	1.309083	1.497038	1.711410	1.955833
55	1.147205	1.315629	1.508266	1.728525	1.980281
56	1.150073	1.322207	1.519578	1.745810	2.005034
57	1.152948	1.328818	1.530975	1.763268	2.030097
58	1.155830	1.335462	1.542457	1.780901	2.059473
59	1.158720	1.342139	1.554026	1.798770	2.081167
60	1.161617	1.348850	1.565681	1.816697	2.107181
61	1.164521	1.355594	1.577424	1.834864	2.133521
62	1.167432	1.362372	1.589254	1.853212	2.160190
63	1.170351	1.365184	1.601174	1.871744	2.187192
64	1.173277	1.376030	1.613182	1.890462	2.214532
65	1.176210	1.382910	1.625281	1.905366	2.242214
66	1.179150	1.389825	1.637471	1.928460	2.270242
67	1.182098	1.396774	1.649752	1.947745	2.298620
68	1.185053	1.403758	1.662125	1.967222	2.327352
69	1.188016	1.410777	1.674591	1.986894	2.356444
70	1.190986	1.417831	1.687151	2.006763	2.385900
71	1.193963	1.424920	1.699804	2.026831	2.415724
72	1.196948	1.432044	1.712553	2.047099	2.445920
73	1.199941	1.439205	1.725397	2.067570	2.476494
74	1.202941	1.446401	1.738337	2.088246	2.507450
75	1.205948	1.453633	1.751375	2.109128	2.538793
76	1.208963	1.460901	1.764510	2.130220	2.570528
77	1.211985	1.468205	1.777744	2.151522	2.602660
78	1.215015	1.475546	1.791077	2.173037	2.635193
79	1.218053	1.482924	1.804510	2.194767	2.668133
80	1.221098	1.490339	1.818044	2.216715	2.701485
81	1.224151	1.497790	1.831679	2.238882	2.735253
82	1.227211	1.505279	1.845417	2.261271	2.769444
83	1.230279	1.512806	1.859257	2.283884	2.804062
84	1.233355	1.520370	1.873202	2.306723	2.839113
85	1.236438	1.527972	1.887251	2.329790	2.874602
86	1.239529	1.535611	1.901405	2.353088	2.910534
87	1.242628	1.543289	1.915666	2.376619	2.946916
88	1.245735	1.551006	1.930033	2.400385	2.983752
89	1.248849	1.558761	1.944509	2.424389	3.021049
90	1.251971	1.566555	1.959092	2.448633	3.058812
91	1.255101	1.574387	1.973786	2.473119	3.097048
92	1.258239	1.582259	1.988589	2.497850	3.135761
93	1.261384	1.590171	2.003503	2.522829	3.174958
94	1.264538	1.598122	2.018530	2.548057	3.214645
95	1.267699	1.606112	2.033669	2.573537	3.254828
96	1.270868	1.614143	2.048921	2.599273	3.295513
97	1.274046	1.622213	2.064288	2.625266	3.336707
98	1.277231	1.630325	2.079770	2.651518	3.378416
99	1.280424	1.638476	2.095368	2.678033	3.420646
100	1.283625	1.646669	2.111084	2.704814	3.463404

Table 4 Compound Interest $(1 + r)^n$ (*Continued*)

n	$1\frac{1}{2}\%$	$1\frac{3}{4}\%$	2%	$2\frac{1}{2}\%$	3%
1	1.015000	1.017500	1.020000	1.025000	1.030000
2	1.030225	1.035306	1.040400	1.050625	1.060900
3	1.045678	1.053424	1.061208	1.076891	1.092727
4	1.061364	1.071859	1.082432	1.103813	1.125509
5	1.077284	1.090617	1.104081	1.131408	1.159274
6	1.093443	1.109702	1.126162	1.159693	1.194052
7	1.109845	1.129122	1.148686	1.188686	1.229874
8	1.126493	1.148882	1.171659	1.218403	1.266770
9	1.143390	1.168987	1.195093	1.248863	1.304773
10	1.160541	1.189444	1.218994	1.280085	1.343916
11	1.177949	1.210260	1.243374	1.312087	1.384234
12	1.195618	1.231439	1.268242	1.344889	1.425761
13	1.213552	1.252989	1.293607	1.378511	1.468534
14	1.231756	1.274917	1.319479	1.412974	1.512590
15	1.250232	1.297228	1.345868	1.448298	1.557967
16	1.268986	1.319929	1.372786	1.484506	1.604706
17	1.288020	1.343028	1.400241	1.521618	1.652848
18	1.307341	1.366531	1.428246	1.559659	1.702433
19	1.326951	1.390445	1.456811	1.598650	1.753506
20	1.346855	1.414778	1.485947	1.638616	1.806111
21	1.367058	1.439537	1.515666	1.679582	1.860295
22	1.387564	1.464729	1.545980	1.721571	1.916103
23	1.408377	1.490361	1.576899	1.764611	1.973586
24	1.429503	1.516443	1.608437	1.808726	2.032794
25	1.450945	1.542981	1.640606	1.853944	2.093778
26	1.472710	1.569983	1.673418	1.900293	2.156591
27	1.494800	1.597457	1.706886	1.947800	2.221289
28	1.517222	1.625413	1.741024	1.996495	2.287928
29	1.539981	1.653858	1.775845	2.046407	2.356565
30	1.563080	1.682800	1.811362	2.097568	2.427262
31	1.586526	1.712249	1.847589	2.150007	2.500080
32	1.610324	1.742213	1.884541	2.203757	2.575083
33	1.634479	1.772702	1.922231	2.258851	2.652335
34	1.658996	1.803724	1.960676	2.315322	2.731905
35	1.683881	1.835290	1.999889	2.373205	2.813862
36	1.709140	1.867407	2.039887	2.432535	2.898278
37	1.734777	1.900087	2.080685	2.493349	2.985227
38	1.760798	1.933338	2.122299	2.555682	2.074783
39	1.787210	1.967172	2.164745	2.619574	3.167027
40	1.814018	2.001597	2.208040	2.685064	3.262038
41	1.841229	2.036625	2.252200	2.752190	3.359899
42	1.868847	2.072266	2.297244	2.820995	3.460696
43	1.896880	2.108531	2.343189	2.891520	3.564517
44	1.925333	2.145430	2.390053	2.963808	3.671452
45	1.954213	2.182975	2.437854	3.037902	3.781596
46	1.983526	2.221177	2.486611	3.113851	3.895044
47	2.013279	2.260048	2.536343	3.191697	4.011895
48	2.043478	2.299599	2.587070	3.271489	4.132252
49	2.074130	2.329842	2.638812	3.353277	4.256219
50	2.105242	2.380789	2.691588	3.437109	4.381906

n	$1\frac{1}{2}\%$	$1\frac{3}{4}\%$	2%	$2\frac{1}{2}\%$	3%
51	2.136821	2.422453	2.745420	3.523036	4.515423
52	2.168873	2.464846	2.800328	3.611112	4.650886
53	2.201406	2.507980	2.856335	3.701390	4.790412
54	2.234428	2.551870	2.913461	3.793925	4.934125
55	2.267944	2.596528	2.971731	3.888773	5.082148
56	2.301963	2.641967	3.031165	3.985992	5.234613
57	2.336493	2.688201	3.091788	4.085642	5.391651
58	2.371540	2.735245	3.153624	4.187783	5.553401
59	2.407113	2.783112	3.216697	4.292478	5.720003
60	2.443220	2.831816	3.281031	4.399790	5.891603
61	2.479868	2.881373	3.346651	4.509784	6.068351
62	2.517066	2.931797	3.413584	4.622529	6.250402
63	2.554822	2.983103	3.481856	4.738092	6.437914
64	2.593144	3.035308	3.551493	4.856544	6.631051
65	2.632042	3.088426	3.622523	4.977958	6.829982
66	2.671522	3.142473	3.694973	5.102407	7.034882
67	2.711595	3.197466	3.768873	5.229967	7.245928
68	2.752269	3.253422	3.844250	5.360716	7.463306
69	2.793553	3.310357	3.921135	5.494734	7.687205
70	2.835456	3.368288	3.999558	5.632103	7.917822
71	2.877988	3.427233	4.079549	5.772905	8.155356
72	2.921158	3.487210	4.161140	5.917228	8.400017
73	2.964975	3.548236	4.244363	6.065158	8.652017
74	3.009450	3.610330	4.329250	6.216787	8.911578
75	3.054592	3.673511	4.415835	6.372207	9.178925
76	3.100411	3.737797	4.504152	6.531512	9.454293
77	3.146917	3.803209	4.594235	6.694800	9.737922
78	3.194120	3.869765	4.686120	6.862170	10.030060
79	3.242032	3.937486	4.779842	7.033724	10.330961
80	3.290663	4.006392	4.875439	7.209567	10.640890
81	3.340023	4.076504	4.972948	7.389806	10.960117
82	3.390123	4.147842	5.072407	7.574552	11.288920
83	3.440975	4.220430	5.173855	7.763915	11.627588
84	3.492590	4.294287	5.277332	7.958013	11.976416
85	3.544978	4.369437	5.382878	8.156964	12.335708
86	3.598153	4.445902	5.490536	8.360888	12.705779
87	3.652125	4.523706	5.600347	8.569910	13.086953
88	3.706907	4.602870	5.712354	8.784158	13.479561
89	3.762511	4.683421	5.826601	9.003762	13.883948
90	3.818948	4.765380	5.943133	9.228856	14.300466
91	3.876233	4.848775	6.061995	9.459577	14.729480
92	3.934376	4.933628	6.183235	9.696066	15.171365
93	3.993392	5.019967	6.306900	9.938468	15.626506
94	4.053293	5.107816	6.433038	10.186930	16.095301
95	4.114092	5.197203	6.561699	10.441603	16.578160
96	4.175804	5.288154	6.692933	10.702643	17.075505
97	4.238441	5.380697	6.826791	10.970209	17.587770
98	4.302017	5.474859	6.963327	11.244464	18.115403
99	4.366547	5.570669	7.102594	11.525576	18.658865
100	4.432046	5.668156	7.244645	11.813715	19.218631

Table 4 Compound Interest $(1 + r)^n$ (*Continued*)

n	$3\frac{1}{2}\%$	4%	$4\frac{1}{2}\%$	5%	$5\frac{1}{2}\%$
1	1.035000	1.040000	1.045000	1.050000	1.055000
2	1.071225	1.081600	1.092025	1.102500	1.113025
3	1.108718	1.124864	1.141166	1.157625	1.174241
4	1.147523	1.169859	1.192519	1.215506	1.238825
5	1.187686	1.216653	1.246182	1.276282	1.306960
6	1.229225	1.265319	1.302260	1.340096	1.378843
7	1.272279	1.315932	1.360862	1.407100	1.454679
8	1.316809	1.368569	1.422101	1.477455	1.534687
9	1.362897	1.423321	1.486095	1.551328	1.619094
10	1.410599	1.480244	1.552969	1.628895	1.708144
11	1.459970	1.539454	1.622853	1.710339	1.802092
12	1.511069	1.601032	1.695881	1.795856	1.901207
13	1.563956	1.665073	1.772196	1.885649	2.005774
14	1.618695	1.731676	1.851945	1.979932	2.116091
15	1.675349	1.800943	1.935282	2.078928	2.232476
16	1.733986	1.872981	2.022370	2.182875	2.355263
17	1.794676	1.947900	2.113377	2.292018	2.484802
18	1.857489	2.025816	2.208479	2.406619	2.621466
19	1.922501	2.106849	2.307860	2.526950	2.765647
20	1.989789	2.191123	2.411714	2.653298	2.917757
21	2.059431	2.278768	2.520241	2.785963	3.078234
22	2.131512	2.369919	2.633652	2.925261	3.247537
23	2.206114	2.464715	2.752166	3.071524	3.426152
24	2.283328	2.563304	2.876014	3.225100	3.614590
25	2.363245	2.665836	3.005434	3.386355	3.813392
26	2.445959	2.772470	3.140679	3.555673	4.023125
27	2.531567	2.883368	3.282010	3.733456	4.244401
28	2.620172	2.998703	3.429700	3.920129	4.477843
29	2.711878	3.118651	3.584037	4.116136	4.724124
30	2.806794	3.243397	3.745318	4.321942	4.983951
31	2.905031	3.373133	3.913857	4.538039	5.258068
32	3.006708	3.508059	4.089981	4.764941	5.547262
33	3.111942	3.648381	4.274030	5.003188	5.852362
34	3.220860	3.794316	4.466362	5.253348	6.174242
35	2.333590	3.946089	4.667348	5.516015	6.513825
36	3.450266	4.103932	4.877376	5.791816	6.872085
37	3.571025	4.268090	5.096861	6.081407	7.250050
38	3.696011	4.438813	5.326219	6.385477	7.648803
39	3.825372	4.616366	5.565899	6.704751	8.069487
40	3.959260	4.801020	5.816365	7.039989	8.513309
41	4.097834	4.993061	6.078101	7.391988	8.981541
42	4.241258	5.192784	6.351616	7.761587	9.475525
43	4.389702	5.400495	6.637438	8.149667	9.996679
44	4.543341	5.616515	6.936123	8.557150	10.546496
45	4.702358	5.841175	7.248248	8.985008	11.126554
46	4.866941	6.074822	7.574420	9.434258	11.738514
47	5.037284	6.317815	7.915269	9.905971	12.384132
48	5.213589	6.570528	8.271456	10.401269	13.065260
49	5.396064	6.833349	8.643671	10.921333	13.783849
50	5.584927	7.106683	9.032636	11.467400	14.541961

n	$3\frac{1}{2}\%$	4%	$4\frac{1}{2}\%$	5%	$5\frac{1}{2}\%$
51	5.780399	7.390950	9.439105	12.040770	15.341768
52	5.982713	7.686588	9.863865	12.642808	16.185566
53	6.192108	7.994052	10.307739	13.274948	17.075772
54	6.408832	8.313814	10.771587	13.938696	18.014939
55	6.633141	8.646366	11.256308	14.635631	19.005761
56	6.865301	8.992221	11.762842	15.367412	20.051079
57	7.105586	9.351910	12.292170	16.135783	21.153887
58	7.354282	9.725986	12.845318	16.942572	22.317351
59	7.611682	10.115026	13.423357	17.789700	23.544805
60	7.878091	10.519627	14.027408	18.679185	24.839769
61	8.153824	10.940412	14.658641	19.613145	26.205957
62	8.439207	11.378028	15.318280	20.593802	27.647284
63	8.734580	11.833149	16.007603	21.623492	29.167885
64	9.040290	12.306475	16.727945	22.704667	30.772118
65	9.356700	12.798734	17.480703	23.839900	32.464585
66	9.684185	13.310684	18.267334	25.031895	34.250137
67	10.023131	13.843111	19.089364	26.283490	36.133895
68	10.373941	14.396835	19.948386	27.597664	38.121259
69	10.737029	14.972709	20.846063	28.977547	40.217928
70	11.112825	15.571617	21.784136	30.426425	42.429914
71	11.501773	16.194482	22.764422	31.947746	44.763559
72	11.904336	16.842261	23.788821	33.545133	47.225555
73	12.320987	17.515951	24.859318	35.222390	49.822961
74	12.752222	18.216589	25.977987	36.983509	52.563223
75	13.198550	18.945253	27.146997	38.832685	55.454201
76	13.660499	19.703063	28.368611	40.774319	58.504182
77	14.138616	20.491186	29.645199	42.813035	61.721911
78	14.633468	21.310833	30.979233	44.953687	65.116617
79	15.145639	22.163266	32.373298	47.201371	68.698030
80	15.675736	23.049797	33.830097	49.561440	72.476422
81	16.224387	23.971789	35.352451	52.039512	76.462625
82	16.792241	24.930660	36.943312	54.641487	80.668069
83	17.379969	25.927887	38.605761	57.373561	85.104813
84	17.988268	26.965002	40.343020	60.242239	89.785578
85	18.617857	28.043602	42.158456	63.254351	94.723785
86	19.269482	29.165346	44.055586	66.417069	99.933593
87	19.943914	30.331960	46.038086	69.737922	105.429940
88	20.641951	31.545238	48.109802	73.224818	111.228587
89	21.364420	32.807048	50.274743	76.886059	117.346159
90	22.112174	34.119330	52.537106	80.730362	123.800198
91	22.886100	35.484103	54.901276	84.766880	130.609209
92	23.687114	36.903467	57.371833	89.005224	137.792715
93	24.516163	38.379606	59.953566	92.455486	145.371314
94	25.374229	39.914790	62.651470	98.128260	153.366736
95	26.262327	41.511381	65.470793	103.034673	161.801907
96	27.181508	43.171836	68.416978	108.186406	170.701011
97	28.132861	44.898710	71.495742	113.595727	180.089567
98	29.117511	46.694658	74.713051	119.275513	189.994493
99	30.136624	48.562444	78.075138	125.239289	200.444190
100	31.191405	50.504942	81.588519	131.501253	211.468620

Table 4 Compound Interest $(1 + r)^n$ (*Continued*)

n	6%	$6\frac{1}{2}\%$	7%	$7\frac{1}{2}\%$	8%
1	1.060000	1.065000	1.070000	1.075000	1.080000
2	1.123600	1.134225	1.144900	1.155625	1.166400
3	1.191016	1.207950	1.225043	1.242297	1.259712
4	1.262477	1.286466	1.310796	1.335469	1.360489
5	1.338226	1.370087	1.402552	1.435629	1.469328
6	1.418519	1.459142	1.500730	1.543302	1.586874
7	1.503630	1.553987	1.605781	1.659045	1.713824
8	1.593848	1.654996	1.718186	1.783478	1.850930
9	1.689479	1.762570	1.838459	1.917239	1.999005
10	1.790848	1.877137	1.967151	2.061032	2.158925
11	1.898299	1.999151	2.104852	2.215609	2.331639
12	2.012196	2.129096	2.252192	2.381780	2.518170
13	2.132928	2.267487	2.409845	2.560413	2.719624
14	2.260904	2.414874	2.578534	2.752444	2.937194
15	2.396558	2.571841	2.759032	2.958877	3.172169
16	2.540352	2.739011	2.952164	3.180793	3.425943
17	2.692773	2.917046	3.158815	3.419353	3.700018
18	2.854339	3.106654	3.379932	3.675804	3.996019
19	3.025599	3.308587	3.616527	3.951489	4.315701
20	3.207135	3.523645	3.869684	4.247851	4.660957
21	3.399564	3.752682	4.140562	4.566440	5.033834
22	3.603537	3.996606	4.430402	4.908923	5.436540
23	3.819750	4.256386	4.740530	5.277092	5.871464
24	4.048935	4.533051	5.072367	5.672874	6.341181
25	4.291871	4.827699	5.427433	6.098340	6.848475
26	4.549383	5.141500	5.807353	6.555715	7.396353
27	4.822346	5.475697	6.213867	7.047394	7.988061
28	5.111687	5.831617	6.648838	7.575948	8.627106
29	5.418388	6.210672	7.114257	8.144144	9.317275
30	5.743491	6.614366	7.612255	8.754955	10.062657
31	6.088101	7.044300	8.145113	9.411577	10.867669
32	6.453387	7.502179	8.715271	10.117445	11.737083
33	6.840590	7.989821	9.325340	10.876253	12.676049
34	7.251025	8.509160	9.978113	11.691972	13.690133
35	7.686087	9.062255	10.676581	12.568870	14.785344
36	8.147252	9.651301	11.423942	13.511535	15.968171
37	8.636087	10.278636	12.223618	14.524901	17.245625
38	9.154252	10.946747	13.079271	15.614268	18.625275
39	9.703507	11.658286	13.994820	16.785338	20.115297
40	10.285718	12.416075	14.974457	18.044239	21.724521
41	10.902861	13.223119	16.022669	19.397557	23.462483
42	11.557032	14.082622	17.144256	20.852373	25.339481
43	12.250454	14.997993	18.344354	22.416301	27.366640
44	12.985482	15.972862	19.628459	24.097524	29.555971
45	13.764610	17.011098	21.002451	25.904838	31.920449
46	14.590487	18.116820	22.472622	27.847701	34.474084
47	15.465916	19.294413	24.045706	29.936278	37.232011
48	16.393871	20.548550	25.728905	32.181498	40.210572
49	17.377504	21.884205	27.529929	34.595112	43.427418
50	18.420154	23.306679	29.457024	37.189745	46.901611

n	6%	$6\frac{1}{2}\%$	7%	$7\frac{1}{2}\%$	8%
51	19.525363	24.821613	31.519016	39.978976	50.653740
52	20.696885	26.435018	33.725346	42.977399	54.706039
53	21.938698	28.153294	36.086121	46.200704	59.082522
54	23.255020	29.983258	38.612149	49.665757	63.809124
55	24.650321	31.932170	41.315000	53.390689	68.913854
56	26.129340	34.007761	44.207049	57.394990	74.426962
57	27.697100	36.218265	47.301543	61.699614	80.381119
58	29.358926	38.572452	50.612651	66.327086	86.811608
59	31.120462	41.079662	54.155536	71.301617	93.756537
60	32.987690	43.749840	57.946424	76.649238	101.257060
61	34.966951	46.593579	61.002673	82.397931	109.357625
62	37.064968	49.622162	66.342861	88.577776	118.106234
63	39.288865	52.847603	70.986861	95.221109	127.554733
64	41.646198	56.282697	75.955941	102.362692	137.759112
65	44.144970	59.941072	81.272857	110.039894	148.779841
66	46.793668	63.837242	86.961957	118.292886	160.682228
67	49.601288	67.986662	93.049294	127.164852	173.536806
68	52.577365	72.405796	99.562744	136.702216	187.415750
69	55.732007	77.112172	106.532136	146.954882	202.413330
70	59.075928	82.124464	113.989385	157.976498	218.606396
71	62.620483	87.462554	121.968642	169.824735	236.094908
72	66.377712	93.147620	130.506447	182.561591	254.982500
73	70.360375	99.202215	139.641898	196.253710	275.381101
74	74.581997	105.650359	149.416831	210.972738	297.411588
75	79.056917	112.517632	159.876009	226.795693	321.204515
76	83.800332	119.831279	171.067330	243.805370	346.900876
77	88.828352	127.620312	183.042042	262.090773	374.652946
78	94.158053	135.915632	195.854985	281.747581	404.625181
79	99.807536	144.750148	209.564834	302.878649	436.995196
80	105.795988	154.158908	224.234372	325.594547	471.954811
81	112.143748	164.179237	239.930778	350.014138	509.711196
82	118.872372	174.850887	256.725932	376.265199	550.488090
83	126.004715	186.216194	274.696748	404.485088	594.527138
84	133.564997	198.320247	293.925519	434.821470	642.089308
85	141.578897	211.211063	314.500305	467.433080	693.456453
86	150.073631	224.939782	336.515326	502.490560	748.932968
87	159.078049	239.560868	360.071399	540.177352	808.847606
88	168.622731	255.132325	385.276396	580.690654	873.555413
89	178.740095	271.715926	412.245744	624.242453	943.439846
90	189.464501	289.377461	441.102946	671.060636	1018.915031
91	200.832371	308.186996	471.980152	721.390183	1100.428236
92	212.882312	328.219151	505.018761	775.494447	1188.462491
93	225.655252	349.553396	540.370075	833.656529	1283.539492
94	239.194566	372.274366	578.195979	896.180769	1386.222649
95	253.546240	396.472200	618.669698	963.394325	1497.120463
96	258.759014	422.242893	661.976577	1035.648900	1616.890095
97	284.884555	449.688681	708.314935	1113.322566	1746.241303
98	301.977628	478.918445	757.896980	1196.821759	1885.940604
99	320.096286	510.048144	810.949769	1286.583390	2036.815854
100	329.302062	543.201275	867.716251	1383.077144	2199.761119

Table 5 Present Value of a Dollar[a]

$$(1 + r)^{-n}$$

= rate of interest per payment period;
n = number of payment periods

n	$\frac{1}{4}\%$	$\frac{1}{2}\%$	$\frac{3}{4}\%$	1%	$1\frac{1}{4}\%$
1	0.997506	0.995025	0.992556	0.990099	0.987654
2	0.995019	0.990075	0.985167	0.980296	0.975461
3	0.992537	0.985149	0.977833	0.970590	0.963418
4	0.990062	0.980248	0.970554	0.960980	0.951524
5	0.987593	0.975371	0.963329	0.951466	0.939777
6	0.985130	0.970518	0.956158	0.942045	0.928175
7	0.982674	0.965690	0.949040	0.932718	0.916716
8	0.980223	0.960885	0.941975	0.923483	0.905398
9	0.977779	0.956105	0.934963	0.914340	0.894221
10	0.975340	0.951348	0.928003	0.905287	0.883181
11	0.972908	0.946615	0.921095	0.896324	0.872277
12	0.970482	0.941905	0.914238	0.887449	0.861509
13	0.968062	0.937219	0.907432	0.878663	0.850873
14	0.965648	0.932556	0.900677	0.869963	0.840368
15	0.963240	0.927917	0.893973	0.861349	0.829993
16	0.960837	0.923300	0.887318	0.852821	0.819746
17	0.958441	0.918707	0.880712	0.844377	0.809626
18	0.956051	0.914136	0.874156	0.836017	0.799631
19	0.953667	0.909588	0.867649	0.827740	0.789759
20	0.951289	0.905063	0.861190	0.819544	0.780009
21	0.948917	0.900560	0.854779	0.811430	0.770379
22	0.946550	0.896080	0.848416	0.803396	0.760868
23	0.944190	0.891622	0.842100	0.795442	0.751475
24	0.941835	0.887186	0.835831	0.787566	0.742197
25	0.939486	0.882772	0.829609	0.779768	0.733034
26	0.937144	0.878380	0.823434	0.772048	0.723984
27	0.934806	0.874010	0.817304	0.764404	0.715046
28	0.932475	0.869662	0.811220	0.756836	0.706219
29	0.930150	0.865335	0.805181	0.749342	0.697500
30	0.927830	0.861030	0.799187	0.741923	0.688889
31	0.925517	0.856746	0.793238	0.734577	0.680384
32	0.923209	0.852484	0.787333	0.727304	0.671984
33	0.920906	0.848242	0.781472	0.720103	0.663688
34	0.918610	0.844022	0.775654	0.712973	0.655494
35	0.916319	0.839823	0.769880	0.705914	0.647402
36	0.914034	0.835645	0.764149	0.698925	0.639409
37	0.911754	0.831487	0.758461	0.692005	0.631515
38	0.909481	0.827351	0.752814	0.685153	0.623719
39	0.907213	0.823235	0.747210	0.678370	0.616019
40	0.904950	0.819139	0.741648	0.671653	0.608413
41	0.902694	0.815064	0.736127	0.665003	0.600902
42	0.900443	0.811008	0.730647	0.658419	0.593484
43	0.898197	0.806974	0.725208	0.651900	0.586157
44	0.895957	0.802959	0.719810	0.645445	0.578920
45	0.893723	0.798964	0.714451	0.639055	0.571773
46	0.891494	0.794989	0.709133	0.632728	0.564714
47	0.889271	0.791034	0.703854	0.626463	0.557742
48	0.887053	0.787098	0.698614	0.620260	0.550857
49	0.884841	0.783182	0.693414	0.614119	0.544056
50	0.882635	0.779286	0.688252	0.608039	0.537339

[a] Reproduced by permission from A. Mizrahi and M. Sullivan, *Finite Mathematics with Applications*, Wiley, New York, 1973.

n	$\frac{1}{4}\%$	$\frac{1}{2}\%$	$\frac{3}{4}\%$	1%	$1\frac{1}{4}\%$
51	0.880434	0.775409	0.683128	0.602019	0.530705
52	0.878238	0.771551	0.678043	0.596058	0.524153
53	0.876048	0.767713	0.672995	0.590157	0.517682
54	0.873863	0.763893	0.667986	0.584313	0.511291
55	0.871684	0.760093	0.663013	0.578528	0.504979
56	0.869510	0.756311	0.658077	0.572800	0.498745
57	0.867342	0.752548	0.653179	0.567129	0.492587
58	0.865179	0.748804	0.648316	0.561514	0.486506
59	0.863021	0.745079	0.643490	0.555954	0.480500
60	0.860869	0.741372	0.638700	0.550450	0.474568
61	0.858722	0.737684	0.633945	0.545000	0.468709
62	0.856581	0.734014	0.629226	0.539604	0.462922
63	0.854445	0.730362	0.624542	0.534261	0.457207
64	0.852314	0.726728	0.619893	0.528971	0.451563
65	0.850189	0.723113	0.615278	0.523734	0.455988
66	0.848068	0.719515	0.610698	0.518548	0.440482
67	0.845953	0.715935	0.606152	0.513414	0.435044
68	0.843844	0.712374	0.601639	0.508331	0.429673
69	0.841740	0.708829	0.597161	0.503298	0.424368
70	0.839640	0.705303	0.592715	0.498315	0.419129
71	0.837547	0.701794	0.588303	0.493381	0.413955
72	0.835458	0.698302	0.583924	0.488496	0.408844
73	0.833374	0.694828	0.579577	0.483660	0.403797
74	0.831296	0.691371	0.575262	0.478871	0.398811
75	0.829233	0.687932	0.570980	0.474130	0.393888
76	0.827155	0.684509	0.566730	0.469435	0.389025
77	0.825093	0.681104	0.562511	0.464787	0.384222
78	0.823035	0.677715	0.558323	0.460185	0.379479
79	0.820983	0.674343	0.554167	0.455629	0.374794
80	0.818935	0.670988	0.550042	0.451118	0.370167
81	0.816893	0.667650	0.545947	0.446651	0.365597
82	0.814856	0.664329	0.541883	0.442229	0.361083
83	0.812824	0.661023	0.537849	0.437851	0.356625
84	0.810797	0.657735	0.533845	0.433515	0.352223
85	0.808775	0.654462	0.529871	0.429223	0.347874
86	0.806758	0.651206	0.525927	0.424974	0.343580
87	0.804746	0.647967	0.522012	0.420766	0.339338
88	0.802739	0.644743	0.518126	0.416600	0.335148
89	0.800737	0.641535	0.514269	0.412475	0.331011
90	0.798741	0.638343	0.510440	0.408391	0.326924
91	0.796749	0.635168	0.506641	0.404348	0.322888
92	0.794762	0.632008	0.502869	0.400344	0.318902
93	0.792780	0.628863	0.499126	0.396380	0.314965
94	0.790803	0.625735	0.495410	0.392456	0.311076
95	0.788831	0.622622	0.491722	0.388570	0.307236
96	0.786864	0.619524	0.488062	0.384723	0.303443
97	0.784901	0.616442	0.484429	0.380914	0.299697
98	0.782944	0.613375	0.480822	0.377142	0.295997
99	0.780991	0.610323	0.477243	0.373408	0.292342
100	0.779044	0.607287	0.473690	0.369711	0.288733

Table 5 Present Value of a Dollar $(1 + r)^{-n}$ (*Continued*)

n	$1\frac{1}{2}\%$	$1\frac{3}{4}\%$	2%	$2\frac{1}{2}\%$	3%
1	0.985222	0.982801	0.980392	0.975610	0.970874
2	0.970662	0.965898	0.961169	0.951814	0.942596
3	0.956317	0.949285	0.942322	0.928599	0.915142
4	0.942184	0.932959	0.923845	0.905951	0.888487
5	0.928260	0.916913	0.905731	0.883854	0.862609
6	0.914542	0.901143	0.887971	0.862297	0.837484
7	0.901027	0.885644	0.870560	0.841265	0.813092
8	0.887711	0.870412	0.853490	0.820747	0.789409
9	0.874592	0.855441	0.836755	0.800728	0.766417
10	0.861667	0.840729	0.820348	0.781198	0.744094
11	0.848933	0.826269	0.804263	0.762145	0.722421
12	0.836387	0.812058	0.788493	0.743556	0.701380
13	0.824027	0.798091	0.773033	0.725420	0.680951
14	0.811849	0.784365	0.757875	0.707727	0.661118
15	0.799852	0.770875	0.743015	0.690466	0.641862
16	0.788031	0.757616	0.728446	0.673625	0.623167
17	0.776385	0.744586	0.714163	0.657195	0.605016
18	0.764912	0.731780	0.700159	0.641166	0.587395
19	0.753607	0.719194	0.686431	0.625528	0.570286
20	0.742470	0.706825	0.672971	0.610271	0.553676
21	0.731498	0.694668	0.659776	0.595386	0.537549
22	0.720688	0.682720	0.646839	0.580865	0.521893
23	0.710037	0.670978	0.634156	0.566697	0.506692
24	0.699544	0.659438	0.621722	0.552875	0.491934
25	0.689206	0.648096	0.609531	0.539391	0.477606
26	0.679021	0.636950	0.597579	0.526235	0.463695
27	0.668986	0.625995	0.585862	0.513400	0.450189
28	0.659099	0.615228	0.574375	0.500878	0.437077
29	0.649359	0.604647	0.563112	0.488661	0.424346
30	0.639762	0.594248	0.552071	0.476743	0.411987
31	0.630308	0.584027	0.541246	0.465115	0.399987
32	0.620993	0.573982	0.530633	0.453771	0.388337
33	0.611816	0.564111	0.520229	0.442703	0.377026
34	0.602774	0.554408	0.510028	0.431905	0.366045
35	0.593866	0.544873	0.500028	0.421371	0.355383
36	0.585090	0.535502	0.490223	0.411094	0.345032
37	0.576443	0.526292	0.480611	0.401067	0.334983
38	0.567924	0.517240	0.471187	0.391285	0.325226
39	0.559531	0.508344	0.461948	0.381741	0.315754
40	0.551262	0.499601	0.452890	0.372431	0.306557
41	0.543116	0.491008	0.444010	0.363347	0.297628
42	0.535089	0.482563	0.435304	0.354485	0.288959
43	0.527182	0.474264	0.426769	0.345839	0.280543
44	0.519391	0.466107	0.418401	0.337404	0.272372
45	0.511715	0.458090	0.410197	0.329174	0.264439
46	0.504153	0.450212	0.402154	0.321146	0.256737
47	0.496702	0.442469	0.394268	0.313313	0.249259
48	0.489362	0.434858	0.386538	0.305671	0.241999
49	0.482130	0.427379	0.378958	0.298216	0.234950
50	0.475005	0.420029	0.371528	0.290942	0.228107

n	$1\frac{1}{2}\%$	$1\frac{3}{4}\%$	2%	$2\frac{1}{2}\%$	3%
51	0.467985	0.412805	0.364243	0.283846	0.221463
52	0.461069	0.405705	0.357101	0.276923	0.215013
53	0.454255	0.398727	0.350099	0.270169	0.208750
54	0.447542	0.391869	0.343234	0.263579	0.202670
55	0.440928	0.385130	0.336504	0.257151	0.196767
56	0.434412	0.378506	0.329906	0.250879	0.191036
57	0.427992	0.371996	0.323437	0.244760	0.185472
58	0.421667	0.365598	0.317095	0.238790	0.180070
59	0.415435	0.359310	0.310878	0.232966	0.174825
60	0.409296	0.353130	0.304782	0.227284	0.169733
61	0.403247	0.347057	0.298806	0.221740	0.164789
62	0.397288	0.341088	0.292947	0.216332	0.159990
63	0.391417	0.335221	0.287203	0.211055	0.155330
64	0.385632	0.329456	0.281572	0.205908	0.150806
65	0.379933	0.323790	0.276051	0.200886	0.146413
66	0.374318	0.318221	0.270638	0.195986	0.142149
67	0.368787	0.312748	0.265331	0.191206	0.138009
68	0.363337	0.307369	0.260129	0.186542	0.133989
69	0.357967	0.302082	0.255028	0.181992	0.130086
70	0.352677	0.296887	0.250028	0.177554	0.126297
71	0.347465	0.291781	0.245125	0.173223	0.122619
72	0.342330	0.286762	0.240319	0.168998	0.119047
73	0.337271	0.281830	0.235607	0.164876	0.115580
74	0.332287	0.276983	0.230987	0.160855	0.112214
75	0.327376	0.272219	0.226458	0.156931	0.108945
76	0.322538	0.267537	0.222017	0.153104	0.105772
77	0.317771	0.262936	0.217664	0.149370	0.102691
78	0.313075	0.258414	0.213396	0.145726	0.099700
79	0.308449	0.253969	0.209212	0.142172	0.096796
80	0.303890	0.249601	0.205110	0.138705	0.093977
81	0.299399	0.245308	0.201088	0.135322	0.091240
82	0.294975	0.241089	0.197145	0.132021	0.088582
83	0.290615	0.236943	0.193279	0.128801	0.086002
84	0.286321	0.232868	0.189490	0.125660	0.083497
85	0.282089	0.228862	0.185774	0.122595	0.081065
86	0.277920	0.224926	0.182132	0.119605	0.078704
87	0.273813	0.221058	0.178560	0.116687	0.076412
88	0.269767	0.217256	0.175059	0.113841	0.074186
89	0.265780	0.213519	0.171627	0.111065	0.072026
90	0.261852	0.209847	0.168261	0.108356	0.069928
91	0.257982	0.206238	0.164962	0.105713	0.067891
92	0.254170	0.202691	0.161728	0.103135	0.065914
93	0.250414	0.199205	0.158557	0.100619	0.063994
94	0.246713	0.195778	0.155448	0.098165	0.062130
95	0.243067	0.192411	0.152400	0.095771	0.060320
96	0.239475	0.189102	0.149411	0.093435	0.058563
97	0.235936	0.185850	0.146482	0.091156	0.056858
98	0.232449	0.182653	0.143610	0.088933	0.055202
99	0.229014	0.179512	0.140794	0.086764	0.053594
100	0.225629	0.176424	0.138033	0.084647	0.052033

Table 5 Present Value of a Dollar $(1 + r)^{-n}$ (*Continued*)

n	$3\frac{1}{2}\%$	4%	$4\frac{1}{2}\%$	5%	$5\frac{1}{2}\%$
1	0.966184	0.961538	0.956938	0.952381	0.947867
2	0.933511	0.924556	0.915730	0.907029	0.898452
3	0.901943	0.888996	0.876297	0.863838	0.851614
4	0.871442	0.854804	0.838561	0.822702	0.807217
5	0.841973	0.821927	0.802451	0.783526	0.765134
6	0.813501	0.790315	0.767896	0.746215	0.725246
7	0.785991	0.759918	0.734828	0.710681	0.687437
8	0.759412	0.730690	0.703185	0.676839	0.651599
9	0.733731	0.702587	0.672904	0.644609	0.617629
10	0.708919	0.675564	0.643928	0.613913	0.585431
11	0.684946	0.649581	0.616199	0.584679	0.554911
12	0.661783	0.624597	0.589664	0.556837	0.525982
13	0.639404	0.600574	0.564272	0.530321	0.498561
14	0.617782	0.577475	0.539973	0.505068	0.472569
15	0.596891	0.555265	0.516720	0.481017	0.447933
16	0.576706	0.533908	0.494469	0.458112	0.424581
17	0.557204	0.513373	0.473176	0.436297	0.402447
18	0.538361	0.493628	0.452800	0.415521	0.381466
19	0.520156	0.474642	0.433302	0.395734	0.361579
20	0.502566	0.456387	0.414643	0.376889	0.342729
21	0.485571	0.438834	0.396787	0.358942	0.324862
22	0.469151	0.421955	0.379701	0.341850	0.307926
23	0.453286	0.405726	0.363350	0.325571	0.291873
24	0.437957	0.390121	0.347703	0.310068	0.276657
25	0.423147	0.375117	0.332731	0.295303	0.262234
26	0.408838	0.360689	0.318402	0.281241	0.248563
27	0.395012	0.346817	0.304691	0.267848	0.235605
28	0.381654	0.333477	0.291571	0.255094	0.223322
29	0.368748	0.320651	0.279015	0.242946	0.211679
30	0.356278	0.308319	0.267000	0.231377	0.200644
31	0.344230	0.296460	0.255502	0.220359	0.190184
32	0.332590	0.285058	0.244500	0.209866	0.180269
33	0.321343	0.274094	0.233971	0.199873	0.170871
34	0.310476	0.263552	0.233896	0.190355	0.161963
35	0.299977	0.253415	0.214254	0.181290	0.153520
36	0.289833	0.243669	0.205028	0.172657	0.145516
37	0.280032	0.234297	0.196199	0.164436	0.137930
38	0.270562	0.225285	0.187750	0.156605	0.130739
39	0.261413	0.216621	0.179665	0.149148	0.123924
40	0.252572	0.208289	0.171929	0.142046	0.117463
41	0.244031	0.200278	0.164525	0.135282	0.111339
42	0.235779	0.192575	0.157440	0.128840	0.105535
43	0.227806	0.185168	0.150661	0.122704	0.100033
44	0.220102	0.178046	0.144173	0.116861	0.094818
45	0.212659	0.171198	0.137964	0.111297	0.089875
46	0.205468	0.164614	0.132023	0.105997	0.085190
47	0.198520	0.158283	0.126338	0.100949	0.080748
48	0.191806	0.152195	0.120898	0.096142	0.076539
49	0.185320	0.146341	0.115692	0.091564	0.072549
50	0.179053	0.140713	0.110710	0.087204	0.068767

n	$3\frac{1}{2}\%$	4%	$4\frac{1}{2}\%$	5%	$5\frac{1}{2}\%$
51	0.172998	0.135301	0.105942	0.083051	0.065182
52	0.167148	0.130097	0.101380	0.079096	0.061783
53	0.161496	0.125093	0.097014	0.075330	0.058563
54	0.156035	0.120282	0.092837	0.071743	0.055509
55	0.150758	0.115656	0.088839	0.068326	0.052616
56	0.145660	0.111207	0.085013	0.065073	0.049873
57	0.140734	0.106930	0.081353	0.061974	0.047273
58	0.135975	0.102817	0.077849	0.059023	0.044808
59	0.131377	0.098863	0.074497	0.056212	0.042472
60	0.126934	0.095060	0.071289	0.053536	0.040258
61	0.122642	0.091404	0.068219	0.050986	0.038159
62	0.118495	0.087889	0.065281	0.048558	0.036170
63	0.114487	0.084508	0.062470	0.046246	0.034284
64	0.110616	0.081258	0.059780	0.044044	0.032497
65	0.106875	0.078133	0.057206	0.041946	0.030803
66	0.103261	0.075128	0.054743	0.039949	0.029197
67	0.099769	0.072238	0.052385	0.038047	0.027675
68	0.096395	0.069460	0.050129	0.036235	0.026232
69	0.093136	0.066788	0.047971	0.034509	0.024865
70	0.089986	0.064219	0.045905	0.032866	0.023568
71	0.086943	0.061749	0.043928	0.031301	0.022340
72	0.084003	0.059374	0.042037	0.029811	0.021175
73	0.081162	0.057091	0.040226	0.028391	0.020071
74	0.078418	0.054895	0.038494	0.027039	0.019025
75	0.075766	0.052784	0.036836	0.025752	0.018033
76	0.073204	0.050754	0.035250	0.024525	0.017093
77	0.070728	0.048801	0.033732	0.023357	0.016202
78	0.068337	0.046924	0.032280	0.022245	0.015357
79	0.066026	0.045120	0.030890	0.021186	0.014556
80	0.063793	0.043384	0.029559	0.020177	0.013798
81	0.061636	0.041716	0.028287	0.019216	0.013078
82	0.059551	0.040111	0.027068	0.018301	0.012396
83	0.057538	0.038569	0.025903	0.017430	0.011750
84	0.055592	0.037085	0.024787	0.016600	0.011138
85	0.053712	0.035659	0.023720	0.015809	0.010557
86	0.051896	0.034287	0.022699	0.015056	0.010007
87	0.050141	0.032969	0.021721	0.014339	0.009485
88	0.048445	0.031701	0.020786	0.013657	0.008990
89	0.046807	0.030481	0.019891	0.013006	0.008522
90	0.045224	0.029309	0.019034	0.012387	0.008078
91	0.043695	0.028182	0.018215	0.011797	0.007656
92	0.042217	0.027098	0.017430	0.011235	0.007257
93	0.040789	0.026056	0.016680	0.010700	0.006879
94	0.039410	0.025053	0.015961	0.010191	0.006520
95	0.038077	0.024090	0.015274	0.009705	0.006180
96	0.036790	0.023163	0.014616	0.009243	0.005858
97	0.035546	0.022272	0.013987	0.008803	0.005553
98	0.034344	0.021416	0.013385	0.008384	0.005263
99	0.033182	0.020592	0.012808	0.007985	0.004989
100	0.032060	0.019800	0.012257	0.007604	0.004729

Table 5 Present Value of a Dollar $(1 + r)^{-n}$ (*Continued*)

n	6%	$6\frac{1}{2}$%	7%	$7\frac{1}{2}$%	8%
1	0.943396	0.938967	0.934579	0.930233	0.925926
2	0.889996	0.881659	0.873439	0.865333	0.857339
3	0.839619	0.827849	0.816298	0.804961	0.793832
4	0.792094	0.777323	0.762895	0.748801	0.735030
5	0.747258	0.729881	0.712986	0.696559	0.680583
6	0.704961	0.685334	0.666342	0.647962	0.630170
7	0.665057	0.643506	0.622750	0.602755	0.583490
8	0.627412	0.604231	0.582009	0.560702	0.540269
9	0.591898	0.567353	0.543934	0.521583	0.500249
10	0.558395	0.532726	0.508349	0.485194	0.463193
11	0.526788	0.500212	0.475093	0.451343	0.428883
12	0.496969	0.469683	0.444012	0.419854	0.397114
13	0.468839	0.441017	0.414964	0.390562	0.367698
14	0.442301	0.414100	0.387817	0.363313	0.340461
15	0.417265	0.388827	0.362446	0.337966	0.315242
16	0.393646	0.365095	0.338735	0.314387	0.291890
17	0.371364	0.342813	0.316574	0.292453	0.270269
18	0.350344	0.321890	0.295864	0.272049	0.250249
19	0.330513	0.302244	0.276508	0.253069	0.231712
20	0.311805	0.283797	0.258419	0.235413	0.214548
21	0.294155	0.266476	0.241513	0.218989	0.198656
22	0.277505	0.250212	0.225713	0.203711	0.183941
23	0.261797	0.234941	0.210947	0.189498	0.170315
24	0.246979	0.220602	0.197147	0.176277	0.157699
25	0.232999	0.207138	0.184249	0.163979	0.146018
26	0.219810	0.194496	0.172195	0.152539	0.135202
27	0.207368	0.182625	0.160930	0.141896	0.125187
28	0.195630	0.171479	0.150402	0.131997	0.115914
29	0.184557	0.161013	0.140563	0.122788	0.107328
30	0.174110	0.151186	0.131367	0.114221	0.099377
31	0.164255	0.141959	0.122773	0.106252	0.092016
32	0.154957	0.133295	0.114741	0.098839	0.085200
33	0.146186	0.125159	0.107235	0.091943	0.078889
34	0.137912	0.117520	0.100219	0.085529	0.073045
35	0.130105	0.110348	0.093663	0.079562	0.067635
36	0.122741	0.103613	0.087535	0.074011	0.062625
37	0.115793	0.097289	0.081809	0.068847	0.057986
38	0.109239	0.091351	0.076457	0.064044	0.053690
39	0.103056	0.085776	0.071455	0.059576	0.049713
40	0.097222	0.080541	0.066780	0.055419	0.046031
41	0.091719	0.075625	0.062412	0.051553	0.042621
42	0.086527	0.071010	0.058329	0.047956	0.039464
43	0.081630	0.066676	0.054513	0.044610	0.036541
44	0.077009	0.062606	0.050946	0.041498	0.033834
45	0.072650	0.058785	0.047613	0.038603	0.031328
46	0.068538	0.055197	0.044499	0.035910	0.029007
47	0.064658	0.051828	0.041587	0.033404	0.026859
48	0.060998	0.048665	0.038867	0.031074	0.024869
49	0.057546	0.045695	0.036324	0.028906	0.023027
50	0.054288	0.042906	0.033948	0.026889	0.021321

n	6%	6½%	7%	7½%	8%
51	0.051215	0.040287	0.031727	0.025013	0.019742
52	0.048316	0.037829	0.029651	0.023268	0.018280
53	0.045582	0.035520	0.027711	0.021645	0.016925
54	0.043001	0.033352	0.025899	0.020135	0.015672
55	0.040567	0.031316	0.024204	0.018730	0.014511
56	0.038271	0.029405	0.022621	0.017423	0.013436
57	0.036105	0.027610	0.021141	0.016208	0.012441
58	0.034061	0.025925	0.019758	0.015077	0.011519
59	0.032133	0.024343	0.018465	0.014025	0.010666
60	0.030314	0.022857	0.017257	0.013046	0.009876
61	0.028598	0.021462	0.016128	0.012136	0.009144
62	0.026980	0.020152	0.015073	0.011290	0.008467
63	0.025453	0.018922	0.014087	0.010502	0.007840
64	0.024012	0.017767	0.013166	0.009769	0.007259
65	0.022653	0.016683	0.012304	0.009088	0.006721
66	0.021370	0.015665	0.011499	0.008454	0.006223
67	0.020161	0.014709	0.010747	0.007864	0.005762
68	0.019020	0.013811	0.010044	0.007315	0.005336
69	0.017943	0.012968	0.009387	0.006805	0.004940
70	0.016927	0.012177	0.008773	0.006330	0.004574
71	0.015969	0.011433	0.008199	0.005888	0.004236
72	0.015065	0.010736	0.007662	0.005478	0.003922
73	0.014213	0.010080	0.007161	0.005095	0.003631
74	0.013408	0.009465	0.006693	0.004740	0.003362
75	0.012649	0.008887	0.006255	0.004409	0.003113
76	0.011933	0.008345	0.005846	0.004102	0.002883
77	0.011258	0.007836	0.005463	0.003815	0.002669
78	0.010620	0.007358	0.005106	0.003549	0.002471
79	0.010019	0.006908	0.004772	0.003302	0.002288
80	0.009452	0.006487	0.004460	0.003071	0.002119
81	0.008917	0.006091	0.004168	0.002857	0.001962
82	0.008412	0.005719	0.003895	0.002658	0.001817
83	0.007936	0.005370	0.003640	0.002472	0.001682
84	0.007487	0.005042	0.003402	0.002300	0.001557
85	0.007063	0.004735	0.003180	0.002139	0.001442
86	0.006663	0.004446	0.002972	0.001990	0.001335
87	0.006286	0.004174	0.002777	0.001851	0.001236
88	0.005930	0.003920	0.002596	0.001722	0.001145
89	0.005595	0.003680	0.002426	0.001602	0.001060
90	0.005278	0.003456	0.002267	0.001490	0.000981
91	0.004979	0.003245	0.002119	0.001386	0.000909
92	0.004697	0.003047	0.001980	0.001289	0.000841
93	0.004432	0.002861	0.001851	0.001200	0.000779
94	0.004181	0.002686	0.001730	0.001116	0.000721
95	0.003944	0.002522	0.001616	0.001038	0.000668
96	0.003721	0.002368	0.001511	0.000966	0.000618
97	0.003510	0.002224	0.001412	0.000898	0.000573
98	0.003312	0.002088	0.001319	0.000836	0.000530
99	0.003124	0.001961	0.001233	0.000777	0.000491
100	0.002947	0.001841	0.001152	0.000723	0.000455

Table 6 Amount of an Annuity

$$\left(s_{\overline{n}|\,r} = \frac{(1 + r)^n - 1}{r} \right)$$

r = interest rate per payment period; n = number of payment periods

n	$\frac{1}{2}\%$	$\frac{3}{4}\%$	1%	$1\frac{1}{4}\%$
1	1.000000	1.000000	1.000000	1.000000	1.000000
2	2.002499	2.005000	2.007500	2.010000	2.012500
3	3.007505	3.015025	3.022556	3.030100	3.037656
4	4.015023	4.030100	4.045225	4.060401	4.075627
5	5.025060	5.050251	5.075564	5.101005	5.126572
6	6.037623	6.075502	6.113631	6.152015	6.190654
7	7.052717	7.105880	7.159483	7.213535	7.268037
8	8.070347	8.141409	8.213179	8.285670	8.358888
9	9.090523	9.182116	9.274778	9.368527	9.463374
10	10.113249	10.228027	10.344339	10.462212	10.581666
11	11.138532	11.279167	11.421921	11.566834	11.713936
12	12.166377	12.335563	12.507586	12.682502	12.860361
13	13.196793	13.397241	13.601393	13.809327	14.021115
14	14.229784	14.464227	14.703403	14.947421	15.196379
15	15.265359	15.536549	15.813679	16.096895	16.386334
16	16.303521	16.614231	16.932281	17.257864	17.591163
17	17.344280	17.697302	18.059273	18.430442	18.811052
18	18.387640	18.785789	19.194717	19.614747	20.046190
19	19.433609	19.879718	20.338678	20.810894	21.296767
20	20.482192	20.979116	21.491218	22.019003	22.562977
21	21.533398	22.084012	22.652402	23.239193	23.845014
22	22.587230	23.194432	23.822295	24.471585	25.143077
23	23.643699	24.310404	25.000962	25.716301	26.457365
24	24.702807	25.431957	26.188469	26.973463	27.788082
25	25.764564	26.559116	27.384883	28.243198	29.135433
26	26.828975	27.691912	28.590269	29.525630	30.499626
27	27.896046	28.830372	29.804696	30.820886	31.880871
28	28.965785	29.974524	31.028231	32.129095	33.279382
29	30.038200	31.124396	32.260943	33.450386	34.695374
30	31.113295	32.280018	33.502900	34.784890	36.129066
31	32.191078	33.441419	34.754172	36.132739	37.580679
32	33.271555	34.608626	36.014828	37.494066	39.050438
33	34.354734	35.781669	37.284939	38.869006	40.538568
34	35.440620	36.960577	38.564576	40.257696	42.045300
35	36.529221	38.145380	39.853810	41.660273	43.670866
36	37.620543	39.336107	41.152714	43.076876	45.115502
37	38.714594	40.532788	42.461359	44.507645	46.679446
38	39.811380	41.735452	43.779819	45.992721	48.262939
39	40.910909	42.944129	45.108168	47.412248	49.866225
40	42.013185	44.158850	46.446479	48.886371	51.489553
41	43.118218	45.379644	47.794828	50.375234	53.133172
42	44.226012	46.606543	49.153289	51.878987	54.797337
43	45.336577	47.839575	50.521938	53.397776	56.482304
44	46.449918	49.078773	51.900853	54.931754	58.188332
45	47.566043	50.324167	53.290109	56.481072	59.915686
46	48.684957	51.575788	54.689785	58.045882	61.664632
47	49.806669	52.833667	56.099958	59.626341	63.435440
48	50.931185	54.097835	57.520707	61.222604	65.228383
49	52.058514	55.368324	58.952113	62.834830	67.043738
50	53.188659	56.645166	60.384253	64.463178	68.881786

[a] Reproduced by permission from A. Mizrahi and M. Sullivan, *Finite Mathematics with Applications*, Wiley, New York, 1973.

n	$\frac{1}{4}\%$	$\frac{1}{2}\%$	$\frac{3}{4}\%$	1%	$1\frac{1}{4}\%$
51	54.321630	57.928392	61.847210	66.107810	70.742806
52	55.457433	59.218034	63.311064	67.768888	72.627092
53	56.596077	60.514125	64.785897	69.446577	74.534930
54	57.737566	61.816695	66.271791	71.141043	76.466616
55	58.881910	63.125778	67.768830	72.852453	78.422449
56	60.029113	64.441408	69.277096	74.580977	80.402730
57	61.179186	65.763614	70.796674	76.326787	82.407764
58	62.332134	67.092433	72.327649	78.090055	84.437861
59	63.487963	68.427895	73.870107	79.870956	86.493334
60	64.646682	69.770034	75.424132	81.669665	88.574500
61	65.808299	71.118885	76.989813	83.486361	90.681681
62	66.972818	72.474479	78.567236	85.321225	92.815202
63	68.140251	73.836852	80.156491	87.174437	94.975392
64	69.310600	75.206036	81.757665	89.046181	97.162584
65	70.483877	76.582066	83.370847	90.936643	99.377116
66	71.660086	77.964977	84.996128	92.846010	101.619330
67	72.839236	79.354802	86.633599	94.779970	103.889572
68	74.021333	80.751576	88.283351	96.722214	106.188191
69	75.206386	82.155334	89.945476	98.689436	108.515543
70	76.394402	83.566111	91.620067	100.676380	110.871988
71	77.585387	84.983941	93.307217	102.683094	113.257887
72	78.779350	86.408861	95.007022	104.709924	115.673611
73	79.976298	87.840905	96.719574	106.757024	118.119531
74	81.176238	89.280110	98.444971	100.824594	120.596025
75	82.379178	90.726511	100.183308	110.912846	123.103475
76	83.585124	92.180143	101.934683	113.021968	125.642268
77	84.794088	93.641044	103.699193	115.152188	128.212797
78	86.006071	95.109249	105.476936	117.303709	130.815456
79	87.221088	96.584796	107.268014	119.476747	133.450649
80	88.439139	98.067720	109.072523	121.671514	136.118782
81	89.660237	99.558058	110.890567	123.888229	138.820267
82	90.884387	101.055849	112.722246	126.127111	141.555520
83	92.111597	102.561128	114.567663	128.388382	144.324964
84	93.341875	104.073934	116.426920	130.672266	147.129026
85	94.575230	105.594304	118.300123	132.978988	149.968138
86	95.811667	107.122275	120.187373	135.308778	152.842740
87	97.051197	108.657887	122.088778	137.661866	155.753274
88	98.293823	110.201176	124.004444	140.038484	158.700190
89	99.539557	111.752182	125.934477	142.438869	161.683942
90	100.788406	113.310943	127.878986	144.863258	164.704991
91	102.040376	114.877498	129.838078	147.311890	167.763803
92	103.295475	116.451885	131.811864	149.785009	170.860850
93	104.553715	118.034145	133.800453	152.282859	173.996611
94	105.815098	119.624315	135.803956	154.805687	177.171568
95	107.079636	121.222438	137.822486	157.353744	180.386213
96	108.347334	122.828550	139.856154	159.927281	183.641040
97	109.618202	124.442693	141.905075	162.526554	186.936553
98	110.892247	126.064906	143.969368	165.151819	190.273260
99	112.169477	127.695231	146.049133	167.803338	193.651675
100	113.449899	129.333707	148.144501	170.481370	197.072322

Table 6 Amount of an Annuity $\left(s_{\overline{n}|r} = \dfrac{(1 + r)^n - 1}{r} \right)$ *(Continued)*

n	$1\frac{1}{2}\%$	$1\frac{3}{4}\%$	2%	$2\frac{1}{2}\%$	3%
1	1.000000	1.000000	1.000000	1.000000	1.000000
2	2.015000	2.017500	2.020000	2.025000	2.030000
3	3.045225	3.052806	3.060400	3.075625	3.090900
4	4.090903	4.106230	4.121608	4.152515	4.183627
5	5.152267	5.178089	5.204040	5.256328	5.309136
6	6.229551	6.268706	6.308121	6.387737	6.468410
7	7.322994	7.378408	7.434283	7.547430	7.662462
8	8.432839	8.507530	8.582969	8.736116	8.892336
9	9.559332	9.656412	9.754628	9.954518	10.159106
10	10.702722	10.825399	10.949720	11.203381	11.463879
11	11.863262	12.014844	12.168715	12.483466	12.807795
12	13.041211	13.225103	13.412089	13.795552	14.192029
13	14.236830	14.456542	14.680331	15.140441	15.617790
14	15.450382	15.709532	15.973937	16.518952	17.086324
15	16.682138	16.984449	17.293416	17.931926	18.598913
16	17.932370	18.281676	18.639284	19.380224	20.156881
17	19.201355	19.601606	20.012070	20.864730	21.761587
18	20.489376	20.944634	21.412311	22.386348	23.414435
19	21.796716	22.311165	22.840558	23.946006	25.116868
20	23.123667	23.701610	24.297369	25.544656	26.870374
21	24.470522	25.116388	25.783316	27.183273	28.676485
22	25.837580	26.555925	27.298982	28.862855	30.536780
23	27.225143	28.020654	28.844962	30.584426	32.452883
24	28.633521	29.511015	30.421861	32.349036	34.426469
25	30.063024	31.027458	32.030298	34.157762	36.459263
26	31.513969	32.570438	33.670904	36.011706	38.553041
27	32.986678	34.140421	35.344322	37.911999	40.709632
28	34.481478	35.737878	37.051208	39.859799	42.930921
29	35.998701	37.363291	38.792232	41.856294	45.218849
30	37.538681	39.017148	40.568077	43.902701	47.575414
31	39.101761	40.699948	42.379438	46.000268	50.002677
32	40.688288	42.412197	44.227027	48.150275	52.502757
33	42.298612	44.154411	46.111568	50.354032	55.077840
34	43.933091	45.927113	48.033799	52.612883	57.730175
35	45.592088	47.730837	49.994475	54.928205	60.462080
36	47.275969	49.566127	51.994364	57.301409	63.275942
37	48.985109	51.433534	54.034251	59.733945	66.174221
38	50.719885	53.333621	56.114936	62.227293	69.159447
39	52.480683	55.266959	58.237235	64.782976	72.234231
40	54.267894	57.234131	60.401979	67.402550	75.401258
41	56.081912	59.235728	62.610019	70.087614	78.663295
42	57.923141	61.272353	64.862219	72.839804	82.023194
43	59.791988	63.344619	67.159464	75.660799	85.483890
44	61.688868	65.453150	69.502653	78.552318	89.048406
45	63.614201	67.598580	71.892706	81.516126	92.719858
46	65.568414	69.781555	74.330560	84.554030	96.501454
47	67.551940	72.002732	76.817171	87.667880	100.396498
48	69.565219	74.262780	79.353514	90.859577	104.408392
49	71.608698	76.562378	81.940584	94.131066	108.540644
50	73.682828	78.902220	84.579396	97.484343	112.796863

n	$1\frac{1}{2}\%$	$1\frac{3}{4}\%$	2%	$2\frac{1}{2}\%$	3%
51	75.788070	81.283009	87.270984	100.921451	117.180769
52	77.924891	83.705461	90.016403	104.444487	121.696192
53	80.093765	86.170307	92.816731	108.055599	126.347078
54	82.295171	88.678287	95.673065	111.756989	131.137490
55	84.529599	91.230157	98.586527	115.550914	136.071615
56	86.797543	93.826684	101.558257	119.439686	141.153763
57	89.099506	96.468651	104.589422	123.425679	146.388376
58	91.435998	99.156852	107.681210	127.511320	151.780027
59	93.807539	101.892097	110.834834	131.699103	157.333428
60	96.214651	104.675209	114.051531	135.991581	163.053431
61	98.657871	107.507025	117.332562	140.391370	168.945034
62	101.137739	110.388398	120.679212	144.901154	175.013384
63	103.654805	113.320195	124.092797	149.523683	181.263786
64	106.209628	116.303298	127.574652	154.261775	187.701699
65	108.802772	119.338605	131.126145	159.118319	194.332750
66	111.434813	122.427031	134.748668	164.096277	201.162733
67	114.106336	125.569504	138.443642	169.198684	208.197614
68	116.817931	128.766970	142.212514	174.428650	215.443543
69	119.570200	132.020392	146.056764	179.789366	222.906849
70	122.363753	135.330748	149.977899	185.284100	230.594054
71	125.199209	138.699037	153.977457	190.916203	238.511875
72	128.077197	142.126269	158.057006	196.689107	246.667232
73	130.998355	145.613479	162.218146	202.606335	225.067249
74	133.963330	149.161715	166.462508	208.671493	263.719266
75	136.972780	152.772045	170.791759	214.888280	272.630844
76	140.027372	156.445555	175.207593	221.260487	281.809769
77	143.127783	160.183352	179.711746	227.791999	291.264062
78	146.274699	163.986561	184.305980	234.486799	301.001983
79	149.468820	167.856326	188.992100	241.348968	311.032043
80	152.710852	171.793811	193.771941	248.382692	321.363004
81	156.001515	175.800202	198.647380	255.592259	332.003894
82	159.341538	179.876706	203.620327	262.982065	342.964010
83	162.731661	184.024548	208.692734	270.556617	354.252930
84	166.172636	188.244977	213.866588	278.320532	365.880518
85	169.665225	192.539264	219.143920	286.278545	377.856933
86	173.210204	196.908701	224.526798	294.435508	390.192641
87	176.808356	201.354604	230.017333	302.796396	402.898420
88	180.460482	205.878308	235.617680	311.366305	415.985373
89	184.167389	210.481179	241.330033	320.150463	429.464934
90	187.929900	215.164599	247.156633	329.154224	443.348881
91	191.748848	219.929980	253.099766	338.383079	457.649348
92	195.625081	224.778753	259.161761	347.842656	472.378828
93	199.559458	229.712382	265.344996	357.538722	487.550192
94	203.552850	234.732348	271.651895	367.477190	503.176698
95	207.606142	239.840165	278.084933	377.664119	519.271998
96	211.720234	245.037367	284.646631	388.105722	535.850158
97	215.896038	250.325521	291.339564	398.808365	552.925662
98	220.134478	255.706217	298.166354	409.778573	570.513433
99	224.436456	261.181070	305.129682	421.023038	588.628835
100	228.003043	266.751744	312.232215	432.548612	607.287700

Table 6 Amount of an Annuity $\left(s_{\overline{n}|r} = \dfrac{(1 + r)^n - 1}{r} \right)$ *(Continued)*

n	$3\frac{1}{2}\%$	4%	$4\frac{1}{2}\%$	5%	$5\frac{1}{2}\%$
1	1.000000	1.000000	1.000000	1.000000	1.000000
2	2.035000	2.040000	2.045000	2.050000	2.055000
3	3.106225	3.121600	3.137025	3.152500	3.168025
4	4.214943	4.246464	4.278191	4.310125	4.342266
5	5.362466	5.416322	5.470710	5.525631	5.581091
6	6.550152	6.632975	6.716892	6.801913	6.888051
7	7.779407	7.898294	8.019152	8.142008	8.266894
8	9.051687	9.214226	9.380014	9.549109	9.721573
9	10.368496	10.582795	10.802114	11.026564	11.256259
10	11.731393	12.006107	12.288209	12.577892	12.875354
11	13.141992	13.486351	13.841179	14.206787	14.583498
12	14.601961	15.025805	15.464032	15.917126	16.385590
13	16.113030	16.626837	17.159913	17.712983	18.286798
14	17.676986	18.291911	18.932110	19.598632	20.292572
15	19.295680	20.023587	20.784054	21.578563	22.408663
16	20.971029	21.824530	22.719337	23.657492	24.641139
17	22.705015	23.697511	24.741707	25.840366	26.996402
18	24.499691	25.645412	26.855084	28.132384	29.481204
19	26.357180	27.671228	29.063563	30.539004	32.102670
20	28.279681	29.778077	31.371423	33.065954	34.868317
21	30.269470	31.969200	33.783137	35.719251	37.786075
22	32.328901	34.247968	36.303378	38.505214	40.864309
23	34.460413	36.617887	38.937030	41.430475	44.111846
24	36.666527	39.082602	41.689197	44.501998	47.537997
25	38.949855	41.645906	44.565210	47.727098	51.152587
26	41.313100	44.311742	47.570645	51.113453	54.965979
27	43.759059	47.084212	50.711324	54.669126	58.989108
28	46.290626	49.967580	53.993334	58.402582	63.233509
29	48.910798	52.966284	57.423034	62.322711	67.711352
30	51.622675	56.084935	61.007070	66.438846	72.435476
31	54.429469	59.328332	64.752388	70.760789	77.419427
32	57.334500	62.701465	68.666246	75.298828	82.677496
33	60.341208	66.209524	72.756227	80.063770	88.224758
34	63.453150	69.857905	77.030257	85.066958	94.077119
35	66.674010	73.652221	81.496619	90.320306	100.251361
36	70.007600	77.598309	86.163966	95.836321	106.765186
37	73.457866	81.702242	91.041345	101.628137	113.637271
38	77.028891	85.970331	96.138206	107.709544	120.887320
39	80.724903	90.409144	101.464425	114.095021	128.536123
40	84.550274	95.025510	107.030324	120.799772	136.605610
41	88.509534	99.826530	112.846689	127.839761	145.118918
42	92.607367	104.819591	118.924790	135.231749	154.100458
43	96.848625	110.012375	125.276405	142.993336	163.575984
44	101.238326	115.412870	131.913843	151.143003	173.572663
45	105.781668	121.029384	138.849966	159.700153	184.119159
46	110.484026	126.870560	146.098215	168.685160	195.245712
47	115.350967	132.945382	153.672635	178.119419	206.984226
48	120.388251	139.263197	161.587903	188.025389	219.368358
49	125.601839	145.833724	169.859359	198.426659	232.433618
50	130.997904	152.667073	178.503030	209.347992	246.217467

n	$3\frac{1}{2}\%$	4%	$4\frac{1}{2}\%$	5%	$5\frac{1}{2}\%$
51	136.582830	159.773756	187.535667	220.815391	260.759427
52	142.363229	167.164706	196.974772	232.856160	276.101198
53	148.345942	174.851294	206.838636	245.498969	292.286761
54	154.538050	182.845345	217.146375	258.773917	309.362533
55	160.946882	191.159159	227.917962	272.712612	327.377472
56	167.580022	199.805525	239.174270	287.348243	346.383232
57	174.445322	208.797746	250.937112	302.715655	366.434311
58	181.550909	218.149655	263.229282	318.851437	387.588197
59	188.905191	227.875641	276.074601	335.794010	409.905548
60	196.516872	237.990667	289.497957	353.583710	433.450352
61	204.394962	248.510293	303.525365	372.262896	458.290121
62	212.548786	259.450704	318.184607	391.876039	484.496077
63	220.987993	270.828732	333.502287	412.469841	512.143361
64	229.722573	282.661881	349.509890	434.093334	541.311246
65	238.762862	294.968356	366.237835	456.798000	572.083364
66	248.119562	307.767089	383.718538	480.637899	604.547948
67	257.803747	321.077773	401.985872	505.669795	638.798088
68	267.826878	334.920883	421.075236	531.953284	674.931979
69	278.200818	349.317718	441.023622	559.550949	713.053237
70	288.937846	364.290426	461.869685	588.528495	753.271165
71	300.050671	379.862043	483.653821	618.954919	795.701079
72	311.552444	396.056524	506.418243	650.902666	840.464637
73	323.456779	412.898785	530.207064	684.447799	887.690192
74	335.777766	430.414735	555.066382	719.670188	937.513151
75	348.529988	448.631325	581.044370	756.653697	990.076374
76	361.728537	467.576577	608.191366	795.486382	1045.530574
77	375.389035	487.279640	636.559978	836.260701	1104.034758
78	389.527651	507.770825	666.205177	879.073734	1165.756665
79	404.161119	529.081656	697.184410	924.027421	1230.873281
80	419.306757	551.244922	729.557709	971.228793	1299.571310
81	434.982494	574.294718	763.387806	1020.790232	1372.047730
82	451.206880	598.266505	798.740257	1072.829742	1448.510354
83	467.999121	623.197166	835.683570	1127.471228	1529.178424
84	485.379090	649.125051	874.289330	1184.844790	1614.283236
85	503.367357	676.090053	914.632349	1245.087029	1704.068810
86	521.985214	704.133654	956.790805	1308.341380	1798.792593
87	541.254696	733.299000	1000.846391	1374.758448	1898.726187
88	561.198610	763.630957	1046.884479	1444.496370	2004.156123
89	581.840561	795.176195	1094.994280	1517.721189	2115.384712
90	603.204980	827.983241	1145.269024	1594.607245	2232.730868
91	625.317154	862.102572	1197.806130	1675.337609	2356.531064
92	648.203253	897.586673	1252.707404	1760.104489	2487.140272
93	671.890367	934.490139	1310.079238	1849.109716	2624.932984
94	696.406529	972.869744	1370.032805	1942.565195	2770.304297
95	721.780759	1012.784531	1432.684283	2040.693453	2923.671030
96	748.043082	1054.265909	1498.155074	2143.728127	3085.472935
97	775.224590	1097.467747	1566.572051	2251.914536	3256.173945
98	808.357450	1142.366453	1638.067795	2365.510255	3436.263509
99	832.474961	1189.061112	1712.780848	2484.785771	3626.257999
100	862.611582	1237.623554	1790.855984	2610.025058	3826.702184

Table 6 Amount of an Annuity $\left(s_{\overline{n}|r} = \dfrac{(1 + r)^n - 1}{r}\right)$ *(Continued)*

n	6%	$6\frac{1}{2}\%$	7%	$7\frac{1}{2}\%$	8%
1	1.000000	1.000000	1.000000	1.000000	1.000000
2	2.060000	2.065000	2.070000	2.075000	2.080000
3	3.183600	3.199225	3.214900	3.230625	3.246400
4	4.374616	4.407175	4.439943	4.472922	4.506112
5	5.637093	5.693641	5.750739	5.808391	5.866601
6	6.975318	7.063728	7.153291	7.244020	7.335929
7	8.393838	8.522870	8.654021	8.787322	8.922803
8	9.897468	10.076857	10.259802	10.446371	10.636628
9	11.491316	11.731852	11.977989	12.229849	12.487558
10	13.180795	13.494423	13.816448	14.147087	14.486562
11	14.971642	15.371560	15.783599	16.208119	16.645487
12	16.869941	17.370711	17.888451	18.423728	18.977126
13	18.882137	19.499808	20.140643	20.805507	21.495296
14	21.015066	21.767295	22.550487	23.365920	24.214920
15	23.275970	24.182169	25.129022	26.118364	27.152114
16	25.672528	26.754010	27.888053	29.077242	30.324283
17	28.212879	29.493021	30.840217	32.258035	33.750225
18	30.905652	32.410067	33.999032	35.677387	37.450243
19	33.759991	35.516722	37.378964	39.353191	41.446263
20	36.785591	38.825309	40.995491	43.304681	45.761964
21	39.992726	42.348954	44.865176	47.552532	50.422921
22	43.392289	46.101636	49.005738	52.118972	55.456754
23	46.995827	50.098242	53.436140	57.027894	60.893295
24	50.815576	54.354628	58.176669	62.304987	66.764758
25	54.864511	58.887679	63.249036	67.977861	73.105939
26	59.156381	63.715378	68.676469	74.076200	79.954414
27	63.705764	68.856877	74.483821	80.631915	87.350767
28	68.528110	74.332575	80.697689	87.679309	95.338828
29	73.639797	80.164192	87.346527	95.255257	103.965934
30	79.058184	86.374864	94.460783	103.399401	113.283209
31	84.801676	92.989230	102.073039	112.154356	123.345866
32	90.889776	100.033530	110.218151	121.565933	134.213535
33	97.343163	107.535710	118.933422	131.683377	145.950617
34	104.183752	115.525531	128.258761	142.559631	158.626667
35	111.434777	124.034691	138.236874	154.251603	172.316800
36	119.120864	133.096946	148.913455	166.820473	187.102144
37	127.268116	142.748247	160.337397	180.332008	203.070315
38	135.904202	153.026883	172.561014	194.856909	220.315940
39	145.058455	163.973630	185.640285	210.471177	238.941216
40	154.761961	175.631916	199.635105	227.256515	259.056512
41	165.047679	188.047991	214.609562	245.300754	280.781033
42	175.950540	201.271110	230.632231	264.698310	304.243515
43	187.507572	215.353732	247.776488	285.550683	329.582997
44	199.758026	230.331725	266.120841	307.966984	356.949636
45	212.743508	246.324588	285.749300	332.064508	386.505607
46	226.508118	263.335686	306.751749	357.969346	418.426055
47	241.098605	281.452505	329.224373	385.817046	452.900140
48	256.564521	300.746919	353.270078	415.753325	490.132150
49	272.958392	321.295468	378.998984	447.934824	530.342722
50	290.335895	343.179673	406.528912	482.529936	573.770138

n	6%	$6\frac{1}{2}\%$	7%	$7\frac{1}{2}\%$	8%
51	308.756049	366.486352	435.985936	519.719680	620.671751
52	328.281411	391.307965	467.504951	559.698656	671.325489
53	348.978296	417.742982	501.230297	602.676055	726.031528
54	370.916993	445.896276	537.316416	648.876758	785.114049
55	394.172013	475.879534	575.928566	698.542515	848.923175
56	418.822333	507.811705	617.243564	751.933203	917.837026
57	444.951673	541.819465	661.450614	809.328194	992.263989
58	472.648773	578.037730	708.752155	871.027808	1072.645104
59	502.007700	616.610182	759.364807	937.354893	1159.456715
60	533.128160	657.689845	813.520340	1008.656509	1253.213249
61	566.115851	701.439684	871.466765	1085.305746	1354.470310
62	601.082800	748.033264	933.469437	1167.703677	1463.827931
63	638.147769	797.655426	999.812300	1256.281450	1581.934169
64	677.436635	850.503029	1070.799156	1351.502560	1709.488897
65	719.082832	906.785726	1146.755097	1453.865253	1847.248009
66	763.227802	966.726798	1228.027951	1563.905145	1996.027847
67	810.021470	1030.564038	1314.989908	1682.198029	2156.710075
68	859.622755	1098.550703	1408.039199	1809.362883	2330.246878
69	912.200122	1170.956497	1507.601942	1946.065099	2517.666628
70	967.932127	1248.068670	1614.134075	2093.019979	2720.079956
71	1027.008055	1330.193133	1728.123464	2250.996476	2938.686356
72	1089.628537	1417.655689	1850.092102	2420.821210	3174.781254
73	1156.006250	1510.803308	1980.598549	2603.382801	3429.763757
74	1226.366622	1610.005523	2120.240443	2799.636508	3705.144851
75	1300.948621	1715.655881	2269.657275	3010.609246	4002.556443
76	1380.005534	1828.173516	2429.533280	3237.404937	4323.760948
77	1463.805867	1948.004794	2600.600607	3481.210308	4670.661830
78	1552.634216	2075.625104	2783.642642	3743.301081	5045.314764
79	1646.792271	2211.540734	2979.497633	4025.048657	5449.939954
80	1746.599804	2356.290888	3189.062458	4327.927299	5886.935134
81	1852.395794	2510.449792	3413.296833	4653.521842	6358.889949
82	1964.539537	2674.629030	3653.227602	5003.535984	6868.601137
83	2083.411913	1849.479914	3909.953540	5379.801177	7419.089235
84	2209.416623	3035.696113	4184.650276	5784.286270	8013.616357
85	2342.981621	3234.016355	4478.575796	6219.107736	8655.705661
86	2484.560511	3445.227421	4793.076093	6686.540805	9349.162105
87	2634.634147	3670.167201	5129.591424	7189.031364	10098.095077
88	2793.712188	3909.728077	5489.662807	7729.208723	10906.942661
89	2962.334920	4164.860403	5874.939210	8309.899372	11780.498081
90	3141.075010	4436.576330	6287.184940	8934.141819	12723.937900
91	3330.539515	4725.953783	6728.287887	9605.202449	13742.852951
92	3531.371874	5034.140785	7200.268024	10326.592628	14843.281143
93	3744.254194	5362.359933	7705.286788	11102.087059	16031.743671
94	3969.909436	5711.913330	8245.656841	11935.743587	17315.283134
95	4209.104005	6084.187692	8823.852836	12831.924335	18701.505798
96	4462.650238	6480.659896	9442.522521	13795.318672	20198.626205
97	4731.409255	6902.902790	10104.499080	14830.967571	21815.516296
98	5016.293804	7352.591470	10812.814002	15944.290138	23561.757575
99	5318.271438	7831.509906	11570.710987	17141.111877	25447.698181
100	5638.567708	8341.558067	12381.660732	18427.695266	27484.514007

Table 7 Present Value of an Annuity[a]

$$\left(a_{\overline{n}|r} = \frac{1 - (1 + r)^{-n}}{r} \right)$$

r = interest rate per payment period; n = number of payment periods

n	$\frac{1}{4}\%$	$\frac{1}{2}\%$	$\frac{3}{4}\%$	1%	$1\frac{1}{4}\%$
1	0.997506	0.995025	0.992556	0.990099	0.987654
2	1.992524	1.985099	1.977723	1.970395	1.963115
3	2.985061	2.970248	2.955556	2.940985	2.926534
4	3.975123	3.950496	3.926110	3.901965	3.878058
5	4.962716	4.925867	4.889439	4.853431	4.817835
6	5.947846	5.896385	5.845597	5.795476	5.746010
7	6.930519	6.862074	6.794637	6.728194	6.662725
8	7.910741	7.822960	7.736613	7.651677	7.568124
9	8.888520	8.779064	8.671576	8.566017	8.462344
10	9.863860	9.730412	9.599579	9.471304	9.345525
11	10.836767	10.677027	10.520674	10.367628	10.217803
12	11.807249	11.618933	11.434912	11.255077	11.079311
13	12.775310	12.556152	12.342345	12.133740	11.930184
14	13.740957	13.488708	13.243022	13.003702	12.770552
15	14.704197	14.416626	14.136994	13.865052	13.600545
16	15.665033	15.339926	15.024312	14.717873	14.420291
17	16.623475	16.258633	15.905024	15.562251	15.229918
18	17.579525	17.172769	16.779180	16.398268	16.029548
19	18.533192	18.082357	17.646829	17.226008	16.819307
20	19.484480	18.987420	18.508019	18.045552	17.599315
21	20.433396	19.887980	19.362798	18.856982	18.369694
22	21.379946	20.784060	20.211214	19.660379	19.130562
23	22.324136	21.675682	21.053314	20.455820	19.882036
24	23.265970	22.562867	21.889145	21.243386	20.624233
25	24.205456	23.445639	22.718754	22.023155	21.357268
26	25.142599	24.324019	23.542188	22.795203	22.081252
27	26.077405	25.198029	24.359492	23.559607	22.796298
28	27.009879	26.067691	25.170711	24.316442	23.502517
29	27.940030	26.933025	25.975892	25.065784	24.200016
30	28.867859	27.794055	26.775079	25.807707	24.888905
31	29.793376	28.650802	27.568317	26.542284	25.569289
32	30.716584	29.503285	28.355649	27.269588	26.241273
33	31.637490	30.351527	29.137121	27.989691	26.904961
34	32.556099	31.195550	29.912775	28.702665	27.560455
35	33.472417	32.035373	30.682655	29.408579	28.207857
36	34.386451	32.871018	31.446804	30.107504	28.847266
37	35.298205	33.702505	32.205264	30.799509	29.478781
38	36.207685	34.529856	32.958079	31.484662	30.102500
39	37.114898	35.353091	33.705289	32.163032	30.718518
40	38.019848	36.172230	34.446937	32.834685	31.326932
41	38.922541	36.987293	35.183064	33.499688	31.927834
42	39.822983	37.798302	35.913711	34.158107	32.521317
43	40.721180	38.605275	36.638919	34.810007	33.107474
44	41.617136	39.408234	37.358729	35.455452	33.686394
45	42.510859	40.207198	38.073180	36.094507	34.258167
46	43.402353	41.002187	38.782312	36.727235	34.822881
47	44.291624	41.793221	39.486166	37.353698	35.380623
48	45.178676	42.580320	40.184780	37.973958	35.931479
49	46.063518	43.363502	40.878194	38.588077	36.475535
50	46.946152	44.142788	41.566445	39.196116	37.012874

[a] Reproduced by permission from A. Mizrahi and M. Sullivan, *Finite Mathematics with Applications*, Wiley, New York, 1973.

n	$\frac{1}{4}\%$	$\frac{1}{2}\%$	$\frac{3}{4}\%$	1%	$1\frac{1}{4}\%$
51	47.826585	44.918198	42.249573	39.798135	37.543579
52	48.704822	45.689749	42.927616	40.394193	38.067733
53	49.580870	46.457462	43.600612	40.984349	38.585415
54	50.454732	47.221355	44.268597	41.568663	39.096706
55	51.326417	47.981447	44.931610	42.147191	39.601685
56	52.195926	48.737759	45.589687	42.719991	40.100430
57	53.063268	49.490307	46.242866	43.287120	40.593017
58	53.928446	50.239112	46.891182	43.848633	41.079523
59	54.791466	50.984191	47.534672	44.404587	41.560023
60	55.652335	51.725563	48.173372	44.955037	42.034590
61	56.511058	52.463247	48.807317	45.500037	42.503299
62	57.367637	53.197261	49.436542	46.039640	42.966221
63	58.222083	53.927623	50.061085	46.573901	43.423428
64	59.074396	54.654351	50.680977	47.102872	43.874991
65	59.924584	55.377464	51.296255	47.626606	44.320978
66	60.772652	56.096979	51.906953	48.145155	44.761460
67	61.618605	56.812914	52.513105	48.658569	45.196504
68	62.462449	57.525288	53.114744	49.166900	45.626177
69	63.304188	58.234117	53.711905	49.670198	46.050545
70	64.143828	58.939420	54.304620	50.168513	46.469674
71	64.981375	59.641214	54.892923	50.661894	46.883629
72	65.816832	60.339517	55.476847	51.150390	47.292473
73	66.650206	61.034345	56.056424	51.634049	47.696269
74	67.481502	61.725716	56.631686	52.112920	48.095081
75	68.310725	62.413648	57.202666	52.587050	48.488969
76	69.137879	63.098157	57.769395	53.056485	48.877994
77	69.962972	63.779261	58.331906	53.521272	49.262216
78	70.786006	64.456976	58.890229	53.981457	49.641695
79	71.606989	65.131320	59.444396	54.437087	50.016488
80	72.425923	65.802308	59.994438	54.888205	50.386655
81	73.242816	66.469958	60.540385	55.334856	50.752252
82	74.057672	67.134287	61.082268	55.777085	51.113335
83	74.870495	67.795311	61.620117	56.214936	51.469961
84	75.681291	68.453045	62.153962	56.648451	51.822184
85	76.490066	69.107508	62.683834	57.077674	52.170058
86	77.296823	69.758714	63.209760	57.502648	52.513637
87	78.101570	70.406681	63.731772	57.923414	52.852975
88	78.904308	71.051424	64.249898	58.340014	53.188124
89	79.705045	71.692959	64.764167	58.752489	53.519134
90	80.503785	72.331303	65.274607	59.160880	53.846059
91	81.300533	72.966470	65.781248	59.565228	54.168947
92	82.095294	73.598478	66.284117	59.965572	54.487849
93	82.888075	74.227341	66.783242	60.361952	54.802813
94	83.678877	74.853076	67.278652	60.754408	55.113890
95	84.467708	75.475697	67.770375	61.142978	55.421126
96	85.254571	76.095221	68.258436	61.527701	55.724569
97	86.039472	76.711663	68.742865	61.908615	56.024265
98	86.822415	77.325038	69.223687	62.285758	56.320262
99	87.603406	77.935361	69.700930	62.659166	56.612604
100	88.382449	78.542648	70.174620	63.028877	56.901338

Table 7 Present Value of an Annuity $\left(a_{\overline{n}|r} = \dfrac{1 - (1 + r)^{-n}}{r} \right)$ (Continued)

n	$1\frac{1}{2}\%$	$1\frac{3}{4}\%$	2%	$2\frac{1}{2}\%$	3%
1	0.985222	0.982801	0.980392	0.975610	0.970874
2	1.955883	1.948699	1.941561	1.927424	1.913470
3	2.912200	2.897984	2.883883	2.856024	2.828611
4	3.854385	3.830942	3.807729	3.761974	3.717098
5	4.782645	4.747855	4.713459	4.645828	4.579707
6	5.697187	5.648997	5.601431	5.508125	5.417191
7	6.598214	6.534641	6.471991	6.349390	6.230283
8	7.485925	7.405053	7.325481	7.170137	7.019692
9	8.360517	8.260494	8.162236	7.970865	7.786109
10	9.222184	9.101223	8.982585	8.752064	8.530203
11	10.071118	9.927492	9.786848	9.514208	9.252624
12	10.907505	10.739549	10.575341	10.257764	9.954004
13	11.731532	11.537641	11.348373	10.983185	10.634955
14	12.543381	12.322005	12.106248	11.690912	11.296073
15	13.343233	13.092880	12.849263	12.381377	11.937935
16	14.131264	13.850496	13.577709	13.055002	12.561102
17	14.907649	14.595082	14.291871	13.712197	13.166118
18	15.672561	15.326862	14.992031	14.353363	13.753513
19	16.426168	16.046056	15.678462	14.978891	14.323799
20	17.168639	16.752881	16.351433	15.589162	14.877475
21	17.900137	17.447549	17.011209	16.184548	15.415024
22	18.620824	18.130269	17.658048	16.765413	15.936916
23	19.330861	18.801247	18.292204	17.332110	16.443608
24	20.030405	19.460685	18.913925	17.884985	16.935542
25	20.719611	20.108781	19.523456	18.424376	17.413147
26	21.398632	20.745731	20.121035	18.950611	17.876842
27	22.067617	21.371726	20.706897	19.464010	18.327031
28	22.726717	21.986954	21.281272	19.964888	18.764108
29	23.376076	22.591601	21.844384	20.453549	19.188454
30	24.015838	23.185849	22.396455	20.930292	19.600441
31	24.646146	23.769876	22.937701	21.395407	20.000428
32	25.267139	24.343858	23.468334	21.849177	20.388765
33	25.878954	24.907969	23.988563	22.291880	20.765792
34	26.481728	25.462377	24.498591	22.723786	21.131836
35	27.075595	26.007250	24.998619	23.145157	21.487220
36	27.660684	26.542752	25.488842	23.556251	21.832252
37	28.237127	27.069044	25.969453	23.957318	22.167235
38	28.805052	27.586284	26.440640	24.348603	22.492461
39	29.364583	28.094628	26.902588	24.730344	22.808215
40	29.915845	28.594229	27.355478	25.102775	23.114772
41	30.458961	29.085237	27.799489	25.466121	23.412400
42	30.994050	29.567801	28.234793	25.820606	23.701359
43	31.521232	30.042064	28.661562	26.166445	23.981902
44	32.040622	30.508171	29.079962	26.503849	24.254274
45	32.552337	30.966262	29.490159	26.833023	24.518712
46	33.056490	31.416473	29.892313	27.154169	24.775449
47	33.553192	31.858942	30.286581	27.467482	25.024708
48	34.042554	32.293800	30.673119	27.773153	25.266706
49	34.524683	32.721180	31.052077	28.071369	25.501657
50	34.999688	33.141209	31.423605	28.362311	25.729764

n	$1\frac{1}{2}\%$	$1\frac{3}{4}\%$	2%	$2\frac{1}{2}\%$	3%
51	35.467673	33.554013	31.787848	28.646157	25.951227
52	35.928742	33.959718	32.144949	28.923080	26.166240
53	36.382997	34.358445	32.495048	29.193249	26.374990
54	36.830539	34.750315	32.838282	29.456828	26.577660
55	37.271467	35.135445	33.174787	29.713979	26.774427
56	37.705879	35.513950	33.504693	29.964857	26.965464
57	38.133871	35.885946	33.828130	30.209617	27.150935
58	38.555537	36.251544	34.145226	30.448407	27.331005
59	38.970973	36.610854	34.456104	30.681372	27.505830
60	39.380269	36.963985	34.760886	30.908656	27.675564
61	39.783516	37.311041	35.059692	31.130396	27.840353
62	40.180804	37.652129	35.352639	31.346728	28.000343
63	40.572221	37.987351	35.639842	31.557783	28.155672
64	40.957853	38.316806	35.921414	31.763691	28.306478
65	41.337786	38.640596	36.197465	31.964577	28.452891
66	41.712105	38.958817	36.468103	32.160562	28.595040
67	42.080891	39.271564	36.733434	32.351768	28.733049
68	42.444228	39.578933	36.993563	32.538311	28.867038
69	42.802195	39.881015	37.248591	32.720303	28.997124
70	43.154872	40.177902	37.498619	32.897857	29.123421
71	43.502337	40.469682	37.743744	33.071080	29.246040
72	43.844667	40.756445	37.984062	33.240078	29.365087
73	44.181938	41.038275	38.219669	33.404954	29.480667
74	44.514224	41.315258	38.450656	33.565809	29.592881
75	44.841600	41.587477	38.677114	33.722740	29.701826
76	45.164138	41.855014	38.899131	33.875844	29.807598
77	45.481910	42.117950	39.116795	34.025214	29.910290
78	45.794985	42.376364	39.330191	34.170940	30.009990
79	46.103433	42.630333	39.539403	34.313112	30.106786
80	46.407323	42.879934	39.744513	34.451817	30.200763
81	46.706723	43.125242	39.945601	34.587138	30.292003
82	47.001697	43.366331	40.142746	34.719159	30.380586
83	47.292313	43.603274	40.336025	34.847960	30.466588
84	47.578633	43.836142	40.525515	34.973620	30.550085
85	47.860722	44.065004	40.711289	35.096214	30.631151
86	48.138643	44.289930	40.893421	35.215819	30.709855
87	48.412456	44.510988	41.071981	35.332506	30.786267
88	48.682222	44.728244	41.247040	35.446348	30.860454
89	48.948002	44.941763	41.418667	35.557412	30.932479
90	49.209854	45.151610	41.586929	35.665768	31.002407
91	49.467837	45.357847	41.751891	35.771481	31.070298
92	49.722007	45.560538	41.913618	35.874616	31.136212
93	49.972421	45.759742	42.072175	35.975235	31.200206
94	50.219134	45.955521	42.227622	36.073400	31.262336
95	50.462201	46.147932	42.380022	36.169171	31.322656
96	50.701675	46.337034	42.529433	36.262605	31.381219
97	50.937611	46.522883	42.675915	36.353761	31.438077
98	51.170060	46.705537	42.819524	36.442694	31.493279
99	51.399074	46.885048	42.960318	36.529458	31.546872
100	51.624704	47.061472	43.098351	36.614105	31.598905

Table 7 Present Value of an Annuity $\left(a_{\overline{n}|r} = \dfrac{1 - (1 + r)^{-n}}{r} \right)$ (Continued)

n	$3\frac{1}{2}\%$	4%	$4\frac{1}{2}\%$	5%	$5\frac{1}{2}\%$
1	0.966184	0.961538	0.956938	0.952381	0.947867
2	1.899694	1.886095	1.872668	1.859410	1.846320
3	2.801637	2.775091	2.748964	2.723248	2.697933
4	3.673079	3.629895	3.587526	3.545950	3.505150
5	4.515052	4.451822	4.389977	4.329477	4.270284
6	5.328553	5.242137	5.157873	5.075692	4.995530
7	6.114544	6.002055	5.892701	5.786373	5.682967
8	6.873955	6.732745	6.595886	6.463213	6.334566
9	7.607686	7.435331	7.268791	7.107822	6.952195
10	8.316605	8.110896	7.912718	7.721735	7.537626
11	9.001551	8.760477	8.528917	8.306414	8.092536
12	9.663334	9.385074	9.118581	8.863252	8.618518
13	10.302738	9.985648	9.682852	9.393573	9.117078
14	10.920520	10.563123	10.222825	9.898641	9.589648
15	11.517411	11.118387	10.739546	10.379658	10.037581
16	12.094117	11.652295	11.234015	10.837770	10.462162
17	12.651320	12.165669	11.707191	11.274066	10.864608
18	13.189682	12.659297	12.159992	11.689587	11.246074
19	13.709837	13.133939	12.593294	12.085321	11.607653
20	14.212403	13.590326	13.007937	12.462210	11.950382
21	14.697974	14.029160	13.404724	12.821153	12.275244
22	15.167125	14.451115	13.784425	13.163003	12.583170
23	15.620410	14.856841	14.147775	13.488574	12.875042
24	16.058367	15.246963	14.495478	13.798642	13.151699
25	16.481514	15.622080	14.828209	14.093945	13.413933
26	16.890352	15.982769	15.146611	14.375185	13.662495
27	17.285364	16.329585	15.451303	14.643034	13.898100
28	17.667019	16.663063	15.742874	14.898127	14.121422
29	18.035767	16.983714	16.021889	15.141074	14.333101
30	18.392045	17.292033	16.288889	15.372451	14.533745
31	18.736276	17.588493	16.544391	15.592810	14.723929
32	19.068865	17.873551	16.788891	15.802677	14.904198
33	19.390208	18.147645	17.022862	16.002549	15.075069
34	19.700684	18.411197	17.246758	16.192904	15.237033
35	20.000661	18.664613	17.461012	16.374194	15.390552
36	20.290494	18.908282	17.666041	16.546852	15.536068
37	20.570525	19.142579	17.862240	16.711287	15.673998
38	20.841087	19.367864	18.049990	16.867893	15.804738
39	21.102500	19.584485	18.229656	17.017041	15.928662
40	21.355072	19.792774	18.401584	17.159086	16.046125
41	21.599103	19.993052	18.566110	17.294368	16.157464
42	21.834883	20.185627	18.723550	17.423208	16.262999
43	22.062688	20.370795	18.874210	17.545912	16.363032
44	22.282791	20.548841	19.018383	17.662773	16.457851
45	22.495450	20.720040	19.156347	17.774070	16.547726
46	22.700918	20.884653	19.288371	17.880066	16.632915
47	22.899438	21.042936	19.414709	17.981016	16.713664
48	23.091244	21.195131	19.535607	18.077158	16.790203
49	23.276564	21.341472	19.651298	18.168722	16.862751
50	23.455618	21.482184	19.762008	18.255925	16.931518

n	$3\frac{1}{2}\%$	4%	$4\frac{1}{2}\%$	5%	$5\frac{1}{2}\%$
51	23.628616	21.617485	19.867950	18.338977	16.996699
52	23.795764	21.747582	19.969330	18.418073	17.058483
53	23.957260	21.872675	20.066345	16.493403	17.117045
54	24.113295	21.992966	20.159182	18.565146	17.172555
55	24.264053	22.108612	20.248021	18.633472	17.225170
56	24.409713	22.219819	20.333034	18.698545	17.275043
57	24.550447	22.326749	20.414387	18.760519	17.322316
58	24.686423	22.429567	20.492236	18.819542	17.367124
59	24.817800	22.528429	20.566733	18.875754	17.409596
60	24.944734	22.623490	20.638022	18.929290	17.449854
61	25.067376	22.714894	20.706241	18.980276	17.488013
62	25.185870	22.802783	20.771523	19.028834	17.524183
63	25.300358	22.887291	20.833993	19.075080	17.558468
64	25.410974	22.968549	20.893773	19.119124	17.590965
65	25.517849	23.046682	20.950979	19.161070	17.621767
66	25.621110	23.121809	21.005722	19.201019	17.650964
67	25.720879	23.194048	21.058107	19.239066	17.678639
68	25.817275	23.263507	21.108236	19.275301	17.704871
69	25.910410	23.330295	21.156207	19.309810	17.729736
70	26.000397	23.394515	21.202112	19.342677	17.753304
71	26.087340	23.456264	21.246040	19.373987	17.775644
72	26.171343	23.515639	21.288077	19.403788	17.796819
73	26.252505	23.572730	21.328303	19.432179	17.816890
74	26.330923	23.627625	21.366797	19.459218	17.835914
75	26.406689	23.680408	21.403634	19.484970	17.853947
76	26.479892	23.731162	21.488884	19.509495	17.871040
77	26.550621	23.779963	21.472616	19.532853	17.887242
78	26.618957	23.826888	21.504896	19.555098	17.902599
79	26.684983	23.872007	21.535785	19.576283	17.917155
80	26.748776	23.915392	21.565345	19.596460	17.930953
81	26.810411	23.957107	21.593632	19.615677	17.944031
82	26.869962	23.997219	21.620700	19.633978	17.956428
83	26.927500	24.035787	21.646603	19.651407	17.968178
84	26.983092	24.072872	21.671390	19.668007	17.979316
85	27.036804	24.108531	21.695110	19.683816	17.989873
86	27.088699	24.142818	21.717809	19.698873	17.999879
87	27.138840	24.175787	21.739530	19.713212	18.009364
88	27.187285	24.207487	21.760316	19.726869	18.018355
89	27.234092	24.237969	21.780207	19.739875	18.026876
90	27.279316	24.267278	21.799241	19.752262	18.034954
91	27.323010	24.295459	21.817455	19.764059	18.042610
92	27.365227	24.322557	21.834885	19.775294	18.049868
93	27.406017	24.348612	21.851565	19.785994	18.056747
94	27.445427	24.373666	21.867526	19.796185	18.063267
95	27.483504	24.397756	21.882800	19.805891	18.069447
96	27.520294	24.420919	21.897417	19.815134	18.075306
97	27.555839	24.443191	21.911403	19.823937	18.080858
98	27.590183	24.464607	21.924788	19.832321	18.086122
99	27.623365	24.485199	21.937596	19.840306	18.091111
100	27.655525	24.504999	21.949853	19.847910	18.095839

Table 7 Present Value of an Annuity $\left(a_{\overline{n}|r} = \dfrac{1 - (1 + r)^{-n}}{r}\right)$ *(Continued)*

n	6%	$6\frac{1}{2}\%$	7%	$7\frac{1}{2}\%$	8%
1	0.943396	0.938967	0.934579	0.930233	0.925926
2	1.833393	1.820626	1.808018	1.795565	1.783265
3	2.673012	2.648475	2.624316	2.600526	2.577097
4	3.465106	3.425799	3.387211	3.349326	3.312127
5	4.212364	4.155679	4.100197	4.045885	3.992710
6	4.917324	4.841014	4.766540	4.693846	4.622880
7	5.582381	5.484520	5.389289	5.296601	5.206370
8	6.209794	6.088751	5.971298	5.857304	5.746639
9	6.801692	6.656104	6.515232	6.378887	6.246888
10	7.360087	7.188830	7.023581	6.864081	6.710081
11	7.886875	7.689042	7.498674	7.315424	7.138964
12	8.383844	8.158725	7.942686	7.735278	7.536078
13	8.852683	8.599742	8.357651	8.125840	7.903776
14	9.294984	9.013842	8.745468	8.489154	8.244237
15	9.712249	9.402669	9.107914	8.827120	8.559479
16	10.105895	9.767764	9.446649	9.141507	8.851369
17	10.477260	10.110577	9.763223	9.433960	9.121638
18	10.827603	10.432466	10.059087	9.706009	9.371887
19	11.158116	10.734710	10.335595	9.959078	9.603599
20	11.469921	11.018507	10.594014	10.194491	9.818147
21	11.764077	11.284983	10.835527	10.413480	10.016803
22	12.041582	11.535196	11.061240	10.617191	10.200744
23	12.303379	11.770137	11.272187	10.806689	10.371059
24	12.550357	11.990739	11.469334	10.982967	10.528758
25	12.783356	12.197877	11.653583	11.146946	10.674776
26	13.003166	12.392373	11.825779	11.299485	10.809978
27	13.210534	12.574998	11.986709	11.441381	10.935165
28	13.406164	12.746477	12.137111	11.573378	11.051078
29	13.590721	12.907490	12.277674	11.696165	11.158406
30	13.764831	13.058676	12.409041	11.810386	11.257783
31	13.929086	13.200635	12.531814	11.916638	11.349799
32	14.084043	13.333929	12.646555	12.015478	11.434999
33	14.230230	13.459089	12.753790	12.107421	11.513888
34	14.368141	13.576609	12.854009	12.192950	11.586934
35	14.498246	13.686957	12.947672	12.272511	11.654568
36	14.620987	13.790570	13.035208	12.346522	11.717193
37	14.736780	13.887859	13.117017	12.415370	11.775179
38	14.846019	13.979210	13.193473	12.479414	11.828869
39	14.949075	14.064986	13.264928	12.538989	11.878582
40	15.046297	14.145527	13.331709	12.594409	11.924613
41	15.138016	14.221152	13.394120	12.645962	11.967235
42	15.224543	14.292162	13.452449	12.693918	12.006699
43	15.306173	14.358837	13.506962	12.738528	12.043240
44	15.383182	14.421443	13.557908	12.780026	12.077074
45	15.455832	14.480228	13.605522	12.818629	12.108401
46	15.524370	14.535426	13.650020	12.854539	12.137409
47	15.589028	14.587254	13.691608	12.887943	12.164267
48	15.650027	14.635919	13.730474	12.919017	12.189137
49	15.707572	14.681615	13.766799	12.947922	12.212163
50	15.761861	14.724521	13.800746	12.974812	12.233485

n	6%	$6\frac{1}{2}\%$	7%	$7\frac{1}{2}\%$	8%
51	15.813076	14.764808	13.832473	12.999825	12.253224
52	15.861393	14.802637	13.862124	13.023093	12.271506
53	15.906974	14.838157	13.889836	13.044737	12.288432
54	15.949976	14.871509	13.915735	13.064872	12.304103
55	15.990543	14.902825	13.939939	13.083602	12.318614
56	16.028814	14.932230	13.962560	13.101025	12.332050
57	16.064919	14.959840	13.983701	13.117233	12.344491
58	16.098980	14.985766	14.003459	13.132309	12.356010
59	16.131113	15.010109	14.021924	13.146334	12.366676
60	16.161428	15.032966	14.039181	13.159381	12.376552
61	16.190026	15.054428	14.055309	13.171517	12.385696
62	16.217006	15.074580	14.070383	13.182807	12.394163
63	16.242458	15.093503	14.084470	13.193308	12.402003
64	16.266470	15.111270	14.097635	13.203078	12.409262
65	16.289123	15.127953	14.109940	13.212165	12.415983
66	16.310493	15.143618	14.121439	13.220619	12.422207
67	16.330654	15.158327	14.132186	13.228483	12.427969
68	16.349673	15.172138	14.142230	13.235798	12.433305
69	16.367617	15.185106	14.151617	13.242603	12.438245
70	16.384544	15.197282	14.160389	13.248933	12.442820
71	16.400513	15.208716	14.168588	13.254821	12.447005
72	16.415578	15.219452	14.176251	13.260299	12.450977
73	16.429791	15.229532	14.183412	13.265394	12.454608
74	16.443199	15.238997	14.190105	13.270134	12.457971
75	16.455848	15.247885	14.196359	13.274543	12.461084
76	16.467781	15.256230	14.202205	13.278645	12.463967
77	16.479039	15.264065	14.207668	13.282460	12.466636
78	16.489659	15.271423	14.212774	13.286010	12.469107
79	16.499679	15.278331	14.217546	13.289311	12.471396
80	16.509131	15.284818	14.222005	13.292383	12.473514
81	16.518048	15.290909	14.226173	13.295240	12.475476
82	16.526460	15.296628	14.230069	13.297897	12.477293
83	16.534396	15.301998	14.233709	13.300370	12.478975
84	16.541883	15.307041	14.237111	13.302669	12.480532
85	16.548947	15.311775	14.240291	13.304809	12.481974
86	16.555610	15.316221	14.243262	13.306799	12.483310
87	16.561896	15.320395	14.246040	13.308650	12.484546
88	16.567827	15.324315	14.248635	13.310372	12.485691
89	16.573421	15.327995	14.251061	13.311974	12.486751
90	16.578699	15.331451	14.253328	13.313464	12.487732
91	16.583679	15.334696	14.255447	13.314851	12.488641
92	16.588376	15.337742	14.257427	13.316140	12.489482
93	16.592808	15.340603	14.259277	13.317340	12.490261
94	16.596988	15.343289	14.261007	13.318455	12.490983
95	16.600932	15.345812	14.262623	13.319493	12.491651
96	16.604653	15.348180	14.264134	13.320459	12.492269
97	16.608163	15.350404	14.265546	13.321357	12.492842
98	16.611475	15.352492	14.266865	13.322193	12.493372
99	16.614599	15.354452	14.268098	13.322970	12.493863
100	16.617546	15.356293	14.269251	13.323693	12.494318

Answers to Odd-Numbered Exercises

CHAPTER 1

Exercise 1.1 (pages 6–7)

1. **c., e., f., g., h., i.,** and **j.** are well-defined sets.

3. **a., b., d.,** and **f.** are true statements.

5. **b., c., d., g.,** and **h.** are finite sets.

7. **d.** and **f.** are equal to A.
   b. and **e.** are equal to B.

9. { }, {Bob}, {Charles}, {Dick}, {Edward}, {Bob, Charles}, {Bob, Dick}, {Bob, Edward}, {Charles, Dick}, {Charles, Edward}, {Dick, Edward}, {Bob, Charles, Dick}, {Bob, Charles, Edward}, {Bob, Dick, Edward}, {Charles, Dick, Edward}, {Bob, Charles, Dick, Edward} are 16 subsets of $\mathcal{U}$. All subsets of $\mathcal{U}$ except $\mathcal{U}$ itself are proper subsets of $\mathcal{U}$.

Exercise 1.2 (pages 13–15)

1. a.

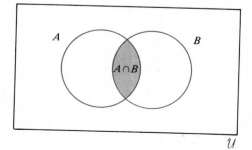

b.

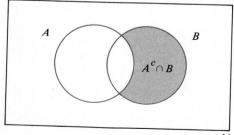

c. **d.**

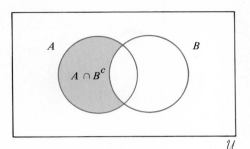

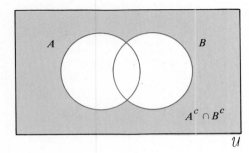

3. a. {1, 7, 8, 9, 10} **b.** {1, 2, 3, 5, 9} **c.** {2, 3, 4, 5, 6, 7, 8, 10}
 d. {4, 6} **e.** {1, 2, 3, 5, 7, 8, 9, 10} **f.** {1, 9}
 g. {1, 9} **h.** {1, 2, 3, 5, 7, 8, 9, 10}

5. a. the set of secretaries or the stockholders of an insurance company
 b. the set of secretaries and the stockholders of an insurance company
 c. the set of stockholders and key-punch operators in an insurance company
 d. the set of stockholders or key-punch operators in an insurance company
 e. the set of secretaries or key-punch operators in an insurance company
 f. the set of secretaries and key-punch operators in an insurance company
 g. the set of either the secretaries and the stockholders or the secretaries and key-punch operators in an insurance company
 h. the set of those who are secretaries, key-punch operators, and stockholders in an insurance company

Exercise 1.3 (pages 20–23)
 1. a. 3 **b.** 8
 3. a. 20 **b.** 29 **c.** 12 **d.** 21 **e.** 42 **f.** 41 **g.** 29 **h.** 38
 5. a. 151 **b.** 19 **c.** 105
 7. a. 68 **b.** 18 **c.** 12 **d.** 44
 9. a. 93 **b.** 7 **c.** 35 **d.** 11 **e.** 11
 11. a. 193 **b.** 126 **c.** 183 **d.** 57

Exercise 1.4 (pages 25–26)
 1. a. {(2, 5), (2, 6), (3, 5), (3, 6), (4, 5), (4, 6)}
 b. {(5, 2), (5, 3), (5, 4), (6, 2), (6, 3), (6, 4)}
 c. {(2, 2), (2, 3), (2, 4), (3, 2), (3, 3), (3, 4), (4, 2), (4, 3), (4, 4)}
 d. {(5, 5), (5, 6), (6, 5), (6, 6)}
 3. a. {(1, 3), (1, 4), (1, 5), (2, 3), (2, 4), (2, 5), (3, 3), (3, 4), (3, 5)}
 b. {(1, 6), (1, 7), (1, 8), (2, 6), (2, 7), (2, 8), (3, 6), (3, 7), (3, 8)}
 c. {(3, 6), (3, 7), (3, 8), (4, 6), (4, 7), (4, 8), (5, 6), (5, 7), (5, 8)}

d. $\{(3, 1), (3, 2), (3, 3), (4, 1), (4, 2), (4, 3), (5, 1), (5, 2), (5, 3)\}$
e. $\{(6, 1), (6, 2), (6, 3), (7, 1), (7, 2), (7, 3), (8, 1), (8, 2), (8, 3)\}$
f. $\{(6, 3), (6, 4), (6, 5), (7, 3), (7, 4), (7, 5), (8, 3), (8, 4), (8, 5)\}$
5. a. $\varnothing$ **b.** $\varnothing$
    $n(A \times B) = 0; n(B \times A) = 0$
7. a. 20   **b.** 20   **c.** 30   **d.** 15   **e.** 12
9. a. $\{(1, 6), (2, 5), (3, 4), (4, 3), (5, 2), (6, 1)\}$
   b. $\{(1, 1), (2, 2), (3, 3), (4, 4), (5, 5), (6, 6)\}$
11. a. $\{HHH\}$ **b.** $\{HTH, THH, HHT\}$ **c.** $\{HTT, THT, TTH\}$

CHAPTER 2

Exercise 2.1 (pages 36–38)

1. a., f., and h. are functions.
3. b., c., e., and f. are functions.
5. a., b., d., and e. are functions.
7. a. domain: set of reals
     range: set of reals
   b. domain: set of reals
     range: set of reals
   c. domain: set of reals
     range: set of non-negative reals
   d. domain: set of reals
     range: set of reals greater than or equal to -4
   e. domain: set of nonzero reals
     range: set of reals
   f. domain: set of reals between -3 and 3, inclusive
     range: set of reals between 0 and 3, inclusive
9. a. 11   **b.** 6   **c.** 51   **d.** 3   **e.** 11   **f.** 123
11. a. 8   **b.** 10   **c.** 17   **d.** 1   **e.** -18 **f.** 73

13.

p	$d(p)$
0	100
1	96
2	84
3	64
4	36
5	0

15.

x	$f(x)$	$\dfrac{f(x)}{x}$
1	103	103
2	102	51
3	97	32.3
4	88	22
5	75	15
6	58	9.66
7	37	5.29

Exercise 2.2 (pages 42–43)

3. a. 6   **b.** 9   **c.** 6   **d.** 14   **e.** 20   **f.** 14
5. Shipping by train is cheaper.

Exercise 2.3 (pages 51–53)

1. a. (i) 100 (ii) 75 (iii) 50 (iv) 25 (v) 0

b.

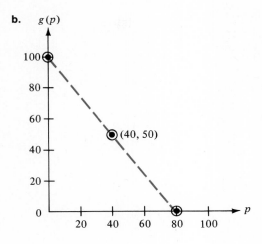

3. a.

p	$D(p)$
$1	440
$2	400
$3	360
$4	320
$6	240
$12	0

b.

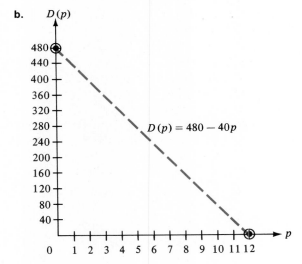

5. a.

x	$f(x)$	$g(x) = \dfrac{f(x)}{x}$
1	150	150
2	180	90
3	190	63.33
4	180	45
5	150	30
6	100	16.66

b.

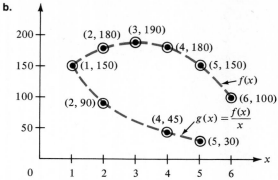

7. a. $R(x) = 5000 + 150x - 5x^2$

b. $\{0, 1, 2, \ldots, 40\}$

c.

x	$R(x)$ (in dollars)
0	5000
5	5625
10	6000
15	6125
20	6000
25	5625
30	5000
35	4125
40	3000

d.

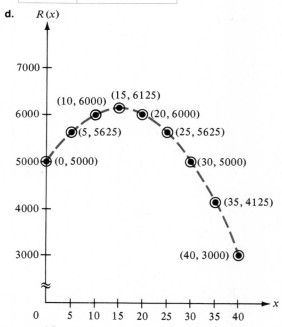

e. $x = 15$

f. $x = 34$

9. $c(x) = \$0.50 + 0.10(x - 1); x = 1, 2, 3, 4, 5, 6, 7, 8, \ldots$
  a. $\$0.60$ **b.** $\$0.80$ **c.** $\$1.00$ **d.** $\$1.20$

11.

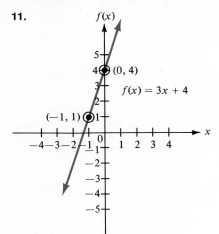

13.

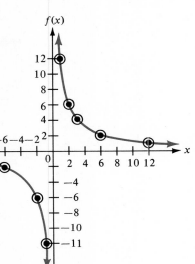

15.

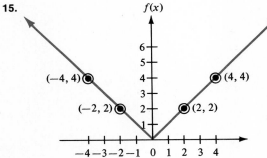

Exercise 2.4 (page 55)

1. $f(x) + g(x) = x^2 + 3x$
  $f(x) - g(x) = x^2 - 3x$
  $f(x) \cdot g(x) = 3x^3$
  $\dfrac{f(x)}{g(x)} = \dfrac{x^2}{3x} = \dfrac{x}{3}, x \neq 0$

3. $f(x) + g(x) = x^2 + \dfrac{1}{x}, x \neq 0$

  $f(x) - g(x) = x^2 - \dfrac{1}{x}, x \neq 0$

  $f(x) \cdot g(x) = x, x \neq 0$

  $\dfrac{f(x)}{g(x)} = x^3, x \neq 0$

5. $f(x) + g(x) = 2x, x \neq 0$

$f(x) - g(x) = \dfrac{2}{x}, x \neq 0$

$f(x) \cdot g(x) = x^2 - \dfrac{1}{x^2}, x \neq 0$

$\dfrac{f(x)}{g(x)} = \dfrac{x^2 + 1}{x^2 - 1}, x \neq 0, 1, -1$

7. a.

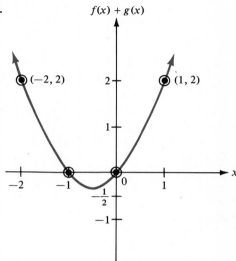

b.

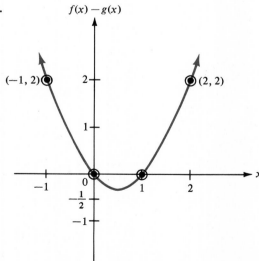

c.

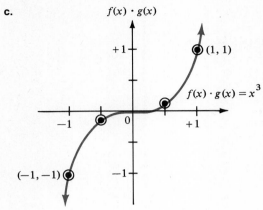

9. a.

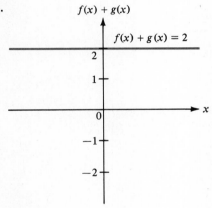

b.

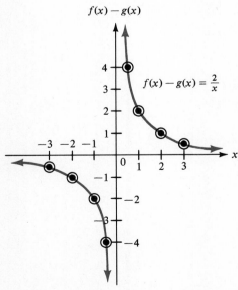

c.

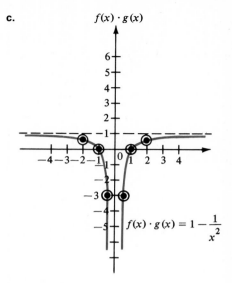

$f(x) \cdot g(x) = 1 - \dfrac{1}{x^2}$

Exercise 2.5 (page 60)

1. $g[f(1)] = 13; g[f(2)] = 19; g[f(3)] = 25; g[f(4)] = 31; g[f(5)] = 37;$
$g[f(6)] = 43$

3. $g[f(1)] = 31; g[f(2)] = 43; g[f(3)] = 55; g[f(4)] = 67; g[f(5)] = 79$
$f[g(1)] = 25; f[g(2)] = 37; f[g(3)] = 49; f[g(4)] = 61; f[g(5)] = 73$

5. $g[f(x)] = \dfrac{3x + 2}{3}; f[g(x)] = x + 2$

7. $g[f(x)] = (2x + 5) + \sqrt{2x + 5}; f[g(x)] = 2(x + \sqrt{x}) + 5$

9. $g[f(x)] = \dfrac{4}{1 + x^2} + 3; f[g(x)] = \dfrac{2}{(2x + 3)^2 + 1}$

11. $g[f(x)] = 9x + 13; f[g(x)] = 9x - 1$

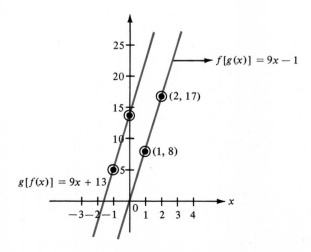

Exercise 2.6 (pages 63–64)

1. a. $\dfrac{x + 4}{5}$; a function **b.** $\dfrac{x - 3}{4}$; a function **c.** $\dfrac{x - 1}{2}$; a function

d. $\dfrac{1}{x}$; a function **e.** $\dfrac{x + 1}{x - 1}$; a function **f.** $x^{1/3}$; a function

3. a.

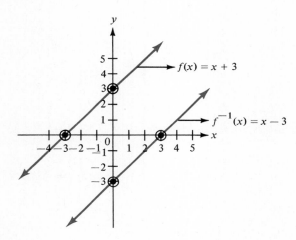

b.

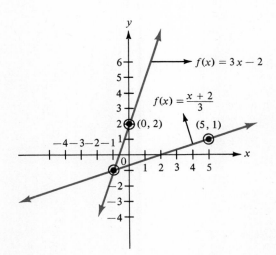

c.

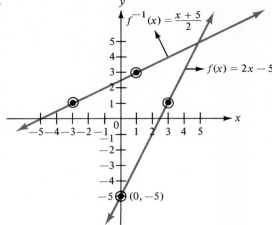

5. a. $\dfrac{x+5}{4}$ **b.** x **c.** x

7. a. $f^{-1}(x) = \dfrac{x-b}{m}$ **b.** x **c.** x

CHAPTER 3

Exercise 3.1 (pages 72–73)
1. a. -1 **b.** 2 **c.** $\frac{3}{7}$ **d.** 2 **e.** $\frac{2}{5}$
3. c. and **e.** are perpendicular to each other.

Exercise 3.2 (pages 81–82)
1. a. $y = 3$ **b.** $y = -2$ **c.** $x = 4$ **d.** $x = -3$
3. a. parallel   **b.** not parallel   **c.** not parallel   **d.** parallel
5. slope $PQ = \frac{1}{5}$, slope $QR = -1$, slope $PR = -\frac{1}{7}$
7. a. slope $= \frac{3}{2}$, y intercept $= 6$
   b. slope $= 1$, y intercept $= 0$
   c. slope $= -\frac{1}{5}$, y intercept $= 2$
   d. slope $= \frac{2}{5}$, y intercept $= 2$
   e. slope $= -\frac{3}{2}$, y intercept $= \frac{15}{2}$
   f. slope $= \frac{3}{4}$, y intercept $= 2$
9. a. $2x + y + 7 = 0$ **b.** $3x - 4y - 25 = 0$ **c.** $2x - 3y + 7 = 0$
   d. $3x + 5y - 13 = 0$ **e.** $x - 3y + 9 = 0$
11. a. $m = 5, b = -6$ **b.** $m = -1, b = 5$ **c.** $m = 2, b = -5$
13. $x + y = 5$

Exercise 3.3 (pages 85–86)
1. $C(x) = \$750 + 15x$; $\$1200$
3. a. $C(x) = \$20 + (0.50)x$ **b.** $\$39$

5. a. $V_{1978} = \$68,000$ **b.** $V_{1984} = \$44,000$
7. $328

9. $y = \dfrac{3}{20} x - 500$

CHAPTER 4

Exercise 4.1 (pages 93–95)

1. a. $x = 1, y = 0$ **b.** $x = 1, y = 2$ **c.** $x = 2, y = -3$
d. $x = 3, y = 2$ **e.** $x = 3, y = 2$ **f.** $x = 4, y = -1$
g. $x = \frac{14}{5}, y = \frac{6}{5}$ **h.** $x = -\frac{22}{5}, y = -\frac{23}{5}$

3. a.

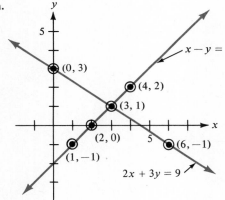

b.

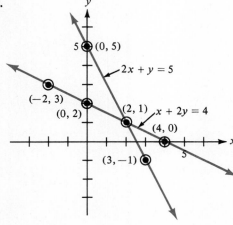

c.

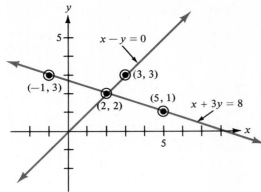

d.

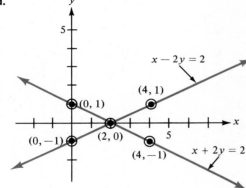

e.

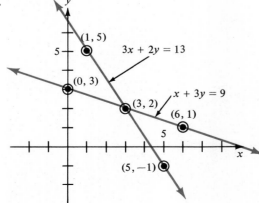

f.

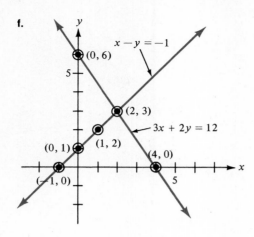

5. shirt $8; tie $4
7. children's tickets: 600, adult's tickets: 1400
9. $4000 at 5 percent and $6000 at 6 percent
11. 50 pounds
13. 22.5 pounds
15. solution A: 90 gallons; solution B: 30 gallons
17. 52.5 gallons

Exercise 4.2 (pages 97–98)

1. 20 units
3. 4000 units
5. 75 percent; 6500 chairs

Exercise 4.3 (page 106)

1.

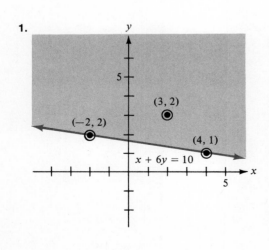

3.

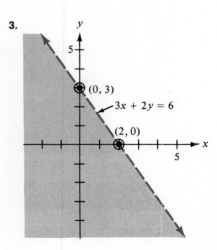

5.

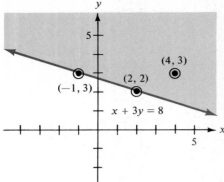

7.

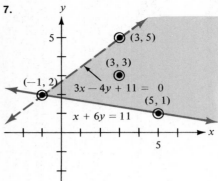

9.

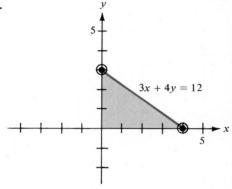

11.

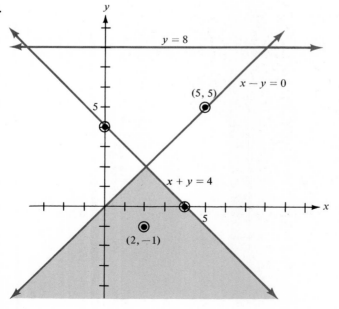

13.

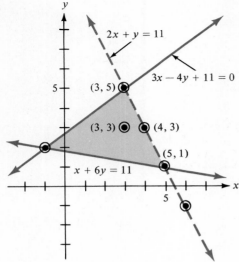

15.

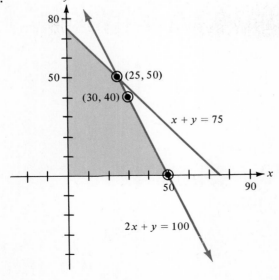

17.

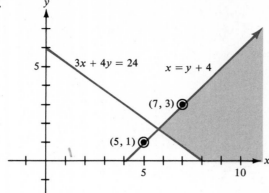

19.

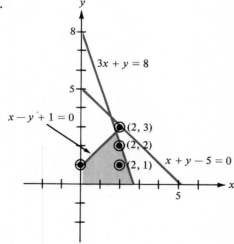

CHAPTER 5

Exercise 5.1 (pages 112–114)

1. a. $(1, 1, 9)$ **b.** $(2, 2, 11)$ **c.** $(16, 12, 53)$

3. a. $(1, 2, -1)$ **b.** $(2, 2, 0)$ **c.** $(2, 0, 3)$

    d. $\begin{pmatrix} \frac{5}{2} \\ -\frac{5}{2} \\ 1 \end{pmatrix}$

5. a. $x = 2$ **b.** $x = 5$

7. $x = 2, y = 1$

9.

	soup	orange juice	eggs (in dozens)	chickens	milk (in gallons)
$\mathbf{a} = ($	5	2	1	2	1	$)$

$$\mathbf{b} = \begin{bmatrix} \$0.31 \\ \$0.73 \\ \$0.95 \\ \$0.79 \\ \$1.53 \end{bmatrix}$$

$\mathbf{ab} = \$7.07$

11.

	stock 1	stock 2	stock 3	stock 4
$\mathbf{a} = ($	40	50	75	80	$)$

$$\mathbf{b} = \begin{bmatrix} \$12.00 \\ \$10.00 \\ \$15.00 \\ \$20.00 \end{bmatrix}$$

$\mathbf{ab} = \$3705$

Exercise 5.2 (pages 120–121)

1. $x = 3, y = 1, z = 4, u = 3$

3. a. $\begin{bmatrix} 3 & 1 \\ 2 & 7 \end{bmatrix}; \begin{bmatrix} -1 & 3 \\ 4 & 1 \end{bmatrix}$ **b.** $\begin{bmatrix} -1 & 1 & -1 \\ 4 & 4 & 4 \end{bmatrix}; \begin{bmatrix} 3 & 3 & 7 \\ 3 & -2 & 0 \end{bmatrix}$

c. $\begin{bmatrix} 6 & -3 & 4 \\ 7 & 2 & 6 \\ 7 & 0 & -2 \\ 0 & 9 & 4 \end{bmatrix}; \begin{bmatrix} -2 & 1 & -2 \\ -3 & 4 & 2 \\ 3 & -2 & 4 \\ 2 & 5 & 2 \end{bmatrix}$ **d.** $\begin{bmatrix} 1 & 3 & 2 & 7 \\ 7 & -2 & 4 & -2 \end{bmatrix}; \begin{bmatrix} 3 & -1 & 4 & 1 \\ 1 & 0 & 0 & 8 \end{bmatrix}$

Exercise 5.3 (pages 132–134)

1. a. 3×5 **b.** 5×5 **c.** 3×3 **d.** 2×4 **e.** 3×4

3. a. $\begin{bmatrix} 10 & 21 \end{bmatrix}$ **b.** $\begin{bmatrix} -7 \\ -11 \\ 0 \end{bmatrix}$ **c.** $\begin{bmatrix} 7 & 0 & 16 \end{bmatrix}$

5. $\begin{bmatrix} 11 & 7 & 17 & 25 & 27 \\ 24 & 21 & 32 & 61 & 61 \\ 31 & 22 & 47 & 74 & 78 \end{bmatrix}$

9. a. $AB = \begin{bmatrix} 8 & 16 \\ 2 & 4 \end{bmatrix} = CB$ but $A \neq C$

11. store 1, \$27.80; store 2, \$27.41; store 3, \$27.64. She should buy at store 2.

CHAPTER 6

Exercise 6.1 (page 145)

1. $x_1 = 2, x_2 = 3$

3. $x_1 = 1, x_2 = 2, x_3 = 1$

5. $x_1 = 2, x_2 = 0, x_3 = 3$

7. $x_1 = 1, x_2 = 1, x_3 = 2$

9. $x_1 = -4, x_2 = 1, x_3 = 3$

11. $x_1 = 1, x_2 = 1, x_3 = 1, x_4 = 1$

13. a. $x_1 = 1, x_2 = -1, x_3 = 2$

b. $x_1 = 1, x_2 = 2, x_3 = 3$

15. a. $x_1 = -1, x_2 = 2, x_3 = 3, x_4 = 4$

b. $x_1 = -2, x_2 = 1, x_3 = 2, x_4 = -1$

c. $x_1 = 1, x_2 = 0, x_3 = 2, x_4 = -1$

Exercise 6.2 (pages 148–149)

1. no solution

3. $x_1 = 3 - 2c, x_2 = c, x_3 = 1$

5. $x_1 = \frac{24}{7} - \frac{3}{7}c, x_2 = \frac{9}{7} + \frac{5}{7}c, x_3 = c$

7. $x_1 = \frac{4}{5} - \frac{2}{5}c, x_2 = \frac{3}{5}c - \frac{11}{5}, x_3 = c$

9. $x_1 = 3, x_2 = 1, x_3 = 2$

Exercise 6.4 (pages 160–162)

1. a. $\frac{1}{2}\begin{bmatrix} 4 & -2 \\ -5 & 3 \end{bmatrix}$
b. $\frac{1}{3}\begin{bmatrix} 2 & -1 \\ -5 & 4 \end{bmatrix}$
c. $\frac{1}{4}\begin{bmatrix} 7 & 10 \\ 6 & 8 \end{bmatrix}$
d. $\frac{1}{9}\begin{bmatrix} 5 & 1 \\ -4 & 1 \end{bmatrix}$

e. $\frac{1}{5}\begin{bmatrix} -8 & 12 & -3 \\ -1 & 4 & -1 \\ 2 & -3 & 2 \end{bmatrix}$
f. $\frac{1}{4}\begin{bmatrix} -2 & -2 & 2 \\ 3 & 1 & -1 \\ -5 & 1 & 3 \end{bmatrix}$
g. $\frac{1}{8}\begin{bmatrix} -10 & 14 & -2 \\ 11 & -13 & 3 \\ -2 & 6 & -2 \end{bmatrix}$

h. $\frac{1}{225}\begin{bmatrix} -59 & -141 & 30 \\ -37 & -138 & 15 \\ 30 & 45 & 0 \end{bmatrix}$
i. $\frac{1}{4}\begin{bmatrix} 2 & 2 & -2 \\ -4 & 0 & 4 \\ 3 & -1 & -1 \end{bmatrix}$
j. $\frac{1}{5}\begin{bmatrix} 3 & -1 & -4 \\ -1 & 2 & 3 \\ -2 & 4 & 1 \end{bmatrix}$

3. $A^{-1} = \frac{1}{25}\begin{bmatrix} 23 & -11 & 8 \\ -5 & 10 & -5 \\ 7 & 1 & -3 \end{bmatrix}$

a. $x_1 = 1, x_2 = 1, x_3 = 1$
b. $x_1 = 1, x_2 = 2, x_3 = 3$

c. $x_1 = 2, x_2 = 0, x_3 = -3$
d. $x_1 = 3, x_2 = 2, x_3 = 1$

5. $A^{-1} = \begin{bmatrix} 9 & -1 & -2 \\ -2 & 1 & 0 \\ -1 & -1 & 1 \end{bmatrix}$

a. $x_1 = 1, x_2 = 2, x_3 = -1$
b. $x_1 = 2, x_2 = 0, x_3 = 3$

c. $x_1 = 1, x_2 = -1, x_3 = 1$
d. $x_1 = 2, x_2 = 1, x_3 = -3$

7. $A^{-1} = \frac{1}{40}\begin{bmatrix} -16 & 6 & 9 \\ 48 & -38 & 3 \\ -24 & 24 & -4 \end{bmatrix}$

a. station wagons, 2; full-size cars, 3; intermediate cars, 4

b. station wagons, 5; full-size cars, 3; intermediate cars, 2

Exercise 6.5 (pages 165–166)

1. industry I, \$100 million; industry II, \$185 million
3. industry I, \$52 million; industry II, \$22 million
5. industry I, \$36.26 million; industry II, \$28.85 million; industry III, \$11.72 million

CHAPTER 7

Exercise 7.1 (pages 182–183)

1. $x_1 = 10, x_2 = 15$ **3.** $x_1 = 20, x_2 = 10$
5. $x_1 = 100, x_2 = 0; x_1 = 30, x_2 = 105$
7. $x_1 = \frac{6}{5}, x_2 = \frac{28}{5}; x_1 = \frac{5}{2}, x_2 = 3$
9. $x_1 = 4, x_2 = 2$ **11.** $x_1 = 3, x_2 = 4$
13. $x_1 = 20, x_2 = 10$ **15.** $x_1 = 15, x_2 = 20$

Exercise 7.2 (pages 189–191)

1. $x_1 = 0, x_2 = 3; x_1 = \frac{10}{3}, x_2 = \frac{4}{3}; P = 60$
3. $x_1 = 8, x_2 = 4; P = 800$
5. product 1, 10 units; product 2, 15 units, $P = \$330$
7. product 1, 40 units; product 2, 10 units; $P = \$230$
9. vitamin A, 6 units; vitamin B, 1 unit; $C = \$0.08$
11. tablets P, 0; tablets Q, 10; $C = \$0.80$
13. fish, 2 pounds; milk, 3 quarts; $P = \$3.40$

Exercise 7.3 (page 202)

1. $x_1 = 100, x_2 = 0; P = 600$ **3.** $x_1 = 4, x_2 = 0; P = 24$
5. $x_1 = 8, x_2 = 4; P = 400$ **7.** $x_1 = 6, x_2 = 0, x_3 = 0; P = 30$
9. $x_1 = 0, x_2 = 6, x_3 = 5; P = 63$ **11.** $x_1 = 5, x_2 = 34, x_3 = 6; P = 118$

Exercise 7.4 (pages 207–208)

1. $y_1 = 3, y_2 = 0; C = 36$ **3.** $y_1 = \frac{18}{11}, y_2 = \frac{10}{11}; C = \frac{158}{11}$
5. $y_1 = \frac{15}{2}, y_2 = \frac{5}{4}; C = 360$ **7.** $y_1 = 12, y_2 = 0; C = 180$
9. $y_1 = 20, y_2 = 10, y_3 = 0; C = 400$ **11.** $y_1 = \frac{3}{5}, y_2 = \frac{21}{40}, y_3 = \frac{29}{80}; C = 37$

CHAPTER 8

Exercise 8.1 (pages 219–223)

1. $x_{11} = 45, x_{12} = 40, x_{13} = 0$
$x_{21} = 0, x_{22} = 35, x_{23} = 30$

3. $x_{11} = 120, x_{12} = 105, x_{13} = 0$
$x_{21} = 0, x_{22} = 65, x_{23} = 75$
$x_{31} = 0, x_{32} = 0, x_{33} = 135$

5. $x_{11} = 115, x_{12} = x_{13} = x_{14} = 0$
$x_{21} = 30, x_{22} = 170, x_{23} = 35, x_{24} = 0$
$x_{31} = x_{32} = 0, x_{33} = 205, x_{34} = 105$

7. a. $x_{11} = 75, x_{12} = 5$
$x_{21} = 0, x_{22} = 60$
b. same as in **a.**

9. a. $x_{11} = 40, x_{12} = 0, x_{13} = 75$
$x_{21} = 35, x_{22} = 50, x_{23} = 0$
b. same as in **a.**

11. a. $x_{11} = 5, x_{12} = 10, x_{13} = 80$
$x_{21} = 0, x_{22} = 50, x_{23} = 0$
$x_{31} = 70, x_{32} = 0, x_{33} = 0$
b. same as in **a.**

13. a. $x_{11} = 90, x_{12} = 10, x_{13} = 0$
$\quad x_{21} = 0, x_{22} = 55, x_{23} = 5$
$\quad x_{31} = 0, x_{32} = 0, x_{33} = 65$
b. $x_{11} = 30, x_{12} = 0, x_{13} = 70$
$\quad x_{21} = 0, x_{22} = 60, x_{23} = 0$
$\quad x_{31} = 60, x_{32} = 5, x_{33} = 0$
c. $x_{11} = 30, x_{12} = 0, x_{13} = 70$
$\quad x_{21} = 60, x_{22} = 0, x_{23} = 0$
$\quad x_{31} = 0, x_{32} = 65, x_{33} = 0$

15. a. $x_{11} = 80, x_{12} = 0, x_{13} = 0$
$\quad x_{21} = 10, x_{22} = 50, x_{23} = 0$
$\quad x_{31} = 0, x_{32} = 20, x_{33} = 35$
Cost \$195
b. $x_{11} = 30, x_{12} = 15, x_{13} = 35$
$\quad x_{21} = 60, x_{22} = 0, x_{23} = 0$
$\quad x_{31} = 0, x_{32} = 55, x_{33} = 0$
Cost \$158.50
c. $x_{11} = 0, x_{12} = 45, x_{13} = 35$
$\quad x_{21} = 35, x_{22} = 25, x_{23} = 0$
$\quad x_{31} = 55, x_{32} = 0, x_{33} = 0$
Cost \$155.50

Exercise 8.2 (pages 233–238)

1. a. Northwest-corner rule:

Iteration	Solution	Cost	Savings over Previous Solution
1	$x_{11} = 90, x_{12} = 10, x_{13} = 0$ $x_{21} = 0, x_{22} = 60, x_{23} = 50$ $x_{31} = x_{32} = 0, x_{33} = 35$	\$1760	
2	$x_{11} = 90, x_{12} = 0, x_{13} = 10$ $x_{21} = 0, x_{22} = 70, x_{23} = 40$ $x_{31} = x_{32} = 0, x_{33} = 35$	\$1700	\$60
3	$x_{11} = 50, x_{12} = 0, x_{13} = 50$ $x_{21} = 40, x_{22} = 70, x_{23} = 0$ $x_{31} = x_{32} = 0, x_{33} = 35$	\$1540	\$160
4	$x_{11} = 15, x_{12} = 0, x_{13} = 85$ $x_{21} = 75, x_{22} = 35, x_{23} = 0$ $x_{31} = 0, x_{32} = 35, x_{33} = 0$	\$1470	\$70

b. Minimum entry method:

Iteration	Solution	Cost	Savings over Previous Solution
1	$x_{11} = 0, x_{12} = 15, x_{13} = 85$ $x_{21} = 90, x_{22} = 20, x_{23} = 0$ $x_{31} = 0, x_{32} = 35, x_{33} = 0$	\$1500	
2	$x_{11} = 15, x_{12} = 0, x_{13} = 85$ $x_{21} = 75, x_{22} = 35, x_{23} = 0$ $x_{31} = 0, x_{32} = 35, x_{33} = 0$	\$1470	\$30

c. Vogel's approximation method:

Iteration	Solution	Cost	Savings over Previous Solution
1	$x_{11} = 15, x_{12} = 0, x_{13} = 85$ $x_{21} = 75, x_{22} = 35, x_{23} = 0$ $x_{31} = 0, x_{32} = 35, x_{33} = 0$	\$1470	

3. a. Northwest-corner rule:

Iteration	Solution	Cost	Savings over Previous Solution
1	$x_{11} = 30, x_{12} = 10, x_{13} = 0$ $x_{21} = 0, x_{22} = 15, x_{23} = 7$ $x_{31} = 0, x_{32} = 0, x_{33} = 8$	\$886	
2	$x_{11} = 22, x_{12} = 18, x_{13} = 0$ $x_{21} = 0, x_{22} = 7, x_{23} = 15$ $x_{31} = 8, x_{32} = x_{33} = 0$	\$798	\$88

b. Minimum entry method:

Iteration	Solution	Cost	Savings over Previous Solution
1	$x_{11} = 30, x_{12} = 10, x_{13} = 0$ $x_{21} = 0, x_{22} = 7, x_{23} = 15$ $x_{31} = 0, x_{32} = 8, x_{33} = 0$	\$814	
2	$x_{11} = 22, x_{12} = 18, x_{13} = 0$ $x_{21} = 0, x_{22} = 7, x_{23} = 15$ $x_{31} = 8, x_{32} = x_{33} = 0$	\$798	\$16

c. Vogel's approximation method:

Iteration	Solution	Cost	Savings over Previous Solution
1	$x_{11} = 22, x_{12} = 18, x_{13} = 0$ $x_{21} = 0, x_{22} = 7, x_{23} = 15$ $x_{31} = 8, x_{32} = x_{33} = 0$	\$798	

5. a. Northwest-corner rule:

Iteration	Solution	Cost	Savings over Previous Solution
1	$x_{11} = 100, x_{12} = 20, x_{13} = 0$ $x_{21} = 0, x_{22} = 70, x_{23} = 5$ $x_{31} = x_{32} = 0, x_{33} = 55$	\$2170	
2	$x_{11} = 100, x_{12} = 15, x_{13} = 5$ $x_{21} = 0, x_{22} = 75, x_{23} = 0$ $x_{31} = 0, x_{32} = 0, x_{33} = 55$	\$2120	\$50
3	$x_{11} = 100, x_{12} = 0, x_{13} = 20$ $x_{21} = 0, x_{22} = 75, x_{23} = 0$ $x_{31} = 0, x_{32} = 15, x_{33} = 40$	\$2045	\$75
4	$x_{11} = 60, x_{12} = 0, x_{13} = 60$ $x_{21} = 40, x_{22} = 35, x_{23} = 0$ $x_{31} = 0, x_{32} = 55, x_{33} = 0$	\$1845	\$200

b. Minimum entry method:

Iteration	Solution	Cost	Savings over Previous Solution
1	$x_{11} = 25, x_{12} = 35, x_{13} = 60$ $x_{21} = 75, x_{22} = x_{23} = 0$ $x_{31} = 0, x_{32} = 55, x_{33} = 0$	$1915	
2	$x_{11} = 60, x_{12} = 0, x_{13} = 60$ $x_{21} = 40, x_{22} = 35, x_{23} = 0$ $x_{31} = 0, x_{32} = 55, x_{33} = 0$	$1845	$70

c. Vogel's approximation method:

Iteration	Solution	Cost	Savings over Previous Solution
1	$x_{11} = 25, x_{12} = 35, x_{13} = 60$ $x_{21} = 75, x_{22} = x_{23} = 0$ $x_{31} = 25, x_{32} = 30, x_{33} = 0$	$1915	
2	$x_{11} = 60, x_{12} = 0, x_{13} = 60$ $x_{21} = 40, x_{22} = 35, x_{33} = 0$ $x_{31} = 0, x_{32} = 55, x_{33} = 0$	$1845	$70

7. a. Minimum entry method:

Iteration	Solution	Cost	Savings over Previous Solution
1	$x_{11} = x_{12} = 0, x_{13} = 52, x_{14} = 43$ $x_{21} = 80, x_{22} = x_{23} = 0, x_{24} = 10$ $x_{31} = 0, x_{32} = 68, x_{33} = 0, x_{34} = 7$	$1556	
2	$x_{11} = 43, x_{12} = 0, x_{13} = 52, x_{14} = 0$ $x_{21} = 37, x_{22} = x_{23} = 0, x_{24} = 53$ $x_{31} = 0, x_{32} = 68, x_{33} = 0, x_{34} = 7$	$1470	$86
3	$x_{11} = 43, x_{12} = 0, x_{13} = 52, x_{14} = 0$ $x_{21} = 30, x_{22} = x_{23} = 0, x_{24} = 60$ $x_{31} = 7, x_{32} = 68, x_{33} = x_{34} = 0$	$1463	$7

b. Vogel's approximation method:

Iteration	Solution	Cost	Savings over Previous Solution
1	$x_{11} = 43, x_{12} = 0, x_{13} = 52, x_{14} = 0$ $x_{21} = 30, x_{22} = x_{23} = 0, x_{24} = 60$ $x_{31} = 7, x_{32} = 68, x_{33} = x_{34} = 0$	$1463	

9. a. Minimum entry method:

Iteration	Solution	Cost
1	$x_{11} = 20, x_{12} = 55, x_{13} = 5, x_{14} = 0$ $x_{21} = 0, x_{22} = 0, x_{23} = 65, x_{24} = 25$ $x_{31} = 75, x_{32} = x_{33} = x_{34} = 0$	$1020

This solution is optimal.
b. Same as in **a.**

Exercise 8.3 (pages 243–244)

1. $x_{11} = 30$, $x_{12} = 120$, $x_{13} = 0$
$x_{21} = 0$, $x_{22} = 0$, $x_{23} = 100$
$x_{31} = 100$, $x_{32} = 0$, $x_{33} = 25$
Cost $3310

3. $x_{11} = 25$, $x_{12} = 60$, $x_{13} = 0$
$x_{21} = 30$, $x_{22} = 0$, $x_{23} = 55$
$x_{31} = 0$, $x_{32} = 30$, $x_{33} = 0$
Cost $1915

5. $x_{11} = 30$, $x_{12} = 20$, $x_{13} = 10$
$x_{21} = 0$, $x_{22} = 0$, $x_{23} = 40$
$x_{31} = 0$, $x_{32} = 20$, $x_{33} = 0$
Cost $1300

Exercise 8.4 (pages 250–252)

1. Assign jobs J_1, J_2, and J_3 to workers W_1, W_3, and W_2, respectively.
3. Assign products P_1, P_2, and P_3 to machines M_2, M_1, and M_3, respectively.
5. Assign regions R_1, R_2, R_3, and R_4 to Jim, Bob, John, and Steve, respectively.
7. Assign Dave, Steve, Peter, Bill, and Vince to machines M_4, M_5, M_3, M_2, and M_1, respectively.

CHAPTER 9

Exercise 9.1 (page 256)

1. 30

3.

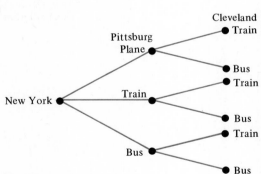

5. 480
7. 6720
9. a. 60   **b.** 320

Exercise 9.2 (pages 259–260)

1. a. 120   **b.** 1680   **c.** 504   **d.** 5040
3. a. 336   **b.** 1680   **c.** 40,320
5. 5040; 720; 120; 1440
7. a. 20,160   **b.** 10,080   **c.** 30,240
9. 600   **11.** 40,320   **13.** 3,628,800; 28,800

Exercise 9.3 (pages 261–262)

1. 20   **3.** 59,049   **5.** 6,760,000
7. a. 360   **b.** 1296   **9. a.** 125   **b.** 60

Exercise 9.4 (page 265)

1. a. $\dfrac{8!}{3!2!}$ **b.** $\dfrac{7!}{(2!)^2}$ **c.** $\dfrac{8!}{(2!)^3}$ **d.** $\dfrac{8!}{2!3!}$

e. $\dfrac{10!}{(2!)^2 3!}$ **f.** $\dfrac{11!}{(2!)^2 3!}$ **g.** $\dfrac{13!}{(2!)^2 4!}$ **h.** $\dfrac{11!}{2!(4!)^2}$

3. $\dfrac{12!}{3!4!5!}$ **5.** 1260

7. 2520; 181,440; 19,958,400 **9.** 181,440

11. a. 39,916,800 **b.** 479,001,600

13. 2880 **15.** 282,240; 0

Exercise 9.5 (pages 270–272)

1. a. 56 **b.** 66 **c.** 19,900

3. 70 **5.** $\dfrac{40!}{9!31!}$ **7.** 1365; 364

9. a. 495 **b.** 425 **11.** 495; 165

13. a. 778,320 **b.** 54,912 **c.** 3744

15. a. 2,598,960 **b.** $\dbinom{4}{2}\dbinom{4}{2}\cdot 44$ **c.** $\dbinom{13}{3}\dbinom{39}{2}$ **d.** $\dbinom{13}{5}\cdot 4$

e. $\dbinom{13}{3}\dbinom{39}{2} + \dbinom{13}{4}\dbinom{39}{1} + \dbinom{13}{5}$ **f.** $\dbinom{4}{2}\dbinom{48}{3}\cdot 2 - \dbinom{4}{2}\dbinom{4}{2}\cdot 44$

17. a. 495 **b.** 120 **19.** $\dbinom{12}{6}\dbinom{50}{7}\dbinom{5}{2}$

21. $\dfrac{12!}{3!4!5!}$ **23.** $\dfrac{13!}{40}$

Exercise 9.6 (pages 277–278)

1. a. $81a^4 + 216a^3b + 216a^2b^2 + 96ab^3 + 16b^4$
b. $243a^5x^5 - 1620a^4bx^4y + 4320a^3b^2x^3y^2 - 5760a^2b^3x^2y^3 + 3840ab^4xy^4 - 1024b^5y^5$
c. $1 - 7x + 21x^2 - 35x^3 + 35x^4 - 21x^5 + 7x^6 - x^7$
d. $1 + 16x + 112x^2 + 448x^3 + 1120x^4 + 1792x^5 + 1792x^6 + 1024x^7 + 256x^8$
e. $x^6 - 12x^5y + 60x^4y^2 - 160x^3y^3 + 240x^2y^4 - 192xy^5 + 64y^6$

f. $x^{11} - 11x^9 + 55x^7 - 165x^5 + 330x^3 - 462x + \dfrac{462}{x} - \dfrac{330}{x^3} + \dfrac{165}{x^5} - \dfrac{55}{x^7} + \dfrac{11}{x^9} - \dfrac{1}{x^{11}}$

3. a. 1.0242 **b.** 1.2763 **c.** 0.9920 **d.** 0.8858

5. a. $\dbinom{17}{3}$ **b.** $\dbinom{2n}{n}$ **c.** $\dbinom{10}{8}$

7. \$1628.89 **9.** 12

CHAPTER 10

Exercise 10.1 (pages 283–284)

1. a. $\{HH, HT, TH, TT\}$

b. $\{(1, H), (1, T), (2, H), (2, T), (3, H), (3, T), (4, H), (4, T), (5, H), (5, T), (6, H), (6, T)\}$

c. Let the five students be labeled A, B, C, D, and E, and let (x, y) represent that student x is the president and student y is the secretary. Then the sample space is space is

$$\{(A, B), (A, C), (A, D), (A, E),$$
$$(B, A), (B, C), (B, D), (B, E),$$
$$(C, A), (C, B), (C, D), (C, E),$$
$$(D, A), (D, B), (D, C), (D, E),$$
$$(E, A), (E, B), (E, C), (E, D)\}$$

d. $\{(A, B), (A, C), (A, D), (A, E),$
$$(B, C), (B, D), (B, E),$$
$$(C, D), (C, E),$$
$$(D, E)\}$$

where A, B, C, D, and E are members of the club.

e. {(diamond, spade), (diamond, club), (diamond, heart), (spade, club), (spade, heart), (club, heart)}

f. $\{H, TH, TTH, TTT\}$

3. $S = \{HHH, HHT, HTH, HTT, THH, THT, TTH, TTT\}$

a. $\{THH, THT, TTH, TTT\}$ **b.** $\{HHH, HTH, THT, TTT\}$

c. $\{HTT, THT, TTH, TTT\}$ **d.** $\{HHH\}$

e. $\{HTH, THH, HHT\}$ **f.** $\{HTH, THH, HHH, HHH\}$

5. Let the ordered pair (x, y) represent that x is the number drawn first and y is the number drawn thereafter. Then

$$S = \{(1, 2), (1, 3), (1, 4), (1, 5),$$
$$(2, 1), (2, 3), (2, 4), (2, 5),$$
$$(3, 1), (3, 2), (3, 4), (3, 5),$$
$$(4, 1), (4, 2), (4, 3), (4, 5),$$
$$(5, 1), (5, 2), (5, 3), (5, 4)\}$$

a. all ordered pairs in S except $(4, 5)$ and $(5, 4)$

b. $\{(2, 4), (4, 2)\}$

c. $\{(1, 2), (1, 4), (2, 1), (2, 3), (2, 5), (3, 2), (3, 4), (4, 1), (4, 3), (4, 5), (5, 2), (5, 4)\}$

d. $\varnothing$

e. $\{(1, 3), (1, 5), (3, 1), (3, 5), (5, 1), (5, 3)\}$

Exercise 10.2 (pages 288–289)

1. a. $\frac{5}{36}$ **b.** $\frac{26}{36}$ **c.** $\frac{15}{36}$

3. a. $\frac{2}{52}$ **b.** $\frac{16}{52}$ **c.** $\frac{26}{52}$ **d.** $\frac{26}{52}$ **e.** $\frac{24}{52}$ **f.** $\frac{26}{52}$

5. a. $\frac{37}{40}$ **b.** $\frac{25}{40}$ **c.** $\frac{27}{40}$ **d.** $\frac{13}{40}$

7. $\frac{1}{3}$

9. $\frac{1}{3}$

11. $\dfrac{8!\,7!}{15!}$

13. a. $\frac{1}{120}$ **b.** $\frac{119}{120}$

Exercise 10.3 (pages 294–296)

1. yes

3. A and B are mutually exclusive;
   B and C are not mutually exclusive;
   A and C are mutually exclusive.
   $P(B \cup C) = \frac{3}{8}$

5. a. The sum of probabilities is less than 1.00.
   b. The sum of probabilities is more than 1.00.
   c. The probability that Mr. Carlson should register for at least two courses should be at least 0.67.

7. a. 0.88   **b.** 0.69   **c.** 0.51   **d.** 0.54

9. a. 0.88   **b.** 0.53   **c.** 0.56   **d.** 0.43

11. a. 0.37   **b.** 0.73   **c.** 0.76   **d.** 0.13
   e. 0.51   **f.** 0.49   **g.** 0.24   **h.** 0.86

13. 0.67

15. a. 0.44   **b.** 0.56   **c.** 0.23   **d.** 0.73   **e.** 0.62

17. 0.5

19. a. $\frac{50}{490}$ **b.** $\frac{40}{490}$ **c.** $\frac{440}{490}$

Exercise 10.4 (pages 298–300)

1. a. $\frac{1}{6}$ **b.** $\frac{1}{2}$ **3.** $\frac{70}{495} \approx \frac{1}{7}$

5. $\frac{7}{15}$ **7.** $\dfrac{4,845}{12,650}$

9. a. $\dfrac{3,003}{15,504}$ **b.** $\dfrac{252}{15,504}$

11. a. $\dfrac{715}{270,725}$ **b.** $\dfrac{13}{270,725}$ **c.** $\dfrac{2,860}{270,725}$

   d. $\dfrac{36}{270,725}$ **e.** $\dfrac{192}{270,725}$ **f.** $\dfrac{82,251}{270,725}$

13. The number of possible drawings is $\binom{18}{5} = 8568$.

   a. $\dfrac{1}{8568}$ **b.** $\dfrac{28}{8568}$ **c.** $\dfrac{27}{8568}$

15. The number of possible selections is $\binom{18}{5} = 8568$.

   a. $\dfrac{700}{8568}$ **b.** $\dfrac{1680}{8568}$ **c.** $\dfrac{5292}{8568}$ **d.** $\dfrac{3276}{8568}$ **e.** $\dfrac{308}{8568}$

Exercise 10.5 (pages 305–307)

1. a. $\frac{13}{52}$ **b.** $\frac{13}{26}$ **c.** $\frac{13}{39}$

3. a. $\frac{1}{7}$ **b.** $\frac{1}{4}$

5. a. $\frac{6}{22}$ **b.** $\frac{3}{7}$ **c.** $\frac{5}{13}$

7. a. $\frac{12}{31}$ **b.** $\frac{12}{38}$ **c.** $\frac{31}{57}$

9. $\frac{3}{8}$

11. a. $\frac{1}{73}$ **b.** $\frac{1}{2}$

13. a. $\frac{3}{7}$ **b.** $\frac{2}{21}$

15. $\dfrac{391}{1155}$

17. a. $\frac{6}{11}$ **b.** $\frac{5}{11}$ **c.** $\frac{1}{22}$ **d.** $\frac{9}{22}$

21. *A* and *B* are independent.
   A and *C* are independent.

23. a. 0.20   **b.** 0.50   **c.** 0.30

Exercise 10.6 (pages 312–313)

1. 0.80   **3.** $\frac{11}{108}$ **5.** 0.40

7. $\frac{27}{71}$; $\frac{12}{71}$ **9.** 0.75   **11.** $\frac{10}{103}$; $\frac{48}{103}$

13. $\frac{9}{28}$

Exercise 10.7 (pages 315–316)

1. 0.375   **3.** 0.0015

5. a. 0.0024   **b.** 0.0284   **c.** 0.1323   **d.** 0.9692

7. 0.0046; 0.9996; 0.0050

9. a. 0.2461   **b.** 0.4102   **c.** 0.2344

11. a. 0.2581   **b.** 0.0317   **c.** 0.9683   **d.** 0.1584

CHAPTER 11

Exercise 11.1 (pages 323–324)

1. 3.00   **3.** 1.00

5. expected loss $400   **7.** favorable to Mr. Smith

9. $1500

11. a. 80   **b.** 45   **c.** 90

13. 50   **15.** 40

Exercise 11.2 (pages 331–332)

1. 0.75; 0.866   **3.** 1.01; 1.005   **5.** 3000; 54.772

7. 200; 100; 10   **9.** 3.6   **11.** 166; 12.884

Exercise 11.3 (page 334)

1. 0.9375   **3.** 0.25

5. The probability is at least 0.96.   **7.** 0.75

Exercise 11.4 (pages 344–345)

1. a. 0.9162   **b.** 0.3849   **c.** 0.0793   **d.** 0.1608   **e.** 0.7994   **f.** 0.0619
3. a. −1.28   **b.** 2.55   **c.** 0.98   **d.** 0.19   **e.** 1.96   **f.** 1.13
   g. −1.00   **h.** 1.03

Exercise 11.5 (pages 348–350)

1. a. 0.0668   **b.** 0.0228   **c.** 0.6915   **d.** 0.6826
3. 0.4207
5. a. 0.6687   **b.** 0.1587   **c.** 0.1587
7. a. 0.0505   **b.** 0.6826   **c.** 0.0228
9. a. 0.4332   **b.** 0.6826   **c.** 0.0228   **d.** 0.0228
11. 88
13. 1116.5 gallons
15. 4.01 percent
17. a. at least 0.36   **b.** 0.7888

Exercise 11.6 (pages 355–356)

1. a. 0.1208   **b.** 0.1173   **3.** 0.0477
5. a. 0.0668   **b.** 0.5934   **c.** 0.1210
7. 0.8531   **9.** 0.0526
11. one customer   **13.** 0.0388

CHAPTER 12

Exercise 12.1 (pages 365–367)

1. a. 31.50

b. Conditional Loss Table

Demand \ Stock	30	31	32	33
30	$0	$6	$12	$18
31	4	0	6	12
32	8	4	0	6
33	12	8	4	0

Conditional Profit Table

Demand \ Stock	30	31	32	33
30	$120	$114	$108	$102
31	120	124	118	112
32	120	124	128	122
33	120	124	128	132

c. Expected Monetary Profit

Stock	Conditional Profit	Probability of Conditional Profit	Expected Profit	Total Expected Profit
30	$120	1.00	$120	$120.00
31	$114	0.10	$11.40	
	124	0.90	111.60	$123.00
32	$108	0.10	$10.80	
	118	0.35	41.30	
	128	0.55	70.40	$122.50
33	$102	0.10	$10.20	
	112	0.35	39.20	
	122	0.50	61.00	
	132	0.05	6.60	$117.00

Expected Loss Table

Stock	Conditional Loss	Probability of Conditional Loss	Expected Loss	Total Expected Loss
30	$0	0.10	$0	
	4	0.35	1.40	
	8	0.50	4.00	
	12	0.05	0.60	$6.00
31	$6	0.10	$0.60	
	0	0.35	0	
	4	0.50	2.00	
	8	0.05	0.40	$3.00
32	$12	0.10	$1.20	
	6	0.35	2.10	
	0	0.50	0	
	4	0.05	0.20	$3.50
33	$18	0.10	$1.80	
	12	0.35	4.20	
	6	0.50	3.00	
	0	0.05	0	$9.00

3. a. 3000   **b.** 3000   **c.** 1200

5. a. 26   **b.** 26   **c.** $98.40   **d.** $104.00

Exercise 12.2 (pages 372–374)

1. a. x: 16   18   20   21   22   23   24   25   26   27   28   29   31   34
     f: 3   5   3   4   2   5   2   4   5   7   5   3   1   1

b. mean = 24
standard deviation = 4.15

3. a. 5.13   **b.** 1.887

5. a. 28.35   **b.** 42.03   **c.** 6.48

7. 22.96   **9.** 59.62

CHAPTER 13

Exercise 13.1 (page 377)

1.

Clark

	Even	Odd
Roger Even	50¢	−50¢
Odd	−50¢	50¢

3.

Cox

	Nickel	Dime	Quarter
Roosevelt Nickel	10¢	−25¢	30¢
Dime	−15¢	20¢	−35¢
Quarter	30¢	−35¢	50¢

5.

Jeanie

	Early	Late
Roger Early	50	10
Late	−10	25

Exercise 13.2 (pages 381–382)

1. saddle point: (2, 1)
   best strategy: R, row 2; C, column 1; $v = 1$
3. saddle point: (1, 1)
   best strategy: R, row 1; C, column 1; $v = 5$
5. saddle point: (2, 1)
   best strategy: R, row 2; C, column 1; $v = 5$
7. saddle point: (2, 2)
   best strategy: Tracey, row 2; Jodey, column 2; $v = -4$
9. saddle point: (1, 1)
   best strategy: R, row 1; C, column 1; $v = 1$
11. saddle point: (2, 2)
   best strategy: Tracey, row 2; Anita, column 2; $v = 6$
13. saddle point: (2, 1)
   best strategy: Karen, row 2; Maryann, column 1; $v = 3$
15. saddle point: (2, 2)
   best strategy: Gail, row 2; Helen, column 2; $v = 4$
17. saddle point: (2, 3)
   best strategy: Jodey, row 2; Jeanie, column 3; $v = 0$

Exercise 13.3 (page 384)

1. 2   **3.** 6

Exercise 13.4 (page 386–387)

1. $P = (\frac{1}{2} \quad \frac{1}{2}); Q = \begin{bmatrix} \frac{1}{2} \\ \frac{1}{2} \end{bmatrix}; v = 0$ **3.** $P = (\frac{4}{7} \quad \frac{3}{7}); Q = \begin{bmatrix} \frac{5}{14} \\ \frac{9}{14} \end{bmatrix}; v = \frac{1}{7}$

5. $P = (\frac{1}{2} \quad \frac{1}{2}); Q = \begin{bmatrix} \frac{1}{2} \\ \frac{1}{2} \end{bmatrix}; v = \frac{1}{2}$ **7.** $P = (\frac{2}{3} \quad \frac{1}{3}); Q = \begin{bmatrix} \frac{3}{5} \\ \frac{2}{5} \end{bmatrix}; v = 1$

Exercise 13.5 (page 389)

1. third row dominates the first row
   first column dominates the third column
   saddle point: (3, 2); $v = 4$
3. first row dominates the third row
   third column dominates the first column
   saddle point: (1, 2); $v = 1$
5. second row dominates the first row
   third and fifth columns dominate the first column
   saddle point: (2, 4); $v = 1$
7. first and third columns dominate the fourth and the second columns, respectively
   best strategy:

$$P = (\frac{2}{3} \quad \frac{1}{3}), Q = \begin{bmatrix} 0 \\ \frac{2}{3} \\ 0 \\ \frac{1}{3} \end{bmatrix}; v = \frac{5}{3}$$

9. second row dominates the first row
second column dominates the third column
best strategy:

$$P = (0 \quad \tfrac{11}{16} \quad \tfrac{5}{16}); Q = \begin{bmatrix} \tfrac{9}{16} \\ 0 \\ \tfrac{7}{16} \end{bmatrix}; v = \tfrac{51}{16}$$

11. first row dominates the second and fourth rows
second column dominates the first column
best strategy:

$$P = (\tfrac{1}{6} \quad 0 \quad \tfrac{5}{6} \quad 0), Q = \begin{bmatrix} \tfrac{2}{3} \\ 0 \\ \tfrac{1}{3} \end{bmatrix}; v = \tfrac{16}{3}$$

Exercise 13.6 (page 398)

1. $P = (\tfrac{3}{7} \quad \tfrac{4}{7}), Q = \begin{bmatrix} \tfrac{1}{7} \\ \tfrac{6}{7} \end{bmatrix}, v = -\tfrac{3}{7}$ **3.** $P = (\tfrac{1}{2} \quad \tfrac{1}{2}), Q = \begin{bmatrix} \tfrac{1}{2} \\ \tfrac{1}{2} \end{bmatrix}, v = \tfrac{3}{2}$

5. $P = (\tfrac{1}{3} \quad \tfrac{2}{3}), Q = \begin{bmatrix} \tfrac{2}{3} \\ \tfrac{1}{3} \\ 0 \end{bmatrix}, v = \tfrac{10}{3}$ **7.** $P = (\tfrac{3}{4} \quad \tfrac{1}{4}), Q = \begin{bmatrix} \tfrac{3}{4} \\ \tfrac{1}{4} \\ 0 \end{bmatrix}, v = \tfrac{1}{4}$

9. $P = (\tfrac{3}{11} \quad \tfrac{8}{11}), Q = \begin{bmatrix} 0 \\ \tfrac{9}{11} \\ \tfrac{2}{11} \end{bmatrix}, v = \tfrac{27}{11}$ **11.** $P = (\tfrac{1}{2} \quad \tfrac{1}{2} \quad 0), Q = \begin{bmatrix} \tfrac{2}{13} \\ \tfrac{1}{13} \\ \tfrac{10}{13} \end{bmatrix}, v = 5$

13. $P = (\tfrac{3}{5} \quad \tfrac{1}{5} \quad \tfrac{1}{5}), Q = \begin{bmatrix} \tfrac{1}{6} \\ \tfrac{4}{15} \\ \tfrac{17}{30} \end{bmatrix}, v = \tfrac{12}{5}$

Exercise 13.7 (pages 405–406)

1.

		Second day	
		Late	On time
First day	Late	0.20	0.80
	On time	0.60	0.40

3.

	1	2	3	4
1	0.25	0.50	0	0.25
2	0.25	0.25	0.50	0
3	0	0.25	0.25	0.50
4	0.50	0	0.25	0.25

5.

	A	B	C
A	0.80	0.10	0.10
B	0.20	0.70	0.10
C	0.12	0.13	0.75

7. 0.61   **9.** 0.46

11. bakery A, 0.37; bakery B, 0.33; bakery C, 0.30

Exercise 13.8 (pages 410–412)

1. a., c., d., e., g., h., m., and **n.** are not regular
   b., f., i., k., and **j.** are regular
   j. is not a transition matrix

3. $T^2 = \begin{bmatrix} 0.6875 & 0.3125 \\ 0.6250 & 0.3750 \end{bmatrix}$, $T^3 = \begin{bmatrix} 0.671875 & 0.328125 \\ 0.656250 & 0.343750 \end{bmatrix}, \cdots$

$T^6 = \begin{bmatrix} 0.66674804 & 0.33325196 \\ 0.66617577 & 0.33382423 \end{bmatrix} \approx \begin{pmatrix} \frac{2}{3} & \frac{1}{3} \\ \frac{2}{3} & \frac{1}{3} \end{pmatrix}$

5. a. $\left(\frac{1}{4}, \frac{3}{8}, \frac{3}{8}\right)$ **b.** $\left(\frac{43}{91}, \frac{23}{91}, \frac{25}{91}\right)$

   c. $\left(\frac{10}{29}, \frac{7}{29}, \frac{12}{29}\right)$ **d., e., f.** $\left(\frac{1}{3}, \frac{1}{3}, \frac{1}{3}\right)$

7. $\left(\frac{1}{5}, \frac{3}{5}, \frac{1}{5}\right)$

CHAPTER 14

Exercise 14.1 (pages 419–420)

1. a. 32   **b.** 27   **c.** 256   **d.** 729   **e.** 26,873,856

   f. 307,546,875   **g.** $\frac{3}{32}$ **h.** $\frac{5}{4}$

3. a. a^8b^4 **b.** $a^6b^9c^{12}$ **c.** a^2b^5 **d.** $\dfrac{1}{a^3bc^6}$ **e.** $\dfrac{d^6}{ca^6}$

   f. ac^6 **g.** $\dfrac{8b}{81a}$ **h.** $\dfrac{72}{a^6b^6}$

5. a. 2   **b.** 4   **c.** -3 **d.** 25   **e.** 81

   f. $\frac{2}{3}$ **g.** $\frac{4}{9}$ **h.** $\frac{4}{7}$

Exercise 14.2 (pages 424–425)

1.

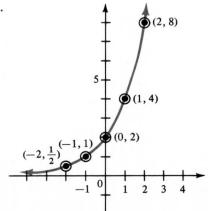

3.

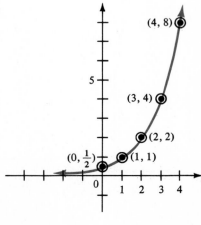

5.

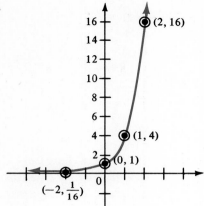

7.

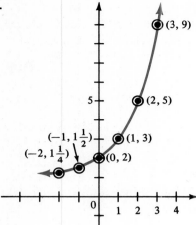

9.

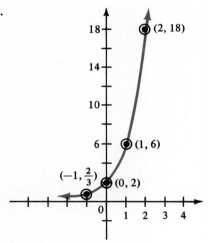

11.

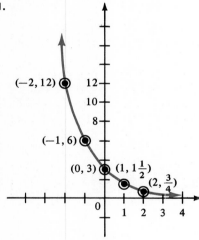

13.

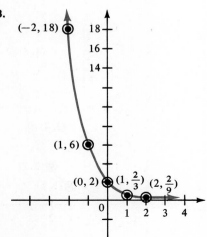

15. a.

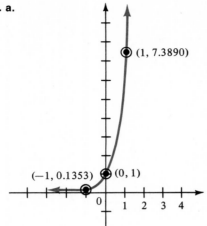

b.

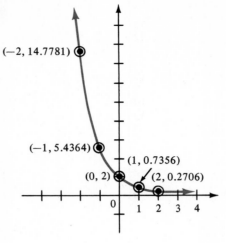

17. $x = 2$ **19.** $x = 3$ **21.** $x = \frac{7}{4}$ **23.** $x = -3$

25. $x = -3$ **27.** $x = 4$ **29.** $x = 5$

Exercise 14.3 (pages 429–430)

1. a. 500 **b.** 911.05 **c.** 2240.84

3. a. $110{,}517$ **b.** $128{,}402$ **c.** $164{,}872$ **d.** $271{,}828$

5.

t	1	2	3	4	5	6	8	10
$P(t)$	\$17,408	\$15,488	\$14,066	\$13,012	\$12,231	\$11,653	\$10,907	\$10,498

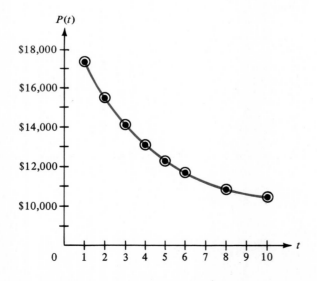

7.

t	$S(t)$
1	14852
2	12943
3	11785
4	11082
5	10657
6	10398
7	10242
8	10147
12	10020

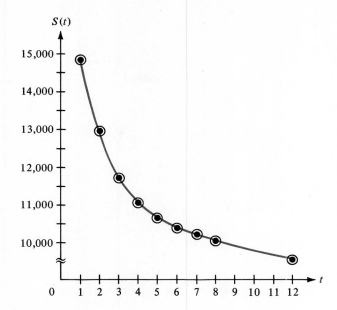

9.

t	$S(t)$
1	2963
2	2195
3	1626
4	1205
5	893
6	661
7	490
8	363
9	269
10	199
11	148
12	109

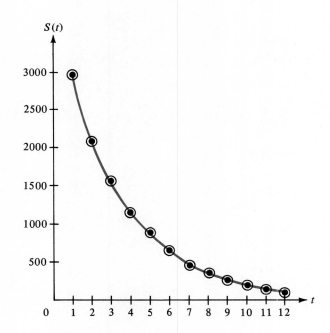

Exercise 14.4 (pages 434–435)

1. a. $\log_2 8 = 3$ **b.** $\log_3 9 = 2$ **c.** $\log_5 625 = 4$ **d.** $\log_{16} 4 = \frac{1}{2}$
   e. $\log_{32} 8 = \frac{3}{5}$ **f.** $\log_{216} 36 = \frac{2}{3}$

3. a. 81   **b.** 128   **c.** 3   **d.** -3
   e. $\frac{1}{25}$ **f.** 3   **g.** 2   **h.** $\frac{1}{2}$
   i. $\frac{1}{5}$ **j.** 7
5. a. -1.26 **b.** 3.05   **c.** 3.56   **d.** 3.22
   e. 4.83   **f.** 5.85
7. $0.6020; 0.7781; 0.9030; 0.9542; 1.0791; 1.2040$

Exercise 14.5 (pages 442–443)
1. a. 3.7185   **b.** 2.7185   **c.** 1.7185   **d.** 0.7185
   e. $0.7185 - 1$ **f.** $0.7185 - 2$
3. a. 1.9243   **b.** 1.5391   **c.** 0.5391   **d.** $2.5391 - 5$
5. a. 103786   **b.** 4.305×10^6 **c.** 8.454   **d.** 3.544×10^3
   e. 1.077×10^1 **f.** 4.023×10^{-3}
7. a. 3.9073   **b.** 1.2620   **c.** 2.0478   **d.** -0.4516
   e. 1.6437   **f.** 1.205
9. a. 1.8756   **b.** 1.2339×10^{-1}

Exercise 14.6 (pages 445–446)
1. a. 8.4115   **b.** 6.1090   **c.** 3.8065   **d.** 1.5040
   e. -0.7985 **f.** -5.4036
3. $s(t) = 20{,}000e^{t(\ln 0.75)}; \; s(8) = 2002.26$

CHAPTER 15

Exercise 15.1 (pages 450–451)
1. a. $1, 4, 7, 10, 13$ **b.** $0, 3, 8, 15, 24$ **c.** $-1, 1, -1, 1, -1$
   d. $3, 8, 15, 24, 35$ **e.** $1, 3, 7, 15, 31$ **f.** $-\frac{1}{2}, \frac{1}{3}, -\frac{1}{4}, \frac{1}{5}, -\frac{1}{6}$

3. a. $3n + 1$ **b.** 3^n **c.** $\dfrac{1}{n}$ **d.** $(-1)^{n+1}$ **e.** $\dfrac{n}{n+1}$ **f.** $\dfrac{1}{2n}$

Exercise 15.2 (pages 454–455)
1. 70

3. $a = 3, d = 5; a_n = 5n - 2, s_n = \dfrac{n}{2}(5n + 1)$

5. $3, 5, 7; 7, 5, 3$
7. a. 1600   **b.** 650   **c.** 1830
9. \$42.50   **11.** \$2850   **13.** 168

Exercise 15.3 (page 459)

1. a. 39,366   **b.** 262,144   **c.** $\dfrac{1}{512}$ **d.** $\dfrac{512}{19{,}683}$ **e.** 1.5513   **f.** 0.3874

3. $4, 8, 16, 32, 64, \ldots ; 4, -8, 16, -32, 64, \ldots$
5. $3, 6, 12; 12, 6, 3$

7. a. 384; 765   **b.** 4374; 6560   **c.** $\dfrac{1}{81}$; $\dfrac{3280}{81}$ **d.** 1.4071; 9.5491

9. $16,727.82; $70,463.66

Exercise 15.4 (pages 461–462)
1. a. $20   **b.** $45   **c.** $60.75   **d.** $9.63   **e.** $15
3. a. $200.00   **b.** $500   **c.** $75.00   **d.** $400
5. 9.89 percent   **7.** $600; 14.29 percent
9. a. 6.38 percent   **b.** 17.65 percent   **c.** 21.95 percent   **d.** 25 percent

Exercise 15.5 (pages 470–471)
1. a. $324.48; $24.48   **b.** $324.73; $24.73   **c.** $324.86; $24.86
3. a. $578.81; $78.21   **b.** $1690.74; $190.74   **c.** $3200.21; $700.21
d. $1643.62; $643.62   **e.** $2542.48; $542.48
5. $9070.09
7. bank A: $6734.28
bank B: $6625.00
The customer should deposit money in bank A.
9. a. 12.36 percent   **b.** 12.55 percent   **c.** 12.68 percent
11. a. $3736.29   **b.** $3720.47   **c.** $3712.35   **d.** $3706.86   **e.** $3704.11
13. $2869.91
15. Interest charged in bank A: $66.00
Interest charged in bank B: $64.30
Mr. Kaplan should borrow from bank B.
17. $D(1) = \$80$; $D(2) = \$144$; $D(3) = \$195.20$; $D(4) = \$236.16$; $D(5) = \$268.93$;
$D(6) = \$295.14$
Resale value after 6 years $= \$104.86$
19. a. $1166.66   **b.** $1037.04

Exercise 15.6 (pages 473–475)
1. $11,051.26   **b.** $40,305.56   **c.** $42,412.20   **d.** $127,236.59
e. $13,874.20   **f.** $13,954.01
3. $24,153.18   **5.** $41,714.41   **7.** $58.25
9. $52.85   **11.** $47.96
13. a. $79.68   **b.** $78.84   **15.** $115.26

Exercise 15.7 (pages 477–478)
1. a. $4329.48   **b.** $22,316.21   **c.** $19,872.26   **d.** $23,628.16   **e.** $23,700.70
3. $22,518.36   **5.** $731.11   **7.** $8516.06   **9.** $848.23
11. a. $188.29   **b.** $154.99   **c.** $132.86   **d.** $105.34
13. $32,256.79   **15.** $214.93

CHAPTER 16

Exercise 16.1 (pages 488–489)
1. 1   **3.** $\frac{2}{3}$ **5.** 0   **7.** 0
9. 0   **11.** limit does not exist   **13.** $\frac{2}{3}$

15. limit does not exist   **17.** limit does not exist
19. 1   **21.** 26   **23.** 26

Exercise 16.2 (pages 497–498)

1. 7   **3.** 39   **5.** limit does not exist
7. 4   **9.** -2 **11.** 1
13. limit does not exist   **15.** limit does not exist **17.** 3
19. 5   **21.** limit does not exist **23.** 2
25. limit does not exist

Exercise 16.3 (pages 502–503)

1. 7   **3.** 0   **5.** 17   **7.** 0
9. 70   **11.** 20   **13.** 3   **15.** -3
17. 12   **19.** -1 **21.** limit does not exist
23. -2 **25.** 1   **27.** $\frac{3}{2}$
29. limit does not exist   **31.** 0
33. limit does not exist   **35.** 1   **37.** 8
39. $\frac{1}{4}$

Exercise 16.4 (pages 508–510)

1. continuous everywhere   **3.** continuous everywhere except $x = 2$
5. continuous everywhere except $x = 5$ **7.** continuous everywhere except $x = 2$
9. discontinuous at $x = 1$ **11.** continuous everywhere
13. discontinuous at $x = 1$ **15.** continuous everywhere
17. $x = 2$ **19.** $x = -2, x = -3$ **21.** continuous
23. $x = 250, x = 500$ **25.** $x = 1, \frac{3}{2}, 2, \frac{5}{2}, 3, \frac{7}{2}, 4$

CHAPTER 17

Exercise 17.1 (pages 520–521)

1. 3   **3.** -5 **5.** $3x^2$ **7.** $-\dfrac{2}{x^3}$

9. $-\dfrac{1}{(x-4)^2}$ **11.** $-\dfrac{3}{x^4}$ **13.** $\dfrac{1}{(x+1)^2}$ **15.** $\dfrac{1}{2\sqrt{x}}$

17. $-\dfrac{1}{2(x+2)^{3/2}}$ **19.** $-\dfrac{1}{2(x+1)^{3/2}}$

21. a. 30   **b.** 10   **c.** 0   **d.** -20
23. a. -16 **b.** -4 **c.** $-\frac{16}{9}$ **d.** -1
25. a. $-\frac{10}{3}$ **b.** $-\frac{5}{2}$

Exercise 17.2 (pages 523–524)

1. $y = 3x - 4$ **3.** $y = 1 - x$ **5.** $y = 3x - 2$
7. $x - 4y + 4 = 0$ **9.** $x - 2y + 2 = 0$

Exercise 17.3 (pages 526–527)

1. a. continuous everywhere   **b.** differentiable everywhere
3. a. continuous everywhere   **b.** differentiable everywhere
5. a. continuous everywhere   **b.** not differentiable at $x = 1$
7. no

Exercise 17.4 (pages 530–532)

1. $4x^3$ **3.** $32x^7$ **5.** $3x^{1/2}$ **7.** $-\dfrac{1}{x^2}$

9. $3x^2 - \dfrac{3}{x^4}$ **11.** $3x^2 + 12x$ **13.** $\dfrac{1}{2\sqrt{x}} - \dfrac{1}{2x^{3/2}}$

15. $12x^2 + 14x + 6 - \dfrac{1}{x^2}$ **17.** $8x^3 + 6x + 5 - \dfrac{7}{2x^{3/2}}$

19. $\frac{5}{4}x^{1/4} + \frac{3}{2}x^{1/2} + \dfrac{1}{2\sqrt{x}}$

21. a. $2x + 5$ **b.** 9 **c.** 11

23. a. $\dfrac{1}{2\sqrt{x}}$ **b.** $\dfrac{1}{2\sqrt{2}}$ **c.** $\dfrac{1}{2\sqrt{3}}$

25. a. $-\dfrac{1}{2\sqrt{2}x^{3/2}}$ **b.** $-\frac{1}{8}$ **c.** $-\dfrac{1}{6\sqrt{6}}$

27. $0.06x + 10$ **29. a.** 2 **b.** $\frac{10}{7}$ **c.** $\frac{20}{17}$

Exercise 17.5 (pages 537–538)

1. $2x + 7$ **3.** $12x + 5$ **5.** $12x + 29$ **7.** $12x - 5$

9. $12x^3 + 38x^2$ **11.** $\frac{3}{2}x^{1/2} + \frac{1}{2}x^{-1/2}$ **13.** $1 + \dfrac{1}{\sqrt{x}}$

15. $-\dfrac{1}{x^2}$ **17.** $\dfrac{2}{(3x + 2)^2}$ **19.** $\dfrac{4}{(2x + 1)^2}$

21. $-\dfrac{4x}{(1 + x^2)^2}$ **23.** $\dfrac{2(x^2 - 1)}{(1 + x + x^2)^2}$

25. a. -1 **b.** $-\frac{1}{9}$ **c.** $-\frac{1}{25}$
27. a. 2 **b.** $\frac{2}{9}$ **c.** $\frac{2}{25}$
29. a. $-\frac{5}{2}$ **b.** $-\frac{5}{18}$ **c.** $-\frac{5}{98}$

Exercise 17.6 (page 542)

1. $8(2x + 3)^3$ **3.** $-18x(6 - 3x^2)^2$

5. $-2(4x + 3)(2x^2 + 3x + 1)^{-3}$ **7.** $\dfrac{3}{2\sqrt{3x + 8}}$

9. $\dfrac{x}{\sqrt{x^2 + 1}}$ **11.** $\dfrac{3x + 1}{\sqrt{2x + 1}}$ **13.** $\frac{5}{2}x^{3/2} + x^{-1/2}$

15. $2x(8x + 7)(3x + 7)^9$ **17.** $2(10x^2 - x + 8)(2x - 1)^7$
19. $8(2x + 3)^3 (3x + 2)^5 + 15(2x + 3)^4 (3x + 2)^4$
21. $3(2x + 1)(x^2 + x + 1)^2(x^2 - x + 1)^4 + 4(2x - 1)(x^2 - x + 1)^3(x^2 + x + 1)^3$

23. $\dfrac{3(2x - 1)^2}{(3x + 2)^4}$ **25.** $\dfrac{-1}{\sqrt{x + 1}(x - 1)^{3/2}}$ **27.** $\dfrac{3}{2\sqrt{2}}$

29. a. 26 **b.** 28

Exercise 17.7 (page 545)

1. $3e^{3x}$ **3.** $2xe^{x^2}$ **5.** $(4x + 3)e^{2x^2 + 3x + 1}$

7. $e^x - e^{-x}$ **9.** $\dfrac{e^{\sqrt{x+1}}}{2\sqrt{x + 1}}$ **11.** $\dfrac{e^{x\sqrt{x-1}}(3x - 2)}{2\sqrt{x - 1}}$

13. $\dfrac{xe^{\sqrt{x^2 - 1}}}{\sqrt{x^2 - 1}}$ **15.** $10^x(1 + x \ln 10)$ **17.** $\dfrac{xe^{\sqrt{x}}(4 + \sqrt{x})}{2}$

19. $2xa^{4x} + (x^2 + 1)a^{4x} \ln a^4$ **21.** $\dfrac{e^x}{(1 + e^x)^2}$

23. $-\dfrac{600e^{0.3x}}{(1 + 10e^{0.3x})^2}$

25. a. $-4000e^{-1}$ **b.** $-4000e^{-2}$ **c.** $-4000e^{-3}$
27. $-1000e^{-0.8}$

Exercise 17.8 (pages 549–550)

1. $\dfrac{1}{x + 1}$ **3.** $\dfrac{1}{2(x + 1)}$ **5.** $\dfrac{3x - 2}{2x(x - 1)}$ **7.** $\dfrac{1}{x \ln x}$

9. $x[1 + 2 \ln 3x]$ **11.** $1 + \dfrac{1}{x}$ **13.** $1 + \ln x$ **15.** $\dfrac{1}{1 + e^x}$

17. $\dfrac{xe^x \ln x - e^x + 1}{2(\ln x)^2 x}$ **19.** $3x^2(x + 1)^5(3x + 1)$

21. $\dfrac{10(1 + x)^4}{(1 - x)^6}$ **23.** $\dfrac{-x}{2\sqrt{x + 1}\,(x + 2)^2}$

25. $(x + 3)^x \ln(x + 3) + x(x + 3)^{x-1}$ **27.** $\dfrac{(\ln x)^{\ln x}}{x}[1 + \ln(\ln x)]$

29. $\dfrac{1}{2\sqrt{x + 1}(x + 2)^{3/2}}$

Exercise 17.9 (pages 552–553)

1. $7x^6$; $42x^5$

3. $50 + \dfrac{x}{100}$; $\dfrac{1}{100}$

5. $4x^3 + 9x^2 + 12x$; $12x^2 + 18x + 12$

7. $\dfrac{1}{(1-x)^2}$; $\dfrac{2}{(1-x)^3}$

9. $\dfrac{6x}{(1+x^2)^2}$; $\dfrac{6(1-3x^2)}{(1+x^2)^3}$

11. $5(ax+b)^4 a$; $20a^2(ax+b)^3$; $60a^3(ax+b)^2$; $120a^4(ax+b)$
13. $\frac{1}{2}(x+1)^{-1/2}$; $-\frac{1}{4}(x+1)^{-3/2}$; $\frac{3}{8}(x+1)^{-5/2}$; $-\frac{15}{16}(x+1)^{-7/2}$
15. $5e^{5x}$; $25e^{5x}$; $125e^{5x}$; $625e^{5x}$

17. $\dfrac{1}{x+3}$; $-\dfrac{1}{(x+3)^2}$; $\dfrac{2}{(x+3)^3}$; $-\dfrac{6}{(x+3)^4}$

19. $\dfrac{3}{3x+4}$; $\dfrac{-9}{(3x+4)^2}$; $\dfrac{54}{(3x+4)^3}$; $\dfrac{-486}{(3x+4)^4}$

Exercise 17.10 (page 556)

1. $\dfrac{1}{\sqrt{x}}$

3. $-\dfrac{x}{4y}$

5. $\dfrac{x}{3y}$

7. $\dfrac{x^2-6y}{6x-y^2}$

9. $-\dfrac{2x+y}{x+2y}$

11. $\dfrac{2\sqrt{xy}+y}{4y\sqrt{xy}-x}$

13. $-\dfrac{xy}{x^2+2y^2}$

15. $\dfrac{x(y^2-2x^2)}{y(2y^2-x^2)}$

17. $-\dfrac{y+\sqrt{y}}{x+\sqrt{x}}$

19. $\dfrac{x(6xy^2-5x^3-8y^4)}{y(5y^3+16xy^2-4x^3)}$

21. $-\dfrac{x}{y}$; $-\dfrac{a^2}{y^3}$

23. $\dfrac{25}{16}\dfrac{x}{y}$; $-\dfrac{625}{16}\dfrac{1}{y^3}$

25. $-\left(\dfrac{y}{x}\right)^{1/3}$; $\left(\dfrac{a^2}{x^4 y}\right)^{1/3}$

27. $3y+4x=25$

29. $x+y-2=0$

31. $3y+11x-36=0$

33. $x+y-3a=0$

35. $3y-x-9=0$

CHAPTER 18

Exercise 18.1 (page 562)

1. relative minimum at $x=-1$; $f(-1)=5$
3. relative maximum at $x=2$; $f(2)=4$
5. relative minimum at $x=2$; $f(2)=-4$
  relative maximum at $x=0$; $f(0)=0$
7. relative minimum at $x=3$; $f(3)=-18$
  relative maximum at $x=1$; $f(1)=4$

Exercise 18.2 (page 564)

1. decreases on $(-\infty, 2)$; increases on $(2, \infty)$
3. decreases on $(-\infty, -3)$; increases on $(-3, \infty)$
5. decreases on $(-1, 1)$; increases on $(-\infty, -1)$ and $(1, \infty)$
7. decreases on $(-1, 3)$; increases on $(-\infty, -1)$ and $(3, \infty)$
9. decreases on $(1, 2)$; increases on $(-\infty, 1)$ and $(2, \infty)$

Exercise 18.3 (pages 570–571)

1. relative minimum at $x = 3$; $f(3) = -1$
3. relative minimum at $x = 2$; $f(2) = 12$
   relative maximum at $x = 1$; $f(1) = 13$
5. relative minimum at $x = -1$ and $x = 1$; $f(-1) = f(1) = 5$
   relative maximum at $x = 0$; $f(0) = 6$
7. relative minimum at $x = -2$ and $x = 2$; $f(-2) = f(2) = -16$
   relative maximum at $x = -3$, $x = 0$, and $x = 3$; $f(-3) = f(3) = 9$; $f(0) = 0$
9. absolute minimum at $x = 2$; $f(2) = 1$
   absolute maximum at $x = 5$; $f(5) = 10$
11. absolute minimum at $x = 2$; $f(2) = -7$
    absolute maximum at $x = -1$; $f(-1) = 11$
13. absolute minima at $x = 1$; $f(1) = -7$
    absolute maxima at $x = 4$; $f(4) = 128$
15. absolute minima at $x = \pm 1$; $f(-1) = f(1) = 0$
    absolute maxima at $x = 3$; $f(3) = 64$
17. $175   19. $x = 15$

Exercise 18.4 (pages 573–575)

1. relative minimum at $x = 2$; $f(2) = -1$
3. relative minimum at $x = 3$; $f(3) = 5$
   relative maximum at $x = 1$; $f(1) = 9$
5. relative minimum at $x = -1$ and $x = 1$; $f(-1) = f(1) = 5$
   relative maximum at $x = 0$; $f(0) = 6$
7. relative minimum at $x = 1$; $f(1) = 2$
9. $x = 6$ 11. $x = 10$ 13. $x = 200$ 15. $x = 10$
17. $x = 70$ 19. $x = 20$

Exercise 18.5 (pages 579–582)

1. The rods should be bent exactly in half, thus forming a square.
3. 15 inches by 10 inches
5. length, $\frac{80}{3}$ inches; width, $\frac{28}{3}$ inches; height, $\frac{8}{3}$ inches
7. length, 1400 ft.; width, 700 ft.
9. 6400 ft.   11. $175; $30,625   13. 45 students   15. $19.00
17. $x = 10$
19. $x = 300$; price, $90 per unit; profit, $47,800

CHAPTER 19

Exercise 19.1 (pages 590–591)

1. 12   **3.** 14   **5.** 34   **7.** $\frac{8}{3}$

9. $\frac{16}{3}$ **11.** $\frac{37}{3}$ **13.** $e^2 - e$ **15.** $\dfrac{e^8 - e^4}{2}$

Exercise 19.2 (page 594)

1. $\frac{3}{2}$ **3.** 14   **5.** 27   **7.** $\frac{21}{2}$
9. $\frac{128}{3}$ **11.** $\frac{27}{2}$ **13.** $\frac{16}{3}$ **15.** 12
17. 750   **19.** $\frac{310}{3}$ **21.** $3(e^2 - 1)$ **23.** $4e^2 - 4e^{-1} + 3$
25. $\frac{98}{3}$ **27.** $2e(e^2 - 1)$ **29.** $\frac{14}{3}$

Exercise 19.3 (pages 597–598)

1. $x^4 + c$ **3.** $-\dfrac{2}{3x^3} + c$ **5.** $(\ln x) + \dfrac{1}{x} + c$

7. $\dfrac{x^3}{3} + \dfrac{x^2}{2} + c$ **9.** $\dfrac{x^3}{3} + 2x^2 + 4x + c$ **11.** $\dfrac{x^2}{2} + \ln x + c$

13. $\dfrac{x^3}{3} - \dfrac{x^2}{2} + \dfrac{x}{4} + c$ **15.** $\dfrac{x^3}{3} - \dfrac{1}{x} + e^x + c$ **17.** $\dfrac{e^x - e^{-x}}{2} + c$

19. $\dfrac{x^2}{2} + c$ **21.** $\frac{62}{5}$ **23.** $\frac{299}{12}$

25. $2e(e^2 - 1)$ **27.** 1   **29.** $x^2 - 3x$

31. $x^3 - 2x^2 - \dfrac{1}{x} + \dfrac{19}{2}$ **33.** $\dfrac{x^3}{3} - \dfrac{3}{2}x^2 + 2x + \dfrac{8}{3}$

Exercise 19.4 (pages 601–602)

1. $\frac{2}{3}(x + 4)^{3/2} + c$ **3.** $\frac{2}{9}(3x + 2)^{3/2} + c$ **5.** $\sqrt{2x + 3} + c$
7. $\frac{1}{18}(x^2 + 1)^9 + c$ **9.** $-\frac{1}{3}(1 - x^2)^{3/2} + c$ **11.** $\frac{2}{3}(x^4 + 2)^{3/2} + c$
13. $\ln(1 + x^2) + c$ **15.** $\frac{1}{2}\sqrt{x^2 + 1} + c$
17. $\frac{2}{5}(x + 1)^{5/2} - \frac{2}{3}(x + 1)^{3/2} + c$ **19.** $\frac{1}{2}e^{x^2} + c$
21. $2e^{\sqrt{x}} + c$ **23.** $e^{x^2 + 3x + 4} + c$ **25.** $\ln(\ln x) + c$

27. $\ln(1 + e^x) + c$ **29.** $-\dfrac{1}{\ln(e^x + e^{-x})} + c$

Exercise 19.5 (page 605)

1. $(x + 1)\ln(x + 1) - x + c$ **3.** $\frac{1}{3}x^3 \ln x - \frac{1}{9}x^3 + c$
5. $\frac{1}{4}e^{2x}(2x - 1) + c$ **7.** $\frac{1}{9}e^{3x}(3x^3 - 3x^2 + 3x - 1) + c$

9. $\frac{1}{5}x^5 + \frac{3}{4}x^4 + x^3 + \frac{1}{2}x^2 + c$ **11.** $\dfrac{44\sqrt{2} - 28}{3}$

Exercise 19.6 (pages 611–614)

1. $6x - \dfrac{x^2}{20} + \dfrac{x^3}{75} + 200$

3. $\sqrt{x^2 + 100} + 990$; $\dfrac{\sqrt{x^2 + 100} + 990}{x}$

5. $200x - 0.0002x^2 + \dfrac{0.01}{3}x^3$ **7.** $1500

9. The machine pays for itself after 7 years.
11. a. $26 per year   **b.** $32 per year
13. $78   **15.** 28,300   **17. a.** 496.631   **b.** 499.98
19. 2186.7

APPENDIX A

Exercise A.1 (pages 621–623)

1. b., c., and **d.** are false; other statements are true.

3. $\dfrac{x^2 + 3x + 10}{2(x + 2)}$ **5.** $\dfrac{4x}{4x^2 - 1}$ **7.** $\dfrac{2x^2 + 6x + 5}{x^2 + 3x + 2}$

9. $\dfrac{x + 3}{x + 1}$ **11.** $\dfrac{1}{4x + 5}$ **13.** $\dfrac{x - y}{x + y}$

15. $\dfrac{-4x}{(x - 2)(x + 2)^2}$ **17.** $x = \frac{29}{7}$ **19.** $x = 5$

21. $x = -1$ **23.** $x = -\frac{3}{4}$ **25.** $x = 3$

Exercise A.2 (page 628)

1. $x < 5$ **3.** $x > 3$ **5.** $x < 5$
7. $x \leq 3$
9. $x \leq 9$

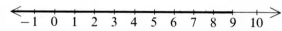

11. $x \leq \frac{9}{4}$

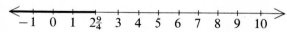

13. $x \geq -\frac{7}{8}$

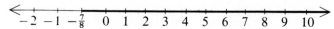

15. $x \leq \frac{1}{4}$

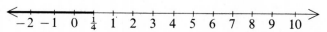

17. $x < 0$ or $x > 1$ **19.** $0 < x < 4$ **21.** $x < 1$ or $x > 2$

23. $2 < x < 3$ **25.** $x \leq -1$ or $x \geq 2$

Exercise A.3 (pages 631–632)

1. $x = 5, x = -1$ **3.** no solution   **5.** $x = 4, x = \frac{4}{3}$

7. $-1 \leq x \leq 1$

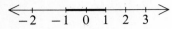

9. $x < -\frac{1}{3}$ or $x > \frac{1}{3}$

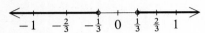

11. $-1 \leq x \leq 5$

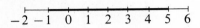

13. $x < 1$ or $x > 5$

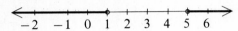

15. $x < -1$ or $x > 5$

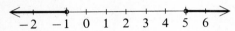

17. $-8 \leq x \leq 4$

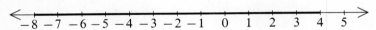

19. $0 \leq x \leq 12$

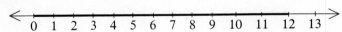

APPENDIX B

Exercise B.1 (page 636)

1. a. $x_1 + x_2 + x_3$
   b. $x_1y_1 + x_2y_2 + x_3y_3 + x_4y_4 + x_5y_5$
   c. $(x_1 + y_1) + (x_2 + y_2) + (x_3 + y_3) + (x_4 + y_4)$
   d. $cx_1 + cx_2 + cx_3 + cx_4 + cx_5$
   e. $x_1 + x_2 + x_3 + x_4 + x_5 + x_6 + 18$
   f. $(x_1 + y_1 + z_1) + (x_2 + y_2 + z_2) + (x_3 + y_3 + z_3)$
3. a. 12 **b.** 50 **c.** 110 **d.** -5 **e.** 42 **f.** 19

Index

79 80 9 8 7 6 5 4 3 2